Semiconductor Physics, Devices, and Circuits

Louis H. Lenert

North American Rockwell Corp.

and

Ohio Technical College

Charles E. Merrill Publishing Company
Columbus, Ohio
A Bell and Howell Company

**Merrill's International Series
in Electrical and Electronics Technology**

SAMUEL L. OPPENHEIMER, *Consulting Editor*

Library of Congress Catalog Card Number: 68-14349

1 2 3 4 5 6 7 8   75 74 73 72 71 70 69 68

PRINTED IN THE UNITED STATES OF AMERICA

To my wife, Phyllis
and to my children—Jenny,
Kevin, Amy, David, Shannon,
and Tracy

Preface

As stated in the title, the scope of this book is threefold. It presents (1) a basic description and analysis of the atomic and molecular phenomena that contribute to the unique operation of semiconductor devices; (2) a detailed development of the characteristics of these devices—the thermistor, junction diode, and transistor; and (3) a description and analysis of the circuitry commonly used to apply them individually and in combination. The reader may pursue a logical path through the microscopic world of the nuclear and molecular physicist to the everyday applications of measurement, regulation, amplification, and information transmission circuitry.

This book presumes no familiarization with electronic circuit design and vacuum tube applications. Algebra, basic trigonometry, and a-c/d-c circuit analysis (Ohm's law and Kirchoff's laws) are ample prerequisites. Physics may be considered a corequisite, although an adequate amount of supporting material is presented in this book.

In the author's opinion, a true appreciation of the intricate phenomena of semiconductor operation and application is impossible without a mathematical framework. Therefore, basic mathematics is used liberally.

However, each mathematical expression is in support of textual description and is generally accompanied by a graphical portrayal of the relationships.

Chapter 1 is devoted to a description and analysis of the structure of matter (both atomic and molecular) and the energy absorptions and emissions constantly exchanged within matter. The relationship of these phenomena to the electrical characteristics of materials is presented in Chapter 2. The simplest semiconductor device, the thermistor, is treated in Chapter 3. First, the electrical characteristics are developed on the previous framework of microscopic structure. With this knowledge in hand, the reader is led through the device applications and the associated analytical techniques. This same procedure is applied to semiconductor diodes, the simplest "junction" device, in Chapter 4, and to the transistor, a more complex "junction" device, in Chapter 5.

The applications of the transistor, which touch every aspect of electronic circuitry functions, could not be treated in a single chapter. Therefore, at this point, the text format changes from the "device" orientation to the "functional applications" orientation. Basic amplifier operation is treated in Chapter 5 through the application of graphical analysis techniques. Small-signal, low-frequency amplification is given a complete mathematical treatment in Chapter 6, with consideration of transistor equivalent circuits; the effects of loads and signal frequencies on amplifier voltage, current, and power gains; the effects of multistage operation; and the effects of negative feedback branches. Chapter 7 describes small-signal, high-frequency amplification and is built upon the analytical framework of Chapter 6. Large-signal amplifiers are described in Chapter 8 which includes a complete analytical treatment of complementary symmetry and compound-connected circuit arrangements that are unique to transistor devices. Again, the analytical framework of Chapter 6 and its relationships to the graphical techniques of Chapter 5 are used. Chapter 9 provides an analysis of transistor amplifier stability (the control of temperature-sensitive variations in the transistor characteristics) and transistor "noise." Chapter 10 presents the design criteria for achieving controlled instability (oscillations) and controlled nonlinear processes (amplitude and frequency modulation and demodulation). The more exotic devices, such as tunnel diodes and field-effect devices are described in Chapter 11.

Throughout the text, the importance of the electronic signal characteristics, before and after transit through the semiconductor device, is stressed in terms of harmonic frequency and amplitude distortions. Appendix C is devoted to a basic description of the harmonic analysis technique, the process whereby nonsinusoidal signals are converted into a series of harmonic sinusoidal components in order to simplify the analysis of electronic circuit "operations."

This book is in no way associated with my work or position at North American Rockwell; nor does it reflect the opinions or preferred techniques of this corporation. It is an independent endeavor, brought about through my part-time association with the evening branch of the Ohio Technical College and the encouragement of Mr. Samuel Oppenheimer, President. The material in this text has been taught for the past three years, in both note and manuscript form, at the Ohio Technical College.

I would like to acknowledge the many students who have directly and indirectly provided an indication of what is needed (and not needed) in a basic transistor text. Special thanks are due to Dorothy Laposki and Sherry Johnston for occupying a lot of their spare time typing portions of the manuscript.

Louis H. Lenert

May, 1968

Table of Contents

Chapter 6

SMALL-SIGNAL CLASS A AUDIO-FREQUENCY AMPLIFIER ANALYSIS   251

1

The Structure of
Matter

Most of the universe is empty. This idea of emptiness has been a part of man's astronomical model for many generations. This model, in its simplest form, portrays a population of very heavy concentrations of matter (stars) separated by immense distances—distances so great that the stars, despite their own vastness, are insignificant points by comparison. To say that the everyday world is equally empty appears contrary to reason. The "solidity" of this world, however, is due to the limitations of man's senses—it does not portray a true picture of the basic structure of matter. To the modern physicist, all matter is an aggragation of particles, held together, to one degree or another, by nuclear, electromagnetic, or gravitational forces, and separated by distances so great in comparison to the size of the particles, that even the most "solid" piece of material consists almost entirely of empty space.

Throughout the universe, many stars harbor their own solar systems. Each solar system consists of a few planets, firmly attached to the parent star by gravitational forces. In the microscopic world of material structure, the atom maintains its own "solar system" of particles held together by electromagnetic forces. The nature and arrangement of these particles

1

determines the physical, chemical, and electrical properties of the resulting material. Through his understanding of these properties, man has learned to manipulate the microscopic particles, control their behavior, and utilize them to his own advantage.

There are many schemes for classifying materials. One such scheme, based on physical appearance, categorizes everything as a gas, a liquid, or a solid. These are called the *states* of matter. Semiconductors fall into the solid category. For this reason, the physics of semiconductors is a specialized part of a broader science known as *solid state physics*. From this study comes the answers to such questions as: "Why is diamond a good insulator and graphite a good conductor when both are composed of the same element (carbon)?" and "Why does the resistance of some materials decrease as temperature rises while the resistance of other materials increases?" In order to answer these questions, as well as a multitude of similar ones, it is necessary to develop a *microphysical model* of matter, which permits an accurate prediction of the nature of materials.

The model to be presented is the simplest one that adequately describes a material's significant electrical properties. In order for this to be true, the model must consider, to some degree, the nature of the atomic nucleus, the chemical combination of atoms, the molecular structure of crystals, and the ever-present influence of *quantum mechanics*. The reader must realize, however, that this model will not answer all questions in these areas—each of which accounts for a separate science in itself. Rather, it is hoped that the reader will develop enough general understanding of the basic relationships governing electrical properties to apply this knowledge, not only to semiconductor devices, but to other electronic devices currently in use or yet to be developed.

1.1 Basic Atomic Structure

Microscopic physics begins with the establishment of the concept of atoms. Every atom is like a miniature solar system in many respects. In the solar system, the central figure is the sun, containing most of the solar system's mass and extending the predominant structuring forces. In an atom, the mass is concentrated in a central core called the *nucleus*. Likewise, this nucleus extends the predominant force holding the atom together. Minute electrical particles occupy orbital levels about the nucleus in a manner similar to the planetary revolutions about the sun. The radius of an atom is on the order of 10^{-10} meter. The orbiting particles and the particles of the nucleus have radii on the order of 10^{-15} meter. Hence, very little of the atomic volume actually contains anything, which leads to the concept that even "solid" objects are "empty."

The structure of the atom is generally separated into two regions: an outer structure containing the orbiting particles, and an inner structure containing the nucleus. The outer structure is well understood. The inner structure is the subject of much current investigation, its exact nature being extremely elusive. Fortunately, the chemical and electrical properties of materials are entirely dependent upon the outer structure, requiring only the simplest of models for the nucleus.

Fundamental Particles and Arrangements

The basic particle of matter having a negative electrical charge is the electron. No smaller charge can exist, and all other charge quantities must be *whole number multiples* of the electron charge value. This value (denoted by Q_e throughout this text) is equal to approximately $-(1.6 \times 10^{-19})$ coulomb. Hence, 6.2×10^{18} electrons must be gathered together in order to accumulate one coulomb of negative charge.

In the normal state, matter is electrically neutral. This indicates the existence of a positively charged particle to counteract the negatively charged electrons. This particle is the *proton*. The proton is also a fundamental charge of value: 1.6×10^{-19} (to be denoted by Q_p) coulomb. Hence, the proton and the electron differ, electrically, only in the sign of their charge.

Protons and electrons do not normally exist in a haphazard manner, scattered individually throughout matter. Rather, they exist together in unique clusters that form the first "structural level" of all materials. These clusters are the *atoms*. From the chemists' viewpoint, each unique atom defines a *chemical element;* i.e., a "pure" substance that cannot be recreated through the chemical combination of any other substances. Thus, the alchemists' ancient dream of forming gold from the more common materials can never be realized from a purely chemical standpoint. It can occur only through the complete restructuring of the fundamental particles.

Table 1–1 provides a partial list of the chemical elements and is produced in order to illustrate an initial model of atomic structure. In all, there are 92 *natural elements* proceeding from hydrogen (the lightest), to uranium (the heaviest). Other *artificial* (man-made) *elements* exist that are heavier than uranium. However, these elements are created through atomic and nuclear restructuring processes, are extremely unstable (explaining why they do not exist in nature), and are of no consequence to this study.

A unique *atomic number* (first column to the right of the elements in Table 1–1) is associated with each element. The atomic number is equal

TABLE 1-1

Partial List of the Elements

Element	Atomic Number	Mass Number
Hydrogen	1	1
Helium	2	4
Lithium	3	7
Beryllium	4	9
Boron	5	11
Carbon	6	12
Nitrogen	7	14
Oxygen	8	16
Fluorine	9	19
Neon	10	20
Sodium	11	23
Magnesium	12	24
Aluminum	13	27
Silicon	14	28
Phosphorus	15	31
Sulfur	16	32
Chlorine	17	35
Argon	18	40
Potassium	19	39
Calcium	20	40
Scandium	21	45
Titanium	22	48
Vanadium	23	51
Chromium	24	52

to the number of electrons normally associated with each atom. Since, in the natural state, the atom is electrically neutral, there must be an equal number of protons associated with the atom. The complete interpretation of the atomic number, then, is that it represents both the number of electrons and the number of protons clustered together to form an atom.

A third particle, having no electrical charge, is also present in the atom. This particle is called the *neutron* and has a mass equal to that of the proton (1.67×10^{-27} kilogram). Since the electron, with a mass of 9.11×10^{-31} kilogram, is approximately 1840 times lighter than either the proton or the neutron, for all practical purposes, the mass of an atom is equal to the combined mass of its protons and neutrons. The *mass number* (second column to the right of the elements in Table 1–1) is a measure of the "relative" atomic mass and is, therefore, equal to the number of protons plus the number of neutrons in the atom. Hydrogen, for example, with an atomic number of one and a mass number of one, has one proton, one electron, and *no* neutrons $(1 - 1 = 0)$. In contrast, helium, with atomic number two and mass number four, has two protons, two electrons, and two neutrons $(4 - 2 = 2)$.

Not all atoms of the same element have the same mass number. A few elements show a rather serious discrepancy. Copper, for instance, contains atoms with a mass number of 63 units and atoms with a mass number of 65 units. It was not until the discovery of the neutron that an adequate explanation for such characteristics was formulated. As stated previously, the hydrogen atom has one proton, one electron and no neutrons. Since the neutron has no electrical charge, its presence or absence does not affect the chemical and electrical characteristics of the atom. *Only the mass and nuclear characteristics are changed.* Hence, an atom with one proton, one electron, and one neutron still has the properties of hydrogen— but it has a mass number of two, rather than one. Atoms of the same element, but with different atomic masses, are called *isotopes*. Almost every element has two or more isotopes. The mass numbers shown in Table 1-1 are for the *most abundant isotope of the elements listed.*

The protons and neutrons associated with an atom are tightly bound together into an atomic core, or *nucleus*. This violates the classical law of electrostatics which states that like charges repel. However, these particles are together in a volume having a radius on the order of 10^{-15} meter. At such small distances, ordinary electromagnetic forces are replaced by a *nuclear force* which violates many classical concepts. Radii for normal atoms (the distance from the center of the nucleus to the outermost orbiting electron) run on the order of 10^{-10} meter. Hence, in terms of volume, most of the matter associated with an atom occupies only 0.0000000000001 per cent of the total. The rest of the atom is empty, with the exception of an occasional electron.

This atomic model consisting of protons, neutrons, and electrons is by no means complete. Over thirty sub-atomic particles, with exotic names such as neutrinos, pions, and muons, have been discovered. These particles appear to be the "bits and pieces" from which the protons, neutrons, and electrons are made. Although such "strange" particles are beyond the scope of discussion here, they are mentioned in order that the reader may realize that much remains to be told in the tale of the fundamental particles of matter.

Electron Energies

The electrons associated with an atom are so far from the nucleus that they do not experience any effects from the nuclear force holding

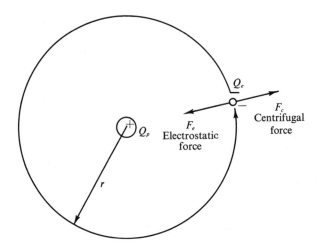

Figure 1-1.   *Simple Hydrogen Atom*

the protons and neutrons together. They do, however, experience a form of electrostatic attraction, as illustrated in Fig. 1–1. The electrostatic force, F_e, tries to draw the electron to the nucleus. The circular motion of the electron produces a countering centrifugal force exactly equal to the force of electrostatic attraction. In order to maintain this balance of forces, the electron velocity must be:

$$v = \sqrt{\frac{Q_e^2}{4\pi\epsilon_0 m_e r}} \quad \text{(meters/second)} \tag{1-1}$$

All quantities in Eq. (1–1) are physical constants with the exception of the distance between the nuclear center and the electron orbit, r. The permittivity of vacuum, ϵ_0, and the mass of the electron, m_e, are given in Appendix A, along with other physical constants. Because of the inverse relationship between v and r, electrons with a lower velocity must orbit at *greater distances from the nucleus*.

The kinetic energy of the electron is:

$$E_k = \left[\frac{Q_e^2}{8\pi\epsilon_0}\right]\frac{1}{r} \quad \text{(joules)} \tag{1-2}$$

The quantity in the brackets is a constant: 1.1×10^{-28} newton·meter². If the electron were to fall to the nucleus, a force, $-F_e$, would act through a distance, r, and work, $W = -F_e r$, would be performed. Hence, as long as the electron stays in its orbit, it has a potential energy of:

$$E_p = -\left[\frac{Q_e^2}{4\pi\epsilon_0}\right]\frac{1}{r} \quad \text{(joules)} \tag{1-3}$$

The bracketed (constant) quantity in this equation is: 2.2×10^{-28} newton·meter^2—two times the value in Eq. (1–2). Note that the potential energy is negative, indicating that it is the result of a force trying to pull the two particles together, as opposed to the positive kinetic energy,

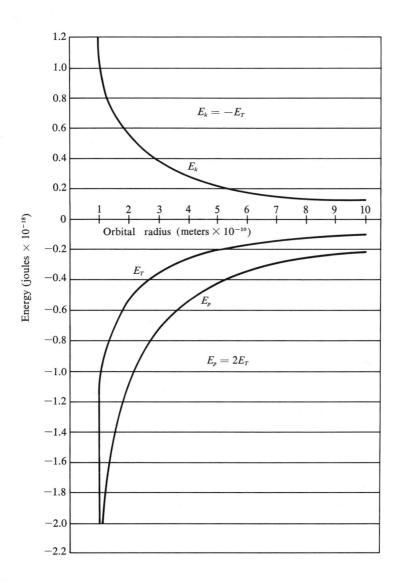

Figure 1-2.   *Energy Profiles in the Hydrogen Model*

whose force tries to separate the particles. The total energy of the electron is the sum of its kinetic and potential energies:

$$E_T = -\left[\frac{Q_e^2}{8\pi\epsilon_0}\right]\frac{1}{r} \qquad \text{(joules)} \qquad \textbf{(1-4)}$$

Equation (1–4) indicates that the total energy of the electron is a negative quantity. From a physical standpoint, this negative total energy demonstrates that the electron has a *natural tendency* to stay attached to the nucleus unless energy is added (from outside the atom).

Figure 1–2 is a plot of Eqs. (1–2), (1–3), and (1–4). This shows that

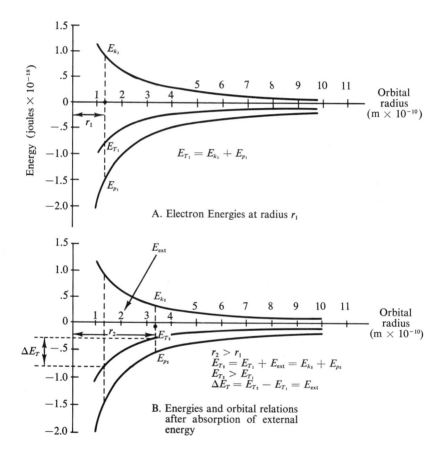

A. Electron Energies at radius r_1

$$E_{T_1} = E_{k_1} + E_{p_1}$$

B. Energies and orbital relations after absorption of external energy

$$r_2 > r_1$$
$$E_{T_2} = E_{T_1} + E_{ext} = E_{k_2} + E_{p_2}$$
$$E_{T_2} > E_{T_1}$$
$$\Delta E_T = E_{T_2} - E_{T_1} = E_{ext}$$

Figure 1-3. *Electron Energy Interchanges*

although the kinetic energy of the electron *decreases* as it moves farther from the nucleus, the potential energy *increases* by twice this value, resulting in a net *increase* in total energy. (Negative values of small magnitude are greater than are negative values of larger magnitude.)

Figure 1–3, Part A shows the energies associated with an electron in an orbit with radius r_1. When the electron absorbs energy from an external source, the electron energy increases ($E_{T_2} = E_{T_1} + E_{ext}$) as shown in Part B of the figure. This means that the electron must take up a larger orbit (see Fig. 1–2) whose radius, r_2, could be determined from Eq. (1-4) with E_T equal to E_{T_2}. The increase in total energy can be expressed in terms of the two radii:

$$\Delta E_T = - \left[\frac{Q_e^2}{8\pi\epsilon_0}\right]\left[\frac{1}{r_2} - \frac{1}{r_1}\right] \tag{1-5}$$

or in terms of the absorbed energy:

$$\Delta E_T = E_{ext} \tag{1-6}$$

When an electron moves from a larger to a smaller orbit, a process exactly the reverse of that depicted in Fig. 1–3 occurs. The total energy of the electron decreases, resulting in the *emission* of energy with a value, $E_{ext} = -\Delta E_T$ (the minus sign indicates a decrease in electron energy and the emission of energy from the atom).

Example 1-1.   What velocity is associated with a hydrogen electron at an orbital radius of 9.11×10^{-11} meter? What is the velocity at a radius of 8.5×10^{-10} meter?

Solution.   The orbital velocity is given by:

$$v = \sqrt{\frac{Q_e^2}{4\pi\epsilon_0 m_e}} \cdot \sqrt{\frac{1}{r}}$$

$$= \sqrt{\frac{(-1.6 \times 10^{-19})^2}{4\pi(8.85 \times 10^{-12})(9.11 \times 10^{-31})}} \cdot \sqrt{\frac{1}{(9.11 \times 10^{-11})}}$$

$$= 7.4 \times 10^5 \text{ m/sec}$$

in the small orbit, and by:

$$v = 5\sqrt{\frac{1}{8.5 \times 10^{-10}}} = 1.85 \times 10^5 \text{ m/sec}$$

in the larger orbit. These answers support the concept that electrons are slower (have less kinetic energy) in the larger orbit. The 5 used in the second equation is the value of the square root of $Q_e^2/4\pi\epsilon_0 m_e$ in the first equation. Since this part of the equation is constant, it need not be re-evaluated as r changes.

Example 1-2. The electron in a hydrogen atom is initially in an orbit with a radius of 5.3×10^{-11} meter. The atom absorbs 2.04×10^{-18} joule of energy from an external source. What is the associated change in total energy and what is the radius of the new orbit?

Solution. The total energy increases by an amount equal to the absorbed external energy (2.04×10^{-18} joule). The relationship between the change in total energy and orbital radius is:

$$\Delta E_T = E_{\text{ext}} = -\frac{Q_e^2}{8\pi\epsilon_o}\left[\frac{1}{r_2} - \frac{1}{r_1}\right]$$

which, when solved for r_2 (the new radius), yields:

$$r_2 = \frac{1}{(1/r_1) - (8\pi\epsilon_o\Delta E_T/Q_e^2)}$$

$$= \frac{1}{[1/(5.3 \times 10^{-11})] - [(8.61 \times 10^{27})(2.04 \times 10^{-18})]}$$

$$= 7.7 \times 10^{-10} \text{ meter}$$

Discrete Energy Levels

The energy relationships discussed in the previous section are based on the assumption that an electron may absorb or emit any quantity of energy and may, therefore, occupy any radial distance from the nucleus. In reality they cannot do so. Rather, the orbits in the hydrogen atom must satisfy the condition:

$$r = \frac{nh}{2\pi m_e v} \qquad \text{(meters)} \qquad \text{(1-7)}$$

where h is Planck's constant (Appendix A) and n is an integer—1, 2, 3, etc. This condition results from the minute size of the electron, which causes it to obey certain microscopic laws contrary to those associated with large-scale objects. The explanation of these laws is undertaken in a branch of physics known as quantum mechanics, most of which is not essential to the purposes of this text. Quantum mechanics shows the existence of a dual nature for electrons: in some instances electrons have particle-like characteristics; at other times electrons display wave-like properties.

When two waves occur out of phase, they tend to destroy themselves (the resulting sum is less than either individual wave). This process is known as *destructive interference*. An electron travels around its orbit in a wave-like fashion. It does so without interference. In other words, the orbit consists of an *integral number of equivalent wavelengths*, so that

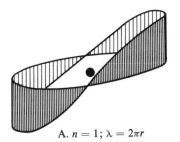

A. $n = 1$; $\lambda = 2\pi r$

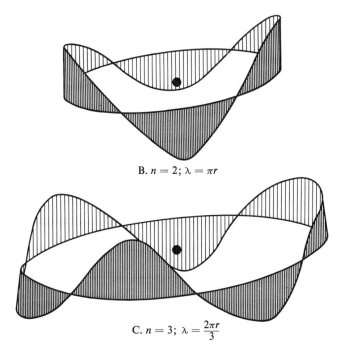

B. $n = 2$; $\lambda = \pi r$

C. $n = 3$; $\lambda = \dfrac{2\pi r}{3}$

Figure 1-4.   *Wave-Like Electron Orbits*

each wave follows exactly the same path that the preceding wave followed. This means that each stable electron orbit has a wavelength:

$$\lambda = \frac{2\pi r}{n} \quad \text{(meters)} \qquad \textbf{(1-8)}$$

associated with it. These orbits are illustrated in Fig. 1–4.

Experiments with electron behavior show that the orbital velocity of the electron is related to its wavelength by:

$$v = \frac{h}{m_e \lambda} \quad \text{(meters/second)} \qquad \textbf{(1-9)}$$

A combination of Eqs. (1–8) and (1–9) yields Eq. (1–7). Hence, the concept of "electron waves" provides the theoretical reason for the existence of discrete electron orbits.

Substituting Eq. (1–9) for v in the kinetic energy equation, and Eq. (1–8) for λ, yields:

$$E_k = \frac{1}{2} m_e v^2 = \frac{h^2 n^2}{8\pi^2 m_e r^2} \quad \text{(joules)} \qquad \textbf{(1-10)}$$

However, the expression at the right must also be equal to the electron kinetic energy expression given by Eq. (1–2). (In order for quantum mechanics to be correct, the quantum principles must explain *both* the microscopic and the classical macroscopic behavior of the electron.) When the two expressions are equivalenced, a complete expression for the discrete orbital radii is obtained:

$$r = \frac{\epsilon_o n^2 h^2}{\pi Q_e^2 m_e} \quad \text{(meters)} \qquad \textbf{(1-11)}$$

Each orbit that an electron may occupy represents a distinct total energy value [from Eqs. (1–4) and (1–11)]:

$$E_T = \frac{-Q_e^2}{8\pi \epsilon_o r} = \frac{-Q_e^4 m_e}{8\epsilon_o^2 n^2 h^2} \qquad \textbf{(1-12)}$$

Values for this expression are shown in Fig. 1–5 for values of n equal to one, two, three, and four.

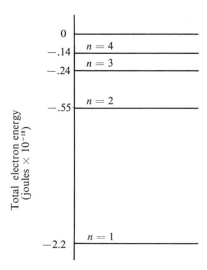

Figure 1-5.   *Discrete Hydrogen Energy Levels*

Example 1-3. What radius is associated with each of the hydrogen atom orbits for n equal to one through n equal to four?

Solution. The permissible orbit radius is given by:

$$r = \frac{\epsilon_o h^2}{\pi Q_e^2 m_e} n^2 = \frac{(8.85 \times 10^{-12})(6.63 \times 10^{-34})^2}{\pi(-1.6 \times 10^{-19})^2(9.11 \times 10^{-31})} n^2$$
$$= (5.3 \times 10^{-11})n^2$$

For n equal to one, two, three, and four, the radius values are 5.3 $\times 10^{-11}$, 2.12×10^{-10}, 4.77×10^{-10}, and 8.5×10^{-10} meter, respectively.

Electron "Shell" Structures

So far, only the hydrogen atom has been treated in detail. The electrons associated with the atoms of all the elements can be modeled in a similar fashion. However, since the nuclei contain more than one unit positive charge (proton), the electrostatic forces of attraction are greater (drawing all the electrons into "tighter" orbits). At the same time, certain, more complex, phenomena associated with quantum mechanics must be taken into consideration. These phenomena include electron "spin," orbital orientation, and the existence of elliptical orbits in addition to circular orbits (illustrated in Fig. 1-6). The so-called *exclusion principle* also

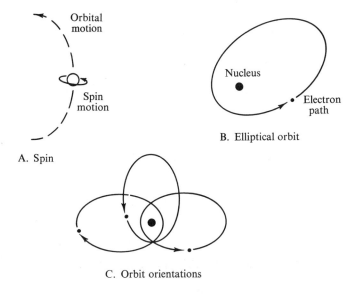

A. Spin

B. Elliptical orbit

C. Orbit orientations

Figure 1-6.   *Additional Orbital Concepts*

becomes a controlling factor. This principle specifies that no two electrons can have exactly the same *quantum state* (the same energy, spin direction, orbit orientation, and orbit shape). All of these concepts are a part of the total quantum atomic model and are not discussed in detail here. It is the final result of this model—the discrete energy levels associated with the electrons of each elemental atom—that is of interest in specifying the electrical charcteristics of a material.

Each orbit represents an electron energy level. However, because of the existence of elliptical orbits, the energy-level value, E_T, for several differently shaped orbits may be equal. Such orbits (or energy levels) are grouped together and are called *orbitals*. These orbitals, in turn, are grouped further into *electron shells*. The shells are denoted by the letters K, L, M, N, O, P and Q—starting at the lowest energy level and proceeding to higher levels. The K-shell contains only one energy level (only one orbital and only one orbit), and each successive shell has an increasing, then decreasing, number of energy levels associated with it, as listed in Table 1–2. The "maximum number of electrons" listed in the table means that the indicated orbital may contain fewer electrons, but *never a greater number*.

TABLE 1-2

Characteristics of the Electron Shells and Orbitals

Shell	Number of Orbitals	Maximum Number of Electrons
K	1	2
L	2	2,6
M	3	2,6,10
N	4	2,6,10,14
O	4	2,6,10,14
P	3	2,6,10
Q	2	2,6

Figure 1–7 presents an "energy diagram" for four of the elements. The filled (containing the maximum number of electrons), partially filled (containing less than the maximum number), and allowable (empty) energy levels are indicated. (The allowable levels for lithium and sodium exist between zero energy and the L_1 and M_1 orbitals, respectively. They are not shown because of scale limitations. They are, in fact, quite closely "packed" into the spaces indicated.) Figure 1–7 also indicates that none of the energy levels have the same value from one element to another.

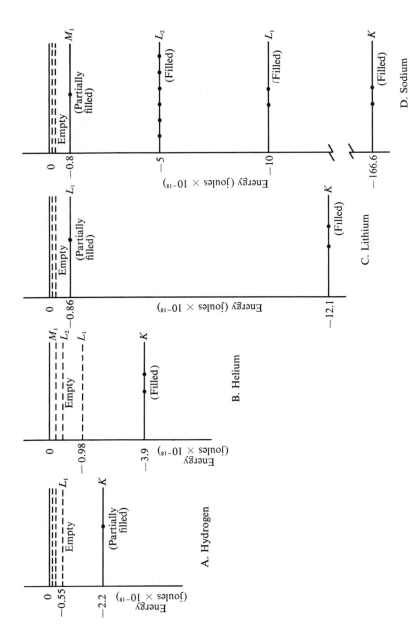

Figure 1-7. *Typical Energy Level Diagrams*

15

This is due to the fact that different numbers of protons and, hence, different attractive forces are involved in each.

Figure 1–8 shows the more complex "orbit representation" of the same elements. This figure illustrates the symmetry associated with the quantum atomic model. Although shown "flat," the reader must realize that the atom is actually a three-dimensional structure. Hence, the multiple orbits of the same shape and size (same energy level) have orientations that vary in all planes. For this reason, and because of electron spin differences, each of these electrons occupies a different quantum state, although all electrons in the same orbital have the same total energy.

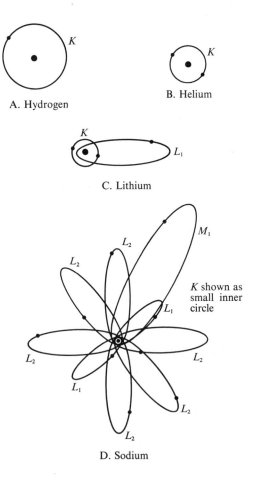

A. Hydrogen

B. Helium

C. Lithium

D. Sodium

Figure 1-8.   *"Physical" Appearance of Electron Orbits*

1.2 Atomic Excitation

When all the electrons associated with an atom are in their lowest possible energy levels (as they are in Figs. 1–7 and 1–8), the atom is said to be in its *ground state*. Such a condition exists only when the surrounding temperature is at absolute zero (0°Kelvin). At all other temperatures, the electrons—particularly the outermost electrons (*K*-shell electrons for hydrogen and helium, *L*-shell electrons for lithium, and *M*-shell electrons for sodium)—are in continuous agitation, jumping back and forth between allowable (and partially filled) energy levels. This agitation is accompanied by the necessary absorption and emission of electromagnetic (thermal) energy. In such a state, an atom is said to be *excited*. Each stage of the excitation (each "jump") remains a stable condition for about 10^{-8} to 10^{-9} second.

Before proceeding to a detailed discussion of atomic excitation, it is convenient to introduce a new unit of energy. The joule is a large unit. When discussing electron energies (as associated with atomic structure) in terms of joules, it becomes necessary to use very large negative powers of ten (as in Fig. 1–7). In order to avoid this, scientists have defined the *electron volt*, which is more nearly related to the microscopic scale of the atom. This energy is equivalent to the amount of work done by an electron as it moves through a potential difference of one volt. The volt is a "joule/coulomb." Multiplying this unit by the electron charge (in coulombs) yields the energy unit, the joule. When one electron travels through a

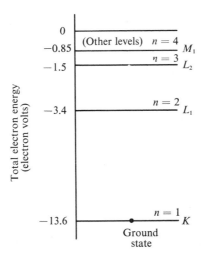

Figure 1-9.   *Hydrogen Energy States*

potential difference of one volt (produces one electron volt of work), this is equivalent to:

$$1 \text{ ev} = 1 \text{ joule/coulomb} \times 1.6 \times 10^{-19} \text{ coulomb}$$
$$= 1.6 \times 10^{-19} \text{ joule}$$

Conversely:

$$1 \text{ joule} = \frac{1 \text{ ev}}{1.6 \times 10^{-19}} = 6.2 \times 10^{18} \text{ ev}$$

Figure 1–9 is a reproduction of Fig. 1–5 in terms of electron volts. Previous equations used to compute electron energy levels can be made to yield electron volts directly by using a modified value for Planck's constant (Appendix A).

Example 1-4.   Express the lowest energy level of the helium atom (Fig. 1–7) in terms of electron volts.

Solution.   The energy value is -3.9×10^{-18} joule. The conversion factor is 6.2×10^{18} ev/joule:

$$(-3.9 \times 10^{-18})(6.2 \times 10^{18}) = -24.18 \text{ ev}$$

Photons

The microscopic particles of matter are in constant agitation, changing energies in abrupt steps of minute size. These step-wise changes in energy result from the absorption or emission of "units" of electromagnetic energy. These units of energy are called *photons* or *quanta*. The electromagnetic waves of classical physics are composed of myriads of these photons, each containing an energy that is dependent on the wave frequency:

$$E_{ph} = hf \quad \text{(joules)} \tag{1-13}$$

where h is Planck's constant (Appendix A).

The individual photons do not follow the laws of classical electromagnetic theory, as dictated by Maxwell's field equations. Rather, they follow the more intricate laws of quantum mechanics and, like electrons, they have a dual nature, sometimes behaving like particles and other times behaving like waves. A more detailed discussion of the relationships between photons and electromagnetic waves is presented in Appendix B.

Energy Absorption

In order for the electrons in their ground states to attain a higher than normal energy level, additional energy must be absorbed. The three primary sources of such energy are: 1) electromagnetic radiations, 2) collisions with other electrons, and 3) the application of an electrical potential difference. Most of the energy jumps (except those very near zero) are far too great to be accomplished through the application of an electric potential difference. Because of the relative size of electrons and the "empty" space around them, electron collisions are fairly remote. The majority of the electron transitions, then, are the result of electromagnetic energy absorption.

The electrons are not restricted to transfers between adjacent energy levels. The only restriction is that the electron must absorb an amount of energy exactly equal to the energy difference between two levels. From Fig. 1-9, if an electron in the K-state absorbs 10.2 ev, it will transfer to the L_1-state. However, it also may absorb 12.1 ev, jumping directly from the K-state to the L_2-state. A third alternative would be for the electron to absorb 10.2 ev, rising to the L_1-state; then, before the excitation time (10^{-8} to 10^{-9} second) elapses, absorb another 1.9 ev—making a second jump to the L_2-state. These transfers only illustrate the process. *Any jump sequence may occur if the proper energy is absorbed.*

The quantized energy absorption process is closely associated with the photons of electromagnetic radiations. Each electron jump to a higher level *in each atom* of a material requires the absorption of at least one photon. *Since the intensity of the radiation determines how many photons there will be, a more intense radiation will result in more atoms being excited.* However, since only specific photon energies can be absorbed, *the radiation frequency is a critical quantity in determining which jumps will actually occur.*

The frequency required to initiate a particular jump can be determined directly from the photon energy relationship [Eq. (1–13)] by substituting the required energy change for E and solving for f. Table 1–3 lists these

TABLE 1-3

Critical Photon Frequencies Required for Specific Electron Transitions

Element	Orbital Transition	Energy Change (ev)	Critical Frequency (cps)
Hydrogen	K to L_1	10.2	2.46×10^{15}
	L_1 to M_1	2.55	6.15×10^{14}
	L_2 to M_1	0.65	1.59×10^{14}
Helium	K to L_1	18.1	4.39×10^{15}
	L_1 to O	7.18	1.7×10^{15}
Lithium	K to L_1	69.7	1.67×10^{16}
	L_1 to O	5.33	1.25×10^{15}
Sodium	K to M_1	1036	2.49×10^{17}
	K to L_1	979	2.36×10^{17}
	L_1 to L_2	31	7.47×10^{15}

"critical" photon frequencies for several possible transitions. All of the transitions, with the exception of those near the zero energy level, require the absorption of very high-frequency photons—photons that, in many instances, occupy the extreme ultraviolet and near X-ray regions of the spectrum. Although such radiations are present under normal conditions, their intensity is at such a low level (the number of photons is very small) that only a few such transitions can occur. For the more complex atoms, having electrons in the higher energy levels, lower frequencies, such as infrared and microwave, can cause transitions. Hence, it is the outer electrons that account for most of the excitation associated with atoms. Once an electron *does* move to a higher level, it takes less energy (a lower critical frequency) to cause it to move still higher. This is true because the spacing between allowable energy levels becomes less as zero energy is approached. When an electron is in one of these levels, an applied electrical potential difference (of practical value) may also contain enough energy to cause the transitions.

Example 1-5.   What is the critical frequency required for an electron to jump from the K orbital to the L_2 orbital in sodium (Fig. 1–7)?

Solution.   The energy difference is 161.6×10^{-18} joule. A photon of exactly this energy is necessary to cause a direct transition from K to L_2. This photon must have a frequency given by:

$$f = \frac{E_{ph}}{h} = \frac{161.6 \times 10^{-18}}{6.63 \times 10^{-34}} = 2.44 \times 10^{17} \text{ cps}$$

which is in the ultraviolet range. This problem can also be worked in terms of electron volts. The energy difference is:

$$(161.6 \times 10^{-18})(6.2 \times 10^{18}) = 1002 \text{ ev}$$

Using h equal to 4.15×10^{-15} ev·sec:

$$f = \frac{1002}{4.15 \times 10^{-15}} = 2.44 \times 10^{17} \text{ cps}$$

Energy Emission

Unless an electron in an energy level above its ground state absorbs additional energy within the excitation period (10^{-8} to 10^{-9} second), it will drop back toward the ground states. This is accompanied by the emission of electromagnetic energy. Just as with the energy absorption process, the emission occurs in quantized units: each electron jump to a lower level results in the emission of a photon. These jumps, again, as with the jumps to a higher level, occur in a random fashion with almost any sequence of jumps being possible. The only restriction is that an amount of energy exactly equal to the difference between two energy levels must be lost. Hence, the associated emissions occur at frequencies specified by Eq. (1–13) and are akin to the critical absorption frequencies already discussed.

Although any of the electron transitions are theoretically possible (leading to the emission of all associated photons), certain emissions predominate in any particular material. This is due to the practical limitations discussed in the previous section. In order for emission to occur, the electron *must first have been raised to an excited state.* Since the energies required for this are concentrated in certain regions of the spectrum, associated concentrations of the emitted energy are to be expected. Man, of course, may control the emissions through artificial excitation processes: by irradiating a substance with specific frequencies, by deliberately heating (and vaporizing) a material, or by applying intense electrical fields.

Example 1-6. What frequency is emitted from the hydrogen atom when an electron transfer from the fifth orbital to the fourth orbital takes place?

Solution. The total electron energy in the fifth orbital is:

$$E_T = \frac{-Q_e^4 m_e}{8\epsilon_0^2 n^2 h^2} = \frac{-(1.6 \times 10^{-19})^4(9.11 \times 10^{-31})}{8(8.85 \times 10^{-12})^2(5^2)(6.63 \times 10^{-34})^2}$$
$$= \frac{6 \times 10^{-106}}{6.9 \times 10^{-87}} = -0.087 \times 10^{-18} \text{ joule}$$

From Fig. 1–5, the total electron energy in the fourth orbital is -0.14×10^{-18} joule. During the transfer process, the difference of 0.053×10^{-18} joule is lost by the electron. Since this energy is emitted as a photon, the photon frequency must be:

$$f = \frac{E_{ph}}{h} = \frac{0.053 \times 10^{-18}}{6.63 \times 10^{-34}} = 8 \times 10^{13} \text{ cps}$$

Ionization

An atom is *ionized;* i.e., has a net electrical charge, when it gains an excess of electrons (to be discussed in the next section), or when one of its normal electrons is broken free from the atom. In the latter case, the fact that all of the nuclear protons are no longer compensated for by electrons results in a net positive charge on the atom. In order to be free from any atom, the electron must have a total energy equal to or greater than zero ($E_T \geq 0$). This (in theory) means that the electron has an orbit with infinite radius. In reality, it means that the electron has moved far enough from its "parent" nucleus to experience an insignificant attraction toward that nucleus.

TABLE 1-4

Ionization Energy for Several Elements

Element	Ionization Energy (ev)
Hydrogen	13.5
Helium	24.5
Lithium	5.37
Beryllium	9.3
Boron	8.26
Carbon	11.2
Nitrogen	14.5
Oxygen	13.5
Fluorine	17.3
Neon	21.5
Sodium	5.1
Magnesium	7.6
Aluminum	6.0
Silicon	8.1

If enough energy were expended, it would be possible to free all the electrons from an atom, resulting in complete ionization. However, from Fig. 1–7, it can be seen that for the more complex atoms, removing electrons below the *highest ground state* can require tremendous energy absorptions. (The *K*-shell electrons for uranium have an energy of −100,000 electron volts.) For this reason, ionization occurs through the removal of one (and, in some instances, two or three) of the electrons in the highest, or outer, ground states. Hence, the *ionization energy* is defined as the energy required to move an electron from the outer ground state to the zero energy level. Table 1–4 lists the values associated with several of the elements.

Example 1-7. What is the ionization frequency for lithium?

Solution. Lithium has an ionization energy of 5.37 ev (Table 1–4). A photon with this energy is required. It must have a frequency given by:

$$f = \frac{E_{ph}}{h} = \frac{5.37}{4.1 \times 10^{-15}} = 1.3 \times 10^{15} \text{ cps}$$

1.3 Molecular Structure

Most of the materials encountered in the everyday world are not elemental in nature. Rather, they are *compounds;* i.e., chemical combinations of two or more of the ninety-two natural elements. So far, the most complex building block discussed has been the atom. When two or more atoms combine to form a compound, the basic building block is known as a *molecule.* Molecules may be very simple, such as the joining of two hydrogen atoms to form a molecule of hydrogen gas; or complex beyond imagination, such as the intricate chain of DNA, the fundamental molecule of human life.

Two or more atoms will form a stable molecule only when the electron energy states associated with it are lower than the energy states associated with the isolated atoms. This is in accordance with the natural tendency for an electron to occupy the lowest permissible energy state; that is, to remain as near a nucleus as existing quantum states will permit. This implies, of course, that new energy states must be associated with the molecule. The existence of new energy states, in turn, implies that the characteristics of a molecule are not usually the same as the characteristics of any of its constituent atoms (or that a compound does not usually behave like any of the elements in it).

Under the influence of ordinary energies, the nuclei of atoms cannot get very close to one another because of their natural electrostatic repulsion. However, the more complex atoms experience a repulsion from the shells of orbiting electrons associated with them—long before the nuclear repulsion takes place. The combination of atoms into a molecule, then, happens only at the outermost fringes of the atoms. This combination may come about through a direct exchange of outer electrons, or through an intermingling (sharing) of the outer electrons. Both of these reactions will be discussed. However, the latter reaction, electron sharing, is of primary importance in discussing the characteristics of most semiconductor materials.

In most solid materials, the molecules line up in an orderly array to form a *crystal lattice.* In such a structure, each molecule (and its atoms) never stray far from a single, fixed position. The vibrations associated with the molecule are centered about this position. In the liquid state, fixed molecular positions do not exist. Rather, the molecules roll around each other much like grains of sand washing across a beach. Finally, in the gaseous state, individual molecules have little regard for the presence of other molecules and an endless, aimless wandering occurs. Special attention will be given to the solid state, since semiconductor materials fall into this category.

Ionic Bonding

When an atom has only one or two electrons in its outer shell, it has a tendency to lose these electrons to an atom having six or seven electrons in its outer shell. Hence, both atoms attain a form of stability with eight electrons in their respective outer shells. The loss of an electron, however, means that the electrical (positive) charge of the nucleus is no longer balanced by an equal negative charge. This results in the formation of a *positive ion*. By a similar line of reasoning, the atom that gains an electron also has an unbalanced electrical charge ("heavy" on the negative side) and becomes a *negative ion*.

Once the two ions are formed, they have a natural electrostatic attraction for each other (since they are of the opposite sign) and begin to move together. However, when they reach a separation (between nuclei) of about 2.6×10^{-10} meter, the electrostatic repulsion of the outer electrons equals the ionic attraction and the movement stops. This represents an equilibrium state: the ions cannot move closer together because of the repulsion; yet they cannot move apart because of the attraction. They are held together through a process known as *ionic bonding*.

Covalent Bonding

Covalent bonding occurs between atoms of the same element or between atoms of different elements having similar outer-shell electron structures. Unlike ionic binding, no electron exchange occurs during the formation of a covalent molecule. Hence, the constituent atoms do not become ionized. Rather, they remain neutral and remain together by "sharing" electrons.

The hydrogen molecule is the simplest covalent bond. Two hydrogen atoms *share* their electrons. There is no experimental way to determine which electron is associated with which nucleus at any particular instant of time. Each electron spends an equal amount of time with each nucleus.

However, both electrons spend most (about two-thirds) of their time "between" the two nuclei. The force of attraction for the electron by *both* nuclei holds the two atoms together.

All molecules that have covalent bonds are governed by essentially the same considerations described for hydrogen. Figure 1–10 shows the covalent bond arrangement in germanium (the internal electron shells are not shown for the sake of clarity). The outer shell for germanium is the *N*-shell with four electrons. Stability can be achieved by a sharing arrangement that provides each germanium atom with four additional electrons. Covalent bonding occurs in "pairs"—leading to the term *electron-pair bonding*, frequently applied to covalent bonds. To do this, each germanium atom surrounds itself with four other germanium atoms. In the final molecule, neither of the germanium atoms "owns" the outer electrons. Rather, they are all shared by each of the five atoms in the molecule. The

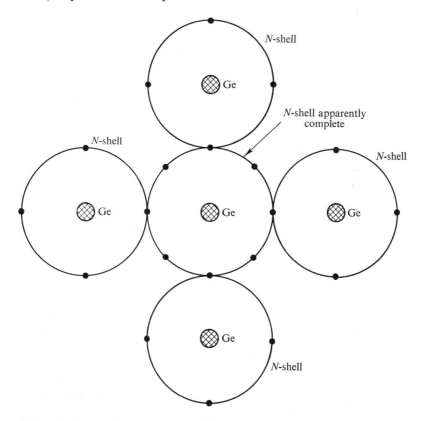

Figure 1-10.   *The Germanium Molecule*

movement of the electrons is considerably more complex than the movement associated with hydrogen. However, each electron again spends more time "between" atoms than in the vicinity of one particular atom.

Metallic Bonding

The last form of molecular bonding to be discussed occurs between atoms having a lone electron that is loosely attached to its parent nucleus. Lithium, boron, sodium, aluminum, copper, and silver are examples of elements falling into this category. The electron orbits and energy levels associated with lithium are shown in Fig. 1–11. The L_1-electron is loosely attached to the nucleus. When several lithium atoms form a "molecular" structure, the atoms move together until their *K*-shell electrons prevent a closer approach.

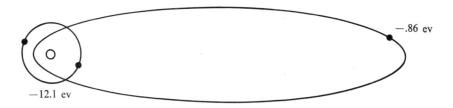

Figure 1-11.   *Lithium Atom Structure*

Metallic bonding occurs only in solid materials and always results in a definite structure such as that shown in Fig. 1–12. The structure is cubical with an atom at each corner and one in the center of each side of the cube. The single outer electron of each atom is far enough from its parent nucleus so that there may actually be other atoms between it and the parent. This decreases the parent attraction for the electron to the point where the "attachment" is actually insignificant. The metallic bond between atoms of the same element does not constitute a molecule in the sense associated with previous bonds, which have contained a specific number of each type atom associated with them. The metallic formation merely consists of long strings of atoms of unspecified number.

Certain elements, including carbon, nickel, cobalt, iron, and manganese, may enter into either a metallic or a covalent bond. The choice depends on the prevailing conditions at the time the bonding occurs. Carbon, for example, normally enters into a metallic bond. However, under extreme conditions of temperature and pressure, carbon atoms unite in a covalent

Figure 1-12.   *The Metallic Crystal* (*Lithium*)

bond to form diamond. The two alternate forms of these materials have entirely different characteristics. These characteristics and the energy phenomena that produce and control them are discussed in the next chapter.

PROBLEMS

1. The density of aluminum is 2.7×10^3 kg/m³. How many atoms are in a cubic meter of aluminum?

2. If it is assumed that the aluminum atoms are perfect spheres, each just touching the other, what is the radius of the aluminum atom and what is the electron velocity in an orbit at this radius?

3. If the potential difference between two plates separated by 0.05 meter is 5000 volts, how far will an electron travel before it reaches a kinetic energy of 10 ev? The electron is released from the negative plate at zero initial velocity.

4. What is the highest state to which a hydrogen atom can be excited by a photon of 12.2 ev?

5. What is the longest wavelength that can be absorbed by a normal hydrogen atom?

6. What frequency photon is required to ionize sodium?
7. For atoms with low atomic number, the (approximate) permissible energy levels are given by $-(Z^4 Q_e^4 m_e)/(8\epsilon_o^2 n^2 h^2)$, where Z is the atomic number of the atom. What are the first four permissible energy levels for helium?

Further Reading

"Basic Theory and Applications of Transistors," TM 11-690. Washington, D.C.: U.S. Government Printing Office, 1959.

Blanchard, C.H., C.R. Burnett, R.G. Stoner, and R.L. Weber, *An Introduction to Modern Physics*. Englewood Cliffs, N.J.: Prentice-Hall, Inc., 1958.

Bush, G.L. and A.A. Silvidi, *The Atom—A Simplified Description*. New York: Barnes and Noble, Inc., 1961.

Cleary, J.F. (ed.), *General Electric Transistor Manual*. Syracuse, N.Y.: General Electric Company, Semiconductor Products Department, 1964.

Ham, J.M. and G.R. Slemon, *Scientific Basis of Electrical Engineering*. New York: John Wiley and Sons, Inc., 1961.

Pierce, J.F., *Transistor Circuit Theory and Design*. Columbus, Ohio: Charles E. Merrill Books, Inc., 1963.

Shive, J.N., *The Properties, Physics, and Design of Semiconductor Devices*. Princeton, N.J.: D. Van Nostrand Co., Inc., 1959.

2

The Electrical Characteristics of Materials

Even the smallest visible sample of a material contains millions of molecules. In most solid inorganic materials, these molecules are arranged in an orderly array known as a *crystal lattice*. The least complicated structure is that of the metals (Fig. 1–12). More complex structures are shown in Fig. 2–1. The stable distance between the atoms depends on the kind of atoms involved, since it is the distance at which the repulsive forces of the outer electrons balance the attractive forces holding the molecule together. The corresponding energy levels in each of the millions of atoms involved cannot occupy exactly the same value. Rather, the individual levels shift slightly to form *energy bands*.

The electrical nature of materials is determined by the relative position of the outer band of electrons and a higher band of allowable energy levels known as the *conduction band*. The lower limit of the conduction band depends on atomic and molecular structure and is different for every element and every combination of elements. The two bands of interest may overlap or may be separated by a forbidden region varying from less than one electron volt to several electron volts in width. From an electrical viewpoint, materials are placed in one of three categories: conduc-

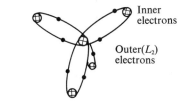

Inner electrons

Outer(L_2) electrons

A. Covalent carbon (diamond) crystal

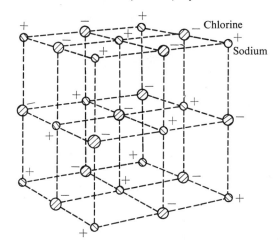

Chlorine

Sodium

B. Ionic sodium chloride (salt) cyrstal

Figure 2-1.   *Typical Crystal Structures*

tors, semiconductors, and insulators—depending upon how well they can support a flow of current (conductivity), or upon how much they impede the flow of current (resistivity). Since resistance is a quantity most commonly used in electronic circuit analysis, most of this discussion will be in terms of resistivity—the resistance offered by a unit cube of material.

Figure 2–2 provides an idea of the relative magnitudes of the resistivities associated with materials in each of the three electrical categories. It is difficult, of course, to specify disinct boundaries for conductors, semiconductors, and insulators. Rather, there is a region of overlap, or transition, where a material may sometimes be considered a conductor, sometimes a semiconductor, or sometimes an insulator. However, this is on the basis of resistivity-magnitude alone. The actual definition of the three categories leaves no question as to which materials fall into each.

As discussed in Chap. 1, metals have many electrons (at least one from

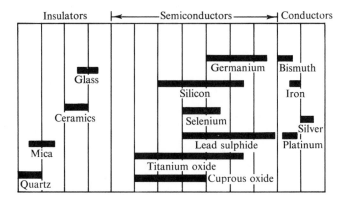

Figure 2-2. *Typical Ranges of Resistivity for the Three Types of Materials*

each atom in the crystal) that are not attached to any of the atoms. Hence, these electrons are free to wander about the material in a random fashion, until they are directed by an electric field (an electric potential difference) to travel in a specific direction. The latter case represents a normal flow of current. In the semiconductor, however, free electrons are not the only medium for supporting current flow; a second medium, referred to as *hole flow*, is also present. Both electron and hole flow will be described in subsequent sections.

The presence of two mechanisms of current flow is not the only distinctive difference between conductors and semiconductors. Their behavior under the influence of a changing temperature is also quite different, as can be seen in Fig. 2–3. At absolute zero (0°K), conductors are *superconductive*, having a negligible resistivity, while semiconductors are *perfect insulators*, supporting no current flow. As the temperature increases, conductors show a gradual, and almost linear, increase in resistivity. Semiconductors, however, show a very rapid decrease in resistivity, leveling off at higher temperatures (when all possible current-carrying particles are being used). Because of this dependence upon temperature, the reader must realize that the classification by resistivity value (Fig. 2–2) is a rather artificial method. In order to be of any use, such a method of comparison must be applied at a standard temperature. The standard to be used throughout this text is room temperature (300°K).

Both of the current mechanisms that have been mentioned occur *inside a solid material*. Hence, the current carriers have a negative total energy. If electrons absorb enough energy, their total energy will become

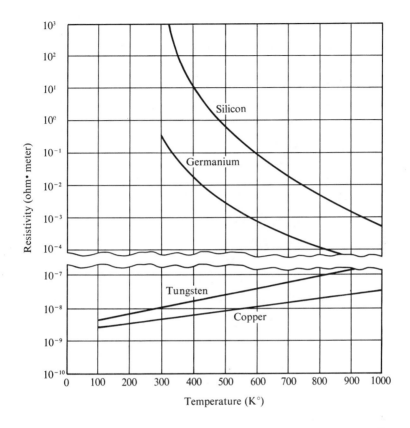

Figure 2-3.   *Thermal Variation of Resistivity for Typical Semiconductors and Conductors*

positive, resulting in a release (emission) from the material itself. This current mechanism is utilized in vacuum tube devices. Since semiconductor devices make use of the *internal mechanisms*, they inherently have lower power losses and a higher reliability (lower failure rate) than tube devices.

2.1 Energy Bands in Solids

When atoms exist in close proximity to each other, a new phenomenon known as *band formation* occurs. This phenomenon is illustrated (for silicon and copper) in Fig. 2–4. As two atoms approach each other, the exclusion principle (and the natural repulsion of electrons) drives the electrons into new energy levels—some lower, some higher. As shown,

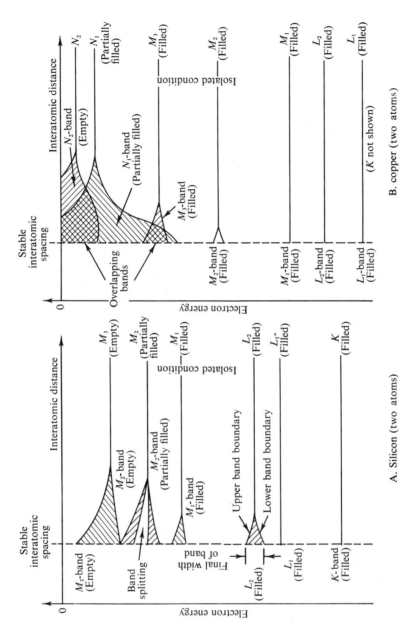

Figure 2-4. *Energy Band Formation*

A. Silicon (two atoms)

B. copper (two atoms)

34

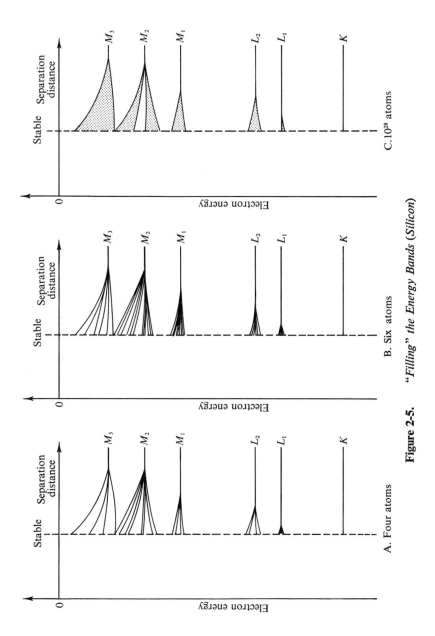

Figure 2-5. *"Filling" the Energy Bands (Silicon)*

35

the "spreading" is more pronounced in the outer electron shells (where repulsive forces are greatest and attraction to the nuclei is weakest) and is insignificant for most of the inner electron shells. The effect also becomes more pronounced as the separation distance decreases. Eventually, some of the bands may begin to overlap (as in copper) or split (as in silicon). The phenomenon reaches its final state when the stable interatomic distance is reached. At this point, the molecular boundaries of each energy band are established. As shown, an energy level that is filled (contains its maximum number of electrons) in the isolated atom results in a filled energy band. Unfilled levels result in unfilled bands.

As more and more atoms enter into combination, each energy level must find its place (Fig. 2–5) within the boundaries of its energy band. Since the band boundaries are dependent upon the type atom and the stable separation distance, the addition of new atoms does not change them. However, each new atom "packs" the levels closer together within the band until it is almost impossible to distinguish them as discrete values. (In the outermost band, the levels are typically from 10^{-22} to 10^{-28} electron volt apart.)

In order to describe the electrical characteristics of solid materials, it is necessary to consider the relative positions and widths of the individual energy bands as they exist within the crystal lattice. Hence, the complete action as a function of separation distance (Figs. 2–4 and 2–5) is not of primary importance. Only the final energy values at the stable separation distance (values along the vertical dashed line in Figs. 2–4 and 2–5) will

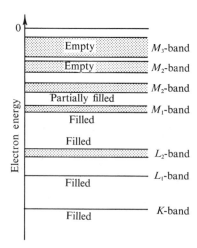

Figure 2-6.   *Simplified Energy Band Diagram (Silicon)*

be considered. This leads to a simplified energy band diagram as shown in Fig. 2–6. In such a diagram, the horizontal scale has no significance: it is used only to provide space for indicating the presence of electrons in the band. Of course, *all the individual levels and electrons within the band are not shown.* (If a scale were chosen large enough for each distinct level to be visible, each band would be several feet wide.)

Ionization in Solids

The formation of energy bands has been discussed in terms of the overall changes in energy levels. Figure 2–7 provides further insight into the phenomenon by showing the change in *energy profiles* of two silicon atoms as they are brought together. An energy profile indicates the region of attractive influence for an atom's nucleus. It is actually three-dimensional, although only two dimensions are shown in the figure. The width of the profile is a measure of an electron's total energy at any particular distance from the nucleus. As the profile width increases, total electron energy increases. Hence, electrons located at the wider portions of the profile are less firmly attached to the parent nucleus. Permissible electron energies (orbits) are indicated by lines within the profile at the appropriate position. The number of electrons that occur in the given energy level is also indicated.

Initially, the two atoms are far enough apart (Fig. 2–7, Part A) to be considered "isolated." Neither atom influences the other, and the energy profiles for both extend to zero in all directions. As the two atoms approach each other, the energy profiles between them blend, and the attractive influence of the two atoms no longer extends to zero in this region. At the same time, the electrons associated with each atom (especially the electrons in the outer shells) experience an attraction from both nuclei and repulsive forces from each other. This results in an energy-level shift, or band formation, as described previously. When the two atoms achieve a stable separation distance, their attractive influence has been reduced considerably in the region between them, and the energy-level shifts have reached a maximum (the band boundaries are fixed at their final values). Figure 2–8 shows five silicon atoms in a covalent molecule, indicating that silicon forms the same covalent bond that germanium, discussed previously, forms. Notice that the band boundaries have not changed, but that the number of levels within each band *has changed*. Notice, also, that there is a further reduction in the attractive influence of the nuclei.

In order for a solid material to support a flow of electrical current, electrons must be outside the influence of the atoms in the material. It has

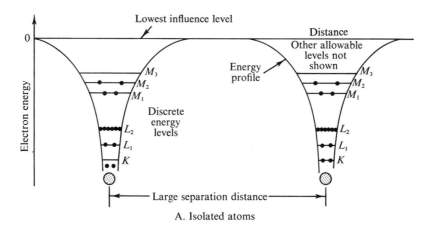

A. Isolated atoms

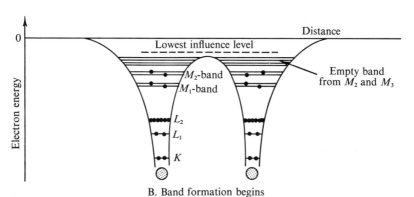

B. Band formation begins

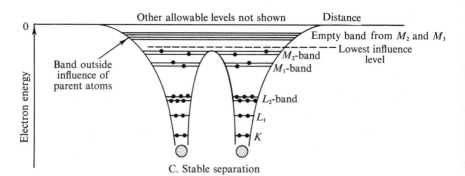

C. Stable separation

Figure 2-7.   *Band Formation and Reduction in Influence Level for Two Silicon Atoms*

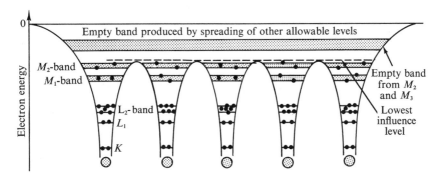

Figure 2-8.   *Band Formation and Reduction in Influence Level for the Covalent Silicon Molecule*

been stated that in order for an electron to be "free" it must reach the zero energy level. The amount of energy that must be absorbed in order to produce this effect has been called the ionization energy. This is exactly true for isolated atoms or, for example, in a gaseous substance where the interatomic spacing is great enough for most atoms to be considered "isolated." In the solid crystalline material, however, an entirely different situation exists due to the reduced influence of the atomic nuclei. An electron need only rise above the "maximum influence level" indicated in Figs. 2–7 and 2–8 in order to be "free." Hence, "ionization" occurs at energy values lower than those previously discussed.

Conduction and Valence Bands

In most crystals, by the time the stable separation distance has been reached, the high-energy allowable levels (above the normal ground state levels) have shifted and split in such a manner that the resulting energy bands overlap and form an almost continuous pattern up to the zero energy level. The lower limit of this region occurs above the influence level of the crystal atoms. Hence, an electron occupying an energy level within this region is free to support an electrical current flow, and this entire group of energy levels is referred to as the *conduction band*.

The inner electron shells do not contribute directly to the electrical characteristics of materials. This is true because they are far removed from the conduction band. The outer (ground state) shell, however, does influence the electrical characteristics of a material. The band of energies associated with this shell is called the *valence band*. Energy diagrams showing only the valence and conduction bands (such as Fig. 2–9) are

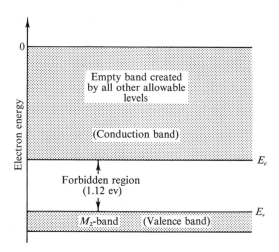

Figure 2-9.   *Conduction and Valence Bands* (*Silicon*)

essential in describing the electrical characteristics of materials *because it is the relative position of these two bands that defines a conductor, a semiconductor, and an insulator.* The upper limit of the valence band is denoted by the energy value, E_v, and the lower limit of the conduction band is denoted by E_c.

2.2 Current Carriers

Under the influence of thermal energy, repulsion from other free electrons, and collisions with atoms (or, at least, the influence of their filled "outer" shells), the free electrons in a material are continuously in motion. As shown in Fig. 2–10, Part A, when no electric field is present to "guide" the electrons, the motion is random, having no particular pattern. Occasionally, an electron may come to rest near an atom. This condition, however, is a momentary one. The electron soon breaks away, perhaps traveling in an entirely new direction. During its translational motion through the material, the electron also changes energy levels. The change is especially significant when the electron makes a "break" from the vicinity of an atom or is "captured" by an atom. This is illustrated in Part B of the figure, along with the concept that the participating electrons must have "room" to transfer to higher and lower, unoccupied (or partially occupied) energy levels.

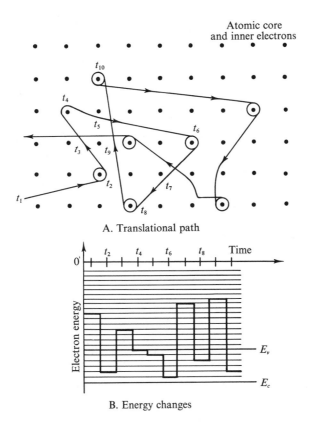

Figure 2-10.   *Random Electron Movement in a Conductor*

Only one electron is shown in Fig. 2–10. Typically, there are on the order of 10^{29} such electrons in a cubic meter of a metal. *Because of the randomness of their motion, these electron movements do not constitute a "current flow."* Mathematically, it can be shown that true randomness requires that every movement in one direction be cancelled by a movement in the opposite direction. Hence, there is no net current flow. The translational velocity of the electrons can be determined from their kinetic energy. Since the electrons are spread over a band of energies, their velocities must be similarly distributed.

When an electric field is impressed on a material (by placing a potential difference across it), the electrons move toward the higher potential (opposite to the $\mathscr{E}$-direction). However, this is not a massive, straight-line migration. Rather, the electrons still follow a zig-zag path but, unlike in the absence of the field, their paths are displaced slightly toward the higher

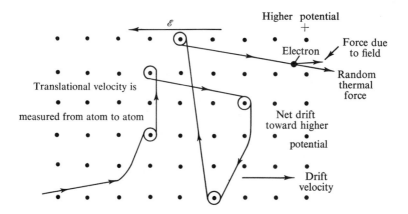

Figure 2-11.   *Drift Current Produced by Electric Fields*

potential. This is shown in Fig. 2–11. All the electrons undergo such a displacement. Hence, there is a definite movement of charged particles in one direction, resulting in a net current flow through the conductor. This is known as a *drift current*. Each electron is subject to two forces (indicated in the figure). One of these is the random force that causes the zig-zag translational motion. The other is the electrical force due to the presence of the field and is always applied in the same direction. Each force produces an acceleration (and velocity) component in its respective direction. The component in the direction of the field is termed the drift velocity.

More will be said about the translational and drift velocities of current carriers in the discussion of conductivity and resistivity. First, however, it is important to understand how the relative positions of the conduction and valence bands affect the availability of current carrying particles in these materials. It has been stated that the carriers have a distribution (or spread) of energies. Since the energy levels in the conduction band are the highest energies associated with a material, the number of electrons that reach these states is limited by both the molecular structure and the application of external (primarily thermal) energy.

Conductors

Figure 2–12 illustrates the overlapping valence and conduction bands associated with copper. *Such an overlap, to one degree or another, is typical of metals and defines a material that falls into the conductor category.* Hence, the energy relationship that defines a conductor is:

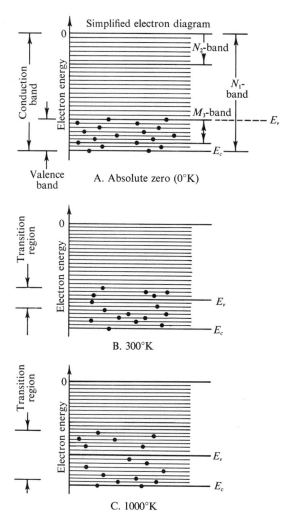

Figure 2-12.   *Electron Distributions in Conductors (Copper)*

$$E_v > E_c \tag{2-1}$$

Notice that, in Part A of the figure, all the electrons are confined within the boundaries of the valence band. This condition is true only at a temperature of absolute zero (0°K). At this temperature, no photons are being absorbed; no energy is being emitted; and no electron movements to higher or lower energy levels occur. Rather, the electrons occupy their lowest possible energy levels (valence band ground states). As the temperature increases (Parts B and C of the figure), electron "jumps" occur, especially near the top of the valence band where allowable levels can be reached with low-frequency photon absorptions. Because of these jumps, the higher energy electrons thin out and are scattered into the previously empty levels. These illustrations represent an "instantaneous" picture. There is a continuous up and down exchange of electrons—at a slightly later instant in time, the electrons shown in the figures will have returned to the valence band and other valence electrons will have jumped up to the higher levels. This exchange reaches an equilibrium point, however, so that the *number of electrons* occupying the higher levels at a particular temperature will remain constant.

Semiconductors

In pure, or *intrinsic*, semiconductor materials the valence and conduction bands are separated by a forbidden region, or *energy gap*, of a few electron volts as shown in Fig. 2–13. Although the electron distribution changes as a function of temperature, the energy gap always exists. Hence, the condition:

$$E_v < E_c \tag{2-2}$$

defines a semiconductor material. At absolute zero, the electrons are confined to the valence band. Since there are no electrons in the conduction band, the semiconductor material will not support current flow and behaves as an "insulator." As the temperature increases, some electrons will jump the energy gap and occupy the lower levels of the conduction band. As the temperature increases further, more of these jumps will occur. This process is known as *thermal activation*. Since these electrons are in the conduction band, they are free to support a current flow. Since more electrons are available at higher temperatures, the semiconductor material moves away from its insulator-like characteristics (at $0°K$) toward a more conductive characteristic. Figure 2–13 provides an "instantaneous" view. The electrons fall back to the valence band after 10^{-8} to 10^{-9} second, only to be replaced (in the conduction band) by other electrons making the upward transition. The return to the valence band is known as *recombination*.

Thermal activation and recombination must occur at the same rate. Thus, the number of electrons in the conduction band is a constant for a given temperature. This is given by:

$$n_{e(i)} = \left[\frac{4\pi m_e k}{h^2} \right]^{3/2} T^{3/2} e^{-E_G/2kT} \tag{2-3}$$

which yields "electron density"—electrons/meter³. In this equation, k

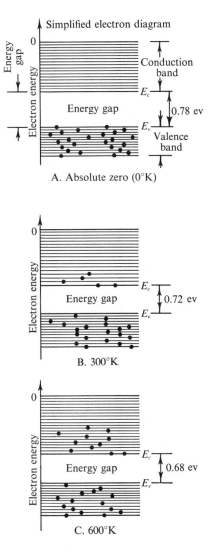

Figure 2-13.   *Electron Distributions in Semiconductors (Germanium)*

is Boltzmann's constant (Appendix A), E_G is the energy gap value, and T is the absolute temperature (°K). The quantity $4\pi m_e k/h^2$, all raised to the 3/2 power, has a value of 5.04×10^{21} meters$^{-3} \cdot$°K$^{-3/2}$. The i-subscript on $n_{e(i)}$ indicates that Eq. (2–3) is valid only for an intrinsic (pure) semiconductor material.

In Fig. 2–13, the energy gap is shown to decrease as temperature increases. This results from the thermal vibration of the atoms and molecules in the crystal. Since the widths and splitting of the energy bands depend on the atomic separation distance (see Fig. 2–4), as this distance fluctuates so must the energy gap fluctuate. The values of E_G (the gap energy) used in the various parts of Fig. 2–13 result from the average separation distance at the specified temperature (except at 0°K where there is no thermal agitation and the separation distance is fixed at the most stable interval).

During the discussion of current carriers in conductors, it was pointed out that vacant energy states must exist around an electron in order for it to participate in a current flow. This permits the electron to change energy states in response to small energy absorptions and emissions as it travels through the crystal. When electrons leave the valence band of a semiconductor material and go into the conduction band, vacant energy states are created in the valence band. Electrons in the conduction band *and the valence band* are surrounded by empty energy states (Fig. 2–13). *Hence, electrons* in both bands can participate in current flow. Since a similar situation exists in a conductor, this may not appear to be of any special interest. However, there is a significant difference between the two similar effects: the conductor transition region covers only a small span of energy values, while the semiconductor transition region covers a much larger span (Fig. 2–14).

As a consequence of the narrow transition region associated with

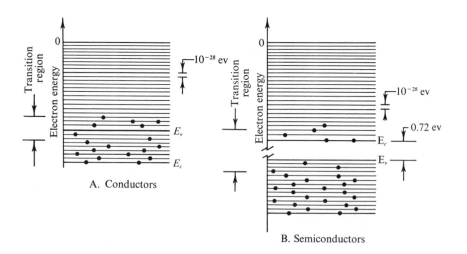

Figure 2-14.   *Comparison of the "Transition Region" in Conductors and Semiconductors*

conductors, all the electrons in this region can be assumed to have similar characteristics as far as movement through the crystal is concerned. Because of this, no distinction is made between current flow supported by valence or conduction band electrons. The relatively large difference in conduction band energies and valence band energies for semiconductor materials causes the electrons in the two regions to have *different movement characteristics*. The valence band electrons, being much more firmly attached to the parent nuclei, do not experience the extreme degree of freedom possessed by the conduction band electrons. Hence, the two electron movements do not contribute equally to the total current flow. In terms of circuit-level observation and measurement, an investigator is led to the conclusion that *two different kinds of current carriers* are involved in the current flow through a semiconductor material. Indeed, the distinction is so great that it has become conventional to assume that semiconductors *do* contain two kinds of current carriers: electrons and *holes*. The electrons are associated with the current component in the conduction band; the holes with the current component in the valence band.

Figure 2–15 is presented to help clarify the electron-hole concept. As an electron leaves a covalent bond to become free, a "hole" is left in the bond. (This thermal activation process is also termed "electron-hole pair formation.") The free electron can move through the crystal at a high energy (high velocity). Meanwhile, an electron in the valence band (near the hole) may absorb enough energy (or, in some instances, lose enough energy) to leave its covalent bond and fill the hole. The hole, then, "moves" to the position previously occupied by the valence electron. This process continues until an electron returns from the conduction band, destroying the hole (recombination occurs). Simultaneously, another electron leaves its covalent bond, goes into the conduction band, and creates another hole—maintaining the equilibrium number of electrons, $n_{e(i)}$, in the conduction band and a similar number of holes, $n_{h(i)}$, in the valence band. The reader has already probably come to the conclusion that, since each electron leaving the valence band creates a hole, the number of electrons and holes must be equal:

$$n_{h(i)} = n_{e(i)} \qquad (2\text{-}4)$$

From this point on, the "free electron" or, simply, "electron" will refer to current carriers in the conduction band, and the "hole" will refer to current carriers in the valence band. An analytical distinction is made between the movement characteristics of these two "particles" in the next section. For the moment, the only distinction to be discussed is the difference in electrical characteristics. From Fig. 2–15 it can be seen that

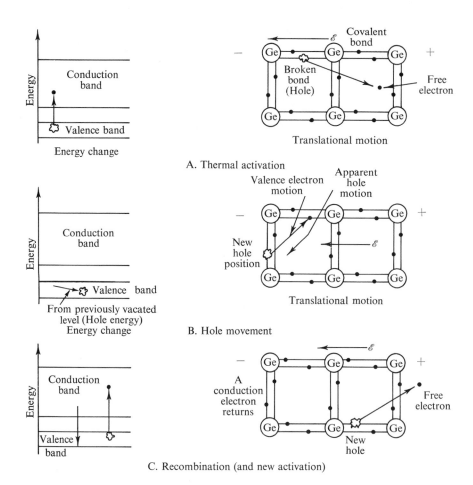

Figure 2-15.   *The Electron-Hole Concept*

all electrons move from left to right (as though a higher potential exists to the right). The holes, however, move from right to left (as if toward a *lower potential*). The only electrical particle that moves toward a lower potential is one with a positive charge. In order to satisfy its direction of movement electrically, the hole is considered to be a *positive charge* with value:

$$Q_h = Q_e \qquad (2\text{-}5)$$

With the introduction of the hole, the transition region of the semiconductor material contains both current carriers as in Fig. 2–16.

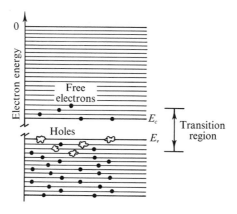

Figure 2-16.   *Electrons and Holes in the Semiconductor Transition Region*

Insulators

Figure 2–17 illustrates the significant difference between semiconductors and insulators. The insulator valence and conduction bands are separated by a much wider energy gap of several electron volts:

$$E_v \ll E_c \qquad\qquad (2\text{-}6)$$

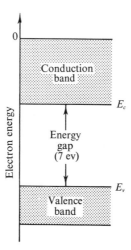

Figure 2-17.   *Insulator Energy Diagram (Diamond)*

Hence, the insulator retains its "insulating" characteristics even as the temperature increases beyond absolute zero. An extremely small number of electrons move to the conduction band [at 300°K (room temperature); use of Eq. (2–3) indicates that there will be one free electron in 10^{35} cubic meters of diamond] until very high temperatures are reached. Generally speaking, the insulator material liquifies or vaporizes before enough electrons are freed to support a significant amount of current flow.

Example 2-1. How many electrons are in the silicon conduction band at 200°K?

Solution. The number of conduction band (free) electrons in an intrinsic material is:

$$n_{e(i)} = \left[\frac{4\pi m_e k}{h^2}\right]^{3/2} T^{3/2} e^{-E_G/2kT}$$

The silicon energy gap is 1.12 ev, so that at 200°K:

$$n_{e(i)} = (5.04 \times 10^{21})(200)^{3/2} e^{-1.12/2(8.55 \times 10^{-5})(200)}$$
$$= 1.83 \times 10^8 \text{ electrons/meter}^3$$

2.3 Conductivity and Resistivity

Figure 2–18 shows a piece of material with a potential difference applied across opposite faces. The application of this potential difference creates an electric field within the material. A current, I, flows as a result of the potential application. However, the charged carriers contributing to this current are distributed across the face of the cube so that a *current density*, $J = I/A$, can be defined. From Ohm's law: $I = V/R$, where R is the macroscopic resistance of the overall material. The value of R is a function of the dimensions of the material sample and the *resistivity* of the material:

$$R = \rho \frac{L}{A} \quad \text{(ohms)} \quad\quad\quad (2\text{-}7)$$

The unit for resistivity, ρ, is the "ohm·meter." The equation is entirely general: it applies to any geometric shape of length L and cross-sectional area A. When Eq. (2–7) is substituted into the Ohm's law relationship and the relationship between potential difference and field intensity is considered, it can be shown that:

$$J = \frac{\mathscr{E}}{\rho} \quad \text{(amperes/meter}^2) \quad\quad\quad (2\text{-}8)$$

Resistivity is numerically equal to the resistance measured between

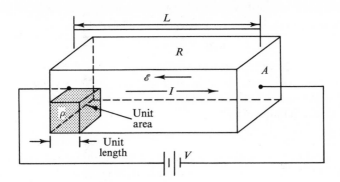

Figure 2-18.   *Resistivity and Resistance*

opposite faces of a unit cube (the shaded cube in Fig. 2–18). Resistivity is preferred over resistance in the following discussions because ρ depends only on the microscopic properties of the material rather than on the macroscopic geometry (size and shape). *Conductivity* is the reciprocal of resistivity and is sometimes used to produce a more convenient form of Eq. (2–8):

$$J = \sigma\mathcal{E} \quad \text{(amperes/meter}^2\text{)} \tag{2-9}$$

The unit for conductivity, σ, is the "mho/meter."

The previous sections have discussed the charged carriers that participate in current flow through various types of material. Caught in the electrical field, such a carrier experiences a force parallel to the direction of the field (Fig. 2–19). This force causes the carrier to accelerate along the

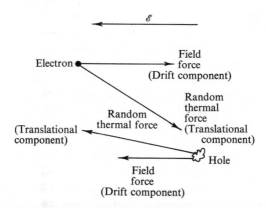

Figure 2-19.   *Carrier Forces in an Electric Field*

field, traveling at a drift velocity that is constant (constant field) or varying (alternating field). The current density can be expressed by:

$$J = nQv_d \qquad \text{(amperes/meter}^2\text{)} \qquad \textbf{(2-10)}$$

where n is the carrier density (carriers/meter^3), Q is the carrier charge (coulombs/carrier), and v_d is the *drift velocity* (meters/second). Equation (2–10) is similar in form to Eq. (2–9). In fact, the drift velocity is proportional to the field intensity:

$$v_d = \mu\mathscr{E} \qquad \text{(meters/second)} \qquad \textbf{(2-11)}$$

where μ is the *carrier mobility*. Substituting Eq. (2–11) into (2–10), equating (2–10) and (2–9), and solving for conductivity leads to:

$$\sigma = nQ\mu \qquad \text{(mhos/meter)} \qquad \textbf{(2-12)}$$

Since resistivity and conductivity are reciprocals:

$$\rho = \frac{1}{nQ\mu} \qquad \text{(ohm} \cdot \text{meters)} \qquad \textbf{(2-13)}$$

The equations used thus far are entirely general. In order to apply them to conductor and semiconductor materials, the different current-carrying mechanisms (electron flow and hole flow) must be considered. For the conductor, this is a simple matter because only electron flow must be considered. Hence, only electron characteristics must be considered:

$$\sigma_c = n_e Q_e \mu_e \qquad \text{(mhos/meter)} \qquad \textbf{(2-14)}$$

$$\rho_c = \frac{1}{n_e Q_e \mu_e} \qquad \text{(ohm} \cdot \text{meters)} \qquad \textbf{(2-15)}$$

where the subscript c refers to conductor characteristics and the subscript e refers to electrons. At room temperature, copper has 1.1×10^{29} electrons/meter^3 and these electrons have a mobility of 3.3×10^{-3} meter^2/volt·second. With these values, Eq. (2–15) yields a resistivity of 1.7×10^{-8} ohm·meter—a value that is in good agreement with the measured resistivity of pure copper.

Two current mechanisms are involved in semiconductors: both electron and hole flow. Since negative carriers (electrons) flow toward the higher potential and positive carriers (holes) flow toward the lower potential, the two current components are *additive:*

$$J_s = J_e + J_h \qquad \textbf{(2-16)}$$

where J_s is the "semiconductor current density." Since the electron and hole paths are parallel paths in the semiconductor material, the "total" conductivity of the semiconductor must be expressed by:

$$\sigma_s = \sigma_e + \sigma_h \qquad \textbf{(2-17)}$$

where σ_e is the "electron conductivity "and σ_h is the "hole conductivity." In terms of the resistivity of parallel paths, the "total" resistivity of the semiconductor material must be:

$$\rho_s = \frac{\rho_e \cdot \rho_h}{\rho_e + \rho_h} \tag{2-18}$$

The resistivity measure yields a difficult expression for examining the overall semiconductor properties. For this reason, it is more convenient to examine the conductivity characteristic—*keeping in mind the fact that resistivity behavior is the inverse of the conductivity behavior.*

From the expression for conductivity [Eq. (2–12)]:

$$\sigma_e = n_e Q_e \mu_e \tag{2-19}$$

$$\sigma_h = n_h Q_h \mu_h \tag{2-20}$$

leading [from Eq. (2–17)] to:

$$\sigma_{s(i)} = n_{e(i)} Q_e (\mu_e + \mu_h) \tag{2-21}$$

TABLE 2-1

Germanium and Silicon Characteristics

Characteristic	Germanium	Silicon
Atomic Number	32	14
Mass Number	73	28
Atoms/Meter³	4.42×10^{28}	4.96×10^{28}
Energy Gap (300°K)	0.72 ev	1.12 ev
Energy Gap (0°K)	0.78 ev	1.21 ev
Stable Separation Distance (meters)	5.66×10^{-10}	5.43×10^{-10}
Electron Mobility (300°K)	0.36	0.15
Hole Mobility (300°K)	0.17	0.05
Electrons (or Holes) per Meter³ (300°K)	2.5×10^{19}	1.6×10^{16}
Conductivity (300°K)	2.12 mho/m	0.00052 mho/m
Resistivity (300°K)	0.47 ohm·m	1950 ohm·m

Note: Mobilities are indicated in units of meters²/volt·sec.

since $n_{h(i)} = n_{e(i)}$ for intrinsic semiconductor materials and $Q_h = Q_e$, always. *This equation is valid only for intrinsic semiconductor materials.*

Table 2–1 lists the characteristics for germanium and silicon, two common semiconductor materials. Since "mobility" is a measure of the velocity attained per unit field intensity (meters/second for each volt/meter, or meters²/volt·second), the holes, having less energy, are "sluggish" and have a lower mobility than the electrons:

$$\mu_h < \mu_e \tag{2-22}$$

as shown in the table.

Example 2-2. At room temperature, nickel has a resistivity of 7.8×10^{-8} ohm·meter. What is the resistance of a nickel plate 0.5 meter long, 0.05 meter thick, and 0.1 meter wide? What is the conductivity of nickel?

Solution. The resistance is given by:

$$R = \rho \frac{L}{A} = (7.8 \times 10^{-8})\, [0.5/(0.05)(0.1)] = 7.8 \times 10^{-6}\ \text{ohm}$$

The conductivity is given by:

$$\sigma = \frac{1}{\rho} = \frac{1}{7.8 \times 10^{-8}} = 1.29 \times 10^7\ \text{mhos/meter}$$

Example 2-3. The free electron density, electron mobility, and hole mobility in pure germanium are given in Table 2–1. Verify the resistivity value listed in the table.

Solution. The most direct approach is to use the reciprocal of the intrinsic semiconductor conductivity expression:

$$\rho_{s(i)} = \frac{1}{\sigma_{s(i)}} = \frac{1}{n_{e(i)} Q_e(\mu_e + \mu_h)}$$
$$= \frac{1}{(2.5 \times 10^{19})(1.6 \times 10^{-19})(0.36 + 0.17)}$$
$$= 0.47\ \text{ohm·meter}$$

Example 2-4. There are 6.02×10^{28} free electrons per cubic meter in a sample of pure aluminum. The resistivity of aluminum is 2.83×10^{-8} ohm·meter. What is the electron mobility in aluminum?

Solution. Aluminum resistivity (and the resistivity for any conductor) is given by:

$$\rho_c = \frac{1}{n_e Q_e \mu_e}$$

which, when solved for mobility, yields:

$$\mu_e = \frac{1}{n_e Q_e \rho_c} = \frac{1}{(6.02 \times 10^{28})(1.6 \times 10^{-19})(2.83 \times 10^{-8})}$$
$$= 3.94 \times 10^{-3} \text{ meter}^2/\text{volt} \cdot \text{second}$$

Effects of Carrier Motion

Two components of motion have been associated with current carriers (see Figs. 2–11 and 2–19): a translational velocity, v_t, and a drift velocity, v_d. The average translational velocity of the electrons in copper is 1.58×10^6 meters/second. In order to investigate the drift velocity, Eq. (2–10) is rearranged to:

$$v_d = \frac{J}{nQ} \quad \text{(meters/second)} \qquad \textbf{(2-10a)}$$

Copper can withstand a *maximum* current density of 10^7 amperes/meter^2 and has a carrier density of 1.1×10^{29} electrons/meter^3. Using these values in Eq. (2–10a), the maximum drift velocity in copper is only 5.7×10^{-4} meter/second—*a value contrary to impressions most readers may have.* However, the general concept that an electron goes charging in one end of a conductor and out the other end is entirely false—as the drift velocity for copper indicates. All electrons in all parts of the material "shift" toward the higher potential as soon as the field is applied. It is this shift that constitutes the initial current flow—not the movement of an electron from one end of the material to another. The current flow is then *maintained* by the slow drift of electrons toward the higher potential. Eventually, of course, an electron will drift from one end of the material to the other. With a drift velocity of 5.7×10^{-4} meter/second, an electron will be displaced one meter from its starting point in approximately 1750 seconds—*slightly over 29 minutes.* In being displaced one meter along the direction of the field, however, the electron actually traverses many times this distance along its zig-zag path (Fig. 2–11).

The mobility factor, μ, has been defined as the drift velocity induced per unit field intensity. The value of μ depends on the number of collisions between an electron and the crystal atoms. During each collision, electron energy is lost, finally resulting in a temporary "capture" of the electron. The distance that the electron travels between captures is called the *mean free* path, ℓ. In copper, at room temperature, the mean free path is 10^{-7} meter. The time it takes the electron to travel this distance is related to the translational velocity of the electron. During this time, ℓ/v_t, the electron accelerates toward the higher potential at the rate

$Q_e\mathscr{E}/m_e$, reaching an average drift velocity of:

$$v_d = \frac{Q_e\ell}{2m_ev_t} \cdot \mathscr{E} \qquad \text{(meters/second)} \qquad \textbf{(2-23)}$$

This equation is of the same form as Eq. (2–11). Hence:

$$\mu_e = \frac{Q_e\ell}{2m_ev_t} \qquad \text{(meters}^2\text{/volt·second)} \qquad \textbf{(2-24)}$$

In view of the translational velocity and mean free path values that have been specified for copper, Eq. (2–24) yields a value of 10^{-2} meter²/volt·second. This does not agree with measured values of copper electron mobility (3.3×10^{-3} meter²/volt·second). The primary reason for this disagreement lies in the fact that Eq. (2–23) does not account for the repulsive forces of electrons traveling in the vicinity of one another. This tends to decrease the acceleration produced by the electric field. Equation (2–23) and Eq. (2–24) are not introduced in order to permit the direct calculation of μ_e, however. Rather, *they are introduced in order to show the general relationship between mobility and mean free path (directly proportional) and between mobility and translational velocity (inversely proportional).* Since resistivity is inversely proportional to mobility [Eq. (2–13)], it must be directly proportional to v_t and inversely proportional to ℓ:

$$\rho_e = \frac{2m_ev_t}{n_eQ_e^2\ell} \qquad \text{(ohm·meters)} \qquad \textbf{(2-25)}$$

The reader must realize that Eq. (2–25) fails to account for inter-electron repulsions also, since it uses a direct substitution of Eq. (2–24) into Eq. (2–13). *It does, however, show the general relationship between ρ and n_e, v_t and ℓ.* Different materials have different values for these factors, depending upon the relationship between E_v and E_c and upon the crystal structure (stable atomic separation distance).

For conductors, the current consists entirely of electrons. By the reciprocal relationship:

$$\sigma_c = \sigma_e = \frac{1}{\rho_e} = \frac{n_eQ_e^2\ell_e}{2m_ev_{t(e)}} \qquad \text{(mhos/meter)} \qquad \textbf{(2-26)}$$

where the *e*-subscript is used on ℓ and v_t in order to associate these values with electrons, specifically. This makes Eq. (2–26) a general equation for conductivity due to electron current flow, and for the conductivity of a "conductor" material.

For semiconductors, both current carriers must be considered. The hole carriers travel through the material under the same haphazard restraints imposed on the electrons, with a general drift induced by the presence of an electric field. Hence, the same derivational procedure [see Eq. (2–26)] can be used to obtain:

$$\sigma_h = \frac{n_h Q_h^2 \ell_h}{2m_h v_{t(h)}} \quad \text{(mhos/meter)} \tag{2-27}$$

This equation can be substituted directly into Eq. (2–21), along with Eq. (2–26) (for electron conductivity), to yield total semiconductor conductivity. However, since $n_h = n_e$, $Q_h = Q_e$, and $m_h = m_e$, the expression simplifies to:

$$\sigma_s = \frac{n_e Q_e^2}{2m_e} \left[\frac{\ell_e}{v_{t(e)}} + \frac{\ell_h}{v_{t(h)}} \right] \tag{2-28}$$

Also, from Eqs. (2–27) and (2–12), it can be noted that:

$$\mu_h = \frac{Q_h \ell_h}{2m_h v_{t(h)}} \quad \text{(meters}^2\text{/volt·second)} \tag{2-29}$$

showing that hole mobility is related to the same general factors as is electron mobility [see Eq. (2–24)]. Repulsive forces produced by holes in the small volume under consideration produce the same inaccuracies in these equations that are encountered in the electron equations. The expressions are presented only to show the inverse relation between mobility (and conductivity) and the translational energy, and the direct relationship between mobility (and conductivity) and the mean free path. *Since holes have less total energy than electrons (they are still attached to atoms, remember), their mean free paths and translational velocities are correspondingly lower.*

Example 2-5. Using the electron mobility in aluminum, as determined in Example 2–4, what is the electron drift velocity in an aluminum conductor 50 meters long with a potential difference of 20 volts across the ends?

Solution. Drift velocity is given by the product of mobility and electric field intensity. The electric field intensity must be determined in terms of potential difference and conductor length. Hence:

$$v_d = \mu \mathscr{E} = \frac{\mu V}{L} = \frac{(3.94 \times 10^{-3})(20)}{50}$$
$$= 1.576 \times 10^{-3} \text{ meter/second}$$

indicating that, on the average, it will take an electron 3.5 hours to travel from one end of the conductor to the other!

Effects of Temperature Variation

The average kinetic energy associated with an object, due to the object's temperature (heat content), is given by

$$E_k = kT \qquad (2\text{-}30)$$

where k is Boltzmann's constant (Appendix A) and T is the absolute temperature. (It is this average energy that accounts for the average, or "most probable," velocity.) As discussed in Appendix B, all particles within an object do not have the same velocity. Rather, they are distributed in accordance with the Maxwell-Boltzmann relationship. Electrons in the conduction band, being free of their parent nuclei and no longer having "orbital evergy," fit these distributions. For this reason, the average translational velocity of the electrons is:

$$v_{t(e)} = \sqrt{\frac{2kT}{m_e}} \qquad (2\text{-}31)$$

Holes follow a distribution also, but have an average translational velocity less than that indicated by Eq. (2–31). This is due to the fact that holes are not free of the parent nuclei in the sense that the electrons are. They still have a component of orbital velocity.

The number of free electrons, n_e, in a conductor is only slightly affected by changes in temperature. In copper, for example, additional free electrons have to come from the M_2-band. This requires that the electrons jump an energy gap on the order of 7 ev. To raise the *average energy* of these electrons by 7 ev requires a temperature *in excess of* 81,000°K. Of course, some of the electrons would jump the gap at lower temperatures. The actual number can be determined from Eq. (2–3). However, a few computations will show that before any significant increase in n_e is obtained, impractical temperatures are required. Hence, the temperature variation of conductor resistivity *is not the result of freeing more electrons*.

It has been shown that the ability of a semiconductor material to support current flow *depends entirely* on the ability of its valence electrons to jump the energy gap to the conduction band. Equation (2–3) is plotted in Fig. 2–20 for germanium and silicon, two commonly used semiconductor materials. From this figure and the semiconductor resistivity in Fig. 2–3, there can be little doubt that the resistivity change associated with temperature change is very closely related to the change in n_e. Actually, the change is even more pronounced than is indicated by Fig. 2–20, because every change in n_e is accompanied by an equal change in n_h.

Since conductor resistivity changes are not brought about by changes in the number of free electrons, they must be the result of changes in electron

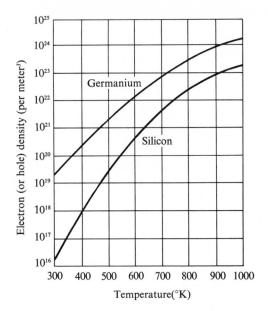

Figure 2-20.   *Carrier Density Variation from* Eq. (2–3)

mobility. Carrier mobility has been related to translational velocity and mean free path. A temperature increase causes an increase in v_t [Eq. (2–31)]. In view of Eqs. (2–24) and (2–25), this change results in decreasing mobility and increasing resistivity. Indeed, this is true of all conductors (Fig. 2–3). However, it is also necessary to examine the temperature change effect on the mean free path before reaching a final conclusion.

Figure 2–21, Part A describes the crystal arrangement at absolute zero. There is no motion of the crystal atoms which maintain a fixed position within the crystal and present a fixed "cross section" to free electrons that must travel through the material. In this situation, electron capture is extremely remote and values of ℓ are quite high. In Part B of the figure (at a temperature above 0°K), the atoms are shown to oscillate about their original positions. In effect, the atoms occupy a larger volume. Since the atoms are "bigger," electrons are more likely to encounter them and be captured by them. Hence, *temperature increases reduce the mean free path.*

From Eqs. (2–24) and (2–25), it can be seen that a reduced mean free path will result in a reduced mobility and an increased resistivity—the same effect associated with increasing v_t. The complete explanation for increases in conductor resistivity with temperature increases lies in the

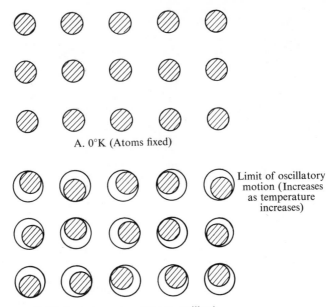

A. 0°K (Atoms fixed)

B. Higher temperature (Atoms oscillate)

Figure 2-21.   *Effective Increase in Collision "Cross Section" with Increasing Temperature*

combined changes in translational velocity and electron mean free path. The two effects compliment one another, resulting in reduced carrier mobility and increased resistivity. The process is reversed when the temperature decreases.

For semiconductors, the change in electron and hole velocities and mean free paths tends to produce lower mobilities and higher resistivities, also. However, unlike the conductor, the semiconductor experiences large increases in carrier density as temperature increases. The increase in carrier density is so pronounced that it overshadows the effects of decreasing carrier mobility, *resulting in a decreased resistivity* when temperature increases.

PROBLEMS

1. What is the free carrier density in intrinsic silicon at 500°K? (Assume that the energy gap variation between 300°K and 500°K is negligible and use data from Table 2–1.)

2. What is the free carrier density in intrinsic germanium at 150°K?

(Assume that the energy gap variation between 300°K and 150°K is negligible and use data from Table 2–1.)

3. What is the free carrier density in diamond at 2000°K if the energy gap is 7 ev?

4. The resistance of a cylindrical conductor 0.005 meter in diameter and 3 meters long is 0.02 ohm. Determine the resistance of a cylindrical conductor of the same material at the same temperature if the diameter is 0.0025 meter and the length is 10 meters.

5. If a current density of 0.5 ampere/meter^2 exists in a piece of intrinsic germanium that has a cross section of 0.0005 meter and a length of 0.001 meter, what electrical potential difference must exist across the ends? (Germanium data appear in Table 2–1.)

6. If electron and hole mobilities change by unequal amounts, but maintain the same ratio associated with 300°K, what are the electron and hole mobilities in intrinsic germanium at 450°K? (Germanium data appear in Table 2–1.)

Further Reading

"Basic Theory and Applications of Transistors." TM 11-690. Washington, D. C.: U.S. Government Printing Office, 1959.

Cleary J. F. (ed.), *General Electric Transistor Manual.* Syracuse, N.Y.: General Electric Company, Semiconductor Products Department, 1964.

Ham, J. M. and G. R. Slemon, *Scientific Basis of Electrical Engineering.* New York: John Wiley and Sons, Inc., 1961.

Pierce, J. F., *Transistor Circuit Theory and Design.* Columbus, Ohio: Charles E. Merrill Books, Inc., 1963.

Shive, J. N., *The Properties, Physics, and Design of Semiconductor Devices.* Princeton, N. J.: D. Van Nostrand Co., Inc., 1959.

Ryder, J. D., *Electronic Fundamentals and Applications.* Englewood Cliffs, N. J.: Prentice-Hall, Inc., 1959.

3

Thermistors

All semiconductor materials have one phenomenon in common: their resistivity decreases, very rapidly, with increasing temperature. These changes may amount to as much as 10 per cent per degree in the vicinity of room temperature. Devices designed specifically to take advantage of this effect are called *thermistors—thermally sensitive resistors*. Even with present-day technology, it is not practical to use pure elemental semiconductor materials, such as germanium or silicon, in the manufacture of these devices. Instead, several *metallic oxides* that satisfy the energy-band definition of semiconductor materials are used. Among these materials are ferrous and ferric oxide, magnesium chromate, and a zinc-titanium oxide alloy. The choice of material depends on the resistivity desired and the temperature sensitivity requirements.

Most thermistors look like normal resistors or like ceramic capacitors. A third type, the *bead thermistor*, is enclosed in a glass or ceramic tube. All types, as shown in Fig. 3–1, have connecting leads attached. The finished devices are light, compact, and rugged.

The extreme temperature sensitivity of thermistors make them well

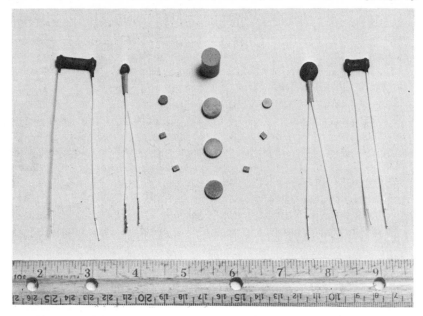

Figure 3-1.   *Thermistors (Photo, Courtesy National Lead Company, Titanium Alloy Manufacturing Division)*

suited to temperature measurement. Other applications include high-frequency power measurement, temperature compensation (offsetting normal resistor changes as temperature changes), and timing and delay circuits. Each of these applications will be discussed, in turn, after a complete description of thermistor characteristics is presented.

3.1 Thermistor Characteristics

The thermistor *material* determines its resistivity which, in combination with the physical dimensions, determines the total circuit resistance [Eq. (2–7)]. Both the resistivity and the resistance are temperature dependent. For this reason it is necessary to characterize a thermistor by its *reference resistance*—specified at room temperature (300°K). Related to this reference resistance is the *power sensitivity*—the power (watts) required to reduce the reference resistance by one per cent.

When appreciable current flows through a thermistor, the temperature of the device is not dependent upon the surrounding (ambient) temperature. Rather, it is dependent upon the internal heating caused by the current flow itself. When only small amounts of current are drawn, so that there is no appreciable internal heating, the thermistor temperature will match the ambient conditions. The exact nature of these effects is related to thermistor *heat capacity*: the amount of heat energy retained in the device per degree rise in temperature (joules/°K), and the *thermal dissipation constant*: the rate at which heat can be dissipated for each degree rise in temperature (watts/°K).

Maximum current, voltage, and power values are usually specified by the manufacturer. Care must be taken to assure that the device is not driven beyond these specified values. The maximum power is usually specified in milliwatts/°C. Hence, the operating temperature of the device must be considered in establishing the maximum power that can be applied in a specific circuit application.

Under dynamic operation, the thermistor displays a time lag before it can match new conditions. Hence, if operation is maintained under one set of conditions (allowing the device to stabilize) and the conditions are then changed, the characteristics will require a definite time to reach their new values.

The Resistance Characteristic

The resistive behavior of semiconductors is thoroughly analyzed in Chap. 2, and is summarized by Fig. 2–3. The semiconductors (germanium and silicon) used in the figure, however, must be highly purified in order to exhibit exactly these characteristics. Very slight amounts of foreign substances will produce an entirely different curve. For this reason, germanium and silicon, as well as any other *elemental* semiconductor materials, are not used in thermistors. The preferred compounds, mentioned in the introduction to this chapter, display a fair degree of "repeatability" between devices, but still have *some variation*. Hence, a resistance characteristic (or any other thermistor characteristic) represents an "average" and does not guarantee identical operation for all devices bearing the same nomenclature. Several typical average resistance characteristics are shown in Fig. 3–2.

The *exponential behavior* of the thermistor resistance as a function of temperature is obvious in Fig. 3–2. *All semiconductor materials display such a characteristic.* Thus, the resistance at any temperature may be computed from:

$$R_T = R_{300}e^{B \cdot [(1/T) - (1/300)]} \tag{3-1}$$

where R_{300} is the reference resistance, B is a constant used to "fit" the exponential equation to the characteristic curve, and T is the temperature (°K) associated with the desired resistance value. B is different for each

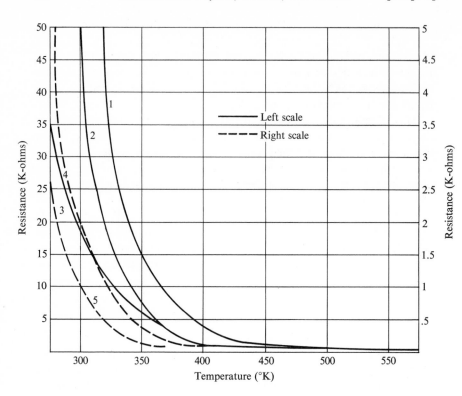

Figure 3-2.   *Resistance Characteristics*

semiconductor material and can be determined from:

$$B = \frac{\ln R_{300} - \ln R_T}{(1/300) - (1/T)} \quad (°K) \tag{3-2}$$

when a resistance characteristic is given. R_T and T represent any particular set of coordinates on the resistance characteristic curve. If it is desirable to know the temperature associated with a particular resistance value:

$$T = \frac{1}{1/300 + 1/B \ln (R_T/R_{300})} \tag{3-3}$$

Figure 3–3 demonstrates the effect of varying B and R_{300} on the resistance characteristic. The value of B depends entirely on the thermistor material. Materials having larger B-values produce thermistors with a less pronounced temperature sensitivity. Although R_{300} is basically dependent upon material (resistivity), any material may be made to have different reference resistances by changing the physical dimensions of the device.

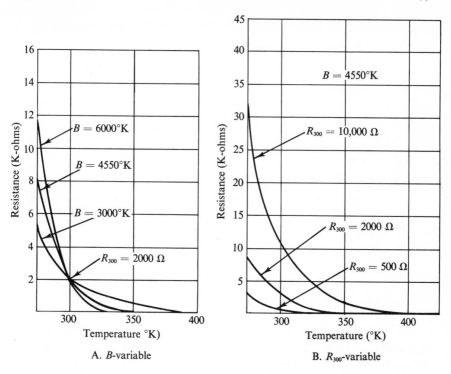

Figure 3-3. *Effects of Independent Variables on Resistance Characteristic*

As shown in the figure, changes in R_{300} shift the characteristic to higher, or lower, overall values.

The Volt-Ampere Characteristic

Figure 3-4 illustrates the nonlinear relationship existing between the potential across a thermistor and the current through the thermistor. From points A to B the thermistor resistance does not change appreciably if the ambient temperature is constant. Hence, the volt-ampere characteristic exhibits the linearity associated with normal resistors. In fact, the straight line between points A and B has a slope equal to R_{300} (as shown). The numbered points along the curve represent the internal temperature associated with the device at the indicated current flow value. As the current increases beyond the value associated with point B, the internal thermistor temperature rises more rapidly, resulting in decreased resistance. At first the decrease is small, so that as current continues to rise, so does the potential—but at a continuously reduced rate. Finally, at point

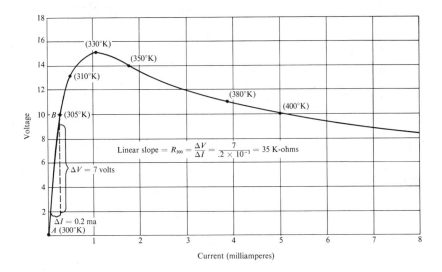

Figure 3-4.   *Typical Thermistor Volt-Ampere Characteristic*

C, the resistance begins decreasing at a significant rate. After this point, the decrease in resistance offsets the increase in current, *resulting in less voltage for increased current.* The exact nature of the volt-ampere characteristic is highly dependent upon the heat capacity and the thermal dissipation constant of the thermistor material.

Example 3-1.   Determine the value of B for thermistor 4 in Fig. 3–2.

Solution.   In general, the value of B is given by:

$$B = \frac{\ln R_{300} - \ln R_T}{(1/300) - (1/T)}$$

From Fig. 3–2, R_{300} for thermistor 4 is 2000 ohms. In order to determine B, it is necessary to select a second temperature and resistance value. If a temperature of 350°K is selected, R_{350} for thermistor 4 is 450 ohms. Hence:

$$B_4 = \frac{\ln 2000 - \ln 450}{(1/300) - (1/350)} = \frac{7.6 - 6.1}{(4.7 \times 10^{-4})} = 3200° \text{ K}$$

Similar values are obtained with other selections of T and the associated R_T.

Example 3-2.   Using the data in Example 3–1, verify the resistance of thermistor 4 at 325°K.

Solution. The resistance at any temperature is:

$$R_T = R_{300}e^{B[(1/T) - (1/300)]}$$

leading to:

$$R_{325} = 2000e^{3200[(1/325) - (1/300)]} = 2000e^{-0.8}$$
$$= 900 \text{ ohms}$$

This figure agrees very well with the corresponding value shown in in Fig. 3–2.

Figure 3–5 shows the variation in internal temperature and power at the volt-ampere characteristic peak as B and the thermal dissipation constant are changed. Since an increase in B causes the peak to occur at a lower temperature (indicating less current flow), this change causes the low-current, linear portion of the characteristic to extend through a smaller range of V-I values. Larger values of thermal dissipation constant produce higher peak powers, leading to a longer range of V-I values for the linear portion.

Straight lines, originating at $V = 0$ and $I = 0$, drawn on the volt-ampere characteristic represent lines of fixed d-c resistance. The intersection of such lines and the volt-ampere characteristic represent points where the thermistor displays the same resistance value (Fig. 3–6). Lines representing constant power can also be drawn by selecting voltage (or current) values arbitrarily, and finding the current (or voltage) that will yield the required power ($P = VI$). These lines are *hyperbolas*, also shown in Fig. 3–6. Intersection points between a power curve and the volt-ampere characteristic represent points where the thermistor is dissipating the specified power.

Plotting the resistance lines and power curves may seem like a tedious and unwarrented task when the resistance at any point on the characteristic is simply V/I and the power is simply VI. However, it has become common practice to plot these characteristics on log-log coordinates (Fig. 3–7). When this is done, lines drawn with a positive slope of 45° represent constant resistance lines, and lines drawn with a negative slope of 45° represent constant power lines. With such a crisscrossed grid, it is possible to rapidly specify the resistance and power associated with any point on the characteristics.

At very large current values (high temperature), the characteristic of decreasing voltage with increasing current ends, and the thermistor displays a linear characteristic similar to the low-current region again. The resistance associated with this new region is very low and is referred to as the *limiting resistance*. This phenomenon occurs at a temperature where *all valence electrons have jumped the energy gap to the conduction band.*

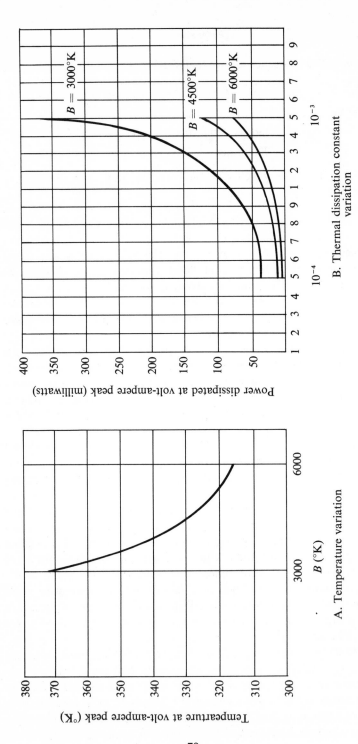

Figure 3-5. *Effect of Independent Variables on Volt-Ampere Peak Characteristics*

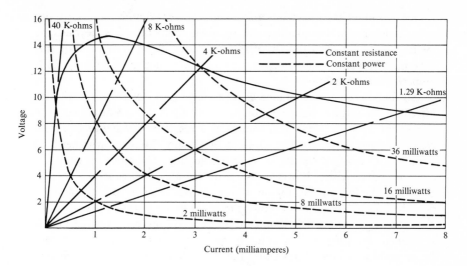

Figure 3-6. *Volt-Ampere Characteristic with Resistance and Power Curves*

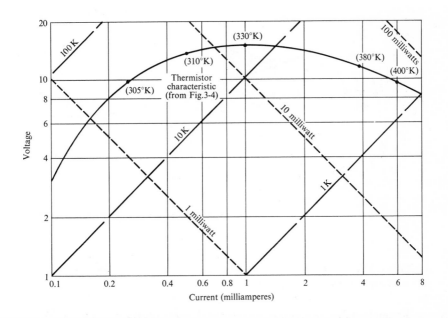

Figure 3-7. *Typical Thermistor Characteristic in Log-Log Coordinates*

Hence, the number of electrons and holes is at a maximum, and resistivity is at a minimum. Frequently, the required temperature is beyond the melting point (or even the vaporization point) of the material. For this reason, the second positive resistance region does not show on many volt-ampere characteristics.

So far, thermistor resistance changes have only been associated with internal temperature changes, brought about by high current values. The thermistor resistance may also change as a result of *ambient temperature changes*. With respect to Eq. (3–1), it makes no difference whether T is the result of internal heating or external heating. The effect on the volt-ampere characteristic, however, is rather drastic. This is shown in Fig. 3–8. Over the low-current region, where internal temperature is not significantly affected by current flow, *the ambient temperature controls the thermistor resistance.* Higher ambient temperatures decrease the thermistor resistance, resulting in less voltage for a given current value, whereas lower ambient temperatures cause the opposite effect. Over the high-current region, the internal heating of the current predominates the thermistor resistance variation, causing the volt-ampere characteristic to vary only slightly with ambient temperature.

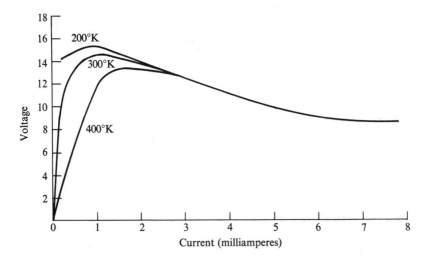

Figure 3-8.   *Thermistor Volt-Ampere Characteristic with Changing Ambient Temperature Conditions*

Example 3-3.   Determine the internal temperature and power for the peak of the volt-ampere characteristic of thermistor 4 in Fig. 3–2 if the thermal dissipation constant is 6×10^{-4} watt/°K.

Solution. From Example 3–1, the *B*-value for thermistor 4 is 3200°K. From Fig. 3–5, Part A, the internal temperature at the peak of the volt-ampere characteristic is 360°K. From Fig. 3–5, Part B, the power is 40 milliwatts if *B* is equal to 3000°K and 15 milliwatts if *B* is equal to 4500°K. For *B* equal to 3200°K, interpolation must be used, and yields approximately 36.7 milliwatts.

Graphical Circuit Analysis

When a circuit is composed of purely linear resistances (resistors made of conductor materials), a knowledge of the supply voltage and a straight-forward application of Ohm's and Kirchoff's laws is sufficient to determine current flow. If a voltage is placed directly across a thermistor, the current flow can be determined directly from the volt-ampere characteristic. However, when a thermistor is used in conjunction with resistive components in an electronic circuit, a graphical construction, known as *load line analysis* must be used.

Regardless of the complexity of the resistor network, the principles of d-c circuit analysis can be used to find a single *equivalent resistance* in series with the thermistor. This equivalent circuit is shown in Fig. 3–9. From Kirchoff's law: the algebraic sum of voltages around a closed loop must equal zero, the equation for this circuit is:

$$V_B - IR - V_{TH} = 0 \qquad (3\text{-}4)$$
$$V_B = V_{TH} + IR \qquad (3\text{-}4a)$$

V_{TH} is dependent upon I (just as the drop across the equivalent resistance,

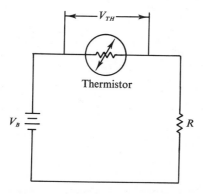

Figure 3-9.   *Basic Thermistor Circuit*

IR, is). However, there is no simple analytical expression for this dependency. The volt-ampere characteristic offers a *graphic* portrayal of this dependency. Hence, Eq. (3–4a) must be solved graphically, in order to find V_{TH} and *I*.

If an analytical expression did exist for V_{TH}, the simultaneous solution of this equation and Eq. (3–4a) would yield the *I*- and V_{TH}-values for the circuit. Graphically, the simultaneous solution of two equations is obtained by finding the *intersection point* between the curves representing the equations. Hence, the point of intersection between the straight line representing Eq. (3–4a) and the nonlinear volt-ampere characteristic of the thermistor will yield the desired values. Since a straight line can be drawn between any two points, selecting any two current values and solving for *IR* would be sufficient. However, a very simple, straightforward procedure consists of finding the voltage-axis and current-axis intercepts. Along the voltage axis, the current is zero. Along the current axis, the voltage is zero. Letting *I* equal zero in Eq. (3–4a) yields:

$$V_B = V_{TH} \tag{3-5}$$

This indicates that the voltage intercept is given by V_B. This is shown in Fig. 3–10. Letting V_{TH} equal zero in Eq. (3–4a) yields:

$$I = \frac{V_B}{R} \tag{3-6}$$

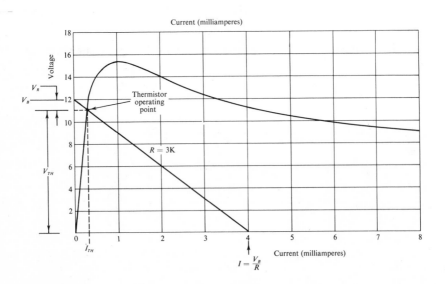

Figure 3-10.   *Load Line Analysis for Thermistor Circuit*

which is the current intercept, as shown in the figure. A straight line between these two points is the plot of Eq. (3–4a). The intersection between
this line and the volt-ampere characteristic defines the thermistor *operating point.* It provides a value for the drop across the thermistor and for
the current through the thermistor (which is also the total circuit current,
I). The voltage drop across the circuit resistance is also given on the
graph ($V_B - V_{TH}$).

The slope of the straight line is the negative of the circuit resistance,
R (Fig. 3–11, Part A). For this reason, the line is termed the circuit load
line. Increasing V_B causes the voltage and current intercept values to be
higher—shifting the load line upward, but not changing its slope (since
R is fixed). Lower battery voltages shift the load line downward. Because
of the nonlinear nature of the volt-ampere characteristic, it is possible for
a load line to intersect it at two points (such as the upper dashed line in
Fig. 3–11, Part A). This is an *unstable condition: two voltage and current
values cannot exist at the same time.* This is not a graphical illusion,

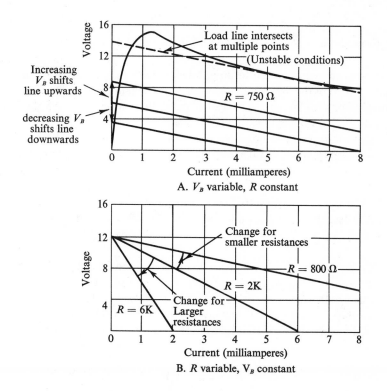

A. V_B variable, *R* constant

B. *R* variable, V_B constant

Figure 3-11.   *Component Variations and Effect on Load Line Analysis*

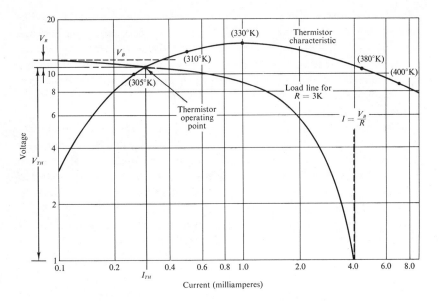

Figure 3-12.   *Load Line in Log-Log Coordinates*

however, and can be used to good advantage in thermistor switching circuits. Part B of the figure shows the effect of changing R for a fixed value of battery voltage. Smaller values of R move the load line toward the horizontal; larger values, toward the vertical.

Equation (3–4a) is not a straight line when it is plotted on log-log coordinates. Rather, it takes on the curve shape shown in Fig. 3–12. It is a curve that is asymptotic (becomes tangent) to two straight lines: one drawn vertically through $I = V_B/R$; the other drawn horizontally through V_B. The curved portion requires point-by-point plotting, obtained by arbitrarily substituting I-values into Eq. (3–4a) and finding the voltage across R.

Example 3-4.   If a thermistor load circuit consists of a 1500-ohm resistor in series with a parallel combination of a 600-ohm resistor and a 1000-ohm resistor, what is the operating current and voltage for the circuit if the volt-ampere characteristic is given by Fig. 3–10? What power is dissipated by the 1500-ohm resistor? (The d-c source voltage is 14 volts.)

Solution.   The voltage intercept is given by:

$$V_{TH} = V_B = 14 \text{ volts}$$

and the current intercept is given by:

$$I = \frac{V_B}{R} = \frac{14}{1500 + \left[\dfrac{600(1000)}{1000 + 600}\right]} = 7.5 \text{ milliamperes}$$

Drawing a straight line between these two points in Fig. 3–10 yields an operating point of 13.2 volts and 0.45 milliampere. Since a total current of 0.45 milliampere flows through the 1500-ohm resistor, the power dissipated in that resistor is:

$$P = I^2R = (4.5 \times 10^{-4})^2(1.5 \times 10^3) = 304 \text{ microwatts}$$

Time-Dependent Characteristics

So far, the discussions of thermistor behavior have been restricted to d-c, or *steady state* operation where conditions have been fixed long enough

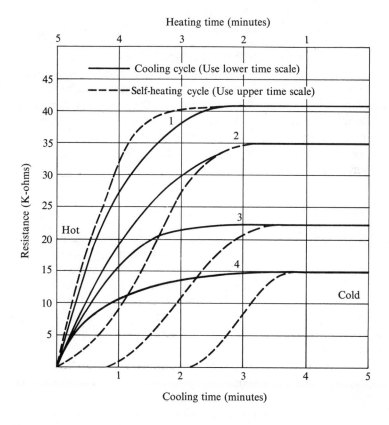

Figure 3-13. *Time Variation of Thermistor Resistance*

for resistance, temperature, and power dissipation to stabilize. If the current through a thermistor is changed from one value to another, the thermistor will alter its characteristics and will *eventually* reach a stable state again. If the change in current is continuous, the thermistor adjustments may follow the changes; may *attempt* to follow the changes, but with a certain degree of lag; *or may ignore the changes*—depending on how rapidly the changes occur.

Figure 3–13 shows the variation in resistance, as a function of time, for a thermistor that has been heated, has the heat source removed, and cools under normal convection and radiation processes. If the thermistor is heated through normal convection and radiation processes, the time variation is the inverse of the cooling variation. However, if the thermistor is heated because of current flow through the device (self-heating), an entirely different variation occurs. This is indicated by the dashed curves in Fig. 3–13.

3.2 Thermistor Applications

The thermal characteristics of the thermistor make it especially suited for temperature measurement and control, power measurement, temperature compensation (stabilization), voltage regulation, and timing (delay) circuits. Each of these applications requires that the thermistor be biased in a particular manner and be operated over a particular region of the volt-ampere characteristic. The thermistor is much more sensitive to temperature changes than are resistance thermometers and ordinary bimetallic thermocouples.

Thermometry

The extreme sensitivity of thermistors to temperature variations makes these devices ideally suited to the accurate measurement of temperature. For this application, a small current flow is maintained through the thermistor. As the temperature changes, the thermistor resistance changes, resulting in a corresponding voltage change that may be calibrated directly in terms of temperature. The voltage change may also serve as a signal to open or close relays (in order to turn on a furnace, for example) in thermostat devices.

Instead of providing for the direct measurement of thermistor voltage, an extremely accurate electric thermometer can be designed by placing the thermistor in a bridge circuit, as shown in Fig. 3–14. The bridge is *balanced* when the ammeter across points *A* and *B* indicates zero current

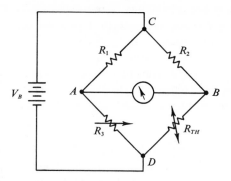

Figure 3-14.   *Bridge Thermometer*

flow. In the balanced condition:

$$\frac{R_1}{R_3} = \frac{R_2}{R_{TH}} \tag{3-7}$$

R_1 and R_2 are fixed resistors. R_3 is variable, and is used to balance the bridge when R_{TH} changes. For this measurement arrangement, R_3 is calibrated directly in terms of temperature. Equation (3–7) can be solved for R_3;

$$R_3 = \frac{R_1}{R_2} R_{TH} \tag{3-8}$$

Changes in R_{TH} and R_3 are of interest:

$$\Delta R_3 = \frac{R_1}{R_2} \Delta R_{TH} \tag{3-9}$$

since this shows the adjustment that is required to achieve bridge balance. If R_1 and R_2 are equal, changes in R_{TH} can be corrected only by equal changes in R_3. However, if R_1 is greater than R_2, small changes in R_{TH} can be corrected by larger changes in R_3. Hence, the ratio R_1/R_2 provides a "scale factor" for the bridge.

In order to serve as a temperature measurement device, the thermistor must be operated over the linear portion of the volt-ampere characteristic. This limits the measurements to temperatures below 600°K. The actual upper limit associated with a particular thermistor can be obtained by investigating the volt-ampere characteristic. The maximum current is just slightly less than the value of current associated with the peak of the characteristic. In practice, an even smaller value of current is used as a limit to assure that the current flow through the thermistor will not heat it appreciably. (The resistance changes of interest are those brought about by the external temperature—not by internal heating effects.)

If the ammeter between points A and B in Fig. 3–14 is replaced by a control relay, or some similar device, the bridge will serve as a temperature control, rather than a measurement, circuit. For this application, R_3 is adjusted to a desired "temperature" value. As long as the temperature at the thermistor is different from this value, an imbalance will occur and current will flow between A and B. When the temperature at the thermistor reaches the preset value, the bridge will be balanced and no current will flow.

Example 3-5. Thermistor 4 in Fig. 3–2 is to be used in a bridge thermometer over a temperature range from 300°K to 350°K. What range of values must be used for the variable resistor if R_1 is to be 10K and R_2 is to be 1K?

Solution. The maximum and minimum resistance for the thermistor over the temperature range can be determined from Fig. 3–2. At 300°K it is 2000 ohms; at 350°K, 450 ohms. R_3 and R_{TH} are related by:

$$R_3 = \frac{R_1}{R_2} R_{TH} = \frac{10K}{1K} R_{TH} = 10R_{TH}$$

At 300°K:

$$R_3 = 10(2000) = 20K$$

At 350°K:

$$R_3 = 10(450) = 4.5K$$

RF Power Measurement

A thermistor may be inserted directly into high-frequency waveguides in order to measure microwave power. This permits the thermistor to absorb all, or a fixed part, of the total power, causing *internal* heating. The thermistor must be biased so that operation occurs over the non-linear region of the volt-ampere characteristic. Power absorbed by the thermistor raises its temperature. The resistance changes are interpreted directly as power readings. A bridge arrangement is used, and the applicable equations are the same.

Temperature Compensation

Figure 3–15 shows the total circuit resistance of a thermistor and a resistor in series at various temperatures. Over a very limited range (points

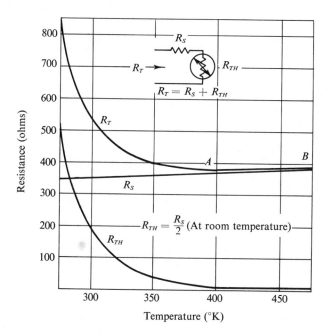

Figure 3-15. *Temperature Variation of Resistance for Series Circuit Arrangement*

A to *B*), the circuit resistance is constant—*independent of temperature.* Such an application is termed *temperature compensation.* Ideal temperature compensation is obtained when the thermistor characteristic (Fig. 3–16) is exactly the inverse of the resistor characteristic. However, the exponential behavior of semiconductor materials and the linear behavior of resistors prevents this, except over very limited ranges.

The parallel combination of a thermistor and a resistor has a characteristic that displays a *nearly linear decrease in resistance with increase in temperature.* Hence, *the combination of a resistor-thermistor parallel arrangement and a series resistor will result in fairly linear operation.* This is shown in Fig. 3–17. Best results are obtained if the thermistor and shunt resistor values are equal to one-half of the series resistor value:

$$R_{SH} = R_{TH} = \frac{R_S}{2} \tag{3-10}$$

at the usual operating temperature. Of course, the total circuit resistance is always more than it would be with only R_S in the circuit. The compensated resistance is approximately:

$$R_C = \frac{5R_S}{4} \tag{3-11}$$

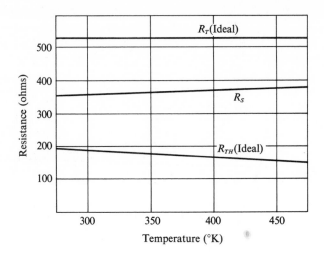

Figure 3-16.   *Ideal Temperature Compensation*

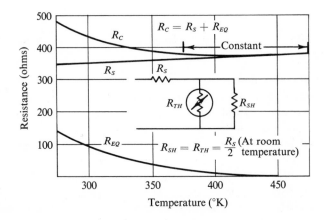

Figure 3-17.   *Compensation of Resistance with Thermistor-Resistor Shunt Circuit*

at room temperature and must be considered in any circuit design calculations.

In order to obtain good temperature compensating characteristics, the designer must assure that the thermistor is subjected directly to the same temperature changes affecting the resistors. Applications of temperature compensating circuits are discussed in Chap. 9.

Example 3-6.   A thermistor-resistor shunt circuit is used to compensate the load resistor in an electronic circuit. The voltage across the load is 10 volts and the load current cannot exceed 2 milliamperes. What value of R_S, R_{SH}, and R_{TH} should be used, and what current will flow at room temperature?

Solution. At high temperatures, the total load resistance (R_C in Fig. 3–17) is a minimum and will approach R_S in value. Since the current cannot exceed 2 milliamperes:

$$R_S = \frac{V}{I_{max}} = \frac{10}{2 \times 10^{-3}} = 5K$$

If R_S is selected as 5K at room temperature, its value at high temperature will exceed 5K slightly—assuring that I_{max} will not be exceeded. This establishes the room temperature value for R_{SH} and R_{TH}:

$$R_{SH} = R_{TH} = \frac{R_S}{2} = \frac{5K}{2} = 2.5K$$

which leads to a total compensated load resistance of:

$$R_C = \frac{5R_S}{4} = \frac{5(5K)}{4} = 6.25K$$

at room temperature. The current at room temperature is:

$$I = \frac{V}{R_C} = \frac{10}{6.25 \times 10^3} = 1.6 \text{ milliamperes}$$

Voltage Regulation

Power supplies, used to convert a-c signal power to d-c power, do not generally provide perfect d-c current and voltage. Rather, there will be a

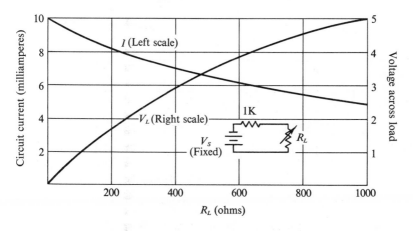

Figure 3-18.   *Effects of Load Variation*

definite "ripple" associated with the output. There are also many electronic circuit applications where a power source must feed to a device that
displays a variable resistance value. Given a constant source voltage,
changes in the load resistance (Fig. 3–18) will change circuit current,
resulting in different voltage values delivered across the load. Such voltage
changes cannot always be tolerated. Circuit arrangements designed to
produce a constant voltage are termed *voltage regulation* devices. The
thermistor can be made to provide a reasonably constant voltage characteristic over wide variations in current.

Figure 3–19 is a plot of the volt-ampere characteristic for a thermistor

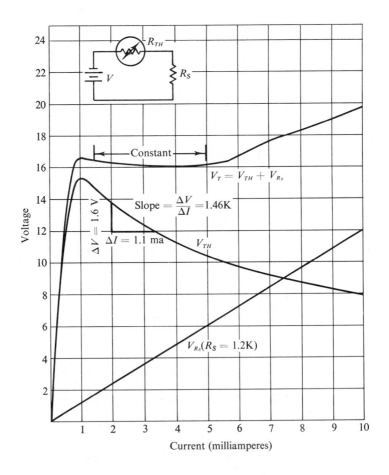

Figure 3-19.   *Volt-Ampere Characteristic for Series Circuit*

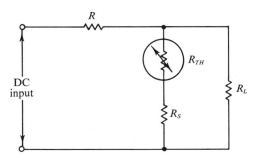

Figure 3-20.   *Thermistor Voltage Regulator*

and a resistor in series. Notice that the resulting characteristic has a fairly constant voltage over a considerable change in current values. When this arrangement is placed in parallel with the circuit load resistance, a fairly constant voltage will be applied to the load. The resulting circuit is shown in Fig. 3–20. Ripples in the input "d-c" voltage will result in more or less voltage across R, but constant voltage will exist across the thermistor-resistor arrangement (and across the load). If the load resistance value changes, the circuit current change is not as pronounced as before, since the equivalent load is the parallel combination of $(R_{TH} + R_S)$ and R_L. Furthermore, when changes do occur, the voltage across R_S and R_{TH} stays constant—forcing the voltage across R_L to stay constant. Again, the resulting voltage fluctuations are absorbed across R.

The greatest degree of regulation can be obtained by making R_S equal to the slope of the thermistor volt-ampere characteristic in the linear region just beyond the peak. The value of the regulation voltage will be approximately twice the voltage value associated with the intersection of the volt-ampere characteristic and the R_S-voltage line when it is plotted as in Fig. 3–19.

Example 3-7. A d-c supply source produces a fluctuating voltage between 21 and 23 volts and is used to feed a 10K-load resistor. If the circuit in Fig. 3–20 is used to regulate the load voltage with the thermistor in Fig. 3–4, what value of R_S and R must be used, and what value of regulated voltage will be maintained?

Solution. The slope of the volt-ampere characteristic in Fig. 3–4 is given by:

$$\text{slope} = \frac{\Delta V}{\Delta I} = \frac{0.6}{0.5 \times 10^{-3}} = 1.2\text{K}$$

in the vicinity of the 350°K-point. This point is chosen because the characteristic appears to be most linear in this region. In fact, if a straight edge is placed on the characteristic at this point, a very high degree of linearity can be seen from about 1.25 to 3.25 milliamperes. Hence, if R_S is made equal to 1.2K, voltage regulation should be maintained between 1.25 and 3.25 milliamperes. If a resistance line for R_S is placed on Fig. 3–4 (as in Fig. 3–19), it will intersect the thermistor characteristic at about 9 volts. The regulation voltage is expected to be about twice this value, or 18 volts. The total voltage variation (from the source) will be from 3 to 5 volts above the regulation value. This voltage must be dropped across R since 18 volts will be dropped across the parallel combination of load resistor and thermistor-R_S combination. If 18 volts is dropped across the 10K-load resistor, a current of 1.8 milliamperes must flow through the resistor. From Fig. 3–4, the current through the thermistor branch must vary from 1.25 to 3.25 milliamperes. This means that the total circuit current must vary between 3.05 and 5.05 milliamperes. When 3.05 milliamperes flows, the drop across the resistor R must be 3 volts. Hence:

$$R = \frac{3}{3.05 \times 10^{-3}} \approx 1\text{K}$$

When 5.05 milliamperes flows, the drop across the resistor R must be 5 volts. Hence:

$$R = \frac{3}{5.05 \times 10^{-3}} \approx 1\text{K}$$

If the two extremes did not yield approximately the same value for R, a compromise value would have to be used. This would be the higher of the two values, and would merely restrict the range of current variation through the thermistor branch to something less than the available range.

Timing and Delay Circuits

In order for a "normally open" relay to close, a certain amount of current must flow through the relay coil. Conversely, in order for a "normally closed" relay (held closed by an energizing current) to open, the current must be reduced below a certain "holding current" value. The thermistor can be used to accomplish either task *with a built-in time delay.*

Figure 3–21 illustrates the circuit arrangement for closing a normally open relay. The thermistor is placed in series with the relay coil so that its

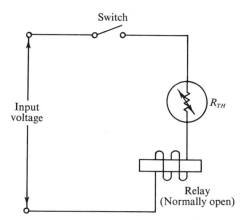

Figure 3-21.   *Thermistor Delay for Closing a Normally Open Relay*

high resistance will prevent the excitation current, I_e, from flowing in the circuit. In order to do this, the reference resistance of the thermistor must satisfy the condition:

$$R_{300} > \frac{V_B}{I_e} - R_r \tag{3-12}$$

where R_r is the relay winding resistance (plus any other series resistance in the circuit). As the current starts flowing, the thermistor resistance slowly decreases, permitting more current to flow. When the thermistor resistance reduces to:

$$R_{TH} = \frac{V_B}{I_e} - R_r \tag{3-13}$$

the circuit current will equal the excitation current, and the relay will close. However, in order for the thermistor to heat properly, the initial current flow (determined by V_B and R_{300} in series with R_r) must be equal to or greater than the I_p-value for the thermistor. This also means that I_e must be greater than I_p —otherwise the relay would close immediately.

A specific time delay is usually dictated by the circuit application. Hence, the thermistor can be selected by consulting a family of curves such as those in Fig. 3–13 (cool thermistor, being heated). Starting with the desired delay time, a thermistor can be selected so that R_{TH} [Eq. (3–13)] will be reached after the required time interval. This thermistor must also have a reference resistance that satisfies Eq. (3–12). Hence, it may be necessary to attempt several combinations (by selecting various values of V_B and by specifying new R_{TH}- and R_{300}-values) before the right thermistor may be selected. Once the current I_e flows in the circuit, the thermistor resistance and temperature will stabilize. A load line analysis (with R_r) would show an intersection (bias point) with a current greater than or equal to I_e flowing through the circuit.

Example 3-8. A normally open relay requiring a 6-milliampere excitation current is to be used in a time delay circuit along with thermistor 2 in Fig. 3–13. The relay winding resistance is 100 ohms. What value of input voltage is required if the relay is to close in 4 minutes? Prove that thermistor 2 can be used in this circuit. (The relay circuit is shown in Fig. 3–21.) Thermistor 2 has a peak current value of 1.5 milliamperes.

Solution. Consulting Fig. 3–13, thermistor 2 has a resistance of 35K at room temperature (R_{300}) and a resistance of 10K after heating for 4 minutes. In order to achieve the proper excitation current the "hot" thermistor resistance must be:

$$R_{TH} = \frac{V_B}{I_e} - R_r$$

Solving for the input voltage:

$$V_B = I_e(R_{TH} + R_r) = (6 \times 10^{-3})[(10 \times 10^3) + (0.1 \times 10^3)]$$
$$= 60 \text{ volts}$$

In order to achieve proper operation, the value of R_{300} must satisfy the inequality:

$$R_{300} > \frac{V_B}{I_e} - R_r = \frac{60}{6 \times 10^{-3}} - 100$$
$$R_{300} > 10\text{K}$$

Since R_{300} is 35K, the inequality is satisfied. At room temperature the circuit current will be:

$$I = \frac{V_B}{R_{TH} + R_r} = \frac{60}{35 \times 10^3} = 1.72 \text{ milliamperes}$$

which is considerably below the excitation value, assuring that the relay will not close immediately, but is above the volt-ampere characteristic peak current, assuring that the thermistor will undergo proper heating.

PROBLEMS

1. Determine the value of B for thermistors 2 and 3 in Fig. 3–2.

2. Plot the resistance versus temperature characteristic for a thermistor with B equal to 6000°K and a room temperature resistance of 10,000 ohms. (Use a temperature range of 200°K to 500°K.)

3. What is the temperature at the peaks of the volt-ampere characteristics for thermistors 2 and 3 in Fig. 3–2?

4. If the voltage and current at the peak of a thermistor volt-ampere characteristic are 10 volts and 2 milliamperes, respectively, and the B-value is 4550°K, what is the thermal dissipation constant of the thermistor material?

5. A thermistor has a room temperature resistance of 15,000 ohms and a thermal dissipation constant of 1×10^{-4} watt/°K. The peak of the volt-ampere characteristic occurs at 380°K. What are the voltage and current values at the peak?

6. What are the operating point values for a thermistor with a volt-ampere characteristic as shown in Appendix D, if the supply voltage is 2 volts and the equivalent circuit resistance is 5000 ohms?

7. A particular application requires that the thermistor with a volt-ampere characteristic as shown in Appendix D be operated with a bias current of 0.1 milliampere. A d-c supply of 10 volts is to be used. What resistance must be placed in series with the thermistor in order to achieve correct operation?

8. The thermistor in Fig. 3–6 is to be operated so that it dissipates 2 milliwatts of power. The equivalent resistance of the rest of the circuit is 2000 ohms. What supply voltage must be used?

9. Thermistor 2 in Fig. 3–2 is to be used in a bridge thermometer to measure a range of temperature variation from 325°K to 450°K. A variable resistor, variable from 500 to 170,000 ohms, is to be used in the circuit for R_3. The dial, however, is to be calibrated directly in terms of temperature. What value of R_3 will correspond to a temperature of 350°K? To a temperature of 400°K?

10. The thermistor in Appendix D is to be used as a temperature compensating device in a precision circuit operating in a high-temperature environment. The thermistor-resistor shunt arrangement in Fig. 3–17 is to be used. The load resistor (placed in parallel with R_{SH}) is 50,000 ohms. The two resistor values increase by 0.015 per cent per degree. Over what range of temperatures can the compensated resistance be made constant?

11. An electronic circuit requires a stable input potential of 3 volts and has an equivalent input resistance of 9000 ohms. The d-c source used with the circuit has a variable output voltage between 8 and 13 volts. The thermistor in Appendix D is to be used in the circuit of Fig. 3–20 to achieve the proper voltage regulation. What value of R_S and R must be used?

12. A normally open relay is to be used in a time delay circuit (Fig. 3–21) designed to produce a delay of about 2.5 minutes. The relay winding resistance is 100 ohms and it has an excitation current of 10 milliamperes. If the thermistors in Fig. 3–13 have I_p-values of 3, 1.5, 1, and 0.9 milliamperes, respectively (for numbers 1 through 4 in the figure), which is the best thermistor to use, and what d-c input voltage must be used?

Further Reading

Shive, J. N., *The Properties, Physics, and Design of Semiconductor Devices*. Princeton, N. J.: D. Van Nostrand Co., Inc.

Surina, T. and C. Herrick, *Semiconductor Electronics*. New York: Holt, Rinehart and Winston, Inc.

4

Semiconductor
Junctions and Diodes

A great deal of effort and large sums of money have been expended in almost every field of manufacturing to produce substances of high purity. The reverse is true in the field of semiconductor devices. *The control and manipulation of impurities in germanium and silicon has led to the development and manufacture of semiconductor devices capable of performing all practical electronic functions.*

The deliberate introduction of impurity atoms, with an excess of electrons, into a basic semiconductor crystal structure results in the formation of an N-*type material.* The electrical nature of this material is controlled by the predominating electron carriers. Atoms having electron deficiencies may also be introduced, resulting in a P-*type material.* Holes predominate and control the characteristics of this material. In combination, the two types form a P-N *junction* which has a predominately unilateral characteristic; i.e., *it passes significant currents in one direction, but not in the other.* Such a *jucntion diode* provides a device capable of performing rectification, voltage regulation, and power switching in less than one-tenth the volume previously occupied by vacuum diodes. Furthermore, the junction diode is a singular structure (no separate cathode and plate;

no heater elements), so that it is more rugged and has a much longer life expectancy.

4.1 Impure Materials

Any disorder in the atomic structure of a material affects its electrical characteristics. In some instances, the disorder may cause an increase in resistivity—in other instances, a decrease. Most solid substances are *polycrystalline* in nature; that is, they are composed of many single crystals butted together in an irregular fashion (Fig. 4-1). All polycrystals contain

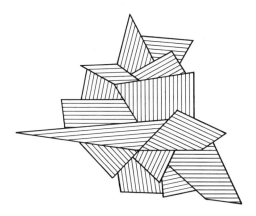

Figure 4-1.   *Polycrystalline Solid*

atomic disorders in the form of crystal discontinuities—the abrupt *grain boundary* that exists between the faces of the single crystals. This disorder is shown in Fig. 4–2 and *always results in increased resistivity*. As shown, the orientation of the atomic lattice is different from one crystal face to another. Such irregular spacings increase the atomic density along the boundary, resulting in an increased likelihood of electron "capture" by one of the atoms. This reduces the average distance that the electron will travel and, in effect, decreases the carrier mobility [see Eq. (2–24)]. These imperfections are present in conductors, semiconductors, and insulators.

Impurities—atoms foreign to the normal molecule composition— constitute the second category of atomic disorder. These impurity atoms may wedge themselves between the normal atoms (Fig. 4–3, Part A), in which case they are termed *interstitial impurities*. This form of intrusion occurs when the foreign atom is small enough and has a low enough

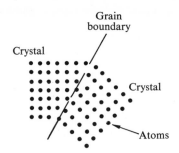

Figure 4-2.   *Atomic Disorder at Crystal Interface*

electron count to overcome the spatial limitations and the repulsive forces (among electrons) that cause the intermediate positions to be vacant. Impurity atoms may also completely displace a normal atom, resulting in the situation shown in Part B of the figure. This is a *substitutional impurity*. Substitution generally requires that the foreign atom be of the same size (or slightly larger) and have reasonably similar valence electron counts. These impurities may exist in conductor, semiconductor, and insulator materials. Metallic alloys are frequently formed by the deliberate introduction of impurities. Nicrome, for example, is arranged so that 60 per cent of the atoms are nickel, 15 per cent are chromium, and 25 per cent are iron. The substitution of impurities tends to increase conductor resistivity. Hence, a metallic alloy will always have a higher resistivity than any one of its components. This increase in resistivity is brought about by the same mechanism associated with the polycrystal boundary: a decrease in the carrier mobility through a reduction in the mean free path. It might appear, from Fig. 4–3, that introducing a few additional, or a few oversized, atoms would not significantly affect the mean free path. However, if the reader will recall (Chap. 2) that the mean free path only spans a few atoms during

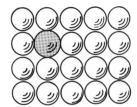

A. Interstitial impurity   B. Substitutional impurity

Figure 4-3.   *Impurities in Solid Crystal Structures*

each translational movement, the significance of the impurity atoms will become more apparent.

In semiconductor materials, impurities of certain types are deliberately introduced in order to *lower the resistivity*. This phenomenon comes about through the introduction of *additional carriers* in sufficient quantities to *offset the reduction in mean free path*. Furthermore, the impurity energy relations are such that the equality between holes and electrons [Eq. (2–4)] is no longer valid. Instead, one carrier or the other predominates the material's electrical characteristics. When the impurity is such that an excessive number of electrons is introduced, an N-*type*, or "negative" type, semiconductor is formed. The introduction of excessive holes produces a P-*type*, or "positive" type, semiconductor material. The addition of these impurities constitutes a process known as *doping*.

Donor Impurities

Silicon and germanium are *tetravalent* atoms; i.e., each atom contains four valence electrons. Because of this, each atom shares electrons with four adjacent atoms to form covalent bonds. Each covalent bond has two electrons common to two bonded atoms (Fig. 2–15).

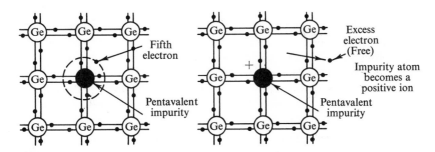

A. Pentavalent substitution (0°K)   B. Small energy absorption (>0°K)

Figure 4-4.   *Donor Impurity and the Semiconductor Crystal*

A *pentavalent* atom; i.e., one having five valence electrons, can easily be substituted for a germanium or silicon atom in this crystal structure. The effect of this substitution is illustrated in Fig. 4-4, Part A. Four of the impurity valence electrons go into covalent bonds with four adjacent semiconductor atoms. From the viewpoint of covalent bonding, the five-atom molecule with an impurity behaves in the same manner. However, the fifth electron associated with the pentavalent impurity *does not enter into a covalent bond.* The fifth electron continues to "orbit" the impurity atom. The attachment is very weak, though, so that very small amounts of energy will free the electron ("jump" it into the conduction band). Once this freedom has been achieved, the excess electron is available to support a current flow, in the same manner that electrons from the valence band contribute to current flow when they are able to jump the energy gap. The excess electron does not create an additional hole, however, *because no covalent bond is broken in the process.* The loss of the electron causes the impurity atom to become a positive ion.

TABLE 4-1

Pentavalent Impurities

Element	Energy Gap (Electron Volts)	
	Germanium	*Silicon*
Phosphorus	0.012	0.039
Arsenic	0.013	0.049
Antimony	0.01	0.039

Table 4–1 lists the pentavalent elements that may be introduced into the semiconductor crystal. Although nitrogen fits this category, it is not used because of handling and combining problems associated with the gaseous state. The impurity atoms are introduced through a carefully controlled process, since the degree of impurity determines the electrical characteristics of the resulting material. A typical doped material will contain on the order of 0.0001 per cent impurity—*one impurity atom per million basic atoms.* The pentavalent atoms are also referred to as *donor impurities* since they "donate" additional electrons. The resulting material is still a semiconductor material, and is distinguished from intrinsic semiconductors by calling it an N-*type semiconductor.*

Acceptor Impurities

When a *trivalent* atom; i.e., one having three valence electrons, is substituted for a silicon or germanium atom, the covalent bonds shown in Fig. 4–5, Part A are produced. Notice that one of the usual covalent bonds is not formed. Because of this, each impurity atom introduces one

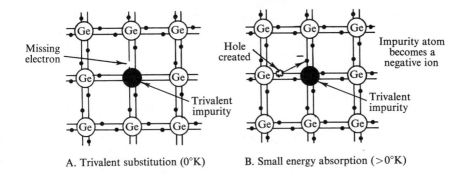

A. Trivalent substitution (0°K)   B. Small energy absorption (>0°K)

Figure 4-5.   *Acceptor Impurity and the Semiconductor Crystal*

empty electron energy state. This empty state can "accept" an electron from a nearby atom, breaking a covalent bond (Part B of the figure). This electron transfer occurs from within the valence band, so that a hole is produced. Hence, each impurity atom that is introduced causes the creation of a permanent hole in the crystal structure. These additional (excess) holes contribute to current flow in the same manner as a thermally activated hole (one created when a valence electron jumps to the conduction band).

TABLE 4-2

Trivalent Impurities

Element	Energy Gap (Electron Volts)	
	Germanium	Silicon
Boron	0.01	0.045
Aluminum	0.01	0.057
Gallium	0.011	0.065
Indium	0.011	0.16

Table 4–2 lists the trivalent elements that may be introduced into the semiconductor crystal. The degree of impurity is carefully controlled, just as with the introduction of the pentavalent impurities. Since each impurity atom creates a vacant energy level that can "accept" electrons from other parts of the crystal, the trivalent elements are termed *acceptor*

impurities. The resulting material is still a semiconductor material, and is distinguished from intrinsic semiconductors by calling it a **P**-*type semiconductor.*

New Energy Bands and Carriers

The introduction of impurity atoms into any material automatically introduces new energy bands, unique to the impurity energy band structure. Hence, regions that previously represented energy gaps—where no electrons can exist—may contain filled, partially filled, or empty (allowable) energy levels when the impurity is added. The impurity atoms are generally so few in number and are so far removed from one another that the associated energy "bands" are not very wide. It is possible for an impurity band to overlap one of the original semiconductor bands. This results in an increased spreading of the original band in order to accommodate the new electron energy states. It may also cause band splitting similar to the phenomenon discussed in Chap. 2.

Energy profiles are discussed in Chap. 2 as a part of the explanation for energy band formation and for an explanation of the decreased ionization energy (presence of the conduction band) in solid materials (see Figs. 2–7 and 2–8, along with the associated text). Figure 4–6 illustrates the energy profile associated with a pentavalent impurity atom in the midst of normal semiconductor atoms. The impurity profile extends to a higher level than that of the semiconductor atoms. Originally, before the molecule is formed, *all of the impurity valence electrons occupy an energy band in the vicinity of the excess electron level shown in the figure.* However, when

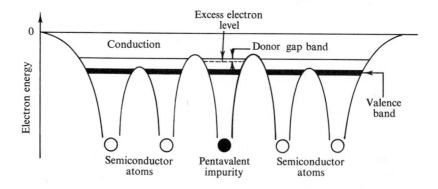

Figure 4-6.   *Energy Profile for Donor Atom in Midst of Normal Semiconductor Atoms*

the molecule is formed, the impurity electrons that enter into the covalent bonds lose energy, ending up as part of the normal semiconductor valence band. This formation leaves the excess electron *just slightly below the lower limit of the conduction band.* As long as the electron stays at this level, it is attached to the impurity atom. This small "donor gap" can be overcome by the absorption of about 0.01 electron volt when the semiconductor material is germanium. Once this energy is absorbed, the electron is free. A similar discussion applies when the semiconductor material is silicon, except that the "donor gap" varies from about 0.04 to 0.05 electron volt, depending upon the impurity selected.

The trivalent impurity energy profile is shown in Fig. 4–7. The energy profile is shown extending only slightly above the energy profiles of the semiconductor atoms. When the impurity atom enters into the crystal formation, its three valence electrons lose energy, becoming part of the semiconductor valence band. This action leaves the unfilled impurity energy state *just above the valence band.* The empty state can accept electrons from the valence band. The "acceptor gap" can be overcome when a valence electron absorbs about 0.01 electron volt (germanium as the basic semiconductor material). When this occurs, the electron becomes attached to the impurity atom. However, when the electron leaves the valence band, a covalent bond is broken and *a hole is created.* Hence, even though the electron does not become a current carrier (since it does not get to the conduction band), current carriers *are* made available. For this reason, the impurity atoms are said to introduce *excess holes.* A parallel discussion applies when the basic semiconductor material is silicon, except that the acceptor gap varies from about 0.045 to 0.2 electron volt, depending upon the impurity selected.

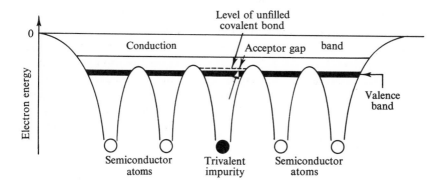

Figure 4-7.   *Energy Profile for Acceptor Atom in Midst of Normal Semiconductor Atoms*

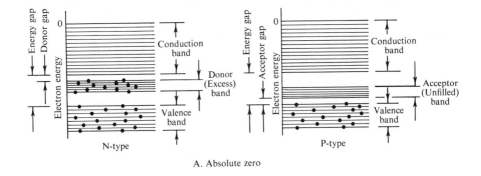

A. Absolute zero

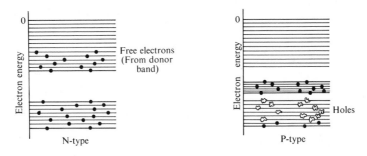

B. Slightly above 0°K

Figure 4-8. *Impurity Electron and Hole Distributions*

Figure 4–8 summarizes the new energy bands associated with N-type and P-type semiconductor materials. Part A of the figure is valid at absolute zero—*before any current carriers are available.* As shown, the excess (donor) electrons exist in a band just below the conduction band, while the excess acceptor (empty) energy states exist in a band just above the valence band. Figure 4–8, Part B, represents the situation at a slightly elevated temperature. In the N-type semiconductor, the excess electrons jump into the conduction band, occupying the lower levels of this band. In the P-type semiconductor, valence electrons jump into the acceptor band, creating an equal number of holes. Each impurity atom contributes one excess electron or hole:

$$n_{e(d)} = N_D \tag{4-1}$$
$$n_{h(a)} = N_A \tag{4-2}$$

where N_D and N_A refer to donor and acceptor atom densities, respectively, and $n_{e(d)}$ and $n_{h(a)}$ refer to the excess electron and hole densities, respectively.

Assuming a concentration of one impurity atom per million germanium atoms, the excess carrier density in either case is 4.42×10^{22} carriers/meter^3 [4.42×10^{28} (from Table 2–1) divided by 10^6]. Solving Eq. (2–3) for temperature, and substituting $E_G = E_D$ (or E_A) = 0.01 electron volt and $n_e = 4.42 \times 10^{22}$, it can be shown that all of the excess carriers will be available to conduct current at a temperature of 20°K. Hence, impure semiconductors can support an appreciable current flow even at low temperatures. Figure 4–9 illustrates the temperature at which *all excess carriers become available* for various impurity concentrations.

So far, the carriers associated with normal thermal activation have not been discussed. This process, the reader will recall, consists of valence electrons jumping into the conduction band, creating both electrons and holes as carriers. The energy gap that must be overcome is still essentially the same (0.72 ev for gemanium; 1.12 ev for silicon). However, an additional complication arises in the impure materials—*the presence of the excess carriers.* The presence of the donor electrons in the lower conduction levels makes it more difficult for valence electrons to transfer to the conduction band; they must achieve energy absorptions greater than the basic E_G-value. Hence, the number of electron-hole pairs generated by thermal activation *at a specific temperature* is less for an impure material

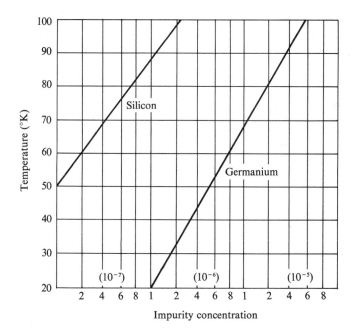

Figure 4-9.   *Temperature Requirements for Complete Excess Carrier Release*

than for an intrinsic material. In the P-type material, the presence of a large number of excess holes in the valence band makes it more difficult for electrons to leave the band. It is easier for them to occupy some of the nearby hole positions. Hence, the same result—fewer electron-hole pairs generated by thermal activation at a specific temperature—is in effect.

When specific numbers of carriers are quoted, it is assumed that the condition of equilibrium has been reached. Since no atom can become excited for long periods of time, the electrons must constantly gain and lose energy, in a rather cyclic manner. Hence, in the N-type material, electrons are in continuous agitation—moving from the donor band to the conduction band and back; moving from the valence band to the donor band and back; and moving from the valence band to the conduction band and back. In the P-type material, electrons move from valence band to acceptor band and back; from acceptor band to conduction band and back; and from valence band to conduction band and back. However, for a particular temperature, these exchanges are in equilibrium, so that there is always a specific number of electrons in the conduction band and a specific number of holes in the valence band. This equilibrium is best expressed by the *mass action law:*

$$n_e n_h = n_{e(i)} n_{h(i)} = n_{e(i)}^2 \qquad \text{(4-3)}$$

where n_e and n_h refer to the total electron and hole densities in an extrinsic material and the i-subscript refers to an intrinsic material. Since $n_{e(i)} n_{h(i)}$ [or $n_{e(i)}^2$] is fixed at a particular temperature, Eq. (4–3) infers that the product of electron and hole densities is fixed (at a particular temperature) regardless of whether the material is intrinsic, N-type, or P-type. For the N-type material, $n_e = n_{e(d)} + n_{e(t)}$, where $n_{e(t)}$ is the number of thermally activated electrons (equal to the number of holes—$n_h = n_{h(t)} = n_{e(t)}$). Similarly, for the P-type material, $n_h = n_{h(a)} + n_{h(t)}$, and $n_e = n_{e(t)} = n_{h(t)}$. Hence, it is impossible to solve Eq. (4–3) directly for the number of thermally activated carriers, unless an approximation, to be discussed in the next section, is made.

4.2 Electrical Characteristics

A complete discussion of the current mechanisms in semiconductor materials is contained in Chap. 2. Although the discussion applies to intrinsic materials, the same basic considerations—electron energy changes, electron and hole translational motion, electron and hole mobilities—also apply to impure, or *extrinsic*, materials. The significant difference between the two types of materials lies in the number of current carriers available, and in the relative number of electrons and holes. At any given temperature, the total number of carriers is equal to the sum of the excess carriers and the thermally activated carriers, as indicated in the previous section. In view of this, and the relationship between conductivity and carrier density [Eqs. (2–17), (2–19), and (2–20)], it is logical to expect that the conductivity of an impure material will be greater than that of a pure material (impure resistivity will be less than pure resistivity). *This is the direct opposite of impurity effects on conductors.*

Since extrinsic materials contain electrons and holes, a drift current must be expected to flow when a potential difference is applied. However, there are also certain internal carrier motions that result in a new kind of current flow mechanism—a *diffusion current*. This current flow is not the result of an applied potential difference. It exists in an electrically neutral material and *cannot be measured externally.*

Majority and Minority Carriers

For an N-type material, the total number of carriers is:

$$n_c = n_{e(d)} + n_{e(t)} + n_{h(t)} \qquad \text{[N-type]} \qquad (4\text{-}4)$$

and, for the P-type material:

$$n_c = n_{h(a)} + n_{e(t)} + n_{h(t)} \qquad \text{[P-type]} \qquad (4\text{-}5)$$

There are 2.5×10^{19} thermally activated electrons (and holes) per cubic meter in intrinsic germanium, as listed in Table 2–1. The previous section has indicated, via the mass action law, that $n_{e(t)}$ (and $n_{h(t)}$) is less than this number in extrinsic materials. Since an N-type material contains 4.42×10^{22} excess electrons/meter³ with a ratio of 10^{-6} impurity atoms, it can be seen that the number of thermally activated electron-hole pairs do not contribute significantly to the total number of carriers. (Adding a number of magnitude 10^{19} to a number of magnitude 10^{22} is akin to adding 1 to 1000.) A similar situation exists in P-type materials. Hence, Eqs. (4–4) and (4–5) can be very reasonably approximated by:

$$n_c = n_{e(d)} = N_D \qquad \text{[N-type]} \qquad (4\text{-}6)$$
$$n_c = n_{h(a)} = N_A \qquad \text{[P-type]} \qquad (4\text{-}7)$$

These approximations are valid at room temperature and for a fairly wide range above room temperature.

Because electrons predominate in the N-type material, they are termed the *majority carrier*, while the holes are termed the *minority carrier*. In the P-type material the situation is reversed; i.e., holes are the majority carrier and electrons are the minority carrier. *For most practical purposes, the characteristics of the extrinsic materials can be described in terms of the applicable majority carrier.*

If the thermally activated component of the majority carrier ($n_{e(t)}$ in N-type materials; $n_{h(t)}$ in P-type materials) is ignored, it is possible to approximate the number of *minority carriers* in an extrinsic material from the mass action law [Eq. (4–3)]:

$$n_{h(t)} = \frac{n_{e(i)}^2}{n_{e(d)}} = \frac{n_{e(i)}^2}{N_D} \quad \text{[N-type]} \tag{4-8}$$

$$n_{e(t)} = \frac{n_{e(i)}^2}{n_{h(a)}} = \frac{n_{e(i)}^2}{N_A} \quad \text{[P-type]} \tag{4-9}$$

At room temperature, $n_{e(i)}^2 = 6.25 \times 10^{38}$ for germanium; 2.56×10^{32} for silicon. Hence, it can be readily seen that the number of minority carriers decreases as the impurity concentration is increased. The quantity, $n_{e(i)}^2$, is temperature dependent, however, and N_D or N_A are not. From Eq. (2–3):

$$n_{e(i)}^2 = \left[\frac{4\pi m_e k}{h^2} \right]^3 \cdot T^3 e^{-E_G/kT} \tag{4-10}$$

where the bracketed term (cubed) is 4.62×10^{46} meters$^{-6} \cdot$°K^{-3}. Substituting Eq. (4–10) into Eqs. (4–8) and (4–9) shows that $n_{h(t)}$, the minority carrier in N-type material, and $n_{e(t)}$, the minority carrier in P-type material, increase exponentially with temperature. This indicates that the normal majority carriers can be overcome by the "minority" carriers at elevated temperatures—a phenomenon of primary importance in explaining extrinsic material behavior under thermal variations. Figure 4–10 illustrates minority carrier density variation as a function of temperature.

Example 4-1   There is one impurity atom per million silicon atoms in a particular P-type material. How many minority carriers are present at 300°K?

Solution.   The minority carriers are the thermally generated electrons in a P-type material and have a density given by:

$$n_{e(t)} = \frac{n_{e(i)}^2}{N_A}$$

Since there are 4.96×10^{28} silicon atoms per cubic meter (Table 2–1), with the substitution of one impurity atom per million silicon atoms:

$$N_A = \frac{4.96 \times 10^{28}}{10^6} = 4.96 \times 10^{22} \text{ atoms/meter}^3$$

This leads to:

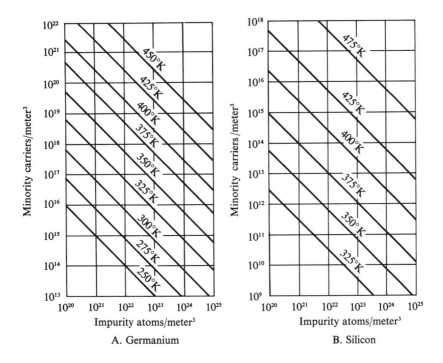

Figure 4-10.   *Variation of Minority Carrier Density with Temperature and Impurity Level*

$$n_{e(t)} = \frac{(2.56 \times 10^{32})}{(4.96 \times 10^{22})} = 5.18 \times 10^9 \text{ electrons/meter}^3$$

where $n_{e(i)}$ is obtained from Table 2–1.

Extrinsic Conductivity and Resistivity

Electron and hole current must be considered in a determination of impurity (extrinsic) conductivity and resistivity [see Eq. (2–17)], just as in any other semiconductor material. However, since the minority carriers are so insignificant in number (at ordinary temperatures), it is possible to determine the extrinsic electrical characteristics by considering only the majority carrier effects. In view of the definition of conductivity [Eq. (2–12) and Eqs. (4–6) and (4–7)]:

$$\sigma_N = N_D Q_e \mu_e \quad \text{[N-type]} \qquad \textbf{(4-11)}$$
$$\sigma_P = N_A Q_e \mu_h \quad \text{[P-type]} \qquad \textbf{(4-12)}$$

The resistivities are given by the reciprocal of these equations. Since

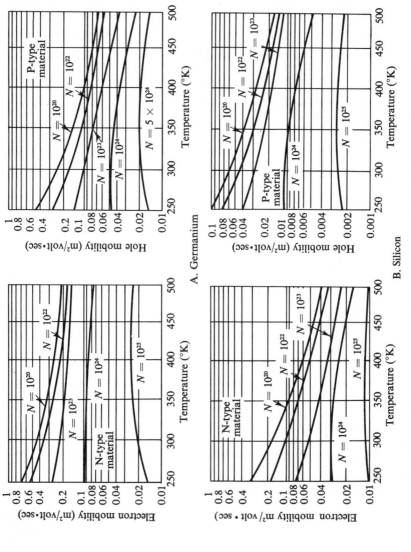

Figure 4-11. *Mobility Variation with Temperature and Impurity Density for the Majority Carriers* (Transistor Engineering, Alvin B. Phillips. Courtesy McGraw-Hill Book Company, Inc.)

electron mobility is always higher than hole mobility, N-*type resistivity must be lower than* P-*type resistivity.* Mobility is decreased by increasing the impurity concentration, as shown in Fig. 4–11. This figure also indicates the variability of mobility as a function of temperature. These changes must be accounted for if Eqs. (4–11) and (4–12) are to yield a reasonable degree of accuracy.

Figure 4–12 presents a typical variation of resistivity for an extrinsic material (with respect to the variation for an intrinsic material). As described in Chap. 2, the resistivity of an intrinsic material *always decreases as temperature increases* because of the ever-increasing number of carriers. The number of carriers also increases in the extrinsic material. However, the resistivity is insensitive to this increase until several hundred degrees is reached. The decreasing resistivity at low temperatures is the result of *increasing mobility.* At a few hundred degrees, the mobility begins to decrease and continues to do so. (This variation can be seen in several

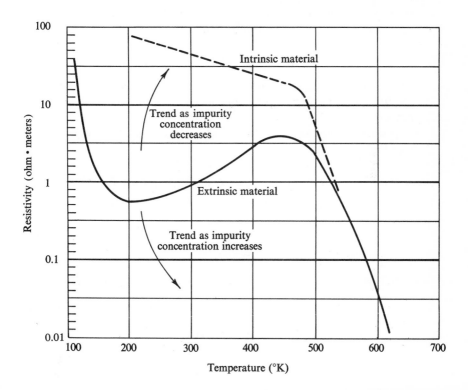

Figure 4-12.   *Resistivity Variation with Temperature for a Particular Semiconductor Material*

of the curves in Fig. 4–11 and is dependent upon impurity concentration.) This reversal of mobility variation causes the resistivity to *increase with increasing temperature* until the minority carrier population begins to make a significant contribution to the total current flow. *From this point on, the extrinsic material is quite similar to an intrinsic material in electrical behavior.*

Example 4-2. What is the resistivity of N-type germanium at 300°K if the impurity concentration is one impurity atom per million germanium atoms? Repeat for P-type germanium under the same temperature and impurity concentration.

Solution. The resistivity is given by:

$$\rho_N = \frac{1}{\sigma_N} = \frac{1}{N_D Q_e \mu_e}$$

when the minority carriers are insignificant with respect to the donor density. For the impurity concentration given:

$$N_D = \frac{4.42 \times 10^{28}}{10^6} = 4.42 \times 10^{22} \text{ atoms/meter}^3$$

(At 300°K, with such an impurity concentration, there are about 5×10^{15} minority carriers per cubic meter—truly insignificant when compared to 4.42×10^{22}.) The value for μ_e depends upon both temperature and impurity concentration, and must be obtained from Fig. 4–11:

$$\rho_N = \frac{1}{(4.42 \times 10^{22})(1.6 \times 10^{-19})(0.29)}$$
$$= 4.89 \times 10^{-4} \text{ ohm} \cdot \text{meter}$$

For P-type gemanium:

$$\rho_P = \frac{1}{N_A Q_h \mu_h}$$

With the same acceptor concentration as for the N-type material:

$$\rho_P = \frac{1}{(4.42 \times 10^{22})(1.6 \times 10^{-19})(0.14)}$$
$$= 1.01 \times 10^{-3} \text{ ohm} \cdot \text{meter}$$

indicating that, for a given impurity concentration and temperature, P-type materials have a higher resistivity than do N-type materials.

Example 4-3. What is the resistivity of the N-type germanium in Example 4–2 at a temperature of 400°K?

Solution. With the impurity density of Example 4–2 (4.42×10^{22} atoms/meter^3) and a temperature of 400°K, the minority carrier density is about 10^{19} holes/meter^3. This number is still insignificant when compared to 4.42×10^{22}, so that resistivity can still be determined from:

$$\rho_N = \frac{1}{N_D Q_e \mu_e} = \frac{1}{(4.42 \times 10^{22})(1.6 \times 10^{-19})(0.21)}$$
$$= 7.3 \times 10^{-4} \text{ ohm} \cdot \text{meter}$$

This is higher than the resistivity in Example 4–2 (4.89×10^{-4} ohm $\cdot$ meter), indicating that the N-type material has an increasing resistivity in the temperature range of 300°K to 400°K (as indicated in Fig. 4–12). At higher temperatures, the number of minority carriers will reach densities equal to or greater than 10^{20} holes/meter^3, and the $1/N_D Q_e \mu_e$-relationship cannot be used. Furthermore, the increase in carrier density will override the decrease in mobility, leading to a lower resistivity (a region of decreasing resistivity, also as shown in Fig. 4–12).

Diffusion Current

In the conduction band, the negatively charged electrons have a natural tendency to move as far from each other as is physically possible. The same is true of the holes in the valence band. This natural repulsion will result in the uniform distribution of carriers throughout the material. If it were possible to introduce impurity atoms in a completely uniform manner, the excess carriers would automatically achieve the same uniform distribution. However, impurity atoms have a tendency to "cluster" in some areas and "thin out" in others, resulting in a nonuniform carrier density as shown in Fig. 4–13, Part A. The more highly concentrated carriers tend to move away toward regions of lower density, seeking the uniformity shown in Part B.

Movement of carriers from regions of high density to regions of low density constitutes a *diffusion current*. This current mechanism is entirely different from the drift current associated with applying an electrical potential difference to the material, since diffusion is a purely local phenomenon and would not result in an external current if a lead were connected between opposite points on the material surface. An external current *cannot flow* because there is no actual potential difference in the material. Figure 4–14 illustrates the neutrality of a normal piece of extrinsic material. The basic atoms and the impurity atoms start out with their electrons equal to their protons in number and in charge. Hence, all atoms are

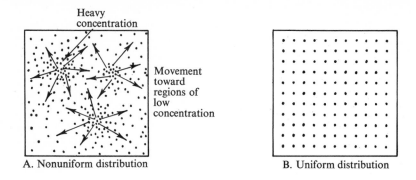

A. Nonuniform distribution   B. Uniform distribution

Figure 4-13.   *Carrier Distributions in Solids*

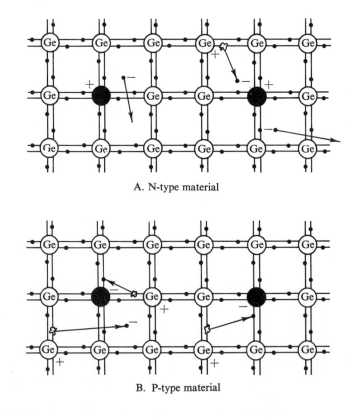

A. N-type material

B. P-type material

Figure 4-14.   *Electrical Neutrality in Extrinsic Semiconductor Materials*

neutral. When a donor atom loses its excess electron, the atom becomes a positive ion (with protons outnumbering electrons by one). When an acceptor atom gains an electron, it becomes a negative ion with electrons exceeding protons by one. However, when the entire material sample is considered, there are still just as many (total) electrons as there are protons, leading to electrical neutrality.

When the diffusion current flows, it is subject to the same resistivity constraints as a normal drift current. Hence, even though an actual potential difference does not exist, it is convenient to speak in terms of an *equivalent potential difference*. In these terms, the diffusion current must satisfy a condition similar to Eq. (2–8):

$$J_d = \frac{\mathscr{E}_T}{\rho} = \frac{V_T}{\ell\rho} \quad \text{(amperes/meter}^2\text{)} \quad \text{(4-13)}$$

where J_d is the diffusion current density and $\mathscr{E}_T$ is an equivalent field intensity due to the thermal energy absorbed by the material. It is more convenient to define an equivalent thermal voltage. Hence, $\mathscr{E}_T$ is replaced by V_T/ℓ, by definition, where ℓ is the diffusion path length. Rearranging Eq. (4–13) yields $V_T = J_d\ell\rho$. However, from Eq. (2–10), current density is also equal to nQv, where v is the carrier velocity. This leads to a new expression for the thermal voltage:

$$V_T = J_d\ell\rho = nQv\ell\rho = \frac{nQv\ell}{nQ\mu}$$

$$= \frac{v\ell}{\mu} = \frac{D}{\mu} \quad \text{(volts)} \quad \text{(4-14)}$$

where the product $v\ell$ has been replaced by D—the *diffusion constant*—which has the units, "meters²/volt·second." The diffusion constant can be measured by indirect experimental methods. Typical values (for room temperature) are listed in Table 4–3. The diffusion constant can be expressed analytically by:

$$D = \frac{\mu kT}{Q} \quad \text{(meters}^2\text{/volt·second)} \quad \text{(4-15)}$$

TABLE 4-3

Diffusion Constants
(Room Temperature)

Carrier	Germanium	Silicon
Electrons	0.728	0.00213
Holes	0.364	0.0986

Note: Values valid for impurity concentration of 10^{-6}
and are in units of meters²/volt·second

showing that its value is dependent upon the carrier type (because of the dependency on mobility) and upon the temperature. The variation of D with temperature is compounded by the fact that mobility is also temperature dependent. Since mobility is also related to the impurity concentration (Fig. 4–11), the diffusion constant must depend on this concentration. Substituting Eq. (4–15) into Eq. (4–14) yields:

$$V_T = \frac{kT}{Q} \quad \text{(volts)} \tag{4-16}$$

showing that the thermal voltage is dependent *only upon the temperature*, or thermal energy content—just as a normal voltage is dependent only upon the electrical energy that produces it. At room temperature, the thermal voltage is approximately 26 millivolts (k must be expressed in joules/°K in these equations).

4.3 The P-N Junction

A piece of N-type material (or P-type material) has no new properties when placed in an electrical circuit. Its general behavior is the same as the behavior of an intrinsic material; i.e., the application of a potential difference will produce a drift current, the drift current may heat the material, and heat causes the material resistivity to decrease. The amount of drift current (for a given potential) is greater in the extrinsic material because the resistivity is lower. The exact nature of the resistivity variation with temperature is also different for the two materials. These differences, however, are not so overwhelming as to suggest any new applications for devices made of extrinsic materials. Rather, it would appear that *more highly sensitive thermistors* are the only devices that extrinsic materials might be applied to. This is true *as long as the two types of extrinsic materials are manufactured and applied separately.*

When a single piece of semiconductor material is formed *with both types of extrinsic materials, a* P-*to*-N *junction is created.* The junction must be an inherent part of the molecular structure. Merely "butting" a piece of N-type material to a piece of P-type material *will not result in the junction phenomenon.* The junction formation requires that the material be started as one type, and that the impurity be gradually changed to the other type, forming a molucular transition from N to P. The electrical characteristics of the junction hold the key to the variety of practical semiconductor devices that have been applied to electronic circuitry. These new electrical characteristics are brought about by the fact that, when the junction is formed, *a diffusion current immediately flows from one type material to the other—creating an electrostatic potential difference across the junction.*

Inherent Carrier Movement

Figure 4–15 provides a simple illustration of the P-N junction microscopic structure at absolute zero. (Although an abrupt change from P to N material is shown, in practice there is a gradual gradation from one material to the other, as discussed previously.) *No current can flow through the material* and there can be no diffusion current. [In Eq. (4–15), if T is zero, D must be zero; likewise, there can be no thermal voltage if there is no thermal energy.] Even though a potential difference might be applied across the materials, no drift current can flow because there are no carriers available.

As the temperature of the material is increased, the diffusion phenomenon begins to act. There are two basic diffusion currents: one occurs within the N-type material (and within the P-type material) as shown in Fig. 4–16, Part A; the other occurs *between the N and P materials* (Part B of the figure). This latter diffusion current occurs because the electrons are much less dense in the P-type material than in the N-type material, and because holes are much less dense in the N-type material than in the P-type material. Hence, the diffusion across the junction transports electrons from the N-type material to the P-type material, and transports holes from the P-type material to the N-type material. This movement creates a potential difference across the junction. The creation of this potential difference is described in subsequent paragraphs. Its presence gradually reduces the diffusion current, until an equilibrium

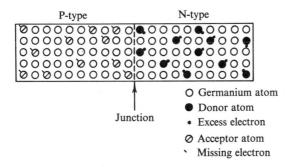

Figure 4-15.   *The P-N Junction at* $0°K$

A. Diffusion within material
P-type   N-type

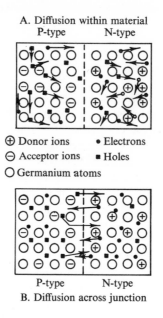

⊕ Donor ions   • Electrons
⊖ Acceptor ions ■ Holes
○ Germanium atoms

P-type   N-type
B. Diffusion across junction

Figure 4-16.   *Carrier Movements ($T > 0°K$)*

condition is reached (the exchange rate is constant). The existence of the diffusion current is an inherent characteristic of the P-N junction. It can be prevented only by maintaining the semiconductor material at absolute zero.

The Depletion Region and Barrier Potential

Electrons flowing from the N material to the P material recombine with holes in the P material (lose energy, returning to the valence band and to the acceptor band in the P material). Likewise, holes flowing from the P material to the N material recombine with electrons in the N material. Electrons that recombine inside a P material can be replaced only through thermal activation from the basic atoms, since the P-impurity atoms only create holes. However, the thermal activation process is already in equilibrium. Hence, the influx of electrons from the N material cannot be replaced when they undergo recombination; they are, in essence, "destroyed." Similarly, holes that recombine inside the N material are replaced only through the thermal activation process, since the N-impurity atoms only create electrons. This leads to the "destruction" of

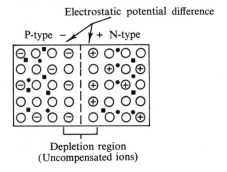

Figure 4-17.   *Creation of Depletion Region*

the holes that diffuse into the N material. Because of the recombination without replacement, *the junction region is almost totally devoid of carriers*, as illustrated in Fig. 4–17. Since there are no carriers available, this section of the semiconductor material is called the *depletion region*. The only charges in the depletion region are those associated with the impurity atoms (now ions) that have lost their neutralizing carriers. These ions are fixed within the crystal structure and cannot, therefore, contribute to the current flow.

The ions located in the depletion region are *uncompensated*. That is, they are no longer neutralized by an equal number of carrier charges of opposite sign. Hence, there is a *net negative charge* in the depletion region *on the* P-*side of the junction* and a *net positive charge* in the depletion region *on the* N-*side of the junction*. The existence of the two oppositely charged regions results in an electrostatic potential difference between them. This *junction potential* is given by:

$$V_j = \frac{kT}{Q} \cdot \ln \left[\frac{n_{e(\text{N})}}{n_{e(\text{P})}} \right] \qquad \text{[N-type]} \qquad \textbf{(4-17)}$$

$$V_j = \frac{kT}{Q} \cdot \ln \left[\frac{n_{h(\text{P})}}{n_{h(\text{N})}} \right] \qquad \text{[P-type]} \qquad \textbf{(4-18)}$$

where $n_{e(\text{N})}$ and $n_{e(\text{P})}$ refer to the electron density in the N and P materials, respectively, and $n_{h(\text{P})}$ and $n_{h(\text{N})}$ refer to the hole density in the P and N materials, respectively. The quantity kT/Q is the thermal voltage [Eq. (4–16)], so that V_T can be substituted directly into Eqs. (4–17) and (4–18). Since the majority carrier densities, $n_{e(\text{N})}$ and $n_{h(\text{P})}$, are equal to N_D and N_A, respectively, and since the minority carriers, $n_{h(\text{N})}$ and $n_{e(\text{P})}$, are given by $n_{h(t)}$ and $n_{e(t)}$, respectively:

$$V_j = V_T \ln \left[\frac{N_D}{n_{e(t)}} \right] \quad \text{[N-type]} \tag{4-19}$$

$$V_j = V_T \ln \left[\frac{N_A}{n_{h(t)}} \right] \quad \text{[P-type]} \tag{4-20}$$

However, in view of Eqs. (4–8) and (4–9), the junction voltage can be simplified to a single equation:

$$V_j = V_T \ln \left[\frac{N_D N_A}{n_{e(t)}^2} \right] \tag{4-21}$$

From this last equation, it can be seen that the junction potential is temperature and impurity concentration dependent. At room temperature, an impurity concentration of 10^{-6} yields a junction potential of about 0.3 volt for germanium; 0.7 volt for silicon.

Figure 4–18 illustrates the junction potential variation with distance across the junction. The junction potential variation indicates that the carrier ratios are not constant across the junction. Indeed, the abrupt change from N to P and the abrupt "ends" of the uncompensated region shown in the various figures are misleading. The changes are gradual, so that the actual position of the junction is ill-defined, as are the ends of the depletion region.

The junction potential is also termed a *barrier potential*. The reason for this is apparent from an examination of Fig. 4–18 in relation to carrier movement. The holes in the P material attempt to maintain the diffusion current across the junction (as do the electrons in the N material). However, as holes from the P material approach the junction, they "see" a force of repulsion from the positive electrostatic potential on the N side.

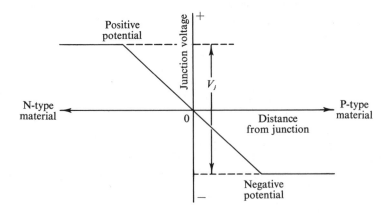

Figure 4-18.   *Barrier Voltage Variation*

Only a few of the holes have sufficient thermal energy to pass through the barrier. Similarly, only a few electrons on the N side can overcome the negative barrier potential on the P side of the junction. Hence, the total equilibrium diffusion current (being the sum of the electron and hole currents) across the junction remains at a small, constant value.

The existence of a potential difference across the junction causes a *drift current* to flow. This drift current is shown in Fig. 4–19 along with the equilibrium diffusion current. Notice that the drift current consists of electrons flowing from the P material toward the N material (toward the positive junction potential) and holes flowing from the N material toward the P material (toward the negative junction potential). The drift electrons are minority carriers in the P material, but become a part of the majority carriers in the N material after the junction is crossed. The same is true of the drift holes. Since these carriers are few in number in the material where they originate, the drift current is also small. In fact, because of the magnitude of the barrier potential, V_j, and its relation to diffusion current, the number of electrons in the drift current equals the number of electrons in the diffusion current. Also, the number of holes in the drift current equals the number of holes in the diffusion current. Since the same number of like carriers cross the junction *in the opposite direction, there is zero net current flowing across the junction* in the equilibrium condition. This is very important; it explains why no current will flow in an external circuit if an ammeter is connected directly from the P material to the N material. The barrier potential is a local, internal phenomenon; the complete piece of semiconductor material *is still electrically neutral.*

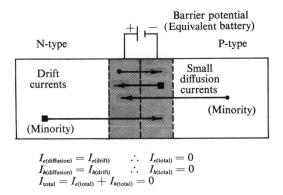

$$I_{e(\text{diffusion})} = I_{e(\text{drift})} \qquad \therefore \quad I_{e(\text{total})} = 0$$
$$I_{h(\text{diffusion})} = I_{h(\text{drift})} \qquad \therefore \quad I_{h(\text{total})} = 0$$
$$I_{\text{total}} = I_{e(\text{total})} + I_{h(\text{total})} = 0$$

Figure 4-19.   *Equilibrium Currents Crossing the Junction*

Example 4-4. What is the barrier potential associated with a P-N junction at room temperature for the impurity concentration indicated in Example 4–1 if equal concentrations exist in both materials?

Solution. The junction potential is given by:

$$V_j = V_T \ln \left[\frac{N_D N_A}{n_{e(i)}^2} \right]$$

For the impurity concentration indicated in Example 4–1 (one impurity atom per million silicon atoms):

$$N_A = N_D = 4.96 \times 10^{22} \text{ atoms/meter}^3$$

if the materials on both sides of the junction have the same concentration. Hence:

$$V_j = (2.6 \times 10^{-2}) \ln \frac{(4.96 \times 10^{22})^2}{(2.56 \times 10^{32})}$$
$$= (2.6 \times 10^{-2})(29.85) = 0.78 \text{ volt}$$

Example 4-5. If the depletion region in Example 4–4 is 10^{-3} meter deep, what total diffusion current density flows in the equilibrium condition?

Solution. Current density is given by:

$$J = \frac{\mathcal{E}}{\rho} = \mathcal{E}\sigma = \frac{V\sigma}{\ell}$$

where V is the potential difference across a region of length ℓ with a conductivity of σ. However, since two materials with two resistivities are involved (as well as two carriers), the relationship:

$$J = J_e + J_h = \frac{V\sigma_N}{\ell} + \frac{V\sigma_P}{\ell} = \frac{V}{\ell}(\sigma_N + \sigma_P)$$

The conductivities, in turn, are given by:

$$\sigma_N = N_D Q_e \mu_e = (4.96 \times 10^{22})(1.6 \times 10^{-19})(0.088)$$
$$= 710 \text{ mhos/meter}$$
$$\sigma_P = N_A Q_h \mu_h = (4.96 \times 10^{22})(1.6 \times 10^{-19})(0.039)$$
$$= 310 \text{ mhos/meter}$$

which leads to:

$$J = \frac{0.78}{(10^{-3})}(710 + 310) = 8 \times 10^5 \text{ amperes/meter}^2$$

where V is V_j (from Example 4–4).

4.4 External Biasing and Currents

The barrier voltage is a local, internal phenomenon associated with the P-N junction; the overall semiconductor material is still electrically neutral; and no net current flow occurs across the junction. Hence, the P-N junction cannot serve as a source of current—an ammeter connected across the junction will register zero. However, if an external d-c voltage source is included in the circuit arrangement, current *will flow*. Furthermore, the current magnitude shows a significant difference when the external source polarity is changed with respect to the P and N materials. The existence of the barrier potential is responsible for this behavior. If a P-type material and an N-type material were merely "butted" together and placed in a circuit, its conduction properties would be the same in either direction. The barrier potential and the relationship between the majority and minority carriers produces a regulating action, permitting large currents to flow in one direction and only small currents in the opposite direction.

Reverse Biasing

The external source arrangement shown in Fig. 4–20, Part A, is termed *reverse biasing*. Notice that the two batteries—the "space charge" battery used to represent the internal junction potential, and the external biasing battery—are connected in *series opposing*. This is an excellent cue for remembering the proper reverse biasing polarities. Notice, also, that the P material is raised to a more negative potential and the N material is raised to a more positive potential. Hence, reverse biasing has the effect of *increasing the barrier potential*, as shown in Part B of the figure.

Figure 4–21 shows the internal phenomena associated with reverse biasing. *The high negative potential draws holes in the* P *material away from the junction, and the high positive potential draws electrons in the* N *material away from the junction.* This causes the depletion region to widen, resulting in more uncompensated ions and a higher barrier potential. The depletion region width stabilizes when the junction voltage reaches external bias voltage. Under this condition the *majority carriers cannot flow across the junction and, therefore, cannot cause any external circuit current to flow.* The increased potential across the junction immediately results in a tendency for increased drift current components (also shown in Fig. 4–21). Since the drift current consists of electrons flowing from P to N and holes flowing from N to P, it is obvious that the reverse biasing arrangement will aid their flow. However, *since these carriers are in the minority within their source materials, the resulting current is not very large.*

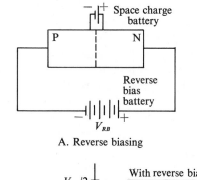

A. Reverse biasing

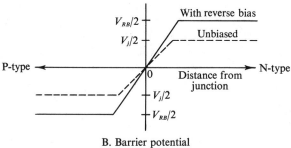

B. Barrier potential

Figure 4-20.   *Reverse Biasing and Effects*

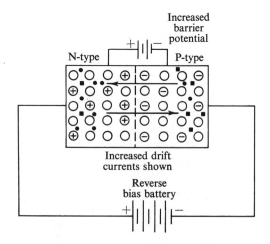

Figure 4-21.   *Internal Phenomena, Reverse Bias*

The total current flow inside the semiconductor material is equal to the sum of the electron and hole components. Since the current flowing in a closed loop must be the same in all parts of the loop, the external current must also be equal to the sum of the electron and hole components. This is not always easy to visualize, since *holes cannot flow in the external conductor.* However, the hole current component *inside* the semiconductor must be compensated for by an equivalent electron current component from the external source, as shown in Fig. 4-22.

The value of the *reverse current* across the P-N junction reaches its *saturation level* (for a given temperature) at fairly low levels of reverse bias voltage. Hence, the reverse current is also termed the *reverse saturation current* or, simply, the *saturation current.* Since the number of minority carriers is temperature dependent, so too is the saturation current.

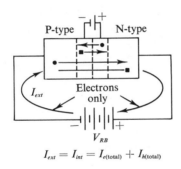

$$I_{ext} = I_{int} = I_{e(total)} + I_{h(total)}$$

Figure 4-22.   *Current Components*

Forward Biasing

Figure 4-23, Part A, illustrates the circuit arrangement for *forward biasing.* By changing the external source polarity from that in Fig. 4-20, a portion of the barrier potential is overcome, as shown in Fig. 4-23, Part B. Notice that the internal and external batteries are now connected in *series aiding*—the condition necessary for forward bias on the P-N junction. This arrangement places the external positive potential on the P material (causing a reduction in the negative barrier potential) and the external negative potential on the N material (causing a reduction in the positive barrier potential). With such a reduction in the barrier, more of the majority carriers will have enough energy (at a given temperature) to penetrate the barrier, establishing a considerably larger diffusion cur-

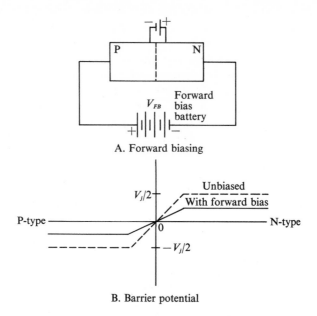

A. Forward biasing

B. Barrier potential

Figure 4-23.   *Forward Biasing and Effects*

rent across the junction. Furthermore, the external polarity is such that the internal drift current (minority carriers) is reduced. The combination of increased diffusion and decreased drift produces a high resultant current through the semiconductor material in the *forward direction*.

The internal phenomena associated with forward biasing are shown in Fig. 4-24. Notice that the external potentials "push" the majority carriers toward the junction, resulting in a reduced *depletion region width*. It might appear that, by increasing the external forward bias voltage, V_{FB}, beyond V_j, the junction potential could be *completely nullified or perhaps even reversed*. This is physically impossible, however, because of the recombination process. Regardless of the external potential, *some* of the electrons and holes "sweeping" across the junction as part of the diffusion current *will always be "destroyed" through recombination.* Hence, although the width of the depletion region is reduced and the depletion region contains charged carriers (the majority carriers moving across the junction), *there is a minimum depletion width and barrier potential that cannot be nullified.* This minimum width depends on the base material (germanium or silicon) and the impurity concentration.

As in the closed loop associated with the reverse biased circuit, the total external circuit current must equal the sum of the internal hole and

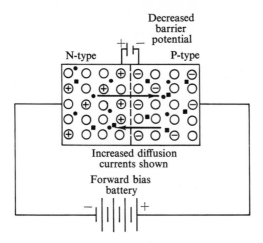

Figure 4-24.   *Internal Phenomena, Forward Bias*

electron components. However, since it is the majority carriers that support the forward current, their high density produces a significant difference between forward and reverse current magnitudes. The forward current density is not as temperature sensitive as the reverse (saturation) current density because majority carriers are involved.

4.5 Junction Diode Characteristics

The characteristics of the P-N junction have been described in terms of the microscopic physical phenomena involved. Because the junction is a two-terminal device (one lead attached to each side of the junction), it is referred to as a *junction diode*. Basically, all junction diodes act as rectifiers; i.e., they convert alternating current to a form of direct current, since the amount of current they pass in one direction is significantly greater than the amount passed in the opposite direction. Various methods exist for categorizing diodes. Most of these categories depend on their specific application (low-power rectifier, high-power rectifier, switch, regulator, etc.), since each application requires that particular diode characteristics be emphasized over all others. In general, however, all diodes have similar characteristics that must be considered in order to design a useful diode circuit. These characteristics include the volt-ampere curve, the *reverse breakdown* phenomenon, certain maximum current and voltage values, temperature characteristics, junction capacitance, and frequency

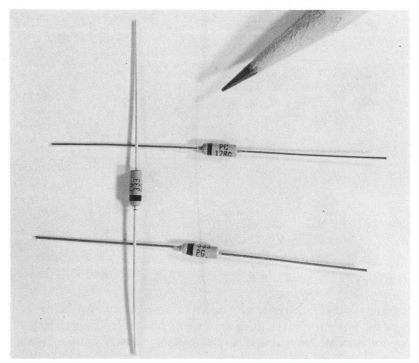

Figure 4-25.   *Physical Characteristics of Junction Diodes* (*Courtesy TRW Electronics*)

limitations. The principal advatages of the junction diode over a vacuum tube diode include reduced size and weight (Fig. 4–25), decreased power requirements (no filament and, hence, no heater current losses), increased ruggedness, and increased lifetime.

The Diode Equation

Figure 4–26 illustrates the typical volt-ampere characteristic shape for a junction diode. When the voltage is applied in the forward direction, a relatively large forward current flows, increasing in value as the forward voltage increases. In contrast, when the reverse voltage is applied, a relatively small reverse current (the forward and reverse current scales *are not the same*) flows, but remains almost constant as the reverse voltage is increased. Since the diode current is always equal to the forward component minus the reverse component, it can be shown that the total diode current is:

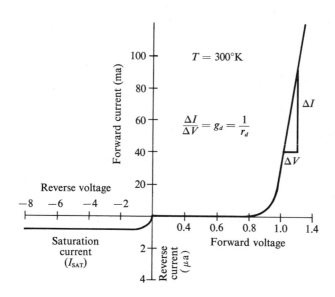

Figure 4-26.   *Typical Volt-Ampere Characteristic*

$$I = I_{sat}(e^{V/V_T} - 1) \tag{4-22}$$

where I_{sat} is the saturation current value. Equation (4–22) is the theoretical *diode equation* and is in close agreement with actual measurements.

The slope of the volt-ampere characteristic, $\Delta I/\Delta V$, (also shown in the figure) is equal to the *dynamic diode conductance*, g_d, or the reciprocal of the *dynamic diode resistance*, r_d. Over a considerable portion of the forward region, the characteristic is nearly linear as shown, so that the dynamic resistance is constant. The reverse characteristic also produces a constant dynamic resistance. However, the forward dynamic resistance is considerably smaller than the reverse dynamic resistance. The value of r_d undergoes considerable variation in the vicinity of the origin.

The dynamic resistance represents the equivalent resistance of the diode when an a-c signal is impressed across it. The changing signal causes operation over a particular voltage range, ΔV, which, in turn, produces a current variation, ΔI. The diode also has a d-c conductance and resistance associated with it. This resistance is simply given by V/I at any point on the characteristic.

Because of the dependency of saturation current upon the number of available minority carriers (Fig. 4–10), silicon diodes have a lower saturation current than do germanium diodes. Silicon diodes also maintain lower forward currents (for specific voltage values). Lower currents over the same voltage ranges indicate that silicon diodes inherently have greater d-c and a-c (dynamic) resistances. However, silicon is not as temperature sensitive and can withstand much higher currents (to *several hundred amperes*) with forced-air cooling. For this reason, silicon devices are applied over a far greater variety of circuits that are the germanium devices.

The diode characteristic in Fig. 4–26 has a forward-to-reverse current of about one thousand, which is typical for all junction diodes. Hence, a diode with a forward current on the order of a few amperes can be expected to have a reverse current of milliampere magnitude. Milliampere forward currents as shown are associated with microampere reverse currents.

Example 4-6. What is the dynamic diode resistance and the d-c resistance of the diode in Fig. 4–26 at a forward voltage of 1.2 volts?

Solution. A forward voltage of 1.2 volts causes a forward current of 90 milliamperes to flow:

$$r_{(d-c)} = \frac{V}{I} = \frac{1.2}{9 \times 10^{-2}} = 13.4 \text{ ohms}$$

Over a small region about this point, the dynamic resistance is:

$$r_d = \frac{\Delta V}{\Delta I} = \frac{1.3 - 1.1}{(120 - 55)(10^{-3})} = 3.08 \text{ ohms}$$

Reverse Breakdown Effects

The diode equation (and the volt-ampere characteristic in Fig. 4–26) does not account for certain phenomena that occur at high reverse voltage values. The electric field, associated with applying a potential difference across the diode, represents an additional source of energy for the valence electrons beyond that supplied by the thermal energy that is always available. Hence, at a given temperature, high electric fields (on the order of 10^7 volts/meter) provide enough additional energy for a significant increase in the number of electrons jumping the silicon energy gap. This increases the number of minority carriers and, therefore, the reverse current value. The point at which this increase in initiated is the *Zener voltage* and the phenomenon is referred to as the *reverse breakdown effect*, or *Zener breakdown*. For silicon diodes, used exclusively as "Zener" diodes, the Zener voltage is approximated by:

$$V_Z = 39\rho_N + 8\rho_P \qquad \text{(volts)} \qquad \text{(4-23)}$$

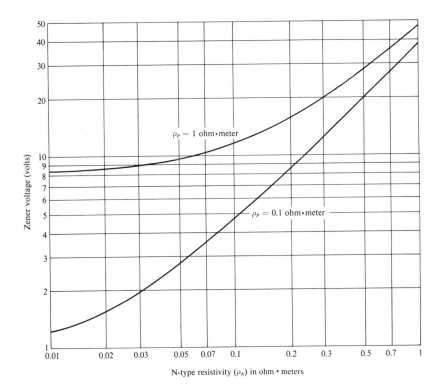

Figure 4-27.   *Variation of Zener Voltage with Semiconductor Resistivity*

Since the Zener voltage can be controlled by controlling ρ_N and/or ρ_P, Zener diodes are available for breakdowns from two or three volts to several hundred volts (Fig. 4–27). Equation (4–23) is experimental in nature. However, this does not mean that the relationship has no theoretical validity. The value of an electric field in a material, and, therefore, the voltage required to produce it, is dependent upon crystal resistivity by definition of resistivity in Chap. 2. Crystal resistivity for P- and N-type materials, in turn, depends on the degree of doping (impurity concentration). When the material has a high concentration of impurity atoms, the barrier potential, which depends on the number of carriers that cross the junction, reaches its equilibrium value while the depletion region is still thin (Fig. 4–28, Part A). *A given voltage applied across a short distance results in a high electric field.* Small increases in the field (small additional reverse bias voltage) will be enough to produce breakdown. This is predicted by Eq. (4–23): higher impurity concentrations produce lower resistivities, and the equation yields lower Zener voltage values. With light

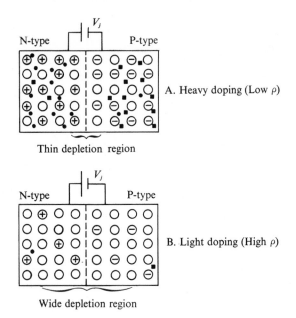

Thin depletion region

Wide depletion region

Figure 4-28.   *Effect of Impurity Concentration on Depletion Region Width*

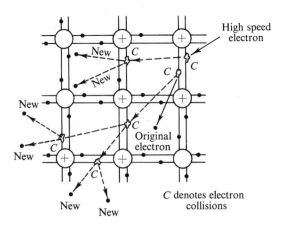

Figure 4-29.   *The Avalanche Effect*

doping, the barrier potential reaches equilibrium with a wide depletion region (Fig. 4–28, Part B). V_j has not changed, however. This means that the barrier field is low and *large amounts of external reverse bias* will be required to produce breakdown. Equation (4–23) predicts the same effect: higher resistivities (lower impurity concentrations) result in higher Zener voltage values.

A second reverse breakdown effect, known as *avalanche breakdown*, also occurs. The electric fields required to produce Zener breakdown cause the carriers to move at extremely high velocities. The associated kinetic

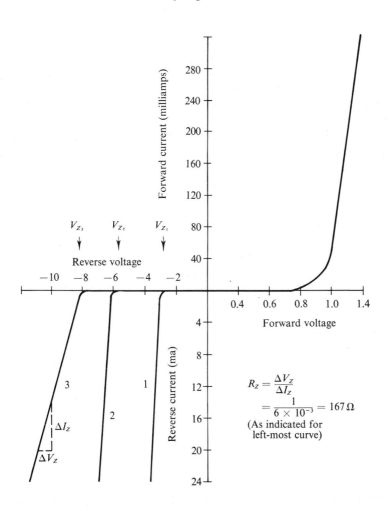

Figure 4-30.   *Typical Reverse Characteristics*

energies are so great that the collision of a carrier with an atom (Fig. 4–29) frequently releases two or three new carriers. Each of these carriers may, in turn, participate in collisions releasing two or three more carriers. Hence, a "carrier chain reaction" or "avalanche" is set off shortly after the reverse voltage exceeds V_Z.

The combined Zener and avalanche breakdown effects result in reverse characteristics as shown in Fig. 4–30. The diode has a high reverse resistance (current stays constant at I_{sat}) until the reverse voltage reaches V_Z. At this point, there is an increase in current flow by a factor of about one thousand. For reverse voltages slightly higher than V_Z, the avalanche effect releases an almost unlimited number of carriers so that the diode essentially becomes a short circuit. The current flow in this region is limited only by an external resistance, thus the diode is "out of control." *Operating a diode in this region does not damage it, as long as the maximum dissipation power of the diode is not exceeded.* Removing the reverse current permits all carriers to return to their normal energy values and velocities.

Figure 4–30 also shows the slope of the volt-ampere characteristic in the reverse breakdown region. It is termed the *Zener resistance* and is defined by:

$$R_Z = \frac{\Delta V_Z}{\Delta I_R} \quad \text{(ohms)} \tag{4-24}$$

This is a dynamic resistance and changes as V_Z changes. (The slope of the breakdown characteristics in Fig. 4–30 are not all the same.) Diodes with higher Zener voltages have smaller Zener resistances.

Example 4-7.   The maximum dissipation for a Zener diode with reverse characteristic 2 in Fig. 4–30 is 120 milliwatts. Can the diode be safely operated with an equivalent external circuit resistance of 500 ohms and a reverse bias of -10 volts?

Solution.   A load line may be constructed on the diode characteristic in much the same manner as on the thermistor volt-ampere characteristic in Chap. 3. The diode is in series with an equivalent external circuit resistance. Hence, when there is no voltage across the diode, there must be:

$$I = \frac{V}{R} = \frac{-10}{500} = -20 \text{ milliamperes}$$

flowing in the circuit. This is the current-axis intercept value. The voltage-axis intercept is given by the supply voltage (-10 volts). If a straight line is drawn between these two points in Fig. 4–30, it will intersect the reverse characteristic 2 at -7.2 milliamperes and -6.4 volts, which is the operating point for this circuit. The dissipated power is:

$$P = (7.2 \times 10^{-3})(6.4) = 46 \text{ milliwatts}$$

which is well within the rated value of 120 milliwatts.

Temperature Effects

All properties and characteristics of semiconductor devices are temperature dependent. The effect of temperature on resistivity has been discussed (Fig. 4–12 and associated text). The effect of temperature on reverse saturation current has been discussed, also. The dependency of Zener voltage upon resistivity and depletion region width makes this voltage value temperature dependent as well. When accounting for temperature effects, it is necessary to consider the internal temperature due to current flowing across the junction, as well as the external (ambient) temperature. The power dissipation characteristics (discussed in the next section) depend very highly on the internal-to-external temperature differential and on the diode's ability to radiate heat into the surrounding medium.

The complex relationship betwen semiconductor properties and temperature makes the development of a complete thermal theory extremely difficult, and impossible within the scope of this text. However, from a practical standpoint, it is possible to develop a straightforward method for discussing diode thermal behavior that accounts for the *total thermal properties*, rather than trying to itemize and investigate each microscopic component.

Temperature is a measure of the amount of heat energy stored in a substance and is related to the *average kinetic energy* of the molecules. Temperature gradient; i.e., the change in temperature from one region to another, determines the direction of heat transfer (flow). Heat inherently flows from regions of high temperature to regions of low temperature until the temperature gradient is zero; i.e., all regions are at the same temperature. Heat flow along or through a substance is termed *conduction*. When the substance, itself, is moving or circulating, the flow is termed *convection*. *Radiation* is the transfer of heat in the form of electromagnetic energy. All three forms enter into the dissipation of heat from a junction diode (Fig. 4–31). *Thermal conductance* is a measure of the heat flow per unit temperature gradient (watts per degree Centigrade). The reciprocal of thermal conductance is termed *thermal resistance*. "Ohm's law" of thermodynamics states that:

$$P_H = (T_1 - T_2)/R_\theta \quad \text{(watts)} \qquad \text{(4-25)}$$

where P_H is the rate of heat flow (power), $(T_1 - T_2)$ is the temperature differential ($T_1 > T_2$), and R_θ is the total thermal resistance between the two regions (°C/watt).

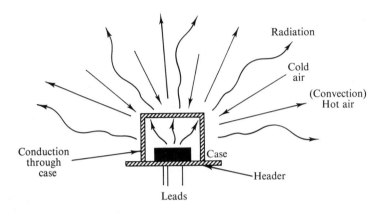

Figure 4-31.   *Heat Transfer Processes*

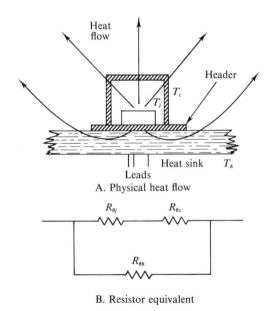

Figure 4-32.   *Heat Flow and Electrical Equivalent*

For the junction diode, the two regions in question are the junction crystal structure and the surrounding "ambient" medium. However, the transfer between the two regions is not direct. The heat flow follows two paths: one from junction to diode case to surroundings, the other from junction through the header and, if available, the heat sink to surroundings (Fig. 4–32, Part A). In terms of thermal resistance (Part B of the figure), the action behaves as a resistor network; i.e., a series connection of $R_{\theta j}$ (junction-to-case) and $R_{\theta c}$ (case-to-ambient), in parallel with $R_{\theta h}$ (heat sink-to-ambient):

$$R_\theta = \frac{(R_{\theta j} + R_{\theta c})R_{\theta h}}{R_{\theta j} + R_{\theta c} + R_{\theta h}} \tag{4-26}$$

which reduces to:

$$R_\theta = R_{\theta j} + R_{\theta c} \tag{4-27}$$

when no heat sink is present. The thermal resistance without a heat sink is generally specified by the manufacturer, along with the permissible

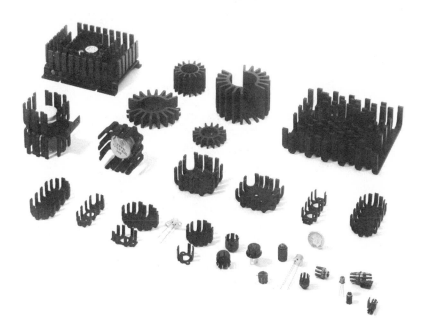

Figure 4-33.   *Typical Heat Sinks for High-Power Applications* (*Courtesy International Electronic Research Corporation*)

junction temperature, T_j. As an alternative, the manufacturer may specify the permissible case temperature, T_c, along with the appropriate thermal resistance. In this case, the value of T_c is chosen so that T_j cannot exceed its maximum permissible value. T_j depends on the base material: for germanium, about 350°K (75°C); for silicon, about 425°K (150°C).

Heat sinks are highly conductive, large-area devices that are attached directly to the diode header. Their design (Fig. 4–33) is such that maximum heat dissipation (radiation) can occur into the surrounding regions. When the diode has no heat sink, the diode may be attached directly to a chassis—with the chassis then serving as a heat sink.

Example 4-8. A silicon diode is capable of dissipating 120 milliwatts of power without a heat sink when the ambient temperature is 300°K. If the junction temperature is 350°K, what is the thermal resistance of the diode? How much power can be dissipated if a heat sink, having a thermal resistance of 200°C/watt, is attached to the diode?

Solution. "Ohm's law" of thermodynamics:

$$P_H = \frac{T_1 - T_2}{R_\theta}$$

must be solved for R_θ:

$$R_\theta = \frac{T_1 - T_2}{P_H} = \frac{(350 - 300)}{0.12} = 417°\text{K/watt}$$

where °K/watt is the same temperature increment as °C/watt. This value is the thermal resistance of the junction-to-case structure and case-to-ambient structure, in total $(R_{\theta j} + R_{\theta c})$. When a heat sink is added:

$$R_\theta = \frac{(R_{\theta j} + R_{\theta c})R_{\theta h}}{(R_{\theta j} + R_{\theta c}) + R_{\theta h}}$$

Hence:

$$P_H = \frac{T_1 - T_2}{(R_{\theta j} + R_{\theta c})R_{\theta h}/[(R_{\theta j} + R_{\theta c}) + R_{\theta h}]}$$
$$= \frac{350 - 300}{(417)200/(417 + 200)} = 380 \text{ milliwatts}$$

Maximum Operating Values

In order to operate a diode in a specific circuit, certain operating values must not be exceeded. These include:

1. maximum forward current;
2. maximum reverse current;
3. peak inverse voltage.

The specified values will have an ambient temperature associated with them—usually room temperature. The reason for specifying temperature, or any of the values, is to prevent the diode from exceeding its *maximum dissipation power*, $P_{D\text{max}}$. This quantity is the most important single characteristic associated with diode operation. Exceeding it in any way for significant periods of time *will destroy the diode*. This is true of both forward and reverse conduction.

Figure 4–34 illustrates a typical variation of maximum dissipation power with temperature. The "constant power curves" shown in the figure are drawn in the same manner discussed for drawing power curves on the thermistor volt-ampere characteristic (Chap. 3). The reason that $P_{D\text{max}}$ must change as ambient temperature changes becomes apparent through an examination of Eq. (4–25). With T_1 fixed (by the specified T_j-, T_c-, or T_h-value) and with R_θ fixed (by diode design), the dissipated power, P_{II}, *must be dependent* upon ambient temperature (substituted for T_2). Hence, $P_{D\text{max}}$ can be obtained—as a function of ambient temperature—by direct substitution of the ambient temperature value in Eq. (4–25) (Fig. 4–35). The variation is usually linear over practical temperature ranges. Non-linearity exists when R_θ is also temperature dependent. The adjustment

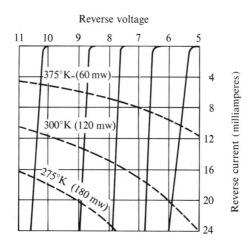

Figure 4-34. *Typical Reverse Characteristics with Maximum Power Dissipation Curves*

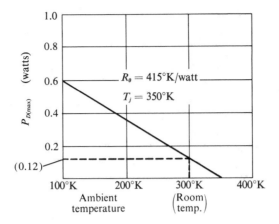

Figure 4-35.   *Variation of Maximum Dissipation Power with Temperature*

that must be made in $P_{D\text{max}}$ is generally specified by the manufacturer as a *temperature derating factor*; i.e., a specific "power/°C" that must be subtracted from the specified $P_{D\text{max}}$-value for increases in ambient temperature above the value associated with $P_{D\text{max}}$. (Similarly, the value may be *added* to $P_{D\text{max}}$ for *decreases* in ambient temperature.) Derating factors for diodes with large heat sinks are lower than those for diodes with small sinks or no sinks.

The peak inverse (or reverse) voltage is specified for rectifier applications; it is equal to V_Z. If a diode is to be used as a rectifier, at no time is it desirable to permit Zener breakdown to occur. Such heavy conduction in the reverse direction defeats the purpose of the rectifier.

Example 4-9.   The silicon diode in Example 4–8 has a temperature derating factor of one milliwatt per degree Centigrade. What is its maximum dissipation power without the heat sink at an external temperature of 400°K?

Solution.   If the diode can be operated with 120 milliwatts dissipation power at 300°K (27°C) and must be derated at one milliwatt per degree centigrade:

$$P_d(400°\text{K}) = P_d(300°\text{K}) - [\Delta T \times (\text{derating factor})]$$
$$= (120 \times 10^{-3}) - (127 - 27)(1 \times 10^{-3})$$
$$= 20 \text{ milliwatts}$$

(Notice that when a temperature difference is involved, a ΔT in degrees Kelvin has the same value as a ΔT in degrees Centigrade.)

Junction Capacitance

The opposite charges in the depletion region are analogous to the charges on the opposite plates of a capacitor. Hence, with no bias applied to the junction, there is a fixed, space-charge capacitance associated with the junction. Capacitance is inversely related to the width of the "dielectric" medium separating the "plates." For this reason, applying a reverse bias to the diode (increasing junction width) decreases the junction capacitance. When a forward bias is applied, there is a considerable increase in the amount of charge in the junction region. There is also a decrease in the junction width. The combination of these effects results in greatly increased junction capacitance with forward bias. The capacitive effect is illustrated in Fig. 4–36.

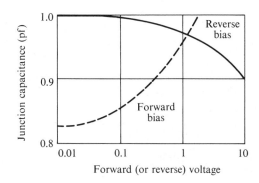

Figure 4-36.   *Junction Capacitance Variation*

The junction capacitance has detrimental effects in some applications, because it limits the frequency at which the diode will operate. However, it can be put to practical use in oscillator and frequency control circuits. Diodes with designed emphasis on the junction capacitance characteristics are termed *variable capacitance diodes* and are available over a wide range of values.

4.6 Rectifiers

Fixed large-scale hydroelectric or steam-driven generators, or small-scale portable units, are readily available to generate a-c power. Since a-c current or voltage can be stepped-up or stepped-down with transformers, a-c power can be efficiently transmitted over vast networks of wires at relatively low costs. On the other hand, d-c power must be obtained from batteries. High voltages can be obtained by operating several batteries in series; high current, by operating several batteries in parallel. However, the resulting power pack is bulky, heavy, and expensive.

Recent advances in more exotic techniques, such as fuel cells, promise to result in d-c power sources that are lighter and smaller for a given rating—especially at higher output levels. Since transformers cannot be used to manipulate d-c voltage and current magnitudes without first employing a mechanical "vibrator" to interrupt the flow regularly (producing a pseudo-a-c signal), the transmission of d-c power over long ranges is impractical. Hence, for purposes of efficiency, flexibility, and cost, a-c power is "ideal," while d-c power is confined to applications requiring self-contained systems operating for short periods. Yet, *almost every electronic circuit requires the use of fixed-value voltages and currents*, as well as *fluctuating voltages and currents*. This leads to a universal requirement for devices capable of converting a-c power to d-c power. The semiconductor diode is such a device.

Rectification is the process of changing a-c voltages (and currents) into *unidirectional* voltages (and currents). The term "unidirectional" indicates that the electrical quantity maintains constant positive or negative *polarity* but does not define pure d-c. This is illustrated in Fig. 4-37. The unidirectional voltage is a fluctuating voltage of uniform polarity, while pure d-c maintains uniform polarity and magnitude. Two basic semiconductor diode circuits, the half-wave and full-wave rectifiers, are capable of producing unidirectional outputs. However, these voltages (and currents) fluctuate widely and, in order for them to approach pure d-c, must be "filtered" or "smoothed" through the use of additional circuit components.

The unilateral nature (conducting strongly in only one direction) of the semiconductor diode permits it to conduct only one-half of an

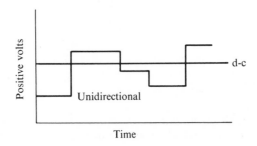

Figure 4-37.   *Comparison of* D-C *and Unidirectional Voltages*

input a-c cycle. Hence, depending upon the arrangement of the diode, only the posive (or negative) half-cycles will result in appreciable signal flow. The slight reverse current characteristic—not present in vacuum tube diodes—can produce undesirable effects in some applications. However, the small value of this current makes its effects insignificant in most practical situations. The entire operation of the diode as a rectifier is destroyed if the reverse voltage (the voltage during the non-conducting half-cycle) *exceeds the Zener voltage.* If V_Z is exceeded, the diode conducts hard in both directions and the output is a-c. For this reason, semiconductor diodes used specifically for rectifier applications have high V_Z-values—usually over a thousand volts.

Half-Wave Rectifiers

Figure 4-38 illustrates the basic *half-wave rectifier* circuit for a semiconductor junction diode. The diode symbol "points" in the direction of

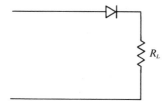

Figure 4-38.   *Half-Wave Rectifier*

hole flow (or, the "conventional" current flow). Actual circuit current; i.e., electron current flow, to be used throughout this text, goes against the direction of the symbolic "arrow." When the input signal is positive, the diode is biased in the forward direction, the majority carriers cross the junction, and a heavy circuit current flows (Fig. 4-39, Parts A, B, and C). Ideally, the output half-cycle would follow the input half-cycle exactly. As shown, the actual output half-cycle is not perfectly sinusoidal due to the nonlinearity of the diode forward characteristic (Fig. 4-26), nor does its peak magnitude equal the peak input magnitude due to voltage lost across the small diode dynamic resistance, r_d. When negative input half-cycles are applied (Parts D, E, and F of the figure), the diode is biased in the reverse direction, only the minority carriers cross the junction, and only a small circuit current, I_{sat}, flows. This produces a low, negative-voltage half-cycle, as shown. The ideal reverse characteristic would

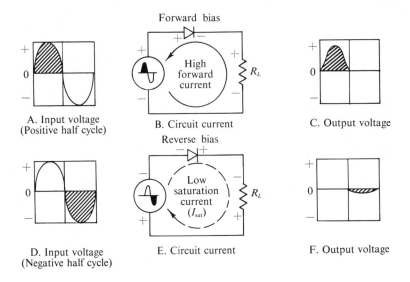

A. Input voltage
(Positive half cycle)

B. Circuit current

C. Output voltage

D. Input voltage
(Negative half cycle)

E. Circuit current

F. Output voltage

Figure 4-39.   *Half-Wave Rectifier Operation*

consist of no output voltage during this time period. The small voltage that *does exist* does not follow the input sinewave because I_{sat} is constant (Fig. 4–26) as long as the peak input voltage does not exceed or equal V_Z. Exceeding V_Z will produce waveforms such as those in Fig. 4–40. Reversing the diode direction in Fig. 4–38 results in an inverted output waveform; i.e., conduction during the negative input half-cycle; nonconduction during the positive input half-cycle.

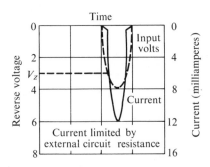

Figure 4-40.   *Heavy Conduction When Exceeding Zener Voltage*

From the waveform analysis relationships (Appendix C), the d-c value associated with the ideal half-wave output is:

$$V_{\text{d-c}} = 0.318\, V_p = 0.45\, V_{\text{rms}} \qquad (4\text{-}28)$$

where V_p is the maximum, or peak, *input* voltage and V_{rms} is the root-mean-square *input* voltage. The same relationship holds true for current, with $I_{\text{d-c}}$, I_p and I_{rms} replacing the analogous voltage values. For most practical designs, the output is near enough to the ideal waveform that use of Eq. (4–28) introduces negligible error. The mathematical analysis of the rectifier circuit is based on replacing the diode with its dynamic resistance (Fig. 4–41) and writing the appropriate Kirchoff equations. Hence:

$$I_{\text{d-c}} = \frac{0.318 V_p}{(r_d + R_L)} = \frac{0.45 V_{\text{rms}}}{(r_d + R_L)} \qquad (4\text{-}29)$$

and

$$V_{\text{d-c}} = 0.318 V_p - I_{\text{d-c}} r_d = 0.45 V_{\text{rms}} - I_{\text{d-c}} r_d \qquad (4\text{-}30)$$

$$= 0.318 V_p\!\left[\frac{r_d + R_L}{r_d}\right]$$

$$= 0.45 V_{\text{rms}}\!\left[\frac{r_d + R_L}{r_d}\right]$$

and

$$P_{\text{d-c}} = I_{\text{d-c}}^2 R_L = \frac{0.1 V_p^2 R_L}{(r_d + R_L)^2} \qquad (4\text{-}31)$$

$$= \frac{0.2 V_{\text{rms}}^2 R_L}{(r_d + R_L)^2}$$

where the d-c voltage, $V_{\text{d-c}}$, and power, $P_{\text{d-c}}$, are measured at the load. The analysis of the reverse conduction is not considered here; it is assumed that the diode can be considered truly unilateral, for all practical purposes.

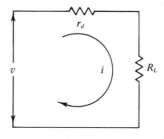

Figure 4-41.   *Rectifier Equivalent Circuit (Forward Conduction)*

The maximum reverse voltage applied to the half-wave rectifying diode is equal to V_p. Hence, the relationship:

$$|V_p| < |V_z| \qquad (4\text{-}32)$$

must be considered as a design limit. This is accomplished either by limiting the range of input voltages for a specific rectifier, or by selecting a diode with a high enough Zener voltage to cover all probable uses of a particular rectifier design.

Example 4-10.   A particular junction diode is to be used in a half-wave rectifier. The maximum dissipation power for the diode is 2 watts at room temperature with 4 volts applied in the forward direction. Assuming that the diode resistance is negligible in comparison, what value load resistance is needed if a 110-volt a-c signal is to be rectified and the diode is to operate at its rated power? What d-c power is delivered to the load?

Solution.   If the maximum dissipation power of 2 watts occurs with 4 volts across the diode, the average (d-c) forward current in the circuit must be 0.5 ampere. In terms of load resistance:

$$I_{\text{d-c}} = \frac{0.45 V_{\text{rms}}}{(r_d + R_L)} = \frac{0.45 V_{\text{rms}}}{R_L}$$

when r_d is negligible. Solving for R_L:

$$R_L = \frac{0.45 V_{\text{rms}}}{I_{\text{d-c}}} = \frac{(0.45)110}{0.5} = 99 \text{ ohms}$$

The d-c power is:

$$P_{\text{d-c}} = I_{\text{d-c}}^2 R_L = (0.5)^2(99) = 24.75 \text{ watts}$$

Full-Wave Rectifiers

Figure 4–42, Part B represents the basic full-wave rectifier circuit for a semiconductor junction diode. When the input signal is positive, diode number one is forward biased (conducting) and diode number two is reverse biased (nonconducting). The load is arranged such that current flow through it produces the polarity indicated in Part B of the figure, with the output waveform indicated in Part C. The ideal waveform is shown, although the actual waveform is subject to the same deviations indicated for the half-wave rectifier. An additional deviation results from the fact that the "nonconducting" diode *does* permit I_{sat} to flow. However, this effect is insignificant. When the input signal is negative, diode number two is forward biased (conducting) and diode number one is reverse biased (nonconducting). This is shown in Part E of the figure, along with current flow and load voltage polarity. Notice that the full-wave rectifier arrangement is such that current through the load is in the same direction, regardless of which diode is conducting. This results in a unidirectional output during *both input half-cycles* (Part F). Reversing *both diodes* results in an inverted full-wave output. Reversing only one diode would result in a half-wave rectifier with twice the current capabilities of a single-diode rectifier. The resulting circuit actually is two half-wave rectifiers operating in parallel.

Since the full-wave output contains twice as many "pulsations" as does the half-wave output, the current and voltage values must be twice as large. From Eq. (4–28):

$$V_{\text{d-c}} = 0.636\ V_p = 0.9\ V_{\text{rms}} \tag{4-33}$$

where the equation can be rewritten for current with $I_{\text{d-c}}$, I_p, and I_{rms} substituted for $V_{\text{d-c}}$, V_p, and V_{rms}, respectively. Assuming that both diodes have the same dynamic resistance:

$$I_{\text{d-c}} = \frac{0.636V_p}{(r_d + R_L)} = \frac{0.9V_{\text{rms}}}{(r_d + R_L)} \tag{4-34}$$

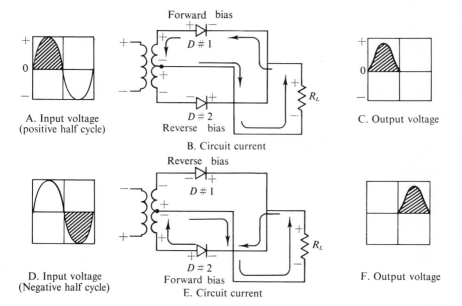

A. Input voltage (positive half cycle)

B. Circuit current

C. Output voltage

D. Input voltage (Negative half cycle)

E. Circuit current

F. Output voltage

Figure 4-42.   *Full-Wave Rectifier Operation*

and with a derivation similar to that shown in Eq. (4-30):

$$V_{d-c} = 0.636 V_p \left[\frac{r_d + R_L}{r_d} \right]$$ (4-35)

$$= 0.9 V_{rms} \left[\frac{r_d + R_L}{r_d} \right]$$

and

$$P_{d-c} = \frac{0.404 V_p^2 R_L}{(r_d + R_L)^2} = \frac{0.81 V_{rms}^2 R_L}{(r_d + R_L)^2}$$ (4-36)

where the d-c voltage and power are measured at the load. These equations clearly indicate that the full-wave rectifier is superior to the half-wave circuit in current, voltage, and power characteristics.

Since, in the nonconducting interval, each diode is subjected to the full transformer secondary voltage with a peak value of $2V_p$, the relationship:

$$|2V_p| < |V_z|$$ (4-37)

must be considered the design limit for the full-wave rectifier diodes.

Example 4-11.   If the diode in Example 4–10 is to be used in a full-wave rectifier circuit with the same a-c source, what load resistance would be used and what d-c output power would be obtained?

Solution.   The average input current cannot exceed 0.5 ampere. Since:

$$I_{d-c} = \frac{0.9 V_{rms}}{(r_d + R_L)} = \frac{0.9 V_{rms}}{R_L}$$

the load value is given by:

$$R_L = \frac{0.9 V_{rms}}{I_{d-c}} = \frac{(0.9)110}{0.5} = 198 \text{ ohms}$$

which is twice the value that must be used in the half-wave rectifier. The d-c power is:

$$P_{d-c} = I_{d-c}^2 R_L = (0.5)^2(198) = 49.5 \text{ watts}$$

which is twice the d-c power of the half-wave rectifier.

Reverse Conduction Characteristics

The previous sections have been based, primarily, on the assumption that the output voltage during the "nonconducting" interval is negligible. Whether or not this assumption is valid depends on the value of I_{sat} and the load value. I_{sat} is fixed for a particular diode. Hence, some care must

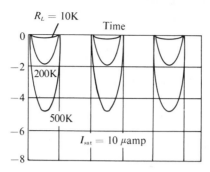

Figure 4-43.   *Variation of Reverse Voltage with Load*

be taken in selecting the load value so that the undesirable "nonconducting" voltage does not exceed some tolerable limit. The variation in voltage, as a function of load, is shown in Fig. 4–43. Although the output voltage during the "conducting" interval will always differ from the "nonconducting" value by a factor of about one thousand, when large load values are used, the "nonconducting" voltage may exceed tolerable limits, depending upon the application. Because of the effect of opposite-polarity waveform segments on effective d-c value (Appendix C), such operation degrades the overall rectifier performance.

Performance Comparisons

The previous sections have indicated that the full-wave rectifier produces twice the current and voltage, and four times the power, of the half-wave rectifier. The main purpose of any rectifier, however, is to convert a-c power into d-c power. Hence, rectifier performance is best specified and compared in terms of this conversion. Two factors: the *ripple factor* and the *rectification efficiency*, are used.

Half-wave and full-wave rectifiers produce pulsating unidirectional outputs. The pulsations are caused by the *harmonic components* of the output waveform. (The rectifier output is nonsinusoidal. Harmonic, or *Fourier*, analysis techniques indicate that nonsinusoidal waveforms are composed of a multitude of sinewaves with frequencies that are integral multiples of a "fundamental" frequency—see Appendix C.)

A measure of the total pulsation associated with a waveform, or the "purity" of the waveform, is called the *ripple factor* (γ). By definition:

$$\gamma = \sqrt{(V_{\text{rms}}/V_{\text{d-c}})^2 - 1} \qquad (4\text{-}38)$$

where V_{rms} now refers to the rms value of the *output* voltage waveform. High values of γ indicate a high degree of pulsation; low values indicate that the waveform is approaching pure d-c ($\gamma = 0$, for pure d-c). Not only does γ provide a theoretical performance comparison factor, it can also be easily measured by using a-c and d-c meters (to determine V_{rms} and $V_{\text{d-c}}$, respectively).

The d-c voltage (or current) values for the half-wave and full-wave outputs have been derived [Eqs. (4–28) and (4–33), respectively; or Eqs. (4–29) and (4–34), respectively]. These values are summarized in Fig. 4–44, along with the rms value. Substituting these values into Eq. (4–38) yields:

$$\gamma = 1.21 \quad \text{[half]} \tag{4-38a}$$

$$\gamma = 0.47 \quad \text{[full]} \tag{4-38b}$$

indicating that the full-wave rectifier has considerably better ripple characteristics than the half-wave. The ripple factor may be converted into *per cent ripple* by multiplying Eq. (4–38) by 100 per cent.

The efficiency of conversion of input a-c power to output d-c power or the *rectification efficiency*, is defined by:

$$\eta_R = \frac{P_{\text{d-c}}(\text{out})}{P_{\text{a-c}}(\text{in})} \times 100 \text{ per cent} \tag{4-39}$$

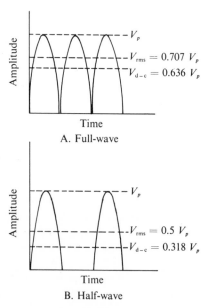

A. Full-wave

B. Half-wave

Figure 4-44.   RMS *and* D-C *Values for Rectified Waveforms*

Notice that P_{d-c} (out) does not represent *all the power dissipated in the load*. It represents the d-c component only. Substituting Eqs. (4–31) and (4–36) for P_{d-c} (out), and the relationship: $[V_p/2(R_L + r_d)]^2$ $(R_L + r_d)$ for P_{a-c} (in) into Eq. (4–39) yields (after considerable algebraic manipulation):

$$\eta_R = \frac{40.6 \text{ per cent}}{1 + r_d/R_L} \qquad \text{[half]} \qquad \textbf{(4-39a)}$$

$$\eta_R = \frac{81.2 \text{ per cent}}{1 + r_d/R_L} \qquad \text{[full]} \qquad \textbf{(4-39b)}$$

indicating that the full-wave rectifier is inherently twice as efficient as the half-wave rectifier. Equations (4–39a) and (4–39b) are plotted in Fig. 4–45 in order to indicate the variation of η_R with r_d and R_L. Maximum efficiency is obtained in both circuits when $R_L \gg r_d$, with 40.6 per cent and 81.2 per cent being the respective limiting values. The requirement that R_L be much greater than r_d in order to achieve high efficiency is compatable with the requirement for low ripple factor.

Example 4-12.   Compare the rectification efficiencies for the half-wave and full-wave rectifiers of Examples 4–10 and 4–11 if the dynamic resistance of the diode is 10 ohms.

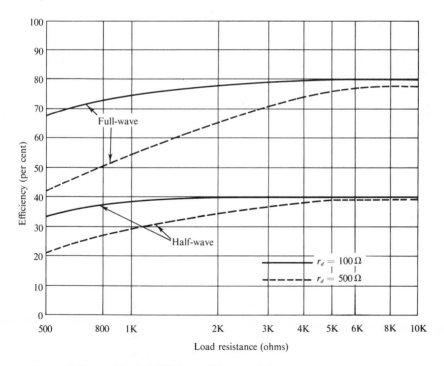

Figure 4-45.   *Typical Efficiency Characteristics*

Solution. For the half-wave rectifier:

$$\eta_R = \frac{40.6 \text{ per cent}}{1 + r_d/R_L} = \frac{40.6 \text{ per cent}}{1 + (10/99)} = 37 \text{ per cent}$$

For the full-wave rectifier:

$$\eta_R = \frac{81.2 \text{ per cent}}{1 + r_d/R_L} = \frac{81.2 \text{ per cent}}{1 + (10/198)} = 77 \text{ per cent}$$

These values indicate high-efficiency operation, which is always achieved when r_d is negligible, and that full-wave efficiency is over twice that of the half-wave rectifier.

Output Smoothing (Filtering)

If the rectifier circuit performed a true conversion of a-c to *pure* d-c, the output voltage would be constant. Furthermore, the ripple factor, γ, would be zero and the rectification efficiency, η_R, would be 100 per cent for both rectifier circuits. All of these conditions indicate the removal of the pulsating output components (the *harmonics* associated with the rectified waveforms). The "removal" of the a-c signal components (harmonics, in this case) can be accomplished by using *filters;* i.e., passive electrical networks that attenuate these signals to insignificant values. Since this text is devoted to semiconductor principles and analyses, rather than to general electrical network analysis, only a brief discussion of two important rectifier filters will be provided, along with design curves that will not be proven or supported here.

Figure 4–46 illustrates the simple RC- or shunt-capacitor filter used in high-voltage, low-(average) current applications with a half-wave rectifier. During the initial output cycle (with R_g, the source resistance, and r_d, the diode resistance, negligible with respect to R_L, the load), the

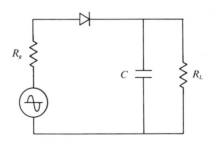

Figure 4-46.   *Half-Wave Rectifier with Shunt-Capacitor Filter*

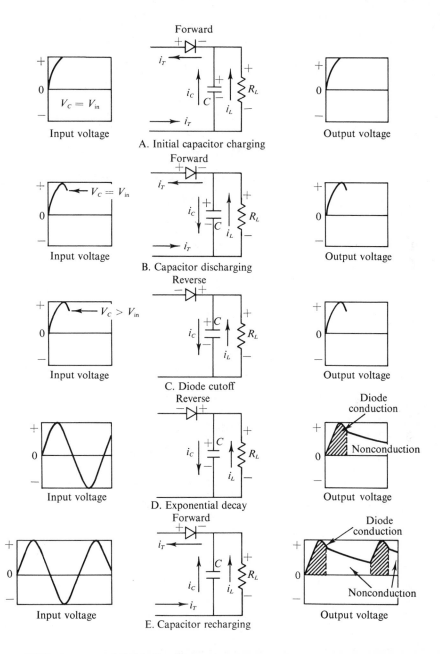

Figure 4-47. *Half-Wave Rectifier Operation with Shunt-Capacitor Filter*

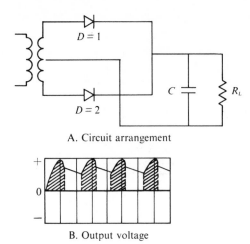

A. Circuit arrangement

B. Output voltage

Figure 4-48. *Full-Wave Rectifier with Shunt-Capacitor Filter*

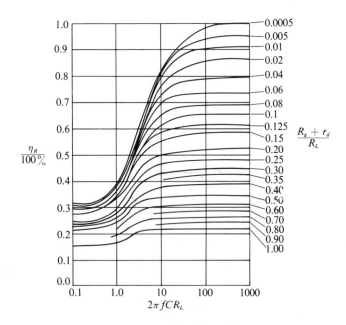

Figure 4-49. *Design Curves (Efficiency) for Half-Wave Rectifier with Shunt-Capacitor Filter (Analysis of Rectifier Operation,* O. H. Schade, July 1943, Proceedings of the Institute of Radio Engineers.)

capacitor charges with its voltage (as well as the parallel load voltage) equal to the input voltage. This is shown in Fig. 4-47, Part A. After the peak voltage is reached and the input voltage begins to decrease, the capacitor (with voltage V_p across it) must discharge into the load, as shown in Part B. The charging time constant for the capacitor is very small (zero, if R_g and r_d are zero). However, the discharging time constant is $R_L C$. Hence, the capacitor voltage does not track the decreasing portion of the input signal as it does the increasing portion. Because of this, the input voltage eventually falls below the capacitor voltage. This results in a reverse bias on the diode, cutting it off, as shown in Part C. The capacitor continues to discharge through the load, with an exponentially decaying output voltage resulting (Part D). During this decay, the input voltage swings through its complete cycle and begins increasing in the forward direction again (also in Part D). When the input voltage exceeds the capacitor voltage, the diode becomes forward biased again and conduction resumes, repeating the previous process (Part E). Notice that diode current flows only between the cut-in and cut-out angles (shaded regions in the figure) and that the output voltage is more nearly constant. A similar reasoning applies to the full-wave rectifier (Fig. 4-48), except that (for a given load value) the output voltage may decrease only slightly during the nonconducting periods.

In actual practice, R_g and r_d, together, are usually *not negligible* with

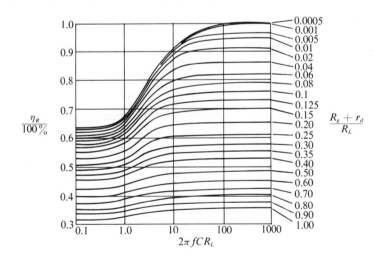

Figure 4-50.   *Design Curves (Efficiency) for Full-Wave Rectifier with Shunt-Capacitor Filter (Analysis of Rectifier Operation,* O. H. Schade, July 1943, Proceedings of the Institute of Radio Engineers.)

respect to R_L. This means that some of the input voltage will be lost. Accounting for R_g and r_d during the conduction period is very tedious, analytically. However, ripple-factor and rectification-efficiency equations *can* be derived, the graphical results being illustrated in Figs. 4-49, 4-50,

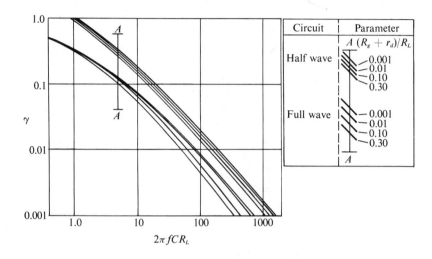

Figure 4-51.   *Design Curves (Ripple Factor) for Half-Wave and Full-Wave Rectifiers with Shunt-Capacitor Filter (Analysis of Rectifier Operation,* O. H. Schade, July 1943, Proceedings of the Institute of Radio Engineers.)

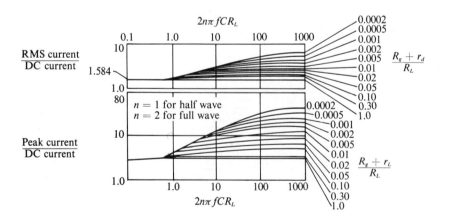

Figure 4-52.   *Design Curves (Current Ratios) for Half-Wave and Full-Wave Rectifiers with Shunt-Capacitor Filter (Analysis of Rectifier Operation,* O. H. Schade, July 1943, Proceedings of the Institute of Radio Engineers.)

and 4–51. These curves, along with Fig. 4–52, represent sufficient material to design an RC-filter for a specific rectifier application. As long as the d-c current does not exceed the maximum diode current, the rectifier will operate properly, *despite the fact that peak current may exceed the specified maximum.*

During nonconduction, the input voltage and capacitor voltage add to form the total reverse voltage on the diode. This results in higher peak reverse voltages than those associated with the unfiltered rectifier. For this reason, the following limiting conditions apply when selecting a diode for the RC-filtered rectifier:

$$|V_z| > |2V_p| \text{[half]}   \text{(4-40a)}$$
$$|V_z| > |3V_p| \text{[full]}   \text{(4-40b)}$$

An inductive filter (Fig 4–53) may be used for low-voltage, high-current

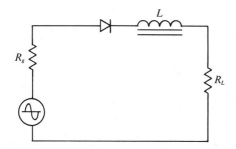

Figure 4-53.   *Half-Wave Rectifier with Series-Inductor Filter*

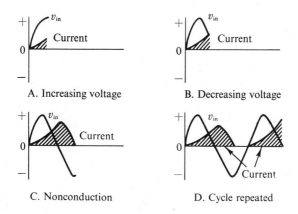

Figure 4-54.   *Half-Wave Rectifier Waveforms with Series-Inductor Filter*

applications. During the initial input cycle, as the voltage increases, the inductor opposes the associated increasing current. This reduces the current (and output voltage) value, as shown in Fig. 4–54, Part A. When the input voltage passes its peak value and begins to decrease, the inductor opposes *this* change and tends to maintain circuit current (and output voltage) values at a high level. This is shown in Part B of the figure. Eventually, however, the stored magnetic energy cannot maintain the conduction and the values drop to zero (Part C), where they remain until the diode begins to conduct again (Part D). The action of the inductor

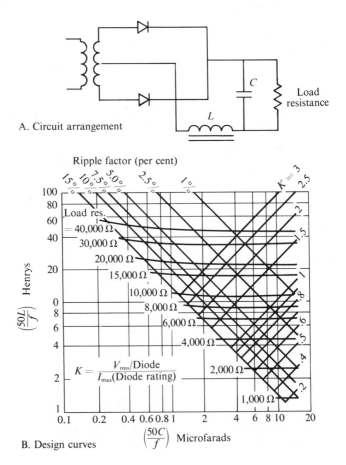

Figure 4-55. *Design of Full-Wave Rectifier with* LC-*Filter, Continuous Conduction* (*Radiotron Designer's Handbook*, 1952, Amalgamated Wireless Valve Company, Sydney, Australia. Reproduced and Distributed in the United States by Radio Corporation of America.)

is such as to "smear" the output pulsations. Component values *can* be selected that will result in continuous (unidirectional) current flow—especially for the full-wave rectifier circuit. Figure 4–55 presents a set of graphs that are useful in designing inductive input filters for the full-wave rectifier. The circuit shown uses both an inductor and a capacitor in order to achieve continuous current flow.

Examples 4-13. A shunt-capacitor filter is to be used in the half-wave rectifier circuit of Example 4–10. Without changing the load resistor value, what value of capacitance must be used if the ripple factor is to be 0.1? (The source and diode resistances, combined, are equal to 23 ohms. The input frequency is 60 cycles per second.) What efficiency is achieved? Is it safe to operate the diode in this circuit?

Solution. Figure 4–51 relates efficiency, load resistance, source resistance, diode resistance, frequency, and capacitance. The parameter value is:

$$\frac{(R_g + r_d)}{R_L} = \frac{23}{99} = 0.23$$

Ripple factor is 0.1 for this condition when:

$$2\pi f C R_L = 14$$

Solving for C:

$$C = \frac{14}{2\pi f R_L} = \frac{7}{\pi(60)(78)} \approx 477 \text{ microfarads}$$

From Fig. 4–49, when $2\pi f C R_L$ is 14 and $(R_g + r_d)/R_L$ is 0.23, the efficiency is 49 per cent, which is an acceptable figure. The ratio of peak to d-c current can be found from Fig. 4–52 with:

$$2n\pi f C R_L = 2\pi f C R_L = 14$$

since $n = 1$ for half-wave rectifiers. With this condition, and with $(R_g + r_d)/R_L = 0.23$, a value of:

$$\frac{I_p}{I_{\text{d-c}}} = 3.5$$

is obtained. With filtering, the peak current may exceed the peak rated current, but the d-c current may not. The d-c current is:

$$I_{\text{d-c}} = \frac{I_p}{3.5} = \frac{1.57}{3.5} = 0.45 \text{ ampere}$$

Since the maximum rated current is 1 ampere, this range of operation is safe.

Example 4-14. It is desirable to completely redesign the full-wave rectifier of Example 4-11 and incorporate an LC-filter with continuous conduction capability. What value of load resistance, inductance, and capacitance must be used in order to achieve a 10-per cent ripple factor at a frequency of 60 cycles per second and an a-c voltage of 2.2 volts across each diode.

Solution. The design curves for a continuous conduction full-wave rectifier with LC-filtering appear in Fig. 4–55. Initially, it is necessary to determine K:

$$K = \frac{V_{rms}}{I_{max}} = \frac{2.2}{1} = 2.2$$

The interpolated line for K equal to 2.2 and the line for γ equal to 10 per cent intersect at a point indicating the need for a 9000-ohm load resistor. This same intersection, projected horizontally to the left and vertically downward, yields:

$$(50L/f) = 10$$
$$(50C/f) = 1.4$$

so that:

$$L = \frac{10f}{50} = \frac{10(60)}{50} = 12 \text{ henries}$$
$$C = \frac{1.4f}{50} = \frac{1.4(60)}{50} = 1.68 \text{ microfarads}$$

This is not a practical circuit design because of the extreme inductance value that is required.

4.7 Voltage Regulation

In many d-c circuit applications it is desirable to maintain a constant voltage across some specific loading device. However, the d-c source voltage may fluctuate (as in the rectifier output or an aging battery) or the load, itself, may change value slowly or in a cyclic fashion. One attempt to maintain a constant load voltage was discussed in Chap. 3, using thermistors. However, the range of constant voltage for such a circuit is very limited. When operated in the breakdown region, the Zener diode will permit a wide variation in current flow while maintaining a voltage equal to V_z. Thus, the Zener diode, operated in the breakdown region, is well suited as a voltage regulation device.

Figure 4–56 illustrates the basic *shunt regulator* circuit. The voltage

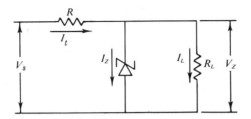

Figure 4-56.   *Basic Shunt Regulator Circuit Utilizing Zener Diode*

across the load (in parallel with the diode) will be maintained at V_Z within the limits of circuit operation. Since there will always be a drop across R, the desired load voltage, V_Z, must be less than the source voltage, V_s. The input resistance to the regulator is given by:

$$R_i = R + \frac{R_Z R_L}{R_Z + R_L} \qquad (4\text{-}41a)$$

but, since R_L is usually much greater than R_Z, this is approximated by:

$$R_i = R + R_Z \qquad (4\text{-}41b)$$

which can be further approximated by:

$$R_i = R \qquad (4\text{-}41c)$$

if R is much greater than R_Z. In either case, Eqs. (4–41b) and (4–41c) indicate that the input resistance of the regulator circuit is constant, even though R_L may vary.

The voltage loop equation for the shunt regulator is:

$$V_s = I_t R_i = I_t R + V_Z \qquad (4\text{-}42)$$

as long as V_Z remains constant, variations in V_s must be accompanied by variations in I_t. If V_s increases, I_t increases; decreasing V_s produces decreases in I_t. The regulating action overcomes this variation in voltage and maintains constant load voltage even though the input voltage is not constant. The voltage differential $(V_s - V_Z)$ is always dropped across R, so that:

$$R = \frac{V_s - V_Z}{I_t} \qquad (4\text{-}43)$$

Since I_t splits into I_Z and I_L, fluctuations in I_Z and I_L must occur when I_t varies.

Since the diode holds the voltage across the load constant, the load current must also be constant. Since the diode shunts the load, when the supply voltage is a minimum, $I_{Z(\text{min})}$ must flow, and when the supply voltage is a maximum, $I_{Z(\text{max})}$ must flow. There is a limit on how small

$I_{Z(\text{min})}$ can become, however, if the diode is to stay in the Zener region. A maximum value for R is given by [from Eq. (4-43)]:

$$R_{(\text{max})} = \frac{V_{s(\text{min})} - V_Z}{I_L + I_{Z(\text{min})}} \qquad (4\text{-}44)$$

Since the diode dissipation capability is limited, $I_{Z(\text{max})}$ is dependent upon the maximum diode power:

$$I_{Z(\text{max})} = \sqrt{P_{\text{max}}/R_Z} \qquad (4\text{-}45)$$

Since the maximum diode current flows when the source voltage is at a maximum, a minimum value for R is given by:

$$R_{(\text{min})} = \frac{V_{s(\text{max})} - V_Z}{I_L + I_{Z(\text{max})}} \qquad (4\text{-}46)$$

Hence, Eq. (4-43) can be used to establish a desirable value for R, given a constant V_s and a desired I_t. When V_s undergoes a known fluctuation, however, this value of R must fall within the limits:

$$R_{(\text{min})} \le R \le R_{(\text{max})} \qquad (4\text{-}47)$$

if proper regulation is to be maintained.

Example 4-15. The voltage regulating circuit of Fig. 4–56 uses a Zener diode with breakdown at 15 volts and 2 microamperes, a maximum dissipation power of 120 milliwatts, and a Zener resistance of 40 ohms. The load resistor is 5K. What value of R should be used if the supply voltage varies from 18 to 24 volts?

Solution. Since the Zener diode will maintain 15 volts across the load, the load current is:

$$I_L = \frac{15}{5000} = 3 \times 10^{-3} \text{ ampere}$$

The minimum permissable Zener current (2 microamperes) is negligible with respect to I_L, so that:

$$R_{(\text{max})} = \frac{V_{s(\text{min})} - V_Z}{I_L} = \frac{18 - 15}{3 \times 10^{-3}} = 1K$$

In order to maintain operation within the dissipation limits of the diode, the current cannot exceed $I_{Z(\text{max})}$:

$$I_{Z(\text{max})} = \sqrt{P_{\text{max}}/R_Z} = \sqrt{(0.12)/(40)} = 55.8 \times 10^{-3} \text{ ampere}$$

In order to prevent the diode current from exceeding this value, R cannot be less than:

$$R_{(\text{min})} = \frac{V_{s(\text{max})} - V_Z}{I_L + I_{Z(\text{max})}} = \frac{24 - 15}{(3 + 55.8)(10^{-3})} = 153 \text{ ohms}$$

Proper regulation can be maintained with R selected between 153 and 1000 ohms.

PROBLEMS

1. An impurity concentration of 6×10^{-6} is used in germanium. At what temperature will the excess carriers be completely transferred to their appropriate energy band?

2. An N-type sample of germanium contains a donor atom for every 100,000 germanium atoms. How many minority carriers are present at 400°K?

3. With an impurity density of 8×10^{23} atoms/meter³, what is the majority-to-minority carrier density ratio at room temperature?

4. What is the resistivity of P-type silicon at 250°K with an impurity concentration of 10^{-5}? At 450°K?

5. What is the room temperature resistance of a device composed of two parallel strips of semiconductor material, each measuring 0.025 meter long by 0.0005 meter wide by 0.0001 meter thick that are butted together? One material is P-type silicon with an impurity concentration of 10^{-6} and the other material is N-type germanium with an impurity concentration of 10^{-8}.

6. What is the diffusion constant for both types of carriers at both temperatures specified in Problem 4?

7. At what temperature will the thermal voltage in a semiconductor material be equal to 32 millivolts?

8. If the two pieces of semiconductor material in Problem 5 are used to form a semiconductor junction, what is the junction potential at room temperature?

9. What is the junction potential in Problem 8 at a temperature of 400°K?

10. The saturation current for a junction diode is 4 microamperes. What is the forward current when a forward voltage of 0.05 volt is applied? With a forward voltage of 0.5 volt applied?

11. A Zener diode is to have a room temperature breakdown voltage of 15 volts. The P-type material has a resistivity of 0.7 ohm·meter. What must the resistivity of the N-type material be?

12. If the P-type material in Problem 11 is silicon, what must its impurity concentration be?

13. A Zener diode with the characteristics given in Appendix D has a maximum dissipation power of 240 milliwatts. If the reverse bias is -20 volts, what circuit resistance must be present to limit the current flow?

14. A diode is operated in an environment with an ambient temperature of 350°K. It has a total thermal resistance of 600°K/watt. What is the junction temperature?

15. A silicon diode without a heat sink is capable of dissipating 300 milliwatts of power at room temperature with a junction temperature of 380°K. The diode derating factor is 0.05 milliwatt/°K. At an ambient temperature of 400°K, specify a heat sink thermal resistance that will permit the diode to continue to dissipate 300 milliwatts.

16. A germanium diode is capable of dissipating 100 milliwatts at room temperature. It has a temperature derating factor of 0.75 milliwatt/°C. How much power can the diode handle at 375°K?

17. It is necessary to deliver 5 watts of rectified d-c power to a 2000-ohm load resistance. The rectification is to be accomplished with a half-wave rectifier, being driven by an a-c signal with an rms value of 110 volts. Specify a maximum current and power rating for the diode used in this circuit. (Assume that the diode resistance is negligible.)

18. If the application described in Problem 17 is to be accomplished with a full-wave rectifier, what maximum current and power rating must the diodes have?

19. A 5000-ohm load is being fed by a 10-volt rectified d-c signal from a half-wave rectifier. When the rectifier diode is in a "nonconducting" state, the current through the load cannot exceed 5 per cent of the forward current value. What is the maximum saturation current that can be associated with the diode?

20. A full-wave rectifier uses diodes with an equivalent dynamic resistance of 100 ohms, and feeds a load resistor of 500 ohms. What is the ripple factor and the efficiency value for the rectifier?

21. A 60-cycle source with an internal resistance of 100 ohms is used to drive a full-wave rectifier with shunt-capacitor filtering. The dynamic resistance of the diode is 15 ohms. What value capacitance should be used in order to achieve a ripple factor of 0.2 when the load resistance is 10,000 ohms? What is the associated rectifier efficiency?

22. The source in Problem 21 is used to drive a half-wave rectifier with shunt-capacitance filtering and provides a peak a-c signal of 50 volts. The rectifier feeds a 3000-ohm load resistance and is to operate at an efficiency of 80 per cent. Specify the maximum dissipation power for the diode.

23. A particular diode has a maximum dissipation power of 0.7 watt at 0.5 ampere forward current. It is to be used in a full-wave rectifier with LC-filtering, designed to feed a 20,000-ohm resistance. What value of inductance and capacitance must be used? What is the associated ripple factor?

24. A Zener diode which breaks down at 10 volts and can dissipate 1 watt is to be used in a voltage regulator circuit. The Zener resistance is 100 ohms. The minimum Zener current is negligible. If the load is 2000 ohms and if the dropping resistor (*R* in Fig. 4–56) is 500 ohms, over what voltage range can the source vary without destroying the diode or causing a degradation in the regulated voltage?

Further Reading

Cleary, J. F. (ed.), *General Electric Transistor Manual*. Syracuse, N.Y.: General Electric Company, Semiconductor Products Department, 1964.

Ham, J. E. and G. R. Slemon, *Scientific Basis of Electrical Engineering*. New York: John Wiley and Sons, Inc., 1961.

Langford-Smith, F. (ed.), *Radiotron Designer's Handbook*. Harrison,N.J.: Radio Corporation of America, Electron Tube Division, 1952.

Martin, T. L., Jr., *Electronic Circuits*. Englewood Cliffs, N.J.: Prentice-Hall, Inc., 1955.

Phillips, A. B., *Transistor Engineering*. New York: McGraw-Hill Book Company, Inc., 1962.

Pierce, J. F., *Transistor Circuit Theory and Design*. Columbus, Ohio: Charles E. Merrill Books, Inc., 1963.

Ryder, J. D., *Electronic Fundamentals and Applications*. Englewood Cliffs, N.J.: Prentice-Hall, Inc., 1959.

Seidman, A. H. and S. L. Marshall, *Semiconductor Fundamentals*. New York: John Wiley and Sons, Inc., 1963.

Shive, J. N., *The Properties, Physics, and Design of Semiconductor Devices*. Princeton, N.J.: D. Van Nostrand Co., Inc., 1959.

Surina, T. and C. Herrick, *Semiconductor Electronics*. New York: Holt, Rinehart and Winston, Inc., 1964.

Tang, K. Y., *Alternating-Current Circuits*. Scranton, Pennsylvania: International Textbook Company, 1951.

5

Transistors and Transistor Amplifiers

A forward biased junction diode represents a low resistance; a reverse biased jucntion diode, a high resistance. With both junctions operating simultaneously in the same device, an inherent *power gain* capability is obtained. Such a device—the transfer resistor, or *transistor*—was first operated in 1948. This initial device was of the *point contact* type; i.e., a design utilizing the contact of two metallic points against a piece of semiconductor material. Such a structure, however, is susceptable to shock damage, contact corrosion, and other degrading effects. Furthermore, its electrical characteristics are rather unstable and not too well defined. The junction transistor, a single-structure, three-element device, was developed in 1949, shortly after the first junction diode.

While the junction diode offers an efficient, small, light-weight and reliable replacement for many vacuum tube diode applications, the transistor offers a like replacement for many vacuum tube triode and pentode applications. From a functional standpoint, transistors may be used as current, voltage, and power amplifiers; oscillators; modulators; demodulators; and nonsinusoidal waveshaping (switching) devices. They are especially desirable in applications requiring high efficiency (no heater element losses), low operating (d-c) voltages, long life, small size, and rugged construction.

The inherent power gain capability of a transistor is illustrated by the circuit in Fig. 5–1. The switch in position (a) permits current to flow through the 10-ohm resistor—a small resistance similar to a forward biased P-N junction. This (Part A) permits one ampere of current to flow, resulting in ten watts of dissipated power. With the switch in position (b), current flows through both resistors, limiting the value to 10 milliamperes. One milliwatt will be dissipated across the 10-ohm resistor; one-tenth watt across the 1000-ohm resistor. The high resistance is analogous to a reverse biased junction. If it were possible to arrange the small resistance as an input resistance of an amplifier and the large resistance as an output resistance of an amplifier, a power gain (P_{out}/P_{in}) of 100 would be realized. The transistor offers such an arrangement of input and output resistance. The transistor operation, of course, is considerably more complex, involving diffusion and drift currents across a double semiconductor junction.

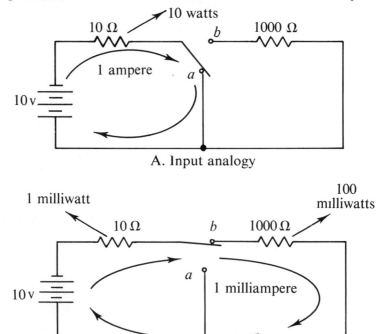

A. Input analogy

B. Input/Output analogy

Figure 5-1.   *Transistor Analogy*

5.1 PNP and NPN Combinations

Since the transistor is a double-junction device, two arrangements are possible. An N-type material may be "sandwiched" between two P-type pieces—forming a PNP *transistor*—or a P-type material may be "sandwiched" between two N-type pieces—forming an NPN *transistor*. Both types are capable of performing the same functions. However, there are differences in biasing requirements, frequency capabilities, and current and power capabilities. In general, the NPN transistor operates at lower frequencies. Similarly, the materials may have either silicon or germanium as a basic semiconductor substance. Again, there are basic differences—silicon is used for high power devices; germanium for higher frequencies.

As with the P-N junction diode, merely "butting" pieces of semiconductor material together will not form the necessary junctions. Rather, the junctions must consist of a single structure where one type material graduates into another type. This is achieved by controlling the introduction of the impurity material.

Emitter, Base, and Collector

The transistor consists of three semiconductor regions, each representing an element of the "triode" device. One end element is termed the

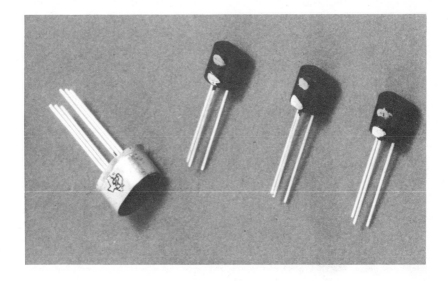

Figure 5-2.   *Typical Commercial Transistors (Courtesy Texas Instruments)*

emitter; the other end, the *collector.* The intermediate region is the *base.* (These elements correspond to the cathode, plate, and grid, respectively, of the vacuum tube triode.) Although in a purely theoretical sense, it makes no difference which end is the collector and which the emitter, in commercial transistors the collector region is larger in area and volume. This permits the collector region to dissipate higher powers, in accordance with the fact that the collector is always in the output loop of a transistor amplifier. Of course, since the semiconductor is encased (Fig. 5–2), it is impossible to identify the three elements directly. In order to circumvent this problem, manufacturers have adopted certain standards for placing the three protruding leads (emitter, base, and collector leads) relative to one another. This is illustrated in Fig. 5–3.

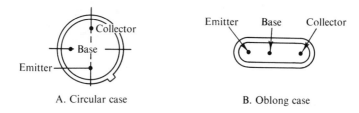

A. Circular case   B. Oblong case

Figure 5-3.   *Transistor Lead Placement*

Figure 5–4 illustrates the standard circuit symbols for the PNP and NPN transistors. The emitter is identified by an arrowhead. The direction of the arrowhead corresponds to the direction of hole flow relative to the base. Hence, it is the arrowhead that identifies the type material used for the base and emitter regions. With P-type material for the emitter, holes flow from the emitter (where they are in the majority) to the base, which is N-type material. This is indicated by the arrowhead pointing *toward*

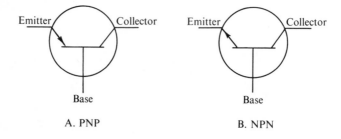

A. PNP   B. NPN

Figure 5-4.   *Transistor Symbols*

the base in the PNP transistor symbol. With N-type material for the emitter, majority holes must flow *from* the P-type base *toward* the emitter. This is indicated by the arrowhead pointing *away from the base* in the NPN transistor symbol.

Barrier Potentials

When the two junctions of the transistor are formed, an initial diffusion current (holes from P material to N material; electrons from N material to P material) flows across the junction. Once across the junction, these carriers recombine, and form a depletion region in the vicinity of each junction. The uncompensated ions in the depletion region form an electrostatic junction, or barrier potential, which eventually limits the diffusion current to a low equilibrium value. The potential on the junctions causes a new carrier movement—a drift current of electrons from the P material to the N material; holes from the N material to the P material. When the junction potential stabilizes, the drift component magnitudes reach equilibrium. This is identical to the P-N jucntion action described in Chap. 4. As with any P-N junction, the drift and diffusion components are equal. This produces zero net current flow across the junction *as long as no biasing potentials are applied from outside.*

The junction voltage is dependent upon temperature [Eqs. (4–15) through (4–20)]. The width of the depletion regions are dependent upon temperature and impurity concentration (Fig. 4–28).

5.2 External Biasing and Currents

In order for the transistor to function as a positive power gain device (amplifier), it is necessary that the emitter, base, and collector be appropriately arranged in a basic amplifier configuration. Proper functioning also requires that the *emitter-to-base junction be forward biased; the collector-to-base junction, reverse biased.* This accommodates the high-resistance/low-resistance combination discussed previously.

Emitter-to-Base Junction

With forward bias on the emitter-to-base junction, the barrier voltage is reduced, permitting increased diffusion (majority carrier movement) across the junction. With the diffusion current components predominating over the drift components, a new *forward current*, composed of holes

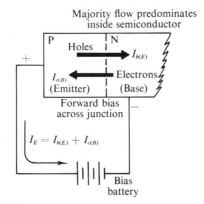

Figure 5-5.   *Emitter-to-Base Junction Characteristics* (PNP)

from emitter to base and electrons from base to emitter, crosses the junction as shown in Fig. 5–5. Because of this net current *inside* the emitter-to-base regions, a compensating (electron) current must flow in the external circuit:

$$I_E = I_{h(E)} + I_{e(B)} \qquad \text{(PNP)} \qquad \text{(5-1)}$$

where $I_{h(E)}$ represents the majority carrier (hole) current originating in the emitter and $I_{e(B)}$ represents the majority carrier (electron) current originating in the base. Typical emitter-to-base bias potential magnitudes are approximately equal to the emitter-to-base junction potential.

Collector-to-Base Junction

The increased barrier voltage on the collector-to-base junction, brought about by reverse biasing the junction, almost completely blocks the diffusion current (majority carriers), but causes an increase in the drift components (minority carriers). This action results in a net *reverse* current, composed of electrons from collector to base and holes from base to collector, across the junction as shown in Fig. 5–6. However, rather than referring to this as a reverse current, for the transistor, it is more properly termed the *cutoff current* since it flows across the "off," or reverse biased junction. A current similar in magnitude, but composed of electron flow only, must flow in the external circuit:

$$I_{CO} = I_{h(B)} + I_{e(C)} \qquad \text{(PNP)} \qquad \text{(5-2)}$$

where the "O" in the subscript denotes the cutoff nature of the collector current, I_C; $I_{h(B)}$ represents the minority carrier (hole current) originating in the base; and $I_{e(C)}$ represents the minority carrier (electron current) originating in the collector.

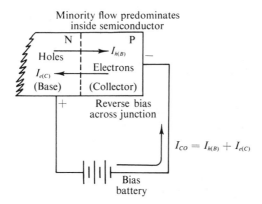

Figure 5-6.   *Collector-to-Base Junction Characteristics* (PNP)

NPN Transistors

The junction actions and external bias requirements for NPN transistors are similar to those for the PNP transistors. The significant difference in external biasing is change of polarity; the batteries shown in Figs. 5–5 and 5–6 must be arranged in reverse polarity to that indicated if the emitter-to-base junction is to be forward biased and the collector-to-base

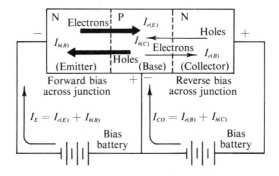

Figure 5-7.   *Junction Characteristics* (NPN)

junction is to be reverse biased. As far as the junction action is concerned, only the types of majority and minority carriers are interchanged. These changes are illustrated in Fig. 5–7. The separately biased junctions support current flows given by:

$$I_E = I_{e(E)} + I_{h(B)} \qquad \text{(NPN)} \qquad \text{(5-3)}$$
$$I_{CO} = I_{e(B)} + I_{h(C)} \qquad \text{(NPN)} \qquad \text{(5-4)}$$

5.3 Transistor Action

The previous section illustrates the biasing arrangements and carrier movements associated with each junction—independent of the effects that the two junctions and two external sources have on each other. The fundamental transistor action consists of the injection of majority carriers from the emitter *through the base region* and into the collector region. This is illustrated, qualitatively, in Fig. 5–8. With the reduced potential on the emitter-to-base junction (forward bias), the majority carrier diffusion across the junction increases. Most of the carriers injected into the base region pass through this (deliberately very narrow) region and into the collector region. A small fraction of the injected carriers, however, are attracted toward the forward bias terminal connected to the base region. This results in a "branching" of the injected carriers in the base region. In addition to these primary currents, there is the ever-present reverse current diffusing across the collector-to-base junction in response to the reverse bias on this junction.

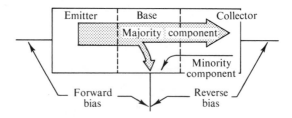

Figure 5-8.   *Transistor Action*

Emitter-to-Collector Current

Figure 5–9, Part A shows the majority carriers (holes) crossing from the emitter region into the base region of a PNP transistor while both junctions are simultaneously biased. Unlike previous illustrations, the

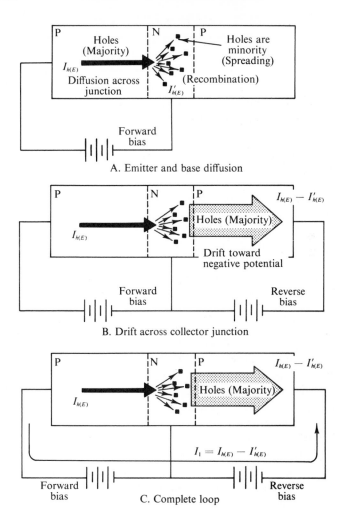

A. Emitter and base diffusion

B. Drift across collector junction

C. Complete loop

Figure 5-9.   *Emitter-to-Collector Action*

base region in Fig. 5–9 is shown narrower than the other two regions. (Even this relative width is exaggerated. In practice, the base region width is deliberately made less than the mean free path of the two carriers.)

Once inside the base region, the holes become minority carriers and, because of the natural tendency toward uniform carrier density, continue to diffuse, spreading throughout the base region. However, because of the narrowness of this region, and the slight negative junction potential on the P-side of the collector-to-base junction, before a high degree of recombination can occur, many of the holes pass through the base and drift across the second junction (Part B of the figure). Once across the collector-to-base junction, the holes (majority carriers again) are attracted toward the high negative potential of the reverse bias battery. Hence, there is a movement of majority carriers—a *forward current*—*through the transistor.* This current "closes the path" from emitter to collector.

If the excess holes in the collector region were allowed to accumulate, the collector would gradually develop an excess positive charge. This would violate the electrical neutrality of the material and cannot occur, since there is also a closed external path. An equivalent current flow must occur *around the entire path, inside and outside the transistor.* Hence, the electrons from the external path must enter the collector region and recombine with the excess holes, maintaining total charge neutrality. Similarly, an equivalent number of electrons must leave the emitter region, attracted to the positive external bias terminal. If they did not, the holes traveling from emitter to collector would allow a gradual accumulation of excess negative charge in the emitter region. Figure 5–9, Part C shows the entire closed-loop, emitter-to-collector current (forward current), given by:

$$I_1 = I_{h(E)} - I'_{h(E)}   \text{(PNP)} \qquad (5\text{-}5)$$

It is this current that flows through a low-resistance junction (emitter-to-base) *and* a high-resistance junction (collector-to-base), giving the transistor an inherent power gain capability. In Eq. (5–5), $I'_{h(E)}$ represents the component of majority carrier (hole) current from the emitter that is "lost" in the base region (undergoes recombination).

A similar mechanism accounts for forward current flow through the NPN transistor. For this arrangement, the electrons are injected into the base, diffuse through the base, drift across the collector-to-base junction, and continue through the collector. In order to achieve the proper biasing conditions, however, the batteries indicated in Fig. 5–9 must be reversed. Electrical neutrality of the material is maintained, since the electron deficiency in the emitter (emitter electron count is decreased due to injection into the base region) is compensated for by electrons flowing from the external forward bias source into the emitter at the same rate. The excess electrons in the collector region are attracted toward the positive reverse bias and continue to flow into the external circuit:

$$I_1 = I_{e(E)} - I'_{e(E)}   \text{(NPN)} \qquad (5\text{-}6)$$

which is analogous to Eq. (5–5), except that the majority carriers originating in the emitter are electrons rather than holes.

Base-to-Emitter Current

The previous section describes the diffusion of majority carriers from the emitter region to the collector region, passing through the base region in the process. The forward bias on the emitter-to-base junction also permits the *majority carriers to diffuse from the base region into the emitter region*. Figure 5-10 shows electrons from the base crossing the junction, where they recombine in the emitter region. At the same time, an equivalent number of holes from the emitter region must recombine in the base region. If they did not, the electrical neutrality of the material would be upset.

Previous discussions have indicated that *most* of the carriers injected into the base cross through to the collector. However, a small percentage of the injected carriers compensate for the electron diffusion into the emitter by undergoing recombination in the base region as illustrated in Fig. 5-10. An associated current must also flow in the external emitter-to-base loop:

$$I_2 = I_{e(B)} + I'_{h(E)} \quad \text{(PNP)} \tag{5-7}$$

Although small in magnitude, the base-to-emitter current is important to several transistor amplifier operating characteristics, since it adds to the total emitter current (amplifier input current):

$$I_E = I_1 + I_2 = I_{h(E)} + I_{e(B)} \quad \text{(PNP)} \tag{5-8}$$

derived from Eqs. (5–5) and (5–7). This, in turn, affects amplifier gain, as will be discussed further in subsequent sections.

A similar base-to-emitter current flows in the NPN transistor. However,

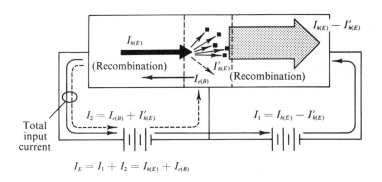

Figure 5-10. *Complete Emitter-to-Base Action*

the respective majority carriers are reversed, so that holes travel from base to emitter, recombining in the emitter. A fraction of the electrons injected from the emitter into the base region must undergo recombination to maintain electrical neutrality in the material:

$$I_2 = I_{h(B)} + I'_{e(E)} \quad \text{(NPN)} \tag{5-9}$$

Hence, as in the PNP transistor, *not all* of the injected carriers cross into the collector region, and the emitter current is slightly higher than it would be if it were dependent only upon the injected carriers:

$$I_E = I_1 + I_2 = I_{e(E)} + I_{h(B)} \quad \text{(NPN)} \tag{5-10}$$

Collector-to-Base Current

The emitter-to-collector and base-to-emitter currents are *forward currents*, since they are composed of majority carriers. The reverse biased collector-to-base junction supports an additional current: the *reverse current* composed of minority carrier movement across the junction. This is a drift current, as opposed to the majority carrier diffusion that has been the topic of discussion so far. The junction potential, further enhanced by the external reverse battery, is responsible for the increased drift component. However, due to the limited number of minority carriers that are available, this reverse current reaches saturation at very low reverse bias values. Indeed, the collector-to-base movement is akin to the *reverse saturation current* defined in Chap. 4. Increasing the reverse bias voltage does not affect the reverse current, unless the Zener and avalanche values are exceeded.

Figure 5-11 illustrates the reverse current effect. As shown, electrons from the P-type collector cross the junction and recombine in the base regions. In order to maintain material charge neutrality, holes from the base region must recombine in the collector. Simultaneously, an equivalent current must flow in the external collector-to-base loop:

$$I_3 = I_{CO} = I_{e(C)} + I_{h(B)} \quad \text{(PNP)} \tag{5-11}$$

This current adds to the total collector current:

$$I_C = I_1 + I_3 = I_{h(E)} + I_{CO} - I'_{h(E)} \quad \text{(PNP)} \tag{5-12}$$

I_{CO} is usually insignificant in comparison to the forward current component, so that it is generally neglected.

Notice that, in the *base branch*, the forward and reverse components flow in *opposite directions*, so that the total base current is the *difference* of the two:

$$I_B = I_2 - I_3 = I_{e(B)} + I'_{h(E)} - I_{CO} \quad \text{(PNP)} \tag{5-13}$$

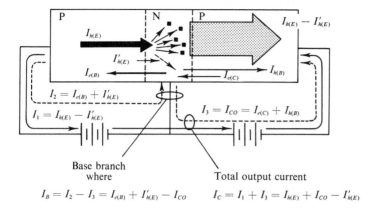

Base branch where

$$I_B = I_2 - I_3 = I_{e(B)} + I'_{h(E)} - I_{CO}$$

Total output current

$$I_C = I_1 + I_3 = I_{h(E)} + I_{CO} - I'_{h(E)}$$

Figure 5-11. *Collector-to-Base Action*

In some applications, the two components are of the same order of magnitude, so that both must be considered when determining the actual base current. *Some applications* permit the reverse component to *exceed* the forward component, leading to a *current reversal* ($-I_B$ in the notation being used) in the base branch.

The NPN transistor supports a similar reverse current—holes from the collector and electrons from the base:

$$I_3 = I_{CO} = I_{h(C)} + I_{e(B)} \quad \text{(NPN)} \tag{5-14}$$

$$I_C = I_1 + I_3 = I_{e(E)} + I_{CO} - I'_{e(E)} \quad \text{(NPN)} \tag{5-15}$$

$$I_B = I_2 - I_3 = I_{h(B)} + I'_{e(E)} - I_{CO} \quad \text{(NPN)} \tag{5-16}$$

Depletion Region Variation and Punchthrough

As described in Chap. 4, the width of the depletion region is directly related to the potential acrosss the junction. For the transistor in the un-biased state, both junctions will be of equal width, unless the impurity concentrations in the various regions are unequal. (The dependency of depletion region width on impurity concentration is also discussed in Chap. 4.) Since the forward emitter-to-base bias reduces the junction potential, this depletion region decreases in width from its unbiased condition. The collector-to-base depletion width increases over the unbiased conditions, since it is reverse biased to a high degree. This is shown in Fig. 5–12, Part A. Because of this variation in depletion region width, the equivalent resistance of both junctions must vary with the bias voltage.

In actual practice, the base region impurity concentration is *lower*

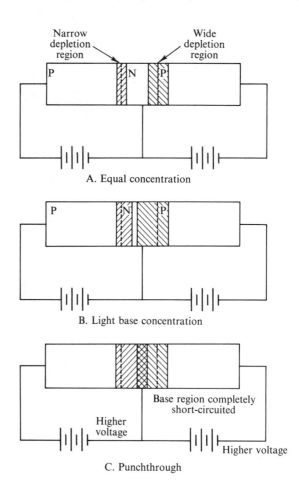

Figure 5-12.   *Depletion Width Variation with Impurity Concentration and Voltage Changes*

than the emitter and collector concentrations in order to achieve more efficient operation. For this reason, changes in the external bias magnitudes produce larger variations in depletion region width *on the base side* of both junctions. This is shown in Part B of the figure. Hence, it is possible to apply a high enough bias across the collector to base to cause the situation illustrated in Part C. This effect is known as *punchthrough*. As shown, the collector-to-base depletion width has increased to the point where the *entire base region is uncompensated.* This condition reduces the overall emitter-to-collector resistance, permitting excessively large currents to pass through the transistor. The ensuing damage is usually permanent.

5.4 Forward Current Transfer Ratio

The forward current transfer ratio, most commonly termed "transistor *alpha*," is defined as the ratio of total collector current to total emitter current:

$$\alpha = \frac{I_C}{I_E} \qquad (5\text{-}17)$$

and, since the collector current is always less than the emitter current, is always less than one in the normal junction transistor. Alpha is also known as the d-c *current gain*. (The term "gain," in its most general sense, refers to the ratio of two electrical quantities and *does not have to be greater than one.*) Alpha is dependent upon three factors: the *emitter efficiency*, the *transport factor*, and the *collector multiplication factor*.

Emitter efficiency expresses the fraction of I_E made up of majority carriers injected from the emitter region into the base region. For the PNP transistor, this represents the portion of I_E composed of holes; for the NPN transistor, the portion composed of electrons. Since there are both holes and electrons composing I_E (Fig. 5–10):

$$\gamma^* = \frac{I_{h(E)}}{I_E} = \frac{I_{h(E)}}{I_{h(E)} + I_{e(B)}} \qquad \text{(PNP)} \qquad (5\text{-}18a)$$

$$\gamma^* = \frac{I_{e(E)}}{I_E} = \frac{I_{e(E)}}{I_{e(E)} + I_{h(B)}} \qquad \text{(NPN)} \qquad (5\text{-}18b)$$

From these equations, it can be seen that forcing the base-to-emitter majority carrier current ($I_{e(B)}$ in PNP; $I_{h(B)}$ in NPN) to be as small as possible is required in order to maintain γ^* near one. This is accomplished by using a low impurity content in the base region.

As the majority carriers diffuse through the base region after being injected from the emitter, some recombine with electrons in the base region. This produces a portion of the base current, I_B. Since these majority carriers do not reach the collector, they are "lost" as far as the transistor action is concerned. The ratio of majority carrier current reaching the collector to majority carrier current leaving the emitter is given by the transport factor:

$$\beta^* = \frac{I_{h(C)}}{I_{h(E)}} = \frac{I_{h(E)} - I'_{h(E)}}{I_{h(E)}} \qquad \text{(PNP)} \qquad (5\text{-}19a)$$

$$\beta^* = \frac{I_{e(C)}}{I_{e(E)}} = \frac{I_{e(E)} - I'_{e(E)}}{I_{e(E)}} \qquad \text{(NPN)} \qquad (5\text{-}19b)$$

In order to keep β^* near one, the base region is made as narrow as possible. The low base region impurity concentration associated with keeping γ^* high also assists in keeping β^* high. This latter control keeps the number of majority carriers down in the base region, thus increasing the chances for the injected emitter carriers (a minority in the base region) to pass through without recombining.

Since the total collector current is composed of the surviving majority current carriers from the emitter and the minority current carriers within the collector region, I_C is actually slightly larger than it would be due to the injected carriers only. This was discussed in the previous section and is accounted for by the collector multiplication factor:

$$\alpha^* = \frac{I_C}{I_1} = \frac{I_{h(E)} + I_{CO} - I'_{h(E)}}{I_{h(E)} + I'_{h(E)}} \qquad \text{(PNP)} \qquad \text{(5-20a)}$$

$$\alpha^* = \frac{I_C}{I_1} = \frac{I_{e(E)} + I_{CO} - I'_{e(E)}}{I_{e(E)} + I'_{e(E)}} \qquad \text{(NPN)} \qquad \text{(5-20b)}$$

With the usual collector impurity concentration, the minority component, I_{CO}, is very small, and α^* is very nearly one.

The forward current transfer factor is equal to the product:

$$\alpha = \gamma^* \beta^* \alpha^* \qquad \text{(5-21)}$$

which corresponds to Eq. (5–17) when the appropriate expressions are substituted for γ^*, β^*, and α^*.

The value of I_{CO} is totally independent of the emitter injected current. Furthermore, since I_{CO} is composed of minority carriers, its magnitude, with respect to $I_{h(E)}$ (or $I_{e(E)}$), is negligible. For these reasons, α is usually written as:

$$\alpha = \left[\frac{I_{h(E)} - I'_{h(E)}}{I_{h(E)} + I'_{e(B)}}\right]^2 \qquad \text{(PNP)} \qquad \text{(5-22a)}$$

$$\alpha = \left[\frac{I_{e(E)} - I'_{e(E)}}{I_{e(E)} + I'_{h(B)}}\right]^2 \qquad \text{(NPN)} \qquad \text{(5-22b)}$$

which means that I_{CO} can be neglected in the equations for I_C, as well:

$$I_C = I_{h(E)} - I'_{h(E)} \qquad \text{(PNP)} \qquad \text{(5-23a)}$$

$$I_C = I_{e(E)} + I'_{e(E)} \qquad \text{(NPN)} \qquad \text{(5-23b)}$$

These equations replace Eqs. (5–12) and (5–15), respectively.

Because the base region is generally kept very narrow, the portion of the injected carriers that undergoes recombination ($I'_{h(E)}$ or $I'_{e(E)}$) is extremely small. In a well-designed transistor, the base region impurity concentration is deliberately low to provide a small value for $I_{e(B)}$. These factors provide an α just below one (0.95 to 0.99) for most transistors.

Table 5–1 summarizes the current relationships in the transistor.

TABLE 5-1

Transistor Current Relationships

Current Component	Microscopic		Conventional (Both Types)
	PNP	NPN	
I_B	$I_{e(B)} + I'_{h(E)} - I_{CO}$	$I_{h(B)} + I'_{e(B)} - I_{CO}$	$(1 - \alpha)I_E - I_{CO}$*
I_E	$I_{h(E)} + I_{e(B)}$	$I_{e(E)} + I_{h(B)}$	I_E
I_C	$I_{h(E)} + I_{CO} - I'_{h(E)}$	$I_{e(E)} + I_{CO} - I'_{e(E)}$	$\alpha I_E + I_{CO}$*

*Assumed negligible for most cases

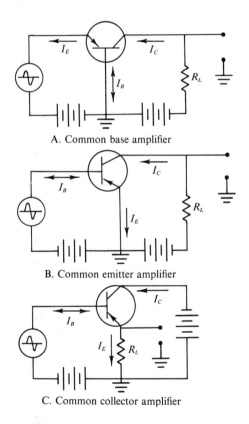

A. Common base amplifier

B. Common emitter amplifier

C. Common collector amplifier

Figure 5-13.   *Conventional Transistor Amplifier Configurations*

The first set of columns is presented in terms of the microscopic current components *inside* the transistor. From a circuit design viewpoint, it is neither convenient, nor necessary, to indicate these components. Rather, the convention illustrated in Fig. 5-13 has been adopted. [The double arrowhead on the base lead indicates that the actual current direction in this lead depends on the relative magnitudes of $(1 - \alpha)I_E$ and I_{co}.] The current relationships associated with this convention are also listed in Table 5-1.

Example 5-1. The base, emitter, and collector impurity concentrations, as well as the base width, of a particular PNP transistor are controlled so that 1 per cent of the holes injected from emitter to base undergo recombinations. The cutoff current is negligible. What is the forward current transfer ratio?

Solution. The forward current transfer ratio is:

$$\alpha = \left[\frac{I_{h(E)} - I'_{h(E)}}{I_{h(E)} + I_{e(B)}}\right]^2$$

when I_{co} is negligible. $I'_{h(E)}$ has been specified as:

$$I'_{h(E)} = 0.01\, I_{h(E)}$$

From Figs. 5-10 and 5-11 and the associated text:

$$I_{e(B)} = I'_{h(E)}$$

Hence:

$$\alpha = \left[\frac{I_{h(E)} - 0.01\, I_{h(E)}}{I_{h(E)} + 0.01\, I_{h(E)}}\right]^2 = \left[\frac{0.99\, I_{h(E)}}{1.01\, I_{h(E)}}\right]^2 = 0.96$$

Example 5-2. What is the value of the emitter efficiency, transport factor, and collector multiplication factor for the transistor in Example 5-1?

Solution. The emitter efficiency is given by:

$$\gamma^* = \frac{I_{h(E)}}{I_{h(E)} + I_{e(B)}} = \frac{I_{h(E)}}{I_{h(E)} + 0.01\, I_{h(E)}}$$

$$= \frac{I_{h(E)}}{1.01\, I_{h(E)}} = 0.99$$

The transport factor is:

$$\beta^* = \frac{I_{h(E)} - I'_{h(E)}}{I_{h(E)}} = \frac{0.99\, I_{h(E)}}{I_{h(E)}} = 0.99$$

The collector multiplication factor is:

$$\alpha^* = \frac{I_{h(E)} - I'_{h(E)}}{I_{h(E)} + I'_{h(E)}} = \frac{I_{h(E)} - 0.01 I_{h(E)}}{I_{h(E)} + 0.01 I_{h(E)}}$$

$$= \frac{0.99 I_{h(E)}}{1.01 I_{h(E)}} = 0.98$$

The transistor α is given by:

$$\alpha = \gamma^* \beta^* \alpha^* = (0.99)(0.99)(0.98) = 0.96$$

which agrees with the answer in Example 5-1.

5.5 Amplifier Configurations and Operation

The transistor amplifier arrangement that has been considered thus far is the one in Part A, Fig. 5–13. For this arrangement, the input signal is applied from emitter to base and the output signal is extracted from collector to base. Hence, *the base terminal is the ground, or common, point in the amplifier.* This leads to the term *common base amplifier configuration* for this circuit. Since there are three transistor terminals, there are three possible common points and three possible amplifier configurations. Part B of the figure illustrates the *common emitter amplifier;* i.e., input signal applied from base to emitter; output signal extracted from collector to emitter. Part C illustrates the *common collector amplifier;* i.e., input signal applied from base to collector; output extracted from emitter to collector. Notice that the load resistor, R_L, is in the *emitter branch* in the common collector circuit.

Each of the configurations has specific characteristics that make each adaptable to different applications. In general, the common base (CB) and common collector (CC) are used as impedance matching devices, yielding some degree of power gain in the process. This gain, however, is lower than the power gain of the common emitter (CE) amplifier. For this reason the CE configuration has become the so-called "conventional" transistor amplifier and is almost always preferred over the other two configurations.

The operation of the transistor is not as straightforward as vacuum tube operation, as must be obvious by this time. The input loop of a vacuum tube amplifier *never draws current*, whereas the input loop of the transistor amplifier *must always draw current*. Hence, the transistor is a *current-controlled device*, as opposed to the *voltage-controlled vacuum tube*. Furthermore, with current flowing in both loops, there is always some degree of *feedback;* i.e., interaction between output loop changes and the input loop values. This is not experienced in the vacuum tube amplifier, which is a unilateral device (working in only one direction—input to output). By comparison, the transistor is a *bilateral* device (working both ways).

Common Base Configuration

Figure 5-14, Part A, illustrates the fundamental common base (CB) amplifier circuit with example values for bias battery voltages, source

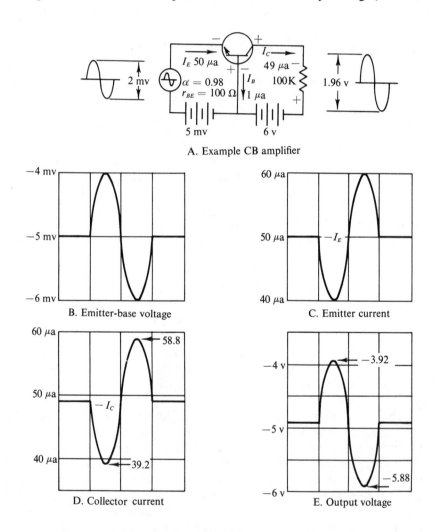

A. Example CB amplifier

B. Emitter-base voltage

C. Emitter current

D. Collector current

E. Output voltage

Figure 5-14.   CB *Amplifier Operation* (NPN)

and output a-c signal voltages, and load. The collector cutoff current, I_{CO}, is ignored because of its usually insignificant contribution. An α of 0.98 is specified in the figure.

A d-c and a-c voltage is applied to the emitter-to-base terminals. (Capital letters will denote d-c components, and lower case letters will denote a-c currents throughout this text.) The *actual transistor input voltage* is the voltage from emitter to base. This is illustrated in Part B of the figure. Notice that during the positive half-cycle, the emitter-to-base voltage is becoming *less negative*. For the NPN transistor, a negative emitter (with respect to the base) is *required for forward bias*. Hence, the interval of less-negative input voltage (positive half-cycle) from the signal source *causes less emitter current to flow*. The negative half-cycle results in a more-negative input voltage (Part B), or more forward bias on the emitter, and produces *greater carrier injection from emitter to base*. This leads to a 180° phase reversal between input current, i_E, and the source and input voltages (Part C).

Since collector current is related to emitter current by α, this current, with a d-c and a-c component, must be in phase with $I_E + i_E$, as shown in Part D. At the same time, the voltage across the load, which rides on a d-c (bias) level of $I_C R_L$, follows the same variations, $i_C R_L$, as is shown in Part E. With $I_C + i_C$ as shown in Part D, the top (negative side) of R_L "sees" a less-negative voltage during the positive half of the source signal. During the negative half of the source signal, the conditions are reversed—increasing forward bias, increasing injected current, and increasing the negative voltage across R_L. Hence, as shown in Part E, the voltage across R_L is *in phase with the source signal*.

Amplifier *current gain* is defined as the ratio of a-c output current to a-c input current:

$$A_{iB} = \frac{i_C}{i_E} = \frac{\alpha i_E}{i_E} = \alpha \qquad (5\text{-}24)$$

indicating that common base amplifier current gain, A_{iB}, is equal to α (0.98 in the example illustrated in Fig. 5–14) and is, therefore, *always less than one*. A gain less than one, of course, indicates that there is actually a loss of current in the CB configuration.

Amplifier *voltage gain* is defined as the ratio of a-c output voltage to a-c input voltage. The a-c output voltage can be written in terms of output current and load ($v_o = i_C R_L = \alpha i_E R_L$). The a-c input voltage must be dropped across the emitter-to-base resistance ($v_i = i_E r_{EB}$), leading to:

$$A_{vB} = \frac{v_o}{v_i} = \frac{\alpha i_E R_L}{i_E r_{EB}} = \alpha \frac{R_L}{r_{EB}} \qquad (5\text{-}25)$$

Since r_{EB} is usually only a few hundred ohms and the load is usually several thousand ohms, common base amplifier voltage gains in excess of one are readily attainable. (For the example in Fig. 5-14, assuming r_{EB} as 100 ohms, a voltage gain of 980 is achieved.)

Amplifier *power gain* is defined as the ratio of a-c power output to a-c power input:

$$A_{pB} = \frac{p_o}{p_i} = \frac{v_o i_C}{v_i i_E} = \alpha^2 \frac{R_L}{r_{EB}} \qquad (5\text{-}26)$$

which, from Eqs. (5-24) and (5-25), is the product of the current and voltage gain:

$$A_{pB} = A_{iB} A_{vB} \qquad (5\text{-}27)$$

Although written in terms of the common base amplifier, Eq. (5-27) is completely general. *Power gain is always the product of the voltage and current gains.* Equation (5-26) indicates that the common base amplifier is capable of providing power gains greater than one. (For the example illustrated in Fig. 5-14, the power gain is 960.)

In summary, the common base amplifier configuration provides no current gain and no phase shift; but does provide appreciable voltage and power gain.

The PNP transistor behaves in a similar manner when connected in the common base configuration. However, the bias polarities and current flow directions are reversed (Fig. 5-15).

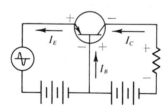

Figure 5-15 CB *Amplifier Operation* (PNP)

Example 5-3. The transistor specified in Example 5-1 is placed in a common base amplifier configuration with a load resistance of 5K. The emitter-to-base junction resistance is 80 ohms. What is the current, voltage, and power gain for the amplifier?

Solution. The current gain is given by:

$$A_{iB} = \alpha = 0.96$$

The voltage gain is given by:

$$A_{vB} = \alpha \frac{R_L}{r_{EB}} = 0.96 \left[\frac{5 \times 10^3}{8 \times 10} \right] = 60$$

The power gain is:

$$A_{pB} = A_{iB}A_{vB} = 0.96(60) = 57.6$$

Common Emitter Configuration

Figure 5-16, Part A illustrates the fundamental common emitter amplifier (CE) circuit with example values. Notice that in this circuit, the base current, I_B, becomes the input current. With this arrangement,

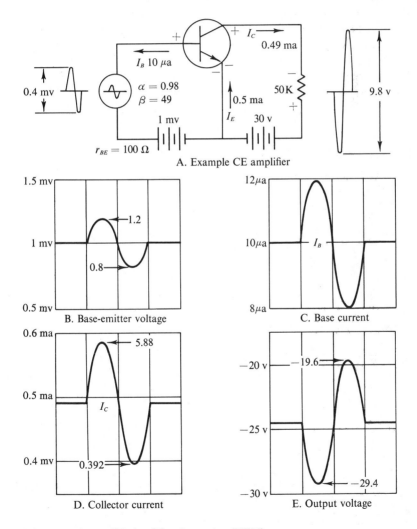

A. Example CE amplifier

B. Base-emitter voltage

C. Base current

D. Collector current

E. Output voltage

Figure 5-16.   CE *Amplifier Operation* (NPN)

the forward current transfer ratio (denoted by β) is given by:

$$\beta = \frac{I_C}{I_B} = \frac{\alpha I_E}{(1 - \alpha)I_E} = \frac{\alpha}{1 - \alpha} \tag{5-28}$$

From this equation, it can be seen that high alpha values (0.95 to 0.99) cause the denominator to be small, resulting in β-values considerably greater than one. For example, the β-value used in Fig. 5–15 is high (49) and is computed from Eq. (5–28) with $\alpha = 0.98$.

The operation of this amplifier can be investigated in much the same manner as the CB amplifier in the previous section. The source signal rides on the d-c bias level, resulting in an a-c *input voltage* from base to emitter (Part B of the figure). This input voltage is driving the base *more positive* during the positive half-cycle generated at the signal source. This is equivalent to applying more forward bias on the base-to-emitter junction. Consequently, more input current, $I_B + i_B$, is flowing during this half-cycle. During the negative half-cycle from the source, the base-to-emitter voltage is being made *less positive* (Part B), resulting in less input current flow. The input *current* is shown in Part C of the figure. It is *in phase* with the source and input voltages. The output current, $I_C + i_C$, being dependent upon the input current, is shown in Part D, and is *in phase* with the input current. In terms of magnitude, the two currents are related by the factor β:

$$(I_C + i_C) = \beta(I_B + i_B) \tag{5-29}$$

The output voltage has a constant bias value, $I_C R_L$, and an a-c variation, $i_C R_L$. The increasing current through R_L associated with the positive half of the source signal, however, causes the top (negative side) of R_L to drive *more negative*. During the negative half of the source signal, when the output current is decreasing, the top side of is R_L driven *less negative*, or *more positive*. This is shown in Part E of the figure and indicates a *phase reversal for the voltage across the load (the output voltage)*.

In view of the definitions of amplifier current, voltage, and power gain, for the CE amplifier configuration:

$$A_{iE} = \frac{i_C}{i_B} = \frac{\beta i_B}{i_B} = \beta \tag{5-30}$$

$$A_{vE} = \frac{v_o}{v_i} = \frac{i_C R_L}{i_B r_{BE}} = \frac{-\beta i_B R_L}{i_B r_{BE}} = -\beta \frac{R_L}{r_{BE}} \tag{5-31}$$

$$A_{pE} = \frac{p_o}{p_i} = \frac{v_o i_C}{v_i i_B} = \frac{(-\beta i_B R_L / r_{BE})\beta i_B}{(i_B r_{BE})i_B}$$

$$= \beta^2 \frac{R_L}{r_{BE}} \tag{5-32}$$

The negative sign in Eq. (5–31) denotes the phase reversal associated with the output voltage. The input junction resistance, r_{BE}, is the same as r_{EB} discussed for the CB configuration. The power gain [Eq. (5–32)] can be derived as shown, or as the product $A_{iE}A_{vE}$ [Eq. (5–27)]. For the illustrated circuit, the current gain is 49, the voltage gain is −24,500, and the power gain is slightly over 1.2×10^6.

In summary, the common emitter amplifier configuration is capable of producing current, voltage, and power gains of substantial amounts, and introduces a voltage phase reversal in the output.

Figure 5–17 illustrates the PNP common emitter amplifier. The operating characteristics are identical to those described for the NPN transistor.

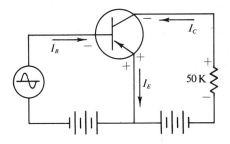

Figure 5-17.   CE *Amplifier Operation* (PNP)

Example 5-4.   The transistor specified in Example 5–1 is placed in a common emitter amplifier configuration. The emitter-to-base junction resistance is 80 ohms. The load resistance is 75K. What is the current, voltage, and power gain of the amplifier?

Solution.   The common emitter forward current transfer ratio must be determined first. It is:

$$\beta = \frac{\alpha}{1-\alpha} = \frac{0.96}{1-0.96} = \frac{0.96}{0.04} = 24$$

This leads to a current gain of:

$$A_{iE} = \beta = 24$$

and a voltage gain of:

$$A_{vE} = -\beta\frac{R_L}{r_{BE}} = -24\left[\frac{7.5 \times 10^4}{8 \times 10}\right] = -22,500$$

The power gain is given by:

$$A_{pE} = A_{iE}A_{vE} = 24(22,500) = 540,000$$

Common Collector Configuration

The fundamental common collector amplifier (CC) configuration is shown in Fig. 5–18, Part A. Example circuit values are indicated. For this circuit, the forward current transfer ratio is given by:

$$\alpha_C = \frac{I_E}{I_B} = \frac{I_E}{I_E - I_C} = \frac{1}{1 - (I_C/I_E)} \tag{5-33}$$

$$= \frac{1}{1 - \alpha} = \beta + 1$$

which shows the relationship to α and β and indicates that α_C and β are similar in magnitude. [The transformation from $1/(1 - \alpha)$ in Eq. (5–33) to $(\beta + 1)$ is obtained by solving Eq. (5–28) for α and substituting the resulting expression in the $1/(1 - \alpha)$ expression.] For the values indicated in Fig. 5–18, α_C is equal to 50.

The common collector configuration is unique among the transistor amplifiers—its load is in *both the input and output loops*. Because the collector is common in the circuit, the actual transistor input voltage must be defined as the *total voltage from base to collector*. Hence, the a-c components are:

$$v_i = v_{BE} + v_o \tag{5-34}$$

$$v_o = i_E R_L \tag{5-35}$$

Figure 5–18, Part B shows the input voltage riding on the d-c bias level (base biased negative with respect to emitter for proper operation). As the source half-cycle is negative, the forward bias (input voltage) is being made less positive, or "negative-going," also. During the positive half-cycle of source voltage, the base is driven more positive. Hence, the input voltage and source voltage are in phase. However, a negative-going base is responsible for less current flow since it is, in reality, less forward bias. Similarly, the positive-going base is responsible for more current flow. Because of this, the input current, $I_B + i_B$, is *in phase* with both voltages. This is shown in Part C. The output current, $I_E + i_E$, must follow the changes in input current (Part D). This leads to an output voltage, $(I_E + i_E)R_L$, that must decrease during the negative half of the input source signal since the lower current will drive the top of R_L to a less-positive value (the same as driving it negative). The positive input half-cycle, in turn, causes an increase in current, and the top of R_L is driven more positive. The output voltage for the CC amplifier, then, is in phase with the source voltage (Part E).

Current gain for the common collector amplifier is given by:

$$A_{iC} = \frac{i_E}{i_B} = \frac{\alpha_C i_B}{i_B} = \alpha_C \tag{5-36}$$

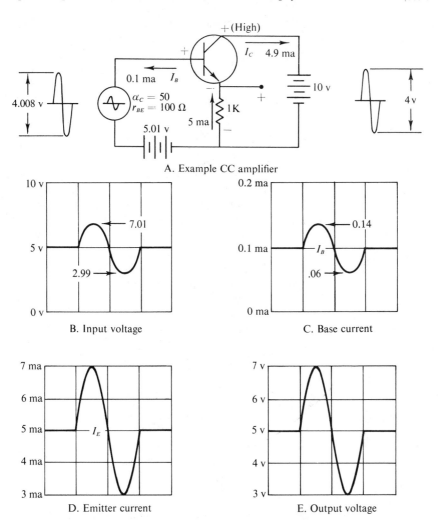

A. Example CC amplifier

B. Input voltage

C. Base current

D. Emitter current

E. Output voltage

Figure 5-18.   CC *Amplifier Operation* (NPN)

which indicates [from Eqs. (5–33) and (5–28)] that the current gain for the CC configuration is greater than one. In fact, it is of the same order as the current gain for the CE amplifier. For the illustrated amplifier, the current gain is 50.

The voltage gain [from Eqs. (5–34) and (5–35)] is given by:

$$A_{vC} = \frac{i_E R_L}{v_{BE} + i_E R_L} = \frac{\alpha_C i_B R_L}{i_B r_{BE} + \alpha_C i_B R_L} \qquad (5\text{-}37)$$

$$= \frac{\alpha_C R_L}{r_{BE} + \alpha_C R_L} \approx 1$$

The presence of r_{BE} in the denominator of Eq. (5–37) will always assure that the denominator is *slightly larger* than the numerator. Hence, the common collector amplifier must always have a *voltage gain less than one*. In most instances, such as in the illustrated example, the deviation from one is negligible.

Since the power gain is the product of current and voltage gains [from Eqs. (5–36) and (5–37)]:

$$A_{pC} = \frac{\alpha_C^2 R_L}{r_{BE} + \alpha_C R_L} \approx \alpha_C \qquad (5\text{-}38)$$

which indicates that the power and current gains are about equal. This is logical, since the voltage gain, in most instances, is approximately one.

In summary, the common collector amplifier has a current gain on the same order as the common emitter amplifier, produces no phase shift, has a voltage gain near one, and a low power gain (approximatley equal to the current gain).

The PNP transistor behaves in a similar manner when connected as a CC amplifier. However, the bias polarities and current flow directions are reversed, as shown in Fig. 5–19.

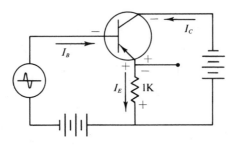

Figure 5-19.   CC *Amplifier Operation* (PNP)

Example 5-5.   The transistor specified in Example 5–1 is placed in a common collector amplifier configuration. The emitter-to-base junction resistance is 80 ohms. The load resistance is 1.5K. What is the current, voltage, and power gain of the amplifier?

Solution.   The common collector forward current transfer ratio must be determined first. From Example 5–4, β is equal to 24, so that:

$$\alpha_C = \beta + 1 = 24 + 1 = 25$$

α_C may also be determined directly in terms of α:

$$\alpha_C = \frac{1}{1 - \alpha} = \frac{1}{1 - 0.96} = 25$$

This leads to a current gain of:

$$A_{iC} = \alpha_C = 25$$

Since r_{BE} is very small, A_{vC} is approximately equal to one. The power gain is:

$$A_{pC} = \alpha_C = 25$$

5.6 Static Characteristics

An adequate description of thermistor operating characteristics consists of a graphical presentation of the volt-ampere relationship (Fig. 3–4). Similarly, a volt-ampere characteristic for the junction diode suffices as a complete description of its operating characteristics (Fig. 4–26). This is true because both of these devices are two-terminal, or two-element devices. Hence, a measurement of the voltage across the device for a particular current flow through the device describes its operation. The transistor, however, is a *three-element device* (Fig. 5–20). Three voltages are present: collector-to-base, V_{CB}; collector-to-emitter, V_{CE}; and emitter-to-base, V_{EB}. Three currents are also present: emitter, I_E; collector, I_C; and base, I_B. Because of the bilateral nature of the transistor, *each of these quantities is affected by the value of all others.* This leads to a total of 15 measurement combinations, or sets of characteristics: V_{CB} versus V_{CE}, V_{CB} versus V_{EB}, V_{CB} versus I_E, V_{CB} versus I_C, V_{CB} versus I_B, V_{CE} versus V_{EB}, V_{CE} versus I_B, etc.

In practice, for a given amplifier configuration, there are only two voltages (input and output) and two currents (input and output) that are of interest. Such a generalization of the transistor is shown in Fig.

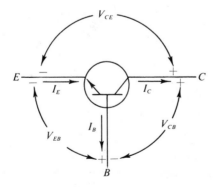

Figure 5-20.   *Transistor as a Three-Element Device*

5-21. The three elements are replaced by an input terminal, I; an output terminal, O; and a common, or grounded, terminal, G. The generalized currents are indicated as an input current, I_I and an output current, I_O. The terminal voltages are generalized as input terminal voltage, V_{IG} and output terminal voltage, V_{OG}. The six possible combinations, or characteristics, are also listed in the figure. However, the V_{OG} versus V_{IG} and V_{OG} versus I_I will differ only by a constant: the amplifier input resistance. Hence, no additional information is gained by having both characteristics, since the input resistance is contained in the V_{IG} versus I_I characteristic. Likewise, the V_{IG} versus I_I and V_{IG} versus I_O characteristics differ only by a constant: the forward current transfer factor (which is contained in the I_O versus I_I characteristic). This redundancy eliminates two of the characteristics, leaving the four standards listed in the left-hand column of Table 5-2.

The order of the variables listed in Table 5-2 has been changed somewhat from the order indicated in Fig. 5-21. Technically, the same information is conveyed regardless of the order. However, it is standard, when portraying a characteristic graphically, to place the *dependent variable* along the ordinate (the vertical axis) and the *independent variable* along the abscissa (the horizontal axis). It has also become standard to have the transistor characteristics represent specific electric quantities, as indicated in the second column of Table 5-2. The general characteristics indicated in Table 5-2 are the result of these standardizations. For example, if the V_{OG}-V_{IG} combination is to represent the *reverse* voltage transfer characteristic, as indicated, it must be graphically portrayed as V_{IG} versus V_{OG} (V_{IG} along the ordinate; V_{OG} along the abscissa). If it were displayed as V_{OG} versus V_{IG}, it would represent the *forward* voltage transfer

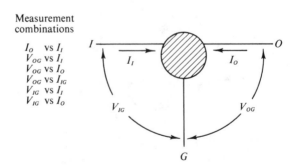

Measurement combinations

I_O vs I_I
V_{OG} vs I_I
V_{OG} vs I_O
V_{OG} vs I_{IG}
V_{IG} vs I_I
V_{IG} vs I_O

Figure 5-21.   *Generalized Transistor Current and Voltage Components*

TABLE 5-2

Standard Transistor Characteristics

General Relationships		Characteristic Name	CB Relationships		CE Relationships		CC Relationships	
Variable	*Constant*		*Variable*	*Constant*	*Variable*	*Constant*	*Variable*	*Constant*
I_O vs I_I	V_{OG}	Forward Current Transfer Characteristic	I_C vs I_E	V_{CB}	I_C vs I_B	V_{CE}	I_E vs I_B	V_{EC}
I_O vs V_{OG}	I_I	Output Conductance Characteristic	I_C vs V_{CB}	I_E	I_C vs V_{CE}	I_B	I_E vs V_{EC}	I_B
V_{IG} vs I_I	V_{OG}	Input Resistance Characteristic	V_{EB} vs I_E	V_{CB}	I_B vs V_{BE}	V_{CE}	V_{BC} vs I_B	V_{EC}
V_{IG} vs V_{OG}	I_I	Reverse Voltage Transfer Characteristic	V_{EB} vs V_{CB}	I_E	V_{BE} vs V_{CB}	I_B	V_{BC} vs V_{EC}	I_B

characteristic. Similar reasoning can be applied to the remaining characteristics.

The "constants" indicated in the left-hand portion of Table 5–2 are essential to the technical validity of the characteristics. By way of illustration, consider the forward current transfer characteristic. I_O is dependent upon V_{OG} as well as upon I_I. Changing V_{OG} will produce changes in I_O, *regardless* of the value of I_I. Hence, in order to get a true relationship between I_O and I_I, no variations in V_{OG} can be tolerated. The forward current transfer characteristic, then, must be obtained for a specific constant V_{OG}-value. For a different V_{OG}-value, an entirely different I_O versus I_I characteristic is obtained. This leads to the requirement that the *complete* forward current transfer characteristic consist of a *family* of I_O versus I_I curves, with each devoted to a specific V_{OG}-value, as illustrated in Fig. 5–22.

Since different amplifier configurations utilize different terminals for input and output, the actual V_{OG}-, V_{IG}-, I_I-, and I_O-values change from one configuration to another. The last three parts of Table 5–2 indicate the specific combinations required to produce the characteristics for each of the three amplifier configurations. This leads to *twelve characteristics* for a complete description of transistor operation. However, since there are three variables involved in each characteristic (over the entire family, a variation of the "constant" quantity can also be obtained), the direct measurement of two families of the characteristics yields enough information to indirectly specify the other two families (for a specific configuration). This will be illustrated in a subsequent section, and reduces the number of characteristics that must be measured to six (two for each of the three configurations). In fact, as will also be demonstrated, because of the algebraic relationships between the voltages and the currents,

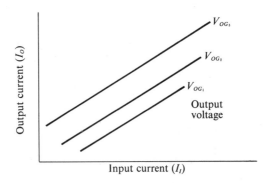

Figure 5-22.   *Generalized Forward Current Transfer Characteristic*

two characteristics will provide enough information to derive all the remaining characteristics.

Although the complete sets of characteristics cover a wide range of variation for the different quantities involved, *any specific point on the curves represents a* d-c *relationship between three quantities.* Therefore, the curves are referred to as the d-c, or *static*, characteristics. Fortunately, from a design standpoint, the a-c signals can be superimposed on the static characteristics and a considerable amount of a-c analysis *can be performed.*

Common Base Configuration

Figure 5–23 represents a typical set of characteristic curves for a transistor arranged in the CB configuration. Notice that some regions of the curves are linear; some regions are nonlinear. Furthermore, some regions display an almost constant quality; others change very rapidly. As will be described in subsequent sections, normal amplifier operation is maintained within the linear regions in order to prevent serious distortions in the signal waveforms. The degree of variation indicates the *sensitivity* of one quantity for another. For example, in the forward current transfer characteristic, there is almost no change in output current, I_C, for a given input current, I_E, as the collector-to-base voltage, V_{CB}, varies. As indicated in the figure, a change of 25 volts in V_{CB} only changes the I_C-I_E relationship by a quarter of a milliampere. The input resistance characteristic also displays a high lack of sensitivity to V_{CB}, becoming more pronounced at higher I_E-values.

A single point on the input resistance characteristic represents the d-c input (emitter-to-base) resistance of the transistor. Two such points are indicated in the figure. At higher values of input current, this resistance decreases. Higher values of V_{CB} also result in lower input resistance, although the reduction is not appreciable. The reverse voltage transfer characteristics indicate that at low input currents, the input voltage is fairly insensitive to the output voltage. At high input currents, when there is more "coupling" from input to output, this effect becomes more pronounced. This coupling is further demonstrated by the output conductance characteristics. As is to be expected, since the collector-to-base junction is reverse biased, the output conductance is very low. However, this conductance increases as I_E is increased, indicating that the forward current flow across the junction overcomes a portion of the reverse bias effect. The forward current transfer characteristic indicates an α of nearly one, with higher α's for higher output voltages, since the higher V_{CB}-values

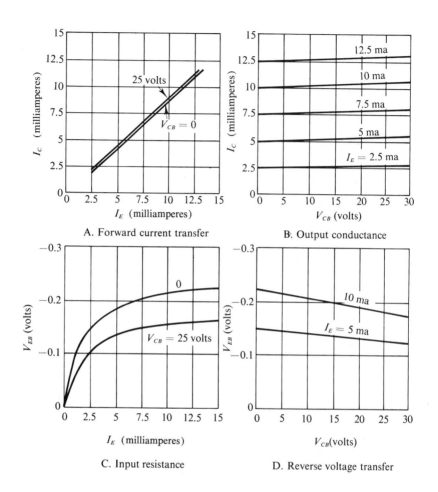

Figure 5-23. CB *Characteristic* (NPN)

"draw" more of the injected carriers across the base region and the collector-to-base junction.

The characteristic curves for NPN and PNP transistors are very much the same. The ones shown in Fig. 5–23 are for NPN transistors. For the PNP type, V_{CB} is a *negative voltage* and V_{EB} is a *positive voltage*.

Common Emitter Characteristics

A set of characteristics for a typical transistor arranged in the CE configuration is shown in Fig. 5–24. The forward current transfer charac-

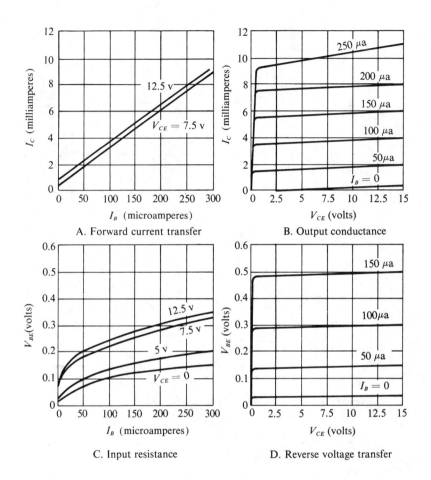

A. Forward current transfer

B. Output conductance

C. Input resistance

D. Reverse voltage transfer

Figure 5-24.   CE *Characteristics* (NPN)

teristics for this configuration are also fairly insensitive to output voltage, but are more sensitive than those for the CB configuration. The remaining characteristics display a significantly greater variation than is associated with the corresponding CB characteristics. The characteristics shown are for an NPN transistor; for the PNP, V_{CE} is a *negative voltage* and V_{BE} is a *negative voltage*.

Common Collector Characteristics

A set of CC configuration characteristics is shown, for an NPN transistor, in Fig. 5–25. These differ, in general, from both the CB and CE

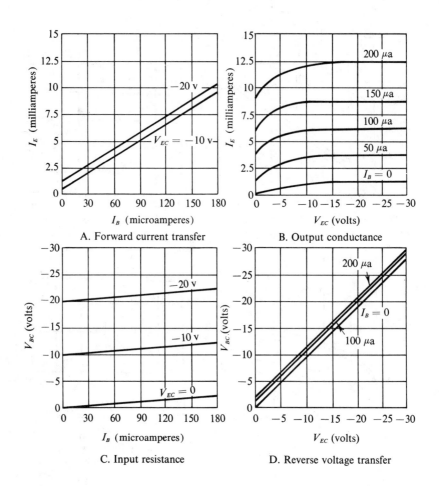

Figure 5-25.   CC *Characteristics* (NPN)

characteristics, with the exception of the output conductance characteristic, which follows the same trend as those for the CE amplifier. For the
PNP transistor, V_{EC} is a *positive voltage* and V_{BC} is a *positive voltage*.

Manufacturer's Characteristics

Since there are only four quantities associated with a particular set of
characteristic curves, and since each characteristic displays three of these
quantities, two properly selected characteristics can be used to derive the

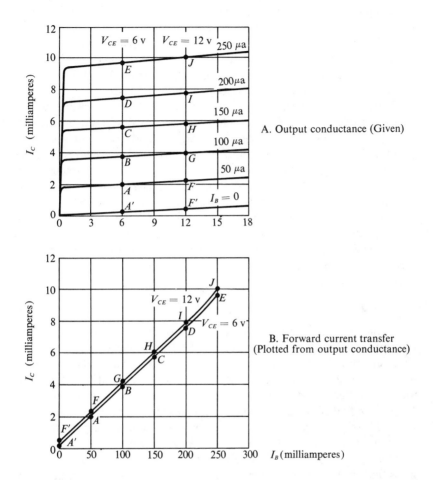

Figure 5-26. *Construction of Characteristics*

remaining two. That is, if two characteristics are chosen which, between them, display all four quantities, all the information regarding the transistor has been specified. Figure 5–26 presents an example of such a derivation for the CE configuration. The output conductance characteristic (displaying I_C, V_{CE}, and I_B) has been selected. The forward transfer characteristic contains the same information as the output conductance characteristic, I_C, I_B, and V_{CE}; only the variables and constants have been interchanged. The forward current characteristic requires that V_{CE} be constant and I_C be plotted against I_B. *Vertical lines on the output conductance characteristic represent constant V_{CE}.* Hence, by selecting vertical lines at the desired V_{CE}-values and indicating the intersections of these lines with the existing output conductance curves, different combinations of I_C and I_B can be obtained (Part A). These are then plotted (Part B) and the points associated with a specific V_{CE}-value are joined. (A similar procedure can be followed to obtain the input resistance curves from the output conductance curves, except that I_B must be maintained constant.)

The procedure described *could be reversed*. That is, the forward current characteristics and the reverse voltage characteristics could be used to derive the output conductance characteristics and the input resistance characteristics, respectively. Furthermore, similar procedures can be followed with the CB characteristics and with the CC characteristics. Using this procedure reduces the number of characteristics that *must be measured to six*, rather than the twelve originally discussed.

An investigation of Fig. 5-20 will provide voltage and current relationships that may be used to *further reduce the number of characteristics that must be measured*. From Kirchoff's equations for voltages around a closed loop and for currents at a junction:

$$V_{EB} + V_{CB} + V_{CE} = 0 \qquad (5\text{-}39)$$
$$I_E + I_B + I_C = 0 \qquad (5\text{-}40)$$

From this, it can be seen that a knowledge of any two voltages and any two currents (four quantities, again) can lead to the derivation of the missing voltage and the missing current. It has just been pointed out that any two of the characteristics for a specific configuration containing all four pertinent quantities can be used to derive the other two characteristics for that configuration. Now, with the aid of Eqs. (5-39) and (5-40), it would appear that *any two characteristics containing any of the four quantities can be used to derive all of the ten remaining characteristics*. This brings about a considerable reduction in the number of characteristics that *must be measured* in order to completely specify a transistor's operating qualities.

In theory, the two measured characteristics may be associated with any of the three amplifier configurations. In practice, considerable error is introduced if either the CB or CC characteristics are used to derive the remaining characteristics. The reason for this can be seen by investigating the three sets of characteristics (Figs. 5-23, 5-24, and 5-25), and comparing the relative magnitudes of the pertinent voltages and currents in actual operating conditions. In operation, the base current is very small [Eqs. (5-13) and (5-16)]. The base-to-emitter voltage is also very small (a few tenths of a volt will forward bias a junction adequately). Yet, in order to show the characteristic variational properties in Figs. 5-23 and 5-24, it is necessary to use large changes in V_{BE} and I_B. Small, realistic operating changes would not show any characteristic difference, unless an extremely large scale were used on the axes. An attempt to make the necessary interpolations from such CB or CC curves would result in very poor approximations of the remaining curves.

On the CE characteristics (Fig. 5–24), both I_B and V_{BE} are available directly in terms of realistic operating values. Hence, an interpolation of very small numbers from much larger numbers is not required. For this reason, the most convenient approach to specifying transistor character-istics is to measure and plot two of the CE characteristics. The two most frequently chosen are the output conductance characteristic and the input resistance characteristic. These CE characteristics are also selected for another reason: the CE configuration is almost universally selected for ampifier applications because it displays current, voltage, and power gains. This limits the need for CB and CC characteristics to the point where it is not economically feasible to measure and distribute them.

Example 5-6.   Given the common emitter output conductance char-acteristic (Fig. 5–26), plot the common collector output conductance characteristics with I_B equal to 50 microamperes, 150 microamperes, and 250 microamperes.

Solution.   The common collector output conductance characteristics consist of a plot of I_E versus V_{EC}, with I_B held constant (Table 5–2 and Fig. 5–25). The two given characteristics contain I_C, V_{CE} (or V_{EC}), and I_B. Since:

$$I_E = -(I_B + I_C)$$

it is possible to calculate values of I_E given values of I_B and I_C. It is of interest to determine I_E (on the basis of the I_B and I_C relationship) with constant I_B, and to determine the value of V_{EC} (or V_{CE}) associated with each I_E-value. Figure E5–6, Part A shows points for V_{CE} and I_C for fixed I_B-values. The results of the I_C-calculations are:

V_{CE}	$I_B = 50 \mu$amps		$I_B = 150 \mu$amps		$I_B = 250 \mu$amps	
	I_C	I_E	I_C	I_E	I_C	I_E
0	0 ma	50 μa	0 ma	150 μa	0 ma	250 μa
6	2 ma	2 ma	5.6 ma	5.6 ma	9.6 ma	9.6 ma
12	2.1 ma	2.1 ma	5.8 ma	5.8 ma	10 ma	10 ma
18	2.4 ma	2.4 ma	6 ma	6 ma	10.4 ma	10.4 ma

Examination of the I_E-data indicates that an abrupt increase, followed by a gradual rise, occurs. This is plotted in Fig. E5–6, Part

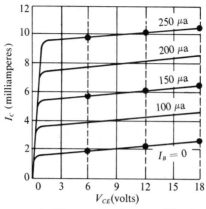

A. CE output conductance (Given)

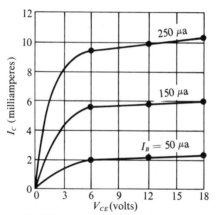

B. CC output conductance (Constructed)

Figure E5-6

B and is similar to the data presented in Fig. 5–25. Because of the approximations made, it is expected that some degree of error will be introduced.

5.7 Static (D-C) Operation

The static characteristics consist of *families* of curves, as previously discussed, in order to portray operational changes over a wide range of voltages and currents. For a particular application, however, each voltage and each current has a specific d-c value. This combination of values is referred to as the *static (or* d-c) *operating point*, or simply, the *operating point*. This operating point must be found through a *graphical load line analysis* similar to that described in Chap. 3 for the thermistor, and mentioned in Chap. 4 for the junction diode.

A generalized transistor amplifier appears in Fig. 5–27. The associated generalized output conductance characteristics are also represented in Fig. 5–27 as plots of I_O versus V_{OG} with various values of I_I establishing the family of curves. These characteristics can be converted to the specific configuration characteristics by consulting Table 5–2 and substituting the specific current and voltage expressions for the general ones. The generalized currents and voltages that will appear in subsequent

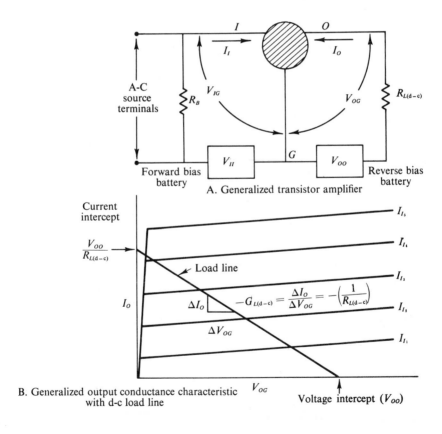

A. Generalized transistor amplifier

B. Generalized output conductance characteristic with d-c load line

Figure 5-27.   *Basis of Transistor Amplifier Analysis*

equations can also be identified for the specific amplifier configurations by referring to Table 5–2. These specific quantities can be substituted for the general quantities in all the equations that will be derived. The "generalization" is used because the procedures to be described in this section, as well as in subsequent sections, can be applied to all three amplifier configurations.

The output loop equation for the circuit (Fig. 5–27) is given by:

$$I_0 R_{L(\text{d-c})} + V_{OG} = V_{OO} \qquad (5\text{–}41)$$

and the input loop equation by:

$$I_I R_B + V_{IG} = V_{II} \qquad (5\text{–}42)$$

where R_B is a bias resistor inserted to limit the flow of input current for practical values of V_{II}. The d-c load resistance, $R_{L(\text{d-c})}$, is indicated specifically in Eq. (5–41) because the d-c and a-c load resistances of an amplifier *do not have to be the same*, as will be discussed in the next section. Following a procedure similar to that described in Chap. 3, the load line can be placed on the output conductance characteristic *by finding the voltage and current intercepts*. The voltage intercept occurs when $I_0 = 0$ or, from Eq. (5–41), when:

$$V_{OG} = V_{OO} \qquad (5\text{–}43)$$

The current intercept occurs when $V_{OG} = 0$ or, from Eq. (5–41), when:

$$I_0 = \frac{V_{OO}}{R_{L(\text{d-c})}} \qquad (5\text{–}44)$$

Both intercepts are shown in Fig. 5–27. The straight line between the two points is the load line. Since the axes are interchanged (to produce output *conductance* characteristics) over those in Chap. 3, the slope of the load line represents the negative of the *load conductance*, $-G_{L(\text{d-c})}$. The negative of the *load resistance* is the reciprocal of this, as shown in the figure.

Since the current intercept is dependent upon $R_{L(\text{d-c})}$, variations in the d-c load will cause changes in the load line orientation. Increasing $R_{L(\text{d-c})}$ reduces the intercept value, moving the load line into a more-horizontal position. (An open output loop, with $R_{L(\text{d-c})}$ equal to infinity, will produce a horizontal line *along the voltage axis*.) Decreasing $R_{L(\text{d-c})}$ increases the current intercept, moving the load line a more-vertical position. (A short circuit, with $R_{L(\text{d-c})}$ equal to zero, will produce a vertical line extending upward from V_{OO}.) These variations are illustrated in Fig. 5–28.

The presence of the load line on the output conductance characteristic does not, in itself, provide a solution for the operating point. It merely provides a line relating all possible V_{OG}-I_0-values that may exist in the

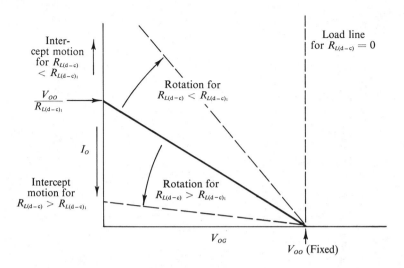

Figure 5-28.   *Variation of Load Line Orientation with Load Value*

circuit. The third variable, I_I, must be specified in order to provide the operating point. From the input loop Eq. (5–42):

$$I_I = \frac{V_{II} - V_{IG}}{R_B} \tag{5-45a}$$

However, V_{II} will usually be several volts and V_{IG} only a few tenths of a volt or less. For this reason, Eq. (5–45a) is very adequately approximated by:

$$I_I = \frac{V_{II}}{R_B} \tag{5-45b}$$

Notice that I_I has been specified without reference to V_{IG} when this approximation is made. The required voltage, V_{IG}, will be developed indirectly as a result of specifying I_I. The actual knowledge of V_{IG} is not essential. (This is the reason for omitting the input resistance characteristic, V_{IG} versus I_I, when specifying transistor characteristics; a common option exercised by the manufacturer.)

Establishing a value for I_I restricts transistor operation to a single curve among the family of output conductance characteristics. In some instances, the desired I_I-value may not be one indicated directly on the characteristics. In this case, the desired curve is obtained by interpolating between two existing curves (Fig. 5–29). Regardless of the I_I-value, the *intersection of the load line and the specified I_I-curve provides the simultaneous solution to Eqs. (5–41) and (5–42).* This simultaneous solution

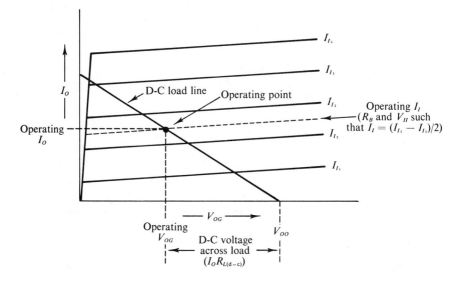

Figure 5-29.   *The Static* (D-C) *Operating Point and Associated Conditions*

yields the operating point, V_{OG}, I_O, and I_I. The operating point specification (also shown in Fig. 5–29) is not complete unless all three values are given.

An amplifier is designed to provide a-c power amplification. This is accomplished by reshaping the d-c power of the source (V_{OO}) into the desired a-c variation. However, all of the power in the output loop—both d-c and a-c—must be supplied by this same source. The d-c power dissipated by the output junction, $I_O V_{OG}$, and by the load, $I_O^2 R_{L(d-c)}$, represents a *power loss* in the output loop because this power is no longer available for conversion to a-c output power.

An additional restriction on the operation of the amplifier results from the fact that there is a maximum power that can be dissipated across the output junction. Junction power dissipation is discussed in Chap. 4, along with the construction of constant power curves on the diode characteristics. An identical procedure can be used to place constant power curves on the transistor output conductance characteristics. Figure 5–30 illustrates the maximum dissipation power curve. On the right side of this curve, an operating point will require the dissipation power to be in excess of the maximum dissipation power, $P_{d(max)}$. Hence, the right side represents an undesirable operating region. On the contrary, the left side of the constant power curve represents the desirable operating region where power dissipation is less than $P_{d(max)}$. The dissipation is exactly equal to $P_{d(max)}$

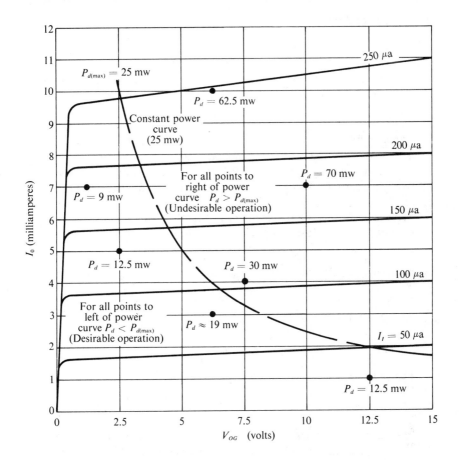

Figure 5-30. *Constant Dissipation Power and Operating Point Placement*

only when the operating point *falls directly on the constant power curve.*

Generally speaking, restricting operation to the safe power dissipation region does not place severe constraints on operating point placement. Other design characteristics are used to place the operating point in an optimum position, as will be described in subsequent sections.

The temperature dependency of $P_{d(max)}$ is discussed in Chap. 4. To account for these variations, the establishment of the safe operating region must be based on the anticipated operating temperature of the amplifier. The manufacturer specifies $P_{d(max)}$ at room temperature. When operation is to occur at elevated temperatures, such as in an unventilated chassis, $P_{d(max)}$ must be reduced by the *derating factor*, which is also specified by the manufacturer:

$$P_{d(\text{max})T} = P_{d(\text{max})} - \theta_{DF}(T - 300°K) \qquad (5\text{-}46)$$

where $P_{d(\text{max})}$ is the maximum dissipation power at temperature T and θ_{DF} is the derating factor. T may be in $°K$ or in $°C$. However, if the centigrade scale is used, the $300°K$ term in Eq. (5–46) must be replaced by $25°C$.

Example 5-7. The transistor with characteristics shown in Fig. 5–24 is used in a common emitter amplifier with a d-c load resistance of 1.5K and a biasing resistor of 100K. Both power supplies are 15-volt batteries. Specify the operating point conditions for the amplifier.

Solution. In order to determine the operating point, it is necessary to plot the static (d-c) load line. The voltage intercept is given by:

$$V_{OG} = V_{OO}$$

From Table 5–2, V_{OG} is V_{CE} in the CE amplifier, leading to:

$$V_{CE} = 15 \text{ volts}$$

and the current intercept is:

$$I_O = \frac{V_{OO}}{R_{L(\text{d-c})}}$$

From Table 5–2, I_O is I_C in the CE amplifier, leading to:

$$I_C = \frac{15}{1.5 \times 10^3} = 10 \text{ milliamperes}$$

A straight line drawn through these two points represents the d-c load line for the amplifier (Fig. 5–7). In order to establish the operating point, the input bias current must be determined:

$$I_I = \frac{V_{II}}{R_B}$$

From Table 5–2, I_I is I_B in the CE amplifier, leading to:

$$I_B = \frac{15}{1 \times 10^5} = 150 \text{ microamperes}$$

Hence, the point of intersection between the d-c load line and the characteristic for I_B equal to 150 microamperes is the operating point. The operating point conditions (Fig. E5–7) are:

$$I_B = 150 \text{ microamperes}$$
$$I_C = 5.8 \text{ milliamperes}$$
$$V_{CE} = 6.5 \text{ volts}$$

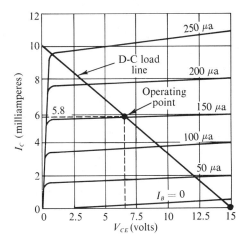

Figure E5-7

Example 5-8. The constant dissipation power curve in Fig. 5–30 represents a maximum dissipation power of 25 milliwatts and is associated with the transistor illustrated by the characteristics in Fig. 5–24. Can the amplifier specified in Example 5–7 operate safely in view of this restriction? If not, what must be done to achieve safe operation when a power supply of 15 volts must be used in the design?

Solution. The operating point specified in Example 5–7 can be placed on Fig. 5–30. When this is done, it can be seen that the operation is to the right of the constant power curve, exceeding safe conditions, as indicated in Fig. E5–8. This could be checked without using a constant power curve. Since V_{CE} is 6.5 volts and I_C is 5.8 milliamperes in Example 5–7, the steady-state power is:

$$P_d = 6.5(5.8 \times 10^{-3}) = 37.7 \text{ milliwatts}$$

which exceeds 25 milliwatts. In order to avoid this condition, while maintaining the same power supply voltage, the load line must be swung toward the horizontal (as in Fig. 5–28) by reducing the current intercept value. This requires an increase in the d-c load resistance. If a straight line is drawn from the 15-volt intercept on the V_{CE}-axis, just tangent to the constant power curve in Fig. 5–30, it will intersect the current axis at:

$$I_C = 6.6 \text{ milliamperes}$$

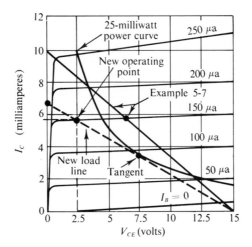

Figure E5-8

This is also shown in Fig. E5–8. Since the current intercept value is given by:

$$I_C = \frac{V_{OO}}{R_{L(\text{d-c})}}$$

the d-c load resistance associated with 6.6 milliamperes and 15 volts is:

$$R_{L(\text{d-c})} = \frac{V_{OO}}{I_C} = \frac{15}{6.6 \times 10^{-3}} = 2.49\text{K}$$

This design establishes a new operating point. If an input bias current of 150 microamperes is maintained:

$$I_B = 150 \text{ microamperes}$$
$$I_C = 5.6 \text{ milliamperes}$$
$$V_{CE} = 2.5 \text{ volts}$$

This represents a steady-state dissipation power of:

$$P_d = 2.5(5.6 \times 10^{-3}) = 14 \text{ milliwatts}$$

which is slightly less than half the maximum dissipation power of the transistor.

5.8 Dynamic (A-C) Operation

The operating bias values, V_{OG}, I_O, and I_I, provide the steady-state voltages and currents, about which the a-c signal components must vary.

This is shown in Fig. 5-31. The a-c input current, i_I, has a peak value of $i_{I(P)}$. Hence, the current reaches a maximum value of:

$$i_{I(\text{max})} = I_I + i_{I(P)} \qquad (5\text{-}47)$$

and a minimum value of:

$$i_{I(\text{min})} = I_I - i_{I(P)} \qquad (5\text{-}48)$$

and varies sinusoidally for all values between $i_{I(\text{max})}$ and $i_{I(\text{min})}$. This a-c input current causes an a-c output current (i_o) and an a-c output voltage (v_{oG}) to be produced, as shown. If the operating point is properly chosen and if the input "swing," $i_{I(\text{max})}$ to $i_{I(\text{min})}$, is not too great, the output current and voltage waveforms will be very nearly sinusoidal (Part A). If, however, the operating point is such that a nonlinear portion of the characteristic curves is utilized, serious distortion will result (Part B). It is also possible to produce a "clipped" waveform as shown in Part C. *For some amplifier applications, clipping is deliberately introduced.* This is especially true for high-power amplifiers and high-frequency, tuned amplifiers, as discussed in Chaps. 7 and 8, and of oscillator and modulator applications, as discussed in Chap. 10.

The voltage, current, and power gains associated with each amplifier configuration have been derived in simple mathematical terms as a part of the previous discussion of amplifier operation. It is also possible to perform a graphical analysis of these gains, using the output conductance characteristics of the transistor. Graphical analysis is somewhat subject to error since it frequently requires interpolations between existing curves in the characteristic family. The error is further accentuated by the fact that transistors of a particular type often display a large deviation from published characteristic curves, since the curves represent an *average* derived from selected samples of the transistor type. Deviations from the average are more prominent in transistor devices than in vacuum tube devices because of the more difficult problems associated with the mass production of semiconductor materials.

Definition of Operating Classes

The *operating class* of an amplifier is defined by the portion of a complete cycle that is reproduced as an output waveform. For the transistor amplifier, as long as an a-c current flows in the input loop, an a-c current flows in the output loop. Hence, output variations that do not conform in duration to an applied signal cycle imply that the *input current flow* (a-c) *ceases during some portion of the signal waveform.* This will occur if a portion of the applied voltage produces a *reverse bias* on the input junction.

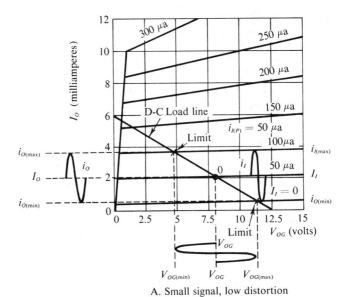

A. Small signal, low distortion

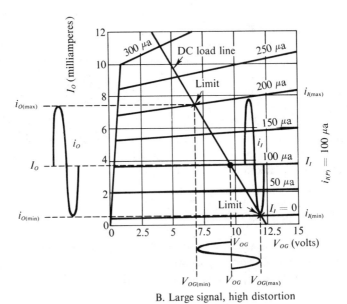

B. Large signal, high distortion

Figure 5-31.   *Examples of Dynamic (A-C) Operation*

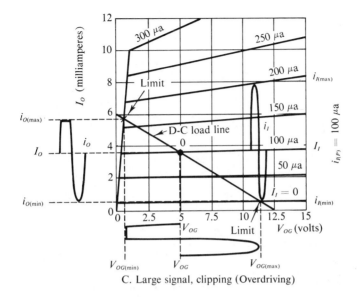

C. Large signal, clipping (Overdriving)

Figure 5-31   (*Continued*)

Figure 5–32 illustrates a generalized input resistance characteristic for a transistor with an input voltage waveform superimposed. *As shown, the input junction voltage does not, in actual practice, have to go into the reverse polarity in order to achieve zero input current.* Although not shown in the figure, it is possible to have nonconduction (zero input current) over a portion of the input voltage waveform regardless of the bias level. Higher value bias levels merely require that larger amplitude voltages be applied before nonconduction will occur. Applications that require conduction during the full signal cycle duration, then, can be assured such operation by using high input biases and small input voltages.

Figure 5–33 illustrates the input current waveforms associated with the four basic amplifier operating classes. The nature of transistor operation requires that the output current and voltage waveforms follow the same patterns, with a phase reversal in the CE configuration only. *Class A* operation requires that conduction occur during the *entire input voltage cycle* (360°, of conduction), as shown in Part A. Part B represents *Class B* operation, which requires that conduction occur *only for one-half of the input voltage cycle* (180° of conduction). This is identical to half-wave rectifier operation. Conduction over less than 360°, and more than 180°,

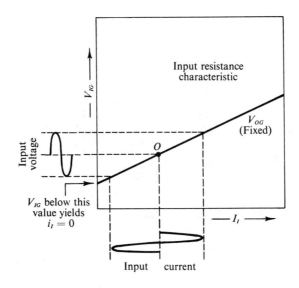

Figure 5-32.   *Input Voltage-Current Relationship*

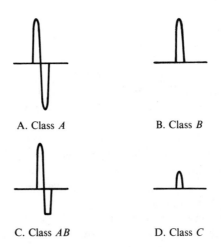

A. Class *A*

B. Class *B*

C. Class *AB*

D. Class *C*

Figure 5-33.   *Input Current Waveforms for the Four Operating Classes (Sinusoidal Input Voltages)*

of the input voltage cycle defines *Class AB* operation (Part C). The last operating class, *Class C*, consists of short "pulses" of less than 180° duration, as shown in Part D.

Although described in terms of sinusoidal waveforms, operating class and amplifier operation, itself, does not require that sinusoidal waveforms be used. Hence, the only characteristic that truly defines operating class is the *conduction duration*.

Figure 5–34 illustrates the relationship between operating points and operating classes. For Class *A* operation:

$$I_I \geq i_{I(P)} \tag{5-49}$$

Generally speaking, for this classs of operation, I_I is considerably greater than $i_{I(P)}$ because the operating point is placed *in the center of the* d-c *load line*. This is done to permit a maximum input current swing (peak-to-peak), while still maintaining Class *A* operation. For Class *B* operation:

$$I_I = 0 \tag{5-50}$$

For Class *AB* operation:

$$i_{I(P)} > I_{I(\text{d-c})} > 0 \tag{5-51}$$

and the operating point may occur anywhere between Q_A and Q_B in the figure. Notice that with Class *B* operation, a small d-c output current continues to flow even during the "nonconducting" period. This current is the normal reverse biased, cutoff current, I_{CO}, that always flows in the

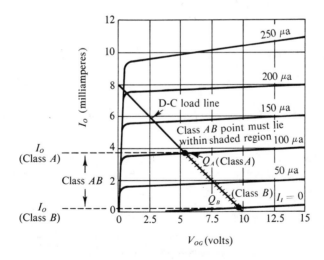

Figure 5-34.   *Location of Operating Points on Output Conductance Characteristics*

output loop. The Class *C* operating point is not indicated in the figure. *Operation in this class requires that the input junction be reverse biased.* The degree of reverse biasing used depends on the amplitude of the input voltage and the desired duration of the output waveform. Conduction will not begin until v_{IG} exceeds a specific value, as indicated in Fig. 5–35.

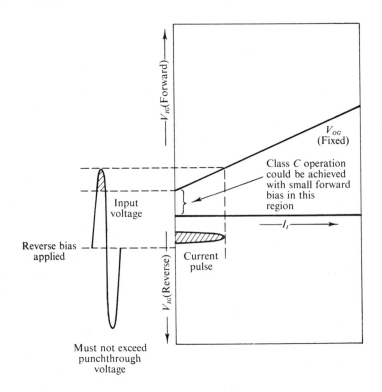

Figure 5-35.   *Bias and Voltage Amplitude Relationships for Class C Operation*

Example 5-9.   If Class *A* operation is to be maintained with the amplifier design described in Example 5–8, what is the maximum input signal current that can be applied?

Solution.   The operating point specified in Example 5–8 is:

$$I_B = 150 \text{ microamperes}$$
$$I_C = 5.6 \text{ milliamperes}$$
$$V_{CE} = 2.5 \text{ volts}$$

with an output-loop source of 15 volts and a d-c load resistance of

2.49K. The d-c load line for this amplifier crosses the near-vertical portion of the characteristics at:

$$I_C = 6.4 \text{ milliamperes}$$
$$V_{CE} = 0.4 \text{ volt}$$

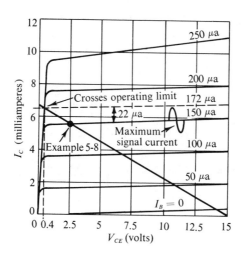

Figure E5-9

as is shown in Fig. E5–9, and occurs when I_B is about 9/20 of the distance between the characteristics for I_B equal to 150 microamperes and I_B equal to 200 microamperes. Interpolating:

$$i_{B(\max)} = I_B + \frac{9}{20}(200 - 150)(10^{-6})$$
$$= (150 \times 10^{-6}) - (22 \times 10^{-6}) = 172 \text{ microamperes}$$

If $i_{B(\max)}$ rises above 172 microamperes, the amplifier will be overdriven (as in Fig. 5–31, Part C). This limits the maximum input signal current to:

$$i_{I(P)} = i_{B(\max)} - I_B = (172 - 150)(10^{-6}) = 22 \text{ microamperes}$$

if Class *A* operation is to be maintained.

Example 5-10. Specify an optimum Class *A* operating point for the amplifier in Example 5–8. Change the ciruit design in order to achieve such operation without exceeding the maximum dissipation power or changing the power supply voltages.

Solution. The optimum placement of the Class *A* operating point is in the center of the d-c load line. For the 2.49K d-c load line and

15-volt output loop power supply specified in Example 5–8, this will require:

$$I_B = 85 \text{ microamperes}$$
$$I_C = 3.2 \text{ milliamperes}$$
$$V_{CE} = 7.6 \text{ volts}$$

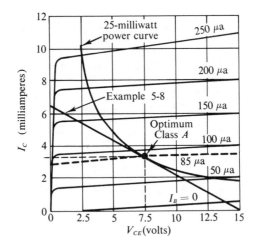

Figure E5-10

This is shown in Fig. E5–10 and represents a steady-state dissipation power of:

$$P_d = 7.6(3.2 \times 10^{-3}) = 24.4 \text{ milliwatts}$$

This operating point is optimum because it permits a maximum input signal current variation ($i_{I(P)} = 85$ microamperes) without over-driving or cutting off the amplifier. Furthermore, since the maximum dissipation power is 25 milliwatts, almost full advantage is made of the transistor's power handling capability. Achieving operation at this point merely requires that I_B be reduced to 85 microamperes. Hence, the bias resistor must be changed to:

$$R_B = \frac{V_{II}}{I_B} = \frac{15}{85 \times 10^{-6}} = 177\text{K}$$

A-C Loads and Load Lines

A single load line has been shown in all the figures presented thus far. In order for an amplifier dynamic analysis to be performed with a single load line, *the d-c and a-c loads must be the same.* This is seldom true in an actual amplifier, because an amplifier is seldom terminated with a single resistor (as has been illustrated thus far) and, in many applications, may not even contain a resistor in the output loop. When an amplifier is delivering a signal to some other device such as a speaker, a cathode ray tube, another amplifier, etc., it is usually not desirable to permit the d-c components, I_O and V_{OG}, to be transferred. Only the a-c components, i_o and v_{og}, are desired. For this reason, multiple amplifier stages and devices driven by amplifiers are connected through *coupling networks.* Three typical coupling networks are shown in Fig. 5-36. For the RC network, the coupling capacitor, C_C, *blocks the* d-c *components* from the device being driven by the amplifier (represented by the single equivalent resistance, R_D). The transformer network, by the very nature of transformer operation, *does not pass* d-c *components.* The impedance network utilizes a coupling capacitor to block d-c and is similar to the RC network. However, the inductance is chosen so that a-c signals are attenuated severly, resulting in only a d-c signal through the inductor. Coupling capacitor values are chosen so that they are essentially short-circuited for a-c signal

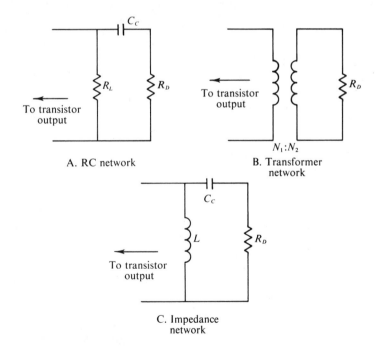

A. RC network

B. Transformer network

C. Impedance network

Figure 5-36. *Coupling Networks*

components. Conversely, most transformers and inductors have such a low winding resistance that they may be assumed to be short-circuited d-c paths. With these considerations in mind, it is possible to derive d-c *and* a-c *equivalent circuits* for the coupling networks as shown in Fig. 5–37.

If the dynamic (a-c) operation of an amplifier is to be considered, the analyses must be performed on the basis *of the* a-c *load*. However, since the operating point is established *by the* d-c *load*, it becomes necessary to consider both in a complete amplifier analysis. These two conditions are essential:

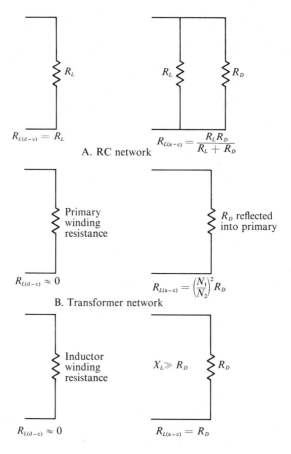

$$R_{L(d-c)} = R_L$$

A. RC network

$$R_{L(a-c)} = \frac{R_L R_D}{R_L + R_D}$$

Primary winding resistance

R_D reflected into primary

$$R_{L(d-c)} \approx 0$$

$$R_{L(a-c)} = \left(\frac{N_1}{N_2}\right)^2 R_D$$

B. Transformer network

Inductor winding resistance

$X_L \gg R_D$

$$R_{L(d-c)} \approx 0$$

$$R_{L(a-c)} = R_D$$

C. Impedance network

Figure 5-37.   *D-C and A-C Equivalent Circuits for Coupling Networks*

1. *Operating point is established directly by* $R_{L(d-c)}$ (*the* d-c *load line*), and

2. *Dynamic operation is established directly by* $R_{L(a-c)}$ (*the* a-c *load line*).

The a-c input current, i_I, must swing about the operating point, as must the a-c output current, i_o, and voltage, v_{OG}. However, the limits of operation are established by the a-c load line (Fig. 5-38) rather than by the d-c load line (Fig. 5-31). Furthermore, when the input signal current is zero, the steady-state (operating point) conditions must persist. For this reason, *the* a-c *and* d-c *load lines must intersect at the operating point*. This is also shown in Fig. 5-38.

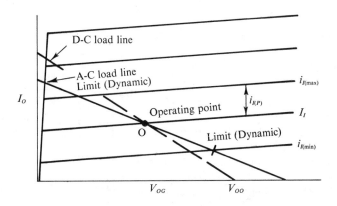

Figure 5-38.   *Operation Established by* A-C *Load Line*

An a-c load line must be drawn in two steps. First, an arbitrary voltage value, V_A, is selected as a voltage-axis intercept, and a current-axis intercept is determined from:

$$I_A = \frac{V_A}{R_{L(a-c)}} \qquad (5\text{-}52)$$

A line is drawn between the two intercepts (the dashed line in Fig. 5-39). This line has the *same slope* as the intended a-c load line, *but does not pass through the operating point*. The second step consists of translating this initial line to the operating point, resulting in the (solid) a-c line in Fig. 5-39. (A straight edge and eye alignment is generally sufficient.)

Since the transformer and inductor d-c resistances are essentially zero, their d-c load lines are represented by a vertical line extending upward

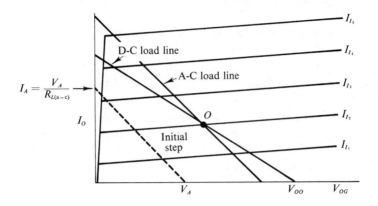

Figure 5-39.   *Procedure for Constructing A-C Load Line*

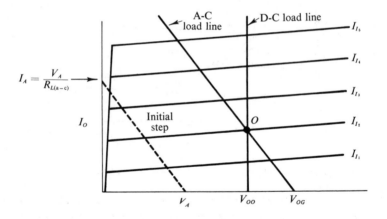

Figure 5-40.   D-C *and* A-C *Load Line Construction with Transformer and Impedance Coupling Networks*

from V_{oo}. This is shown in Fig. 5–40. The procedure for placing the a-c load line is unchanged.

Example 5-11.   The amplifier design specified in Example 5–10 is to be RC coupled to a device having a resistance of 8K. Construct the associated a-c load line. If a peak input signal current of 50 micro-amperes is applied, what maximum and minimum output currents are produced?

Solution. The d-c load resistance in Example 5–10 is 2.49K. When RC coupled to a resistance of 8K, the a-c load (Fig. 5–37, Part A) is:

$$R_{L(a-c)} = \frac{R_{L(d-c)}R_D}{R_{L(d-c)} + R_D} = \frac{(2.49 \times 10^3)(8 \times 10^3)}{(2.49 + 8)(10^3)} = 1.9K$$

The first step toward placing the a-c load line on the output conductance characteristics consists of arbitrarily selecting a voltage intercept (10 volts, for example) and determining the associated current intercept:

$$I_A = \frac{V_A}{R_{L(a-c)}} = \frac{10}{1.9 \times 10^3} = 5.26 \text{ milliamperes}$$

A straight line drawn between these intercepts has the same slope as the desired a-c load line (Fig. E5–11). The second step toward placing the a-c load line consists of drawing a new line through the operating point:

$$I_B = 85 \text{ microamperes}$$
$$I_C = 3.2 \text{ milliamperes}$$
$$V_{CE} = 7.6 \text{ volts}$$

in such a way that it is parallel to the first line of the a-c load line construction. When this is done, it can be seen that the a-c load line intersects the current axis at about 7.2 milliamperes and the voltage axis at about 13.7 volts. With a peak input signal current of 50 micro-

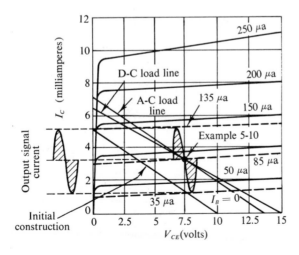

Figure E5-11

amperes, the minimum and maximum base current will be:

$$i_{B(\min)} = I_B - i_{I(P)} = (85 - 50)(10^{-6}) = \ 35 \text{ microamperes}$$
$$i_{B(\max)} = I_B + i_{I(P)} = (85 + 50)(10^{-6}) = 135 \text{ microamperes}$$

The characteristics for $i_{B(\min)}$ and $i_{B(\max)}$ must be drawn by interpolation. This is also shown in Fig. E5–11, along with the intersection of these two characteristics and the a-c load line, which provides the two limiting points of the amplifier's dynamic operation:

$$i_{C(\min)} = 1.3 \text{ milliamperes}$$
$$i_{C(\max)} = 5.1 \text{ milliamperes}$$

Example 5-12. The transistor with characteristics shown in Fig. 5–23 is to be used in a common base amplifier that is transformer coupled to a device with a resistance of 300 ohms. The transformer turns ratio is 3:1 and 15-volt power supplies are to be used. What are the maximum and minimum V_{CB}-values if the peak input signal current is 2.5 milliamperes and the input bias current is 5 milliamperes?

Solution. The d-c load resistance for transformer coupling is essentially zero, leading to a vertical d-c load line intersecting the voltage axis at V_{oo} (15 volts). This is shown in Fig. E5–12, along with the

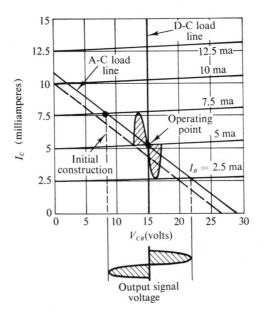

Figure E5-12

operating point conditions:

$$I_B = 5 \text{ milliamperes}$$
$$I_C = 5 \text{ milliamperes}$$
$$V_{CB} = 15 \text{ volts}$$

The a-c load resistance (from Fig. 5–37) is:

$$R_{L(\text{a-c})} = \left(\frac{N_1}{N_2}\right)^2 R_D = 3^2(300) = 2.7\text{K}$$

The a-c load line is constructed in the same manner described in Example 5–11. Arbitrarily selecting 27 volts as a voltage intercept results in a current intercept of:

$$I_A = \frac{V_A}{R_{L(\text{a-c})}} = \frac{27}{2700} = 10 \text{ milliamperes}$$

A straight line between these two points (Fig. E5–12) has the same slope as the desired a-c load line. When a parallel line is drawn through the operating point, the a-c load line construction is complete. With a peak input signal current of 2.5 milliamperes and an input bias current of 5 milliamperes:

$$i_{B(\text{min})} = I_B - i_{I(P)} = (5 - 2.5)(10^{-3}) = 2.5 \text{ milliamperes}$$
$$i_{B(\text{max})} = I_B + i_{I(P)} = (5 + 2.5)(10^{-3}) = 7.5 \text{ milliamperes}$$

The intersection between these characteristics and the a-c load line provide the limit-points for the amplifier's dynamic operation. The collector-to-base voltages are:

$$V_{CB(\text{max})} = 22 \text{ volts}$$
$$V_{CB(\text{min})} = 9 \text{ volts}$$

Maximum Power Transfer

Fig. 5–41 illustrates a simple two-resistor network and the power transfer curve associated with varying one resistor value relative to the other. For low values of R_2 (R_2/R_1 less than one), power delivered to R_2 increases as R_2 increases. For high values of R_2 (R_2/R_1 greater than one) the power delivered to R_2 *derceases* as R_2 increases. This decrease is brought about by the reduction in circuit current as R_2 increases beyond a certain point. *Maximum power is delivered to R_2* when the two resistors are of equal value (R_2/R_1 is equal to one). Satisfying this condition is referred to as *matching*.

Figure 5–42 provides a simple equivalent resistor network for a transistor amplifier input and output loop. The analogy between these equivalent circuits and the circuit in Fig. 5–41 should be obvious. When

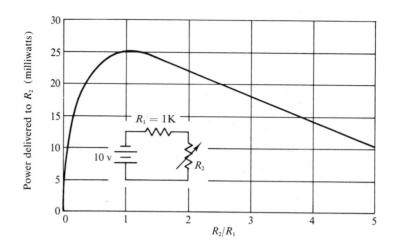

Figure 5-41. *Power Transfer Plot*

R_g (the equivalent source resistance) and r_i (the transistor a-c input resistance) are equal, maximum power will be transfered from the source to the amplifier. When $R_{L(a-c)}$ and r_0 (the transistor a-c output resistance) are equal, maximum power will be transfered from the amplifier to the a-c load. This leads to the conditions for *matching* a transistor amplifier:

$$R_{L(a-c)} = r_0 \qquad (5\text{-}53)$$
$$R_g = r_i \qquad (5\text{-}54)$$

Under matched conditions, an amplifier will operate at its *maximum possible power gain*.

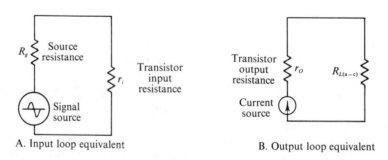

A. Input loop equivalent   B. Output loop equivalent

Figure 5-42. *Transistor Amplifier Input/Output Equivalent Circuits*

Example 5-13. If the output resistance of the CB amplifier specified in Example 5–12 is 60K, what must the transformer turns ratio be in order to achieve maximum power transfer?

Solution.   In order to achieve maximum power transfer:

$$R_{L(\text{a-c})} = r_o = 60\text{K}$$

For the transformer coupled load, the a-c resistance is:

$$R_{L(\text{a-c})} = \left(\frac{N_1}{N_2}\right)^2 R_D$$

Solving for the turns ratio:

$$\left(\frac{N_1}{N_2}\right) = \sqrt{\frac{R_{L(\text{a-c})}}{R_D}} = \sqrt{\frac{6 \times 10^4}{3 \times 10^2}} \approx 14$$

Hence, a transformer turns ratio of 14:1 is required.

Choice of Operating Class

One of the primary uses of an amplifier is to produce increases in a-c signal power. A measure of how well the amplifier converts d-c power to a-c power is called the *output efficiency*, defined by:

$$\eta_0 = \frac{P_{\text{a-c}}}{P_{\text{d-c}}} \times 100 \text{ per cent} \tag{5-55}$$

where $P_{\text{a-c}}$ is the output signal power:

$$P_{\text{a-c}} = i_o^2 R_{L(\text{a-c})} \tag{5-56}$$

and $P_{\text{d-c}}$ is the d-c power supplied to the output loop:

$$P_{\text{d-c}} = I_o V_{oo} \tag{5-57}$$

From Figs. 5–34 and 5–35, it can be seen that $P_{\text{d-c}}$ must change as operating class is changed, since I_o will vary even if V_{oo} remains constant. From Fig. 5–33, it should be obvious that $P_{\text{a-c}}$ must be different for each operating class, also, since different waveforms are involved. Equation (5–55) provides a means of evaluating the resulting differences in output efficiency.

The output loop source must supply *all power in the output loop*. This includes the signal power, $P_{\text{a-c}}$, from Eq. (5–56), the power lost in the d-c load:

$$P_L = I_o^2 R_{L(\text{d-c})} \tag{5-58}$$

and the d-c power dissipated by the transistor:

$$P_d = I_o V_{OG} \tag{5-59}$$

Hence:

$$P_{\text{d-c}} = P_{\text{a-c}} + P_L + P_d \tag{5-57a}$$

and Eq. (5–55) can be written as:

$$\eta_0 = \frac{P_{\text{a-c}}}{P_{\text{a-c}} + P_L + P_d} \times 100 \text{ per cent} \tag{5-55a}$$

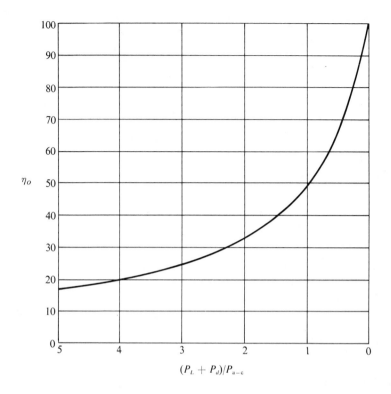

η_O (vertical axis)

$(P_L + P_d)/P_{a-c}$ (horizontal axis)

Figure 5-43.   *Variation of Output Efficiency for Decreasing* D-C *Losses*

From this equation, it can be seen that output efficiency will never be 100 per cent because of the inherent d-c losses in the output loop, $P_L + P_d$. Figure 5–43 presents the variation in output efficiency as the total d-c losses are reduced. Since transformer and inductor winding resistances are very small (assumed zero for most applications), P_L [from Eq. (5–58)] must be negligible for most of these circuits. For this reason, transformer and impedance coupling result in circuits with greater output efficiency than those with RC coupling.

For Class *A* operation, since the full waveform cycle appears in the output, the rms current is:

$$i_o = i_{0(P)}/\sqrt{2} \qquad \textbf{(5-60)}$$

(This is derived in Appendix C and is a general relationship between rms and peak values for sinusoidal waveforms.) Substituting Eq. (5–60) into Eq. (5–56):

$$P_{a-c} = \frac{i_{0(P)}^2 R_{L(a-c)}}{2} \qquad \textbf{(5-56a)}$$

and, with the additional substitution of Eq. (5–57) for $P_{\text{d-c}}$, Eq. (5–55) becomes:

$$\eta_0 = \frac{i_{o(P)}^2 R_{L(\text{a-c})}}{V_{oo} I_o} \times 50 \text{ per cent} \tag{5-55b}$$

Maximum efficiency will always be obtained when i_o is as high as possible for a specific a-c load. For Class A amplifiers, if the operating point is placed in the middle of the d-c load line (see Fig. 5–34), $i_{o(P)}$ can be made to approximate I_o. Substituting I_o for $i_{o(P)}$ in Eq. (5–55b) leads to:

$$\eta_0 = \frac{I_o R_{L(\text{a-c})}}{V_{oo}} \times 50 \text{ per cent} \tag{5-55c}$$

$$= \frac{R_{L(\text{a-c})}}{r_o + R_{L(\text{d-c})}} \times 50 \text{ per cent}$$

The quantity $r_o + R_{L(\text{d-c})}$ can be substituted for V_{oo}/I_o on the basis of the output loop equivalent d-c circuit (Fig. 5–42).

With transformer or impedance coupling, $R_{L(\text{d-c})}$ is essentially zero in most instances. For such a circuit, η_0 will approach 50 per cent if r_o and $R_{L(\text{a-c})}$ are equal. The equality of these two resistances also satisfies the output matching condition for maximum power transfer [Eq. (5–53)] and does, therefore, represent a good practical relationship. With RC coupling, $R_{L(\text{d-c})}$ is not negligible. Since maximum d-c power transfer is achieved when r_o and $R_{L(\text{d-c})}$ are equal, the maximum theoretical efficiency of the RC coupled, Class A amplifier occurs when r_o, $R_{L(\text{d-c})}$, and $R_{L(\text{a-c})}$ are equal. This maximum is 25 per cent.

Table 5–3 lists the maximum theoretical efficiency for Class A, Class B, and Class C amplifiers. These values are presented here for comparitive purposes; the Class B and Class C efficiencies are derived later in the text. A single-transistor Class B amplifier is seldom used. Rather, a two-transistor arrangement is used in such a manner that one transistor develops the positive half-cycle; the other, the negative half-cycle. The two halves are then combined so that the output signal represents a full cycle of conduction (Chap. 8). This amplifier is capable of handling high currents

TABLE 5-3

Operating Class (Theoretical) Efficiencies

Operating Class	Maximum Efficiency
A	25%
B	78.5%
AB	$25\% < \eta_0 < 78.5\%$
C	$> 78.5\%$

and, therefore, high power. The less efficient Class *A* amplifier is seldom used when high output power is required. Instead, the Class *A* amplifier is used primarily as a current or voltage amplifier, boosting very small input signals so that they may be used to *drive* high power Class *B* amplifiers. Class *C*, the most efficient, is used in radio-frequency circuits with a parallel resonant circuit as the load (Chap. 7). The resonance characteristics produce a sinusoidal output despite the fact that the load is "pulsed" by small portions of the input signal waveform.

Example 5-14. What is the efficiency of the Class *A* amplifier specified in Example 5–11?

Solution. The efficiency for Class *A* operation is given by:

$$\eta_o = \frac{i_{o(P)}^2 R_{L(a-c)}}{V_{oo} I_o} \times 50 \text{ per cent}$$

The output current waveform (Fig. E5–11) is symmetrical. Its peak values are:

$$i_{c(P)} = I_c - i_{c(min)} = (3.2 - 1.3)(10^{-3}) = 1.9 \text{ milliamperes}$$
$$i_{c(P)} = i_{c(max)} - I_c = (5.1 - 3.2)(10^{-3}) = 1.9 \text{ milliamperes}$$

indicating that the two halves of the waveform are identical. This leads directly to the amplifier efficiency:

$$\eta_o = \frac{(1.9 \times 10^{-3})^2 (1.9 \times 10^3)}{7.6(3.2 \times 10^{-3})} \times 50 \text{ per cent} = 28.2 \text{ per cent}$$

Hence, it appears that efficiency is in the vicinity of the 25-per cent maximum predicted by theory.

Distortion, Operating Point, and A-C Load (Class *A*)

Fourier analysis indicates that *all nonsinusoidal signals* contain a series of harmonic components with a fundamental component of the same frequency as the basic signal (Appendix C). When a sinewave is converted into a nonsinusoidal signal, such as in Class *B*, Class *AB*, and Class *C* operation, the resulting distortion can be expressed in terms of the harmonic components. In many amplifier applications, harmonic distortion is intolerable or, at least, must be kept to a minimum. In such cases, the Class *A* amplifier is essential, unless special circuitry is used to restore the original undistorted qualities. Even Class *A* operation *does not assure* that there will be no distortion present. However, with the proper selection of a-c load resistance and operating point, distortion can be minimized.

Figure 5–31 illustrates the pronounced change in reproduction quality (degree of distortion) brought about by the improper selection of resistance and operating point for the Class *A* amplifier. Figure 5–28 illustrates the change in load line position as $R_{L(d-c)}$ changes. Since the d-c load establishes the operating point, various degrees of distortion are obviously brought about by varying the d-c load value.

Operating point restrictions have also been established with respect to maximum dissipation power (Fig. 5–30 and associated text). This places more of a restriction on the design of transformer and impedance coupled amplifiers than it does on the design of RC coupled amplifiers. This is illustrated in Fig. 5–44. As shown in Part A of the figure, the use of high supply voltages restricts the operating point to low I_t-values. Since a-c operation must remain in the "safe" region also, all points on the a-c load line must lie to the left of the $P_{d(max)}$-curve. This is also shown in Part A of the figure. Because of this, high supply voltages force the a-c load line toward the horizontal (high values of a-c load). A better operating point placement is illustrated in Part B. This placement leads to a more flexible design since the a-c input signal may vary over a greater range.

The design of an RC coupled amplifier is faced with similar restrictions, as illustrated in Fig. 5–45. With the more optimum placement of the operating point (Part B) and the selection of a supply voltage, the d-c *load resistance has been established* in an indirect manner. The supply voltage is generally selected on the basis of commercially available values—especially if the supply is to be a battery. The operating point is generally placed slightly to the left of the $P_{d(max)}$-curve rather than directly on it. This provides a *margin of safety* to account for variations in transistor manufacturing processsses and in the actual value of the resistor used for $R_{L(d-c)}$. (Ten per cent variation from the coded resistor value is not uncommon.) The d-c resistance necessary to achieve such operation is:

$$R_{L(d-c)} = \frac{V_{oo}}{I_{int}} \tag{5-61}$$

where I_{int} is the intercept current obtained when a straight line is drawn from V_{oo} through the operating point.

For Class *A* operation, distortion is the result of permitting the dynamic operation to occur in a region containing nonlinear characteristics. From Figs. 5–44 and 5–45, it can be seen that the choice of a-c load must also have an effect on distortion. As a matter of fact, minimum distortion criteria can be used to establish an optimum a-c load value. The exact nature of the interactions between operating point, d-c load, a-c load, and distortion are difficult to portray on the output conductance characteristics. However, a *dynamic transfer characteristic* can be constructed to assist in these determinations.

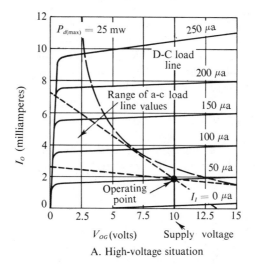

A. High-voltage situation

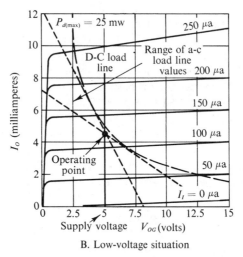

B. Low-voltage situation

Figure 5-44.   *Operating Restrictions Associated with Transformer Coupling*

The dynamic transfer characteristic consists of a family of forward transfer current curves (I_O versus I_I), associated with specific a-c load resistances. Hence, the dynamic characteristic differs from the static characteristic because the static "constant," V_{OG}, is replaced by the dynamic constant, $R_{L(a\text{-}c)}$. The dynamic curves can be obtained directly from the static output conductance curves since I_O and I_I are both present on the curves. The procedure is straightforward, as indicated in Fig. 5–46, which is a reproduction of Fig. 5–45 with a single a-c load line. The intersec-

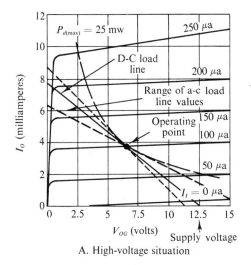

A. High-voltage situation

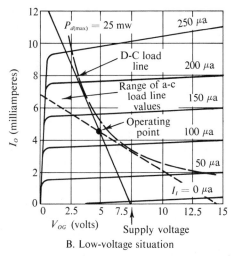

B. Low-voltage situation

Figure 5-45.   *Operating Restrictions Associated with RC Coupling*

tions of this load line with the output conductance curves forms the I_O-I_I-coordinates for a dynamic transfer curve. The I_O-values can be projected directly to the dynamic characteristic I_O-axis if the static I_O-scale is used. The dynamic transfer points must be joined by a smooth line to form the dynamic transfer curve. The complete dynamic transfer characteristic is constructed by following this procedure for several a-c load values. (The curves in Fig. 5–47 are the dynamic curves for all the a-c load values in Fig. 5–45.)

For low I_O-I_I-values, the dynamic transfer curves may be extremely

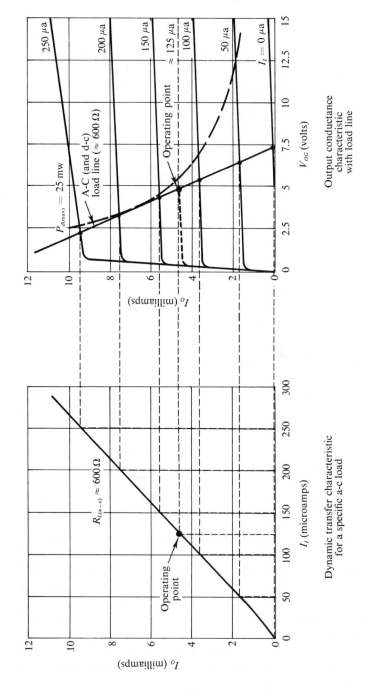

Figure 5-46. Construction of the Dynamic Transfer Characteristic

234

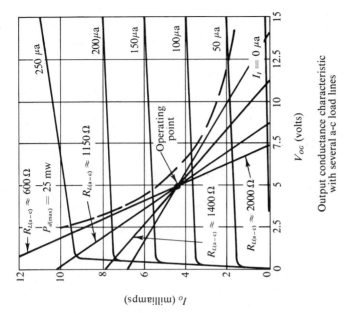

Output conductance characteristic
with several a-c load lines

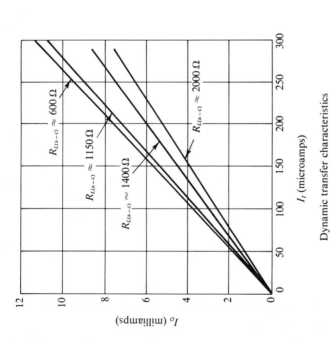

I_I (microamps)

Dynamic transfer characteristics
for several a-c load values

Figure 5-47. *Complete Set of Transfer Characteristics for a Possible Amplifier Design*

235

nonlinear. However, over a wide range of values, a high degree of linearity is displayed. *If amplifier operation is restricted to the linear portion of a dynamic curve, a minimum amount of distortion will be achieved.* Hence, the dynamic characteristic can be used to *make a graphical selection of the optimum* a-c *load* if minimum distortion is the selection criterion.

A dynamic transfer curve can also be used to calculate the specific distortion components associated with the output waveform, i_o. Applying the general expression for a distorted waveform (from Appendix C) to the output current waveform yields:

$$i_o = (I_o + I_{o(D)}) + i_{1(P)} \cos 2\pi f_1 t \qquad \text{(5-62)}$$
$$+ i_{2(P)} \cos 4\pi f_1 t + \cdots$$
$$+ i_{n(P)} \cos 2n\pi f_1 t$$

where $(I_o + I_{o(D)})$ is the total d-c component (output operating current plus the d-c component introduced by the distortion); $i_{1(P)}$, $i_{2(P)}$, and $i_{n(P)}$ are the peak fundamental, second harmonic, and nth harmonic amplitudes; and f_1 is the fundamental frequency(the same as the input frequency). In Eq. (5–62), the peak amplitudes and $I_{o(D)}$ are unknown. Since harmonic amplitudes generally decrease very rapidly, consideration of the third or fourth harmonic is usually sufficient. Consideration of the fourth harmonic requires five equations:

$$I_{o(D)} = \frac{1}{6}(i_{o(\max)} + i_{o(\min)}) \qquad \text{(5-63a)}$$
$$+ \frac{1}{3}(i_o' + i_o'') - I_o$$

$$i_{1(P)} = \frac{1}{3}(i_{o(\max)}' - i_{o(\min)}) \qquad \text{(5-63b)}$$
$$+ \frac{1}{3}(i_o' - i_o'')$$

$$i_{2(P)} = \frac{1}{4}(i_{o(\max)} + i_{o(\min)}) - \frac{I_o}{2} \qquad \text{(5-63c)}$$

$$i_{3(P)} = \frac{1}{6}(i_{o(\max)} - i_{o(\min)}) \qquad \text{(5-63d)}$$
$$- \frac{1}{3}(i_o' - i_o'')$$

$$i_{4(P)} = \frac{1}{12}(i_{o(\max)} + i_{o(\min)}) \qquad \text{(5-63e)}$$
$$- \frac{1}{3}(i_o' + i_o'') + \frac{I_o}{2}$$

The five current values used in these equations are illustrated in Fig. 5–48. The peak output current is $i_{o(\max)}$; $i_{o(\min)}$ is the minimum output current. The value for i_o' is associated with $2\pi ft = 60°$, projected from the i_1-

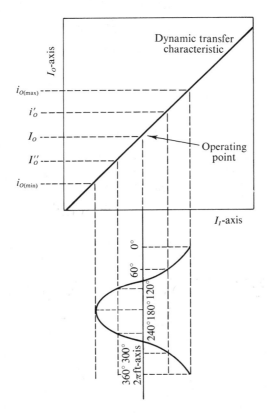

Figure 5-48. *Harmonic Distortion Construction*

waveform. The value for i_o'' is associated with $2\pi ft = 120°$, projected from the i_I-waveform. The input sinewave is difficult to construct precisely. and an alternate technique consists of projecting i_o' from a point *on the* a-c *load line midway between the operating point and the upper limit of operation.* Similarly, i_o'' is obtained by projecting from a point *on the* a-c *load line midway between the operating point and the lower limit of operation.*

Amplifier distortion is usually specified in terms of the per cent of harmonic distortion present. These percentages are given by:

$$D_2 = \frac{i_{2(P)}}{i_{1(P)}} \times 100 \text{ per cent} \qquad (5\text{-}64a)$$

$$D_3 = \frac{i_{3(P)}}{i_{1(P)}} \times 100 \text{ per cent} \qquad (5\text{-}64b)$$

$$D_4 = \frac{i_{4(P)}}{i_{1(P)}} \times 100 \text{ per cent} \qquad (5\text{-}64c)$$

and the total harmonic distortion is:

$$D = \sqrt{D_2^2 + D_3^2 + D_4^2} \qquad (5\text{-}65)$$

The output power associated with any particular harmonic is:

$$P_n = \frac{i_{n(P)}^2}{2} R_{L(\text{a-c})} \qquad (5\text{-}66)$$

where n may be 1, 2, 3 or 4.

Example 5-15. Transistor A in Appendix D is used with an a-c load whose load line has a voltage-axis intercept at 40 volts and a current-axis intercept at 4 milliamperes. The forward bias current is 40 microamperes and the peak input signal current is 20 microamperes. What is the total harmonic distortion for such operation?

Solution. The operating conditions are shown in Fig. E5–15, Part A. The first step in determining harmonic distortion consists of constructing the dynamic transfer characteristic. Based on the intersections between the a-c load line and the indicated base current curves, the following data is obtained:

I_B (μamps)	I_C (ma)
0	0.4
20	0.7
40	1.1
60	1.8
80	2.8
100	3.8

This is plotted in Part B. The operating point is also indicated, along with the input signal current waveform. The "operating" length of the transfer curve is divided into four equal parts, in order to obtain the harmonic data. This yields the five output current values:

$$i_{C(\text{max})} = 2.7 \text{ milliamperes}$$
$$i_C' = 2.2 \text{ milliamperes}$$
$$I_C = 1.8 \text{ milliamperes}$$
$$i_C'' = 1.4 \text{ milliamperes}$$
$$i_{C(\text{min})} = 1.1 \text{ milliamperes}$$

The total harmonic distortion is given by:

$$D = \sqrt{D_2^2 + D_3^2 + D_4^2}$$

where:

$$D_n = \frac{i_{n(P)}}{i_{1(P)}} \times 100 \text{ per cent}$$

The fundamental peak current is:

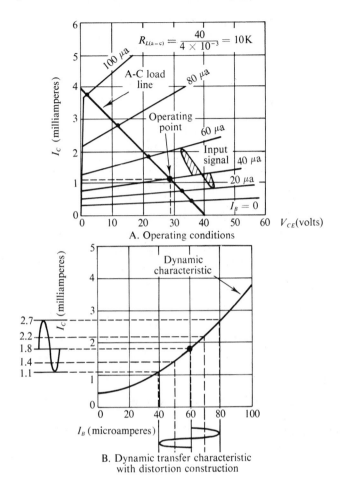

A. Operating conditions

B. Dynamic transfer characteristic
with distortion construction

Figure E5-15

$$i_{1(P)} = \frac{1}{3}(i_{C(\max)} - i_{C(\min)}) + \frac{1}{3}(i_C' - i_C'')$$

$$= \frac{1}{3}[(2.7 - 1.1)(10^{-3})] + \frac{1}{3}[(2.2 - 1.4)(10^{-3})]$$

$$= 0.8 \text{ milliamperes}$$

The second harmonic peak current is given by:

$$i_{2(P)} = \frac{1}{4}(i_{C(\max)} + i_{C(\min)} - \frac{I_C}{2}$$

$$= \frac{1}{4}[(2.7 + 1.1)(10^{-3})] - \frac{1.8 \times 10^{-3}}{2}$$

$$= 0.05 \text{ milliampere}$$

The third harmonic peak current is:

$$i_{3(P)} = \frac{1}{6}(i_{C(\max)} - i_{C(\min)}) - \frac{1}{3}(i'_C - i''_C)$$

$$= \frac{1}{6}[(2.7 - 1.1)(10^{-3})] - \frac{1}{3}[(2.2 - 1.4)(10^{-3})]$$

$$= 0 \text{ [no third harmonic]}$$

The fourth harmonic peak current is:

$$i_{4(P)} = \frac{1}{12}(i_{C(\max)} + i_{C(\min)}) - \frac{1}{3}(i'_C + i''_C) + \frac{I_C}{2}$$

$$= \frac{1}{12}[(2.7 + 1.1)(10^{-3})] - \frac{1}{3}[(2.2 + 1.4)(10^{-3})] + \frac{1.8 \times 10^{-3}}{2}$$

$$= 0.02 \text{ milliampere}$$

Expressed in terms of distortion percentages:

$$D_2 = \frac{i_{2(P)}}{i_{1(P)}} \times 100 \text{ per cent} = \frac{0.05 \times 10^{-3}}{0.8 \times 10^{-3}} \times 100 \text{ per cent}$$

$$= 6.25 \text{ per cent}$$

$$D_3 = 0$$

$$D_4 = \frac{i_{4(P)}}{i_{1(P)}} \times 100 \text{ per cent} = \frac{0.02 \times 10^{-3}}{0.8 \times 10^{-3}} \times 100 \text{ per cent}$$

$$= 2.5 \text{ per cent}$$

This leads to a total distortion of:

$$\sqrt{(6.25 \text{ per cent})^2 + (2.5 \text{ per cent})^2} = 6.75 \text{ per cent}$$

Example 5-16. In view of the distortion currents calculated in Example 5–15, what is the total a-c output power for the amplifier? What is the efficiency of this amplifier if the d-c load resistance is 4K?

Solution. The total a-c power is given by the sum of the individual harmonic powers. The harmonic power, in turn, is given by:

$$P_n = \frac{i_{n(P)}^2}{2} R_{L(\text{a-c})}$$

For the fundamental and harmonic components calculated in Example 5–15 and the a-c load resistance specified in Fig. E5–15:

$$P_1 = \frac{(0.8 \times 10^{-3})^2}{2} (10 \times 10^3) = 3.2 \text{ milliwatts}$$

$$P_2 = \frac{(0.05 \times 10^{-3})^2}{2} (10 \times 10^3) = 0.0125 \text{ milliwatt}$$

$$P_4 = \frac{(0.02 \times 10^{-3})^2}{2} (10 \times 10^3) = 0.004 \text{ milliwatt}$$

This represents a total a-c output power of 3.22 milliwatts.
Amplifier efficiency is defined by:

$$\eta_0 = \frac{P_{\text{a-c}}}{P_{\text{d-c}}} \times 100 \text{ per cent}$$

However, when a distorted waveform is present, the d-c power is not
simply defined by the operating point conditions. The d-c component
of the distorted waveform must also be considered. Using the data
in Example 5–15:

$$I_{C(D)} = \frac{1}{6}(i_{C(\text{max})} + i_{C(\text{min})}) + \frac{1}{3}(i_C' + i_C'') - I_C$$

$$= \frac{1}{6}[(2.7 + 1.1)(10^{-3})] + \frac{1}{3}[(2.2 + 1.4)(10^{-3})] - (1.8 \times 10^{-3})$$

$$= 0.033 \text{ milliampere}$$

This indicates that the average, or d-c, value for the distorted waveform is more than the operating d-c value of 1.8 milliamperes
The effective d-c current flowing in the output loop is:

$$I_{\text{d-c}} = I_C + I_{C(D)} = (1.8 + 0.033)(10^{-3}) = 1.833 \text{ milliamperes}$$

With a d-c load of 4K:

$$P_{\text{d-c}} = I_{\text{d-c}}^2 R_{L(\text{d-c})} = (1.833 \times 10^{-3})^2 (4 \times 10^3) = 13.44 \text{ milliwatts}$$

The efflciency is given by:

$$\eta_0 = \frac{3.22 \times 10^{-3}}{13.44 \times 10^{-3}} \times 100 \text{ per cent} = 24 \text{ per cent}$$

Graphical Gain Calculations

Figure 5–49 illustrates a complete variation of input current, output
current, and output voltage with maximum and minimum values, as shown.
Since current gain is defined as the ratio of output current and input
current:

$$A_{iG} = \frac{i_{O(\text{max})} - i_{O(\text{min})}}{i_{I(\text{max})} - i_{I(\text{min})}} \tag{5-67}$$

The voltage gain is defined by:

$$A_{vG} = \frac{v_{OG(\text{max})} - v_{OG(\text{min})}}{v_{IG(\text{max})} - v_{IG(\text{min})}} \tag{5-68}$$

$$= \frac{v_{OG(\text{max})} - v_{OG(\text{min})}}{(i_{I(\text{max})} - i_{I(\text{min})})r_i}$$

The output power can be determined directly from:

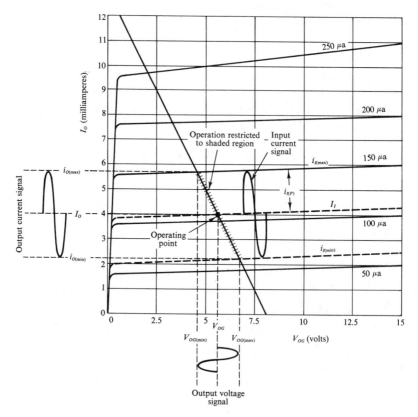

Figure 5-49. *Graphical Determination of Amplifier Operation (Gains)*

$$P_{\text{a-c}} = \frac{(i_{O(\max)} - i_{O(\min)})(v_{OG(\max)} - v_{OG(\min)})}{8} \qquad (5\text{-}69)$$

The constant in the denominator of Eq. (5-69) is required in order to convert the peak-to-peak values into rms power. The power *gain* is merely the product of Eqs. (5-67) and (5-68). The quantity r_i, which is the a-c input resistance, must be specified if the graphical voltage gain is to be used.

Example 5-17. The input resistance for the amplifier in Example 5-11 is 290 ohms. Calculate the current, voltage, and power gains. What is the output power with the input signal specified in Example 5-11?

Solution. The graphical analysis necessary for calculating the gains is shown in Fig. E5-17. The current gain is given by:

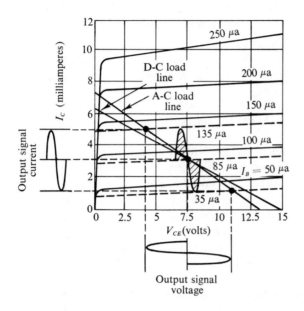

Figure E5-17

$$A_{iE} = \frac{i_{C(max)} - i_{C(min)}}{i_{B(max)} - i_{B(min)}} = \frac{(5.1 - 1.3)(10^{-3})}{(135 - 35)(10^{-6})}$$
$$= 38$$

The voltage gain is:

$$A_{vE} = \frac{v_{CE(max)} - v_{CE(min)}}{(i_{B(max)} - i_{B(min)})r_i} = \frac{11 - 4}{(135 - 35)(10^{-6})290}$$
$$= 241$$

The power gain is:

$$A_{pE} = A_{iE}A_{vE} = 38(241) = 9150$$

The output power can be determined directly by:

$$P_{\text{a-c}} = \frac{(i_{C(max)} - i_{C(min)})(v_{CE(max)} - v_{CE(min)})}{8}$$
$$= \frac{[(5.1 - 1.3)(10^{-3})](11 - 4)}{8} = 3.33 \text{ milliwatts}$$

It may also be determined indirectly by using the power gain and the input power:

$$P_{in} = i_I^2 r_i = \left[\frac{50 \times 10^{-6}}{1.414}\right]^2 (290) = 0.361 \text{ microwatt}$$

$$P_{a\text{-}c} = A_{pE}P_{in} = (1.305 \times 10^4)(3.61 \times 10^{-3})$$
$$= 3.31 \text{ milliwatts}$$

The two methods are in close agreement. As waveforms become more distorted, however, the error associated with the graphical determination of current, voltage, and power gain will increase.

5.9 Biasing Arrangements

As has been stated previously, transistors are *current operated devices;* i.e., the output current and voltage are controlled by the input current. Furthermore, the design procedures have stressed the importance of establishing the proper forward bias (d-c) current in order to achieve efficient and, where required, undistorted operation. The forward bias voltage, V_{IG}, required to produce adequate values of I_I is minute in most cases. Batteries of such small value as to be connected directly across the input elements (Figs. 5–14 and 5–16) are out of the realm of reality. It becomes necessary to utilize batteries of larger voltage rating in series with a biasing resistor (R_B in Fig. 5–27) of such a value as to establish the desired I_I [Eq. (5–45)].

All of the transistor amplifier circuits presented in this chapter have utilized *two bias voltage sources:* one for forward biasing; the second for reverse biasing. This *fixed biasing arrangement* is neither an efficient nor economic way to bias the amplifiers. In reality, a single source is achieved through a *self-biasing network.* The source is placed in the output loop, supplying the reverse bias voltage directly, and the network is arranged to provide the proper forward bias current and voltage to the input loop.

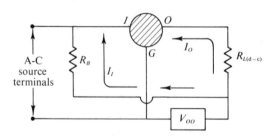

Figure 5-50.   *Self-Biasing Voltage Divider Network*

The resistor arrangement (voltage divider) shown in Fig. 5–50 is common. The resistor is very large, selected in accordance with:

$$R_B = \frac{V_{oo}}{I_I} \tag{5-70}$$

Because of this, almost the entire voltage, V_{oo}, is dropped across R_B; only a minute amount is dropped across the input junction as V_{IG}. The input junction resistance is so small with respect to R_B that it can be ignored.

A second self-biasing arrangement is shown in Fig. 5-51. This arrangement permits a small portion, I_I, of the output current, I_O, to be fed back to the input loop. Since V_{IG} is a negligible voltage, the voltage between the output terminal, O, and the input terminal, I, is essentially equal to V_{OG}. Hence:

$$R_F = \frac{V_{OG}}{I_I} \tag{5-71}$$

indicating that the operating point must be selected (through a d-c load line analysis) before R_F can be specified. In general, R_F is much larger than $R_{L(d-c)}$.

The economy and efficiency obtained through the use of self-biasing networks is not achieved in the sense of "getting something for nothing." The a-c operation is degraded somewhat through a loss of amplifier gain. The exact nature of this degradation is discussed in Chap. 6. Advantages other than the simple elimination of a bias battery are also obtained, however. These are discussed in subsequent chapters. In general, the advantages outnumber the disadvantages—leading to an almost universal application of self-biasing designs.

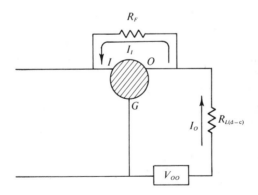

Figure 5-51.   *Common Feedback-Type Self-Biasing Network*

Example 5-18. The amplifier design specified in Example 5-10 uses two 15-volt power supplies with the input bias current (85 microamperes) controlled by a 177K biasing resistor. If only one power supply of 15 volts is to be retained in the circuit, what biasing resistor value must be used in a self-biasing voltage-divider network such as the one in Fig. 5–50? What biasing resistor value must be used in a feedback self-biasing network such as the one shown in Fig. 5–51?

Solution.   For the voltage-divider network:

$$R_B = \frac{V_{oo}}{I_B} = \frac{15}{85 \times 10^{-6}} = 177K$$

Hence, only the resistor connection needs to be changed (from the arrangement in Fig. 5–27 to the arrangement in Fig. 5–50). For the feedback network:

$$R_F = \frac{V_{CE}}{I_B} = \frac{7.6}{85 \times 10^{-6}} = 89.5K$$

where V_{CE} is obtained from the operating conditions desired in Example 5–10.

PROBLEMS

1. The emitter efficiency for a particular transistor is 0.97. The cutoff current is negligible. What is the forward current transfer ratio?
2. The cutoff current for a particular transistor is neglible. If the forward current transfer factor is to be 0.98, what fraction of the carriers emitted from the emitter to the base may undergo recombination during the transfer?
3. A particular line of transistors has a base-to-emitter junction resistance of 100 ohms, but each type in this line has a different forward current transfer ratio. A common base amplifier is to be built, with an a-c load of 2K and a power gain of 19. What value of forward current transfer ratio must be selected in order to achieve this design goal?
4. A particular transistor has a forward current transfer ratio of 42 when used in the common emitter configuration. What is the forward current transfer ratio in the common base and common collector configurations?
5. The transistor in Problem 4 is used in a common emitter amplifier with an a-c load of 10K. The base-to-emitter resistance is 50 ohms. What is the power gain for this amplifier?
6. Using the output conductance and input resistance characteristics for Transistor *B* in Appendix D, plot the common emitter reverse

voltage characteristics for a base current of 20, 60, and 100 micro-amperes. Plot the forward current transfer characteristic for the two collector-to-emitter voltages shown.

7. Using the output conductance and input resistance characteristics for Transistor *B* in Appendix D, plot the common collector reverse voltage transfer characteristics for a base current of 40 and 80 micro-amperes.

8. Using the characteristics for Transistor *B* in Appendix D and the additional characteristics developed in Problem 6, plot the four sets of characteristic curves for the common base configuration.

9. Transistor *E* in Appendix D is used in a common emitter amplifier with two 9-volt batteries as power supplies. An operating point with a base current of 90 microamperes, a collector current of 5 milliamperes, and a collector-to-emitter potential of 5 volts is desired. What biasing resistance and d-c load resistance must be used?

10. A common base amplifier with a 27-volt source in the output loop and a 9-volt source in the input loop has a d-c load resistance of 4.5K and a biasing resistance of 3K. Transistor *F* of Appendix D is used in the amplifier. Specify the operating point.

11. Transistor *C* in Appendix D is used in a common emitter amplifier with an 18-volt source in the output loop and a d-c resistance of 1.8K. The base biasing current is 8 milliamperes. Does such operation exceed the maximum dissipation power of the transistor?

12. Transistor *E* in Appendix D is to be used in a common emitter amplifier with a 9-volt source in the output loop. The amplifier is to be operated Class *A*. What is the minimum d-c load resistance that can be used without exceeding the maximum dissipation power? Specify the optimum Class *A* operating point for this d-c load.

13. The amplifier in Problem 5 uses RC coupling to drive a device with an equivalent resistance of 20K. What is the d-c load resistance used in the amplifier?

14. Transistor *F* in Appendix D is used in a common base amplifier with a 27-volt source in the output loop and a 9-volt source in the input loop. A biasing resistance of 3K is used. The amplifier is to be transformer coupled to a device having an equivalent resistance of 2K. The transformer turns ratio is 2:1. What is the a-c load resistance for the amplifier?

15. Transistor *C* in Appendix D is used in a common emitter amplifier with an operating point specified by a base current of 8 milliamperes, a collector current of 0.3 ampere, and a collector-to-emitter potential of 10 volts. The amplifier is transformer coupled to a device with an equivalent resistance of 10 ohms, using a turns ratio of 3:1. What

is the maximum input current that can be applied without overdriving the amplifier?

16. Transistor B in Appendix D is used in a common emitter amplifier. The amplifier is RC coupled to a device having an equivalent resistance of 2K. The amplifier uses a 9-volt source in the output loop and has an operating point specified by a base current of 60 microamperes, a collector current of 7 milliamperes, and a collector-to-emitter potential of 2.5 volts. An input signal with a peak current of 20 microamperes is applied. What is the efficiency of this amplifier?

17. What is the efficiency of the amplifier in Problem 15 when the maximum input current (for Class A operation) is applied?

18. Transistor A in Appendix D is used in an amplifier with an operating point specified by a base current of 0.6 microampere, a collector current of 1 milliampere, and a collector-to-emitter potential of 6 volts. The a-c load resistance is 3K. Calculate the total harmonic distortion for the amplifier when a peak-to-peak signal current of 0.8 microampere is applied.

19. An amplifier has a d-c output current of 5 milliamperes and a d-c load resistance of 3K. Harmonic analysis shonws that the fundamental and the second, third, and fourth harmonics, respectively, have an a-c power of 6 milliwatts, 0.3 milliwatt, 0.1 milliwatt, and 0.05 milliwatt. What is the efficiency of this amplifier?

20. What is the total harmonic distortion of the amplifier in Problem 19 if the a-c load resistance is 3K?

21. What is the total harmonic distortion of the amplifier in Problem 15 when the maximum input current (for Class A operation) is applied?

22. The amplifier in Problem 9 is RC coulped to a device with an equivalent resistance of 15K. A peak input signal of 90 millivolts is applied to the amplifier. What is the current, voltage, and power gain if the input resistance of the amplifier is 1500 ohms?

23. The amplifier in Problem 10 is RC coupled to a device with an equivalent resistance of 15K. A peak-to-peak signal current of 4 milliamperes is applied to the amplifier. What is the current, voltage, and power gain of the amplifier? What is the a-c power output? What peak signal voltage must be applied if the input resistance of the amplifier is 100 ohms?

24. What is the output power of the amplifier in Problem 15 when the maximum input current (for Class A operation) is applied?

25. What is the output power of the amplifier in Problem 16?

26. What is the current, voltage, and power gain of the amplifier in Problem 18?

27. Plot a curve depicting total harmonic distortion versus output power for the amplifier in Problem 18 using the applied peak signal current, but a variety of a-c load resistance values.

28. The amplifier in Problem 9 is to be biased with a single 9-volt supply in the output loop. The feedback network in Fig. 5–51 is to be used. What value of feedback resistance is needed?

29. In Problem 10, the voltage divider network of Fig. 5–50 is to be used with the 27-volt supply in the output loop. What value resistance must be used to achieve the same operating point?

30. The amplifier in Problem 12 must be forward biased with the feedback network of Fig. 5–51. What value resistance must be used to achieve the optimum Class *A* operating point?

Further Reading

"Basic Theory and Applications of Transistors" TM11-690. Washington, D.C.: U.S. Government Printing Office, 1959.

Cleary, J. F. (ed.), *General Electric Transistor Manual.* Syracuse, N.Y.: General Electric Company, Semiconductor Products Department, 1964.

Martin, T. L., Jr., *Electronic Circuits.* Englewood Cliffs, N.J.: Prentice-Hall, Inc., 1955.

Pierce, J. F., *Transistor Circuit Theory and Design.* Columbus, Ohio: Charles E. Merrill Books, Inc., 1963.

Ryder, J. D., *Electronic Fundamentals and Applications.* Englewood Cliffs, N.J.: Prentice-Hall, Inc., 1959.

Seidman, A. H. and S. L. Marshall, *Semiconductor Fundamentals.* New York: John Wiley and Sons, Inc., 1963.

Surina, T. and C. Herrick, *Semiconductor Electronics.* New York: Holt, Rinehart, and Winston, Inc., 1964.

6

Small-Signal Class *A* Audio-Frequency Amplifier Analysis

Although the graphical analysis of transistor amplifiers yields a great deal of insight into actual device and circuit operation, the most detailed analysis is obtained with a fictitious network of resistors, voltage generators, and current generators in the place of the transistor. Such an approach to the analysis of an electronic device is called *equivalent circuit analysis.* An equivalent circuit is a mathematical tool, and must be treated as such. There are many possible equivalent circuits for the transistor—some based on the physical characteristics of the device; others based on the terminal electrical characteristics. A complete discussion of electrical equivalent circuits is beyond the scope of this text. The intent of this chapter is to present and utilize the transistor equivalent obtained through an application of these "black box" theories to the transistor.

One of the primary requirements associated with the development of an equivalent circuit is that the device be *linear* in its operating characteristics. Since the transistor is *nonlinear*, the application may appear to be misplaced. Over certain ranges of operation, however, the transistor *is a linear device* as can be seen by examining the characteristic curves of Chap. 5. Hence, an immediate restriction arises for this mathematical tool:

operation must be Class A, and the signal amplitudes must be small enough to maintain operation over a linear region. Since every transistor has different characteristics, the definition of "small signal" is somewhat ambiguous. Since the a-c load resistance controls the linearity boundaries for a specific amplifier, the selection of this resistance (as discussed in Chap. 5) will also affect the limits associated with the "small signal."

One of the most direct equivalent circuits for the transistor is shown in Fig. 6–1. This circuit is easily understood on the basis of the transistor's physical characteristics: r_{BE} is the base-emitter junction resistance, r_B is the ohmic resistance of the base region, r_C is the high resistance of the collector-to-base junction, and the current generator represents the current transfer phenomena. An analysis of current gain, voltage gain, and power gain for the circuit in Fig. 6–1 will yield exactly the same equations presented in Chap. 5 [Eqs. (5–24) through (5–38)]. Since it is impossible to obtain values for r_{BE}, r_B, and r_C by direct measurement, manufacturer's specifications do not provide them. Indirect measurement of the values are subject to considerable error. For these reasons, the equivalent T-circuit is inadequate for analytical purposes.

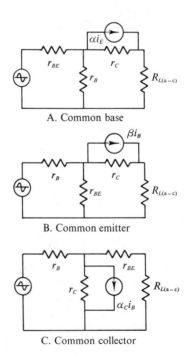

A. Common base

B. Common emitter

C. Common collector

Figure 6-1.   *T-Equivalent for Transistor*

The equivalent circuit that has been almost universally adopted uses the four basic transistor characteristics: input resistance, forward current transfer factor, reverse voltage transfer factor, and output conductance, defined in Chap. 5. These characteristics represent a resistance, a current ratio, a voltage ratio, and a conductance—a mixture of quantities, or parameters. For this reason, the resulting circuit is termed the *hybrid equivalent* and its components are referred to as the *hybrid*, or *h-parameters*. The *h*-parameters, as derived from the characteristic curves, represent the slope of the curves. This implies that a small increment of the dependent and independent variables is associated with the *h*-parameters, as shown in Fig. 6–2. This may be entirely different from the static values associated

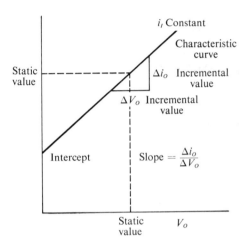

Figure 6-2.   *Definition of Hybrid Parameter as Slope of a Linear Characteristic*

with the same region of the curve (also shown in the figure). Since static values represent d-c conditions, and incremental changes are associated with a-c conditions, the hybrid equivalent circuit represents *an* a-c *equivalent circuit*. For this reason, only the a-c circuit components will be discussed throughout this chapter. Although the d-c load, the batteries, and any other d-c components will not be shown in the subsequent figures, the reader must realize that the proper d-c bias conditions *must exist*. This is an additional requirement associated with equivalent circuit analysis. The appropriate values for d-c operation can only be obtained through the *graphical analysis* procedures of Chap. 5.

Although the passive components of the equivalent circuits will be presented as purely resistive components in most cases, transistor behavior is frequency dependent because of the junction capacitances (Chaps. 4 and 5). Amplifier circuit components external to the transistor also have a frequency-dependent behavior. This should be obvious from the fact that capacitors and inductors are used in the various coupling networks. Although the most serious degradations occur at radio frequencies, even the full range of audio frequencies (approximately 20 cps to 20 kcps) produces severe changes in operation for some of the amplifier configurations.

Many other parameters, beside the hybrid and the resistance parameters, also exist, and are frequently used to construct transistor equivalent circuits. Although these are not discussed in detail in this text, Appendix E presents a summary of these parameters and their relationship to the hybrid parameters.

6.1 The Hybrid Parameters and Equivalent Circuits

TABLE 6-1

General Transistor Characteristic Relationships

Variable	Constant
I_O vs I_I	V_{OG}
I_O vs V_{OG}	I_I
V_{IG} vs I_I	V_{OG}
V_{IG} vs V_{OG}	I_I

The generalized transistor is presented in Chap. 5 (Fig. 5–21), along with the generalized and specific configuration variables and constants (Table 5–2). The generalized variables and constants are repeated in Table 6–1, for convenience. Notice that the *dependent variables* are the output current, I_O, and input voltage, V_{IG}, while the *independent variables* are the input current, I_I, and output voltage, V_{OG}. Furthermore, each of the dependent variables depends on *both* independent variables if a specific value is to be established. This is why V_{OG} must be held constant while I_I is varied (to obtain I_O versus I_I), and I_I must be held constant while V_{OG} is varied (to obtain I_O versus V_{OG}). A similar statement can be made for V_{IG}, I_I, and V_{OG}. Mathematically, it is said that I_O and V_{IG} are *functions* of V_{OG} and I_I:

$$I_O = f_1(V_{OG}, I_I) \tag{6-1}$$

$$V_{IG} = f_2(V_{OG}, I_I) \tag{6-2}$$

The "functional" notation can best be described by taking a simple algebraic expression such as: $y = 2x + 3z$, or $y = f(x, z)$. Here, the function of x and z—$f(x, z)$—*is known*. It is: $2x + 3z$. In Eqs. (6–1) and (6–2), the *functional relationships are not known. The characteristic curves are a graphical representation of these functions.* It would be possible, through the summation of many exponential terms, to develop a fairly accurate equation for the graphical curves. This approach is necessary since the characteristics are nonlinear. However, the small-signal equivalent circuit is derived on the basis of "assumed" linearlity. This is a reasonable assumption *as long as the signal does not drive the transistor into a nonlinear region.*

A straight line can be represented by a simple algebraic equation:

$$y = \frac{\Delta y}{\Delta x} \cdot x + c \tag{6-3}$$

where $\Delta y / \Delta x$ is the slope of the line and c is the y-axis intercept (Fig. 6–2). If the general relationships in Table 6–1 are assumed to be linear, the equations in Table 6–2 are obtained. The special notation to indicate constant V_{OG} and I_I is noted along with the table. The total effect on I_O (and V_{IG}) requires two equations. However, for a specific dependent variable (I_O or V_{IG}, in this case), *any number* of linear equations may be added in order to obtain an equation for *the total effect.* Hence, Eqs. (6–1) and (6–2) become:

$$I_O = \frac{\Delta I_O}{\Delta I_I}\bigg|_{V_{OG}} \cdot I_I + \frac{\Delta I_O}{\Delta V_{OG}}\bigg|_{I_I} \cdot V_{OG} \tag{6-1a}$$

$$V_{IG} = \frac{\Delta V_{IG}}{\Delta I_I}\bigg|_{V_{OG}} \cdot I_I + \frac{\Delta V_{IG}}{\Delta V_{OG}}\bigg|_{I_I} \cdot V_{OG} \tag{6-2a}$$

TABLE 6-2

Linear Equations for Approximating General Transistor
Characteristic Relationships

$I_O = \dfrac{\Delta I_O}{\Delta I_I}\bigg|_{V_{OG}} \cdot I_I$	$I_O = \dfrac{\Delta I_O}{\Delta V_{OG}}\bigg|_{I_I} \cdot V_{OG}$
$V_{IG} = \dfrac{\Delta V_{IG}}{\Delta I_I}\bigg|_{V_{OG}} \cdot I_I$	$V_{IG} = \dfrac{\Delta V_{IG}}{\Delta V_{OG}}\bigg|_{I_I} \cdot V_{GO}$

Note: The vertical bar indicates that the subscript quantity
is to be constant while other quantities vary.

Since the quantities $(\Delta I_0/\Delta I_I)\,|\,V_{OG}$, and so on, merely represent the *slope* of the characteristic curves, and since the *h*-parameters are *defined* by these slopes, the *h*-parameters can be substituted directly into Eqs. (6–1a) and (6–2a). Furthermore, the equations are now a-c equations and can be written as:

$$i_o = h_{fG}i_I + h_{oG}v_{OG} \tag{6-1b}$$

$$v_{IG} = h_{iG}i_I + h_{rG}v_{OG} \tag{6-2b}$$

The double subscript on the *h*-parameters is used as an identification tag. The first subscript identifies a specific parameter: *f* denotes the forward current transfer parameter, *o* denotes the output conductance parameter, *i* denotes the input resistance parameter, and *r* denotes the reverse voltage transfer parameter. The second subscript identifies the circuit configuration: *G* for general, *B* for common base, *E* for common emitter, and *C* for common collector. The *h*-parameters are summarized in Table 6–3. As should be expected, since there are twelve sets of characteristic curves for a particular transistor, there are also twelve *h*-parameters: four for each of the three configurations. Since the characteristics for each of the configurations differ (see Figs. 5–23, 5–24, and 5–25), the *h*-parameters for each of the configurations *must have different values*.

TABLE 6-3

Summary of Hybrid Parameters

General Parameter	Parameter Name	CB Parameter	CE Parameter	CC Parameter
h_{fG}	Forward Current Transfer Parameter	h_{fB}	h_{fE}	h_{fC}
h_{iG}	Input Resistance Parameter	h_{iB}	h_{iE}	h_{iC}
h_{rG}	Reverse Voltage Transfer Parameter	h_{rB}	h_{rE}	h_{rC}
h_{oG}	Output Conductance Parameter	h_{oB}	h_{oE}	h_{oC}

Equation (6–1b) describes the output loop current for the transistor in terms of equivalent components. Equation (6–2b) describes the terminal

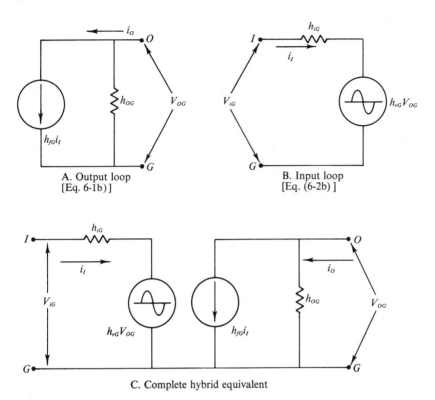

A. Output loop
[Eq. 6-1b)]

B. Input loop
[Eq. (6-2b)]

C. Complete hybrid equivalent

Figure 6-3.   *Synthesis of Hybrid Equivalent Circuit*

voltage for the input loop in terms of equivalent components. In view of this, it should be possible to draw an equivalent input and output loop and construct the transistor equivalent circuit. This is done in Fig. 6–3. The term $h_{fG}i_I$ in Eq. (6–1b) is produced by a *current generator*, while the term $h_{oG}v_{OG}$ is a passive current relationship (*parallel output conductance* times the voltage across it). This is shown as the output loop in Part A of the figure. The term $h_{rG}v_{OG}$ in Eq. (6–2b) is a *voltage generator*, while the $h_{iG}i_I$ term is a passive voltage relationship (*series input resistance* times the current through it). This is shown as the input loop in Part B. Since the two loops have a common ground point, they may be joined (Part C) to form the transistor equivalent circuits.

The development of the hybrid parameters and the equivalent circuit may appear to be artificial and unnecessary. It *is* artificial, in that it replaces the transistor with a nonexistent set of linear electrical components. It is far from unnecessary, however, as will be shown in subsequent sections. It offers a powerful tool for predicting the behavior of a transistor amplifier before it is built, and permits the establishment of general relationships showing trends in performance as various amplifier components are changed. Furthermore, the mathematical process has a much more rigorous foundation than that shown here. The process of deriving equivalent network equations and the associated circuits represents a branch of engineering known as *network synthesis*. The assumption of linearity may also be discarded if the more powerful techniques of calculus are applied. This, of course, is beyond the scope of this text.

It is not meant to imply that the equivalent circuit technique yields perfectly accurate results. The *h*-parameters, like the characteristic curves, may vary from one transistor to another, even though the transistors have the same identity.

Forward Current Transfer Parameter

The forward current transfer parameter is defined by:

$$h_{fG} = \left. \frac{\Delta I_0}{\Delta I_I} \right|_{V_{OG}} \tag{6-4}$$

The value can be determined directly from the forward current transfer characteristics, or indirectly from the output conductance characteristics. This is demonstrated in Fig. 6–4, Parts A and B, respectively, for the CE configuration. From Table 6–3 and Table 5–2, it is possible to show the analogous expressions for all three configurations:

$$h_{fB} = \left. \frac{\Delta I_C}{\Delta I_E} \right|_{V_{CB}} = \alpha \tag{6-4a}$$

$$h_{fE} = \left. \frac{\Delta I_C}{\Delta I_B} \right|_{V_{CE}} = \beta \tag{6-4b}$$

$$h_{fC} = \left. \frac{\Delta I_E}{\Delta I_B} \right|_{V_{EC}} = \alpha_c \tag{6-4c}$$

The extreme right-hand equality in these three equations indicates the identity between the hybrid current transfer parameters and the physical forward current transfer factors, as described in Chap. 5.

Example 6-1. Using the forward current transfer characteristics illustrated in Fig. 5–23, determine the value of h_{fB} for this transistor.

Solution. The parameter is given by:

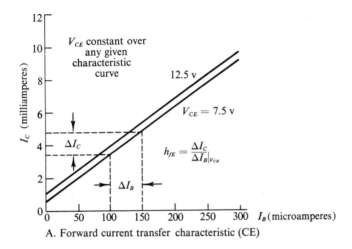

A. Forward current transfer characteristic (CE)

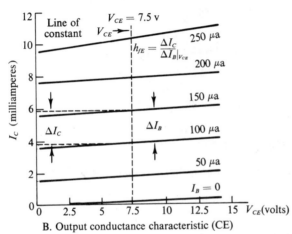

B. Output conductance characteristic (CE)

Figure 6-4.   *Graphical Determination of Forward Current Transfer Parameter*

$$h_{fB} = \frac{\Delta I_C}{\Delta I_E}\bigg|_{V_{CB}}$$

The two characteristics in Fig. 5–23, Part A are parallel. Therefore, the fixed value of V_{CB} may be either of the two shown. For V_{CB} equal to zero:

$$h_{fB} = \frac{(7.5 - 5)(10^{-3})}{(8.75 - 6)(10^{-3})} = \frac{2.5 \times 10^{-3}}{2.75 \times 10^{-3}} = 0.91$$

Because of the linearity of these characteristics, the actual specification of ΔI_C is arbitrary. The value of ΔI_E must, of course, correspond to the increment in I_C. The increment used in this example is shown in Fig. E6-1.

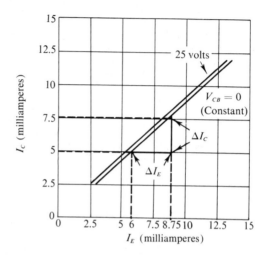

Figure E6-1

Output Conductance Parameter

The output conductance parameter is defined by:

$$h_{oG} = \left.\frac{\Delta I_o}{\Delta V_{OG}}\right|_{I_I} \tag{6-5}$$

The value can be determined directly from the output conductance characteristics, or indirectly from the forward current transfer characteristics. From Table 6-3 and Table 5-2, it is possible to show the analogous expressions for all three configurations:

$$h_{oB} = \left.\frac{\Delta I_C}{\Delta V_{CB}}\right|_{I_E} \tag{6-5a}$$

$$h_{oE} = \left.\frac{\Delta I_C}{\Delta V_{CE}}\right|_{I_B} \tag{6-5b}$$

$$h_{oC} = \left.\frac{\Delta I_E}{\Delta V_{EC}}\right|_{I_B} \tag{6-5c}$$

Example 6-2. Using the output conductance characteristics in Fig. 5–24, determine the value of h_{oE} for this transistor when the base current is 150 microamperes.

Solution. The parameter is given by:

$$h_{oE} = \frac{\Delta I_C}{\Delta V_{CE}}\bigg|_{I_B}$$

With I_B constant at 150 microamperes:

$$h_{oE} = \frac{(6 - 5.6)(10^{-3})}{13.75 - 2.5} = \frac{4 \times 10^{-4}}{11.25} = 35.5 \times 10^{-6} \text{ mho}$$

This increment is shown in Fig. E6–2. Since all the characteristics (except for I_B equal to 250 microamperes) are essentially parallel, this value of h_{oE} applies across most of the transistor operating region.

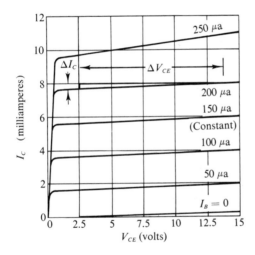

Figure E6-2

Input Resistance Parameter

The input resistance parameter is defined by:

$$h_{iG} = \frac{\Delta V_{IG}}{\Delta I_I}\bigg|_{V_{OG}} \tag{6-6}$$

The value can be determined directly from the input resistance characteristics, or indirectly from the reverse voltage transfer characteristics. From Table 6–3 and Table 5–2, it is possible to show the analogous expressions for all three configurations:

$$h_{iB} = \frac{\Delta V_{EB}}{\Delta I_E}\bigg|_{V_{CB}} \tag{6-6a}$$

$$h_{iE} = \frac{\Delta V_{BE}}{\Delta I_B}\bigg|_{V_{CE}} \tag{6-6b}$$

$$h_{iC} = \frac{\Delta V_{BC}}{\Delta I_B}\bigg|_{V_{EC}} \tag{6-6c}$$

Example 6-3.   Using the reverse voltage transfer characteristics in Fig. 5–23, determine the value of h_{iB} for this transistor in the vicinity of V_{CB} equal to 15 volts.

Solution.   The parameter is given by:

$$h_{iB} = \frac{\Delta V_{EB}}{\Delta I_E}\bigg|_{V_{CB}}$$

Determining the value from the reverse voltage transfer characteristic is an indirect way of specifying h_{iB}. The determination would

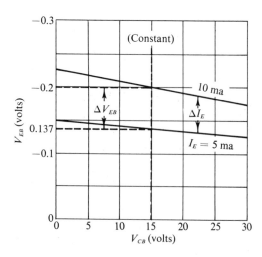

Figure E6-3

normally be made from the input resistance characteristics. However, in Fig. 5–23, Part D, with V_{CB} equal to 15 volts:

$$h_{iB} = \frac{0.2 - 0.137}{(10 - 5)(10^{-3})} = \frac{6.3 \times 10^{-2}}{5 \times 10^{-3}} = 12.6 \text{ ohms}$$

This increment is shown in Fig. E6–3. Since the two reverse voltage transfer characteristics are not parallel, h_{iB} will vary from point to point. In view of the nonlinearity in Fig. 5–23, Part C, such a variation is to be expected.

Reverse Voltage Transfer Parameter

The reverse voltage transfer parameter is defined by:

$$h_{rG} = \frac{\Delta V_{IG}}{\Delta V_{OG}}\bigg|_{I_I} \tag{6-7}$$

The value can be determined directly from the reverse voltage transfer characteristics, or indirectly from the input resistance characteristics. From Table 6–3 and Table 5–2, it is possible to show the analogous expressions for all three configurations:

$$h_{rB} = \frac{\Delta V_{EB}}{\Delta V_{CB}}\bigg|_{I_E} \tag{6-7a}$$

$$h_{rE} = \frac{\Delta V_{BE}}{\Delta V_{CE}}\bigg|_{I_B} \tag{6-7b}$$

$$h_{rC} = \frac{\Delta V_{BC}}{\Delta V_{EC}}\bigg|_{I_B} \tag{6-7c}$$

Example 6-4. Using the reverse voltage transfer characteristics in Fig. 5–25, determine the value of h_{rC} for this transistor.

Solution. The parameter is given by:

$$h_{rC} = \frac{\Delta V_{BC}}{\Delta V_{EC}}\bigg|_{I_B}$$

Since all three characteristics in Fig. 5–25, Part D are parallel, the selection of a fixed I_B-value is arbitrary. Using an I_B-value of 100 microamperes:

$$h_{rC} = \frac{20 - 15}{20 - 15} = \frac{5}{5} = 1$$

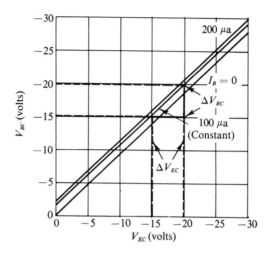

Figure E6-4

This value of one is, as a rule, a valid approximation for all common collector arrangements. The increment is shown in Fig. E6–4.

Hybrid Parameter Conversions and Comparisons

Manufacturers commonly specify h-parameters for the CB configuration, the CE configuration, or a mixture of the two. However, all four parameters are not, as a rule, specified. Rather, h_{fB} (or h_{fE}) and h_{iE} are usually given. The value of h_{oE} can be determined directly from the CE output conductance characteristics, which are usually given. Since Eqs. (6–4), (6–5), (6–6), and (6–7) provide four equations for four unknown quantities, it should be possible to calculate h_{rG}, given h_{iG}, h_{fG}, and h_{oG}:

$$h_{rG} = \frac{h_{iG}h_{oG}}{|h_{fG}|} \qquad (6\text{-}8)$$

Unfortunately, in practice, this turns out to be only an approximation for the CB and CE configurations, and does not hold true at all for the CC configuration:

$$h_{rB} \approx \frac{h_{iB}h_{oB}}{|h_{fB}|} \qquad (6\text{-}8a)$$

$$h_{rE} \approx \frac{h_{iE}h_{oE}}{|h_{fE}|} \qquad (6\text{-}8b)$$

$$h_{rC} \approx 1 \qquad (6\text{-}8c)$$

TABLE 6-4

Hybrid Parameter Conversion Equations

From **CB** to **CE**	From **CB** to **CC**
$h_{iE} = \dfrac{h_{iB}}{1 + h_{fB}}$	$h_{iC} = \dfrac{h_{iB}}{1 + h_{fB}}$
$h_{fE} = \dfrac{-h_{fB}}{1 + h_{fB}}$	$h_{fC} = \dfrac{-1}{1 + h_{fB}}$
$h_{rE} = \dfrac{h_{iB}h_{oB}}{1 + h_{fB}} - h_{rB}$	$h_{rC} = \dfrac{1 - h_{iB}h_{oB}}{1 + h_{fB}} + h_{rB}$
$h_{oE} = \dfrac{h_{oB}}{1 + h_{fB}}$	$h_{oC} = \dfrac{h_{oB}}{1 + h_{fB}}$
From **CE** to **CB**	From **CE** to **CC**
$h_{iB} = \dfrac{h_{iE}}{1 + h_{fE}}$	$h_{iC} = h_{iE}$
$h_{fB} = \dfrac{-h_{fE}}{1 + h_{fE}}$	$h_{fC} = -(1 + h_{fE})$
$h_{rB} = \dfrac{h_{iE}h_{oE}}{1 + h_{fE}} - h_{rE}$	$h_{rC} = 1$
$h_{oB} = \dfrac{h_{oE}}{1 + h_{fE}}$	$h_{oC} = h_{oE}$

TABLE 6-5

Example Values of Hybrid Parameters

Common Base	Common Emitter	Common Collector
$h_{iB} = 21.7$	$h_{iE} = 2410$	$h_{iC} = 2410$
$h_{fB} = -0.991$	$h_{fE} = 110$	$h_{fC} = -111$
$h_{rB} = 3.25 \times 10^{-4}$	$h_{rE} = 7.37 \times 10^{-4}$	$h_{rC} = 1$
$h_{oB} = 2.92 \times 10^{-7}$	$h_{oE} = 3.25 \times 10^{-5}$	$h_{oC} = 3.25 \times 10^{-5}$

Note: h_{fB} and h_{fC} must always be used as a negative quantity in order to make the design equations (to be derived) valid, and to maintain proper equivalent circuit phase relationships.

Chapter 5 contains a graphical technique for determining the sets of characteristic curves for two configurations when given the set for the third configuration. Since the *h*-parameters represent the slopes of linear approximations to the characteristic curves, it is reasonable to expect that the knowledge of one set of *h*-parameters should be sufficient to obtain the remaining two sets. Such a conversion *is* possible, as indicated in Table 6–4. In order to provide a "feel" for the relative values of the *h*-parameters for a particular transistor, Table 6–5 is presented. This is not to imply that all transistor *h*-parameters fall into these values—each transistor has its own distinctive set.

Example 6-5.   With the values for the *h*-parameters in Table 6–5, derive the value for h_{rE} when h_{iE}, h_{oE}, and h_{fE} are given.

Solution.   The approximation for h_{rE} is:

$$h_{rE} = \frac{h_{iE}h_{oE}}{|h_{fE}|} = \frac{(2.41 \times 10^3)(3.25 \times 10^{-5})}{110}$$

$$= \frac{7.85 \times 10^{-2}}{110} = 7.1 \times 10^{-4}$$

This is in close agreement with the h_{rE}-value specified in Table 6–5.

Example 6-6.   The *h*-parameters for a particular transistor are:

$$h_{iE} = 2000 \text{ ohms} \qquad h_{rE} = 5.5 \times 10$$
$$h_{fE} = 49 \qquad h_{oE} = 2.5 \times 10$$

Determine the common base parameter values.

Solution.   From Table 6–4, to convert from CE parameters to CB parameters:

$$h_{iB} = \frac{h_{iE}}{1 + h_{fE}} = \frac{2000}{1 + 49} = \frac{2000}{50} = 40 \text{ ohms}$$

$$h_{fB} = \frac{-h_{fE}}{1 + h_{fE}} = \frac{-49}{1 + 49} = \frac{-49}{50} = -0.98$$

$$h_{rB} = \frac{h_{iE}h_{oE}}{1 + h_{fE}} - h_{rE}$$

$$= \frac{(2 \times 10^3)(2.5 \times 10^{-5})}{1 + 49} - (5.5 \times 10^{-4})$$

$$= (10 - 5.5)(10^{-4}) = 4.5 \times 10^{-4}$$

$$h_{oB} = \frac{h_{oE}}{1 + h_{fE}} = \frac{2.5 \times 10^{-5}}{1 + 49} = \frac{2.5 \times 10^{-5}}{50} = 5 \times 10^{-7} \text{ mho}$$

6.2 Hybrid Equivalent Circuits

The hybrid equivalent for the transistor (Fig. 6–3) is analogous to the generalized transistor in Fig. 5–21. A generalized amplified circuit can be

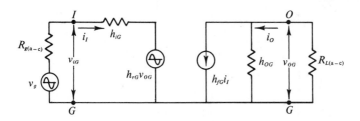

Figure 6-5.   *Generalized Hybrid Equivalent Transistor Amplifier*

constructed by adding the a-c load resistance and the a-c source resistance. This is shown in Fig. 6–5. The a-c load resistance may actually consist of several resistances in series or parallel combination, the resistance reflected through a transformer (see Figs. 5–36 and 5–37), or any number of electrical networks. The same is true of the a-c source resistance: it is the equivalent of any combination of components as seen from the terminals *I-G*, looking back toward the a-c source. (Examples are indicated in Fig. 6–6.)

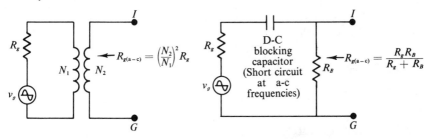

A. Transformer coupled input   B. Capacitor coupled input

Figure 6-6.   *Examples of Equivalent A-C Source Resistance*

The generalized amplifier circuit in Fig. 6–5 can be redrawn to represent any of the specific amplifier configurations by associating the generalized terminals with the specific terminals (Figs. 5–20 and 5–21) and arranging the a-c load and a-c source resistance in accordance with the basic designs (Fig. 5–13). The resulting a-c equivalent amplifier configurations are shown in Fig. 6–7.

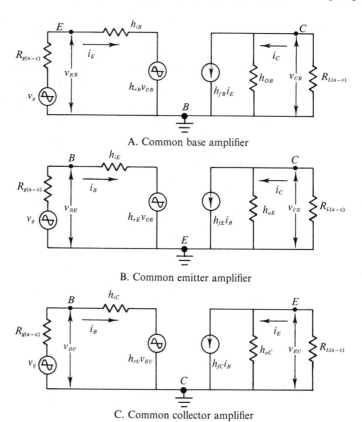

Figure 6-7. *Hybrid Equivalent Amplifier Configurations*

6.3 Design Equations

One of the fundamental reasons for synthesizing the transistor equivalent circuit is to permit the derivation of design equations for current gain, voltage gain, power gain, input resistance, and output resistance. These derivations will be performed for the generalized amplifier circuit (Fig. 6-5). However, the resulting equations can be converted to design equations for specific amplifier configurations *merely by substituting the appropriate h-parameters for the generalized parameters*. This is accomplished by consulting Table 6-3.

Current Gain

Current gain is defined as the ratio of a-c output current to a-c input current:

$$A_{iG} = \frac{i_o}{i_I} \tag{6-9}$$

Consideration of the output loop of the a-c equivalent circuit (Fig. 6–5) yields the Kirchoff current equation:

$$h_{fG}i_I + h_{oG}v_{OG} + i_O = 0 \tag{6-10}$$

This equation could be solved for i_O and the resulting expression could be substituted for i_O in Eq. (6–9). However, the resulting expression would contain i_I and v_{OG}—which is not a desirable expression, since the design equations should contain only h-parameters, $R_{L(a-c)}$, and $R_{g(a-c)}$. With this in mind, it is desirable to express v_{OG} in terms of a current. From Ohm's law:

$$v_{OG} = i_O R_{L(a-c)} \tag{6-11}$$

Substituting Eq. (6–11) for v_{OG} in Eq. (6–10) yields:

$$h_{fG}i_I + h_{oG}i_O R_{L(a-c)} + i_O = 0 \tag{6-10a}$$

or:

$$i_O(h_{oG}R_{L(a-c)} + 1) = -h_{fG}i_I \tag{6-10b}$$

Equation (6–10b) can be arranged as the ratio i_O/i_I, which, from Eq. (6–9), is the current gain:

$$A_{iG} = \frac{-h_{fG}}{h_{oG}R_{L(a-c)} + 1} \tag{6-9a}$$

Example 6-7. Calculate the current gain for a common emitter amplifier using the transistor described in Table 6–5. The d-c load resistor for the amplifier is 10K. The amplifier is RC coupled to a device with an equivalent resistance of 2K.

Solution. The current gain for the CE amplifier is given by:

$$A_{iE} = \frac{h_{fE}}{h_{oE}R_{L(a-c)} + 1}$$

For this amplifier the a-c load is:

$$R_{L(a-c)} = \frac{(10 \times 10^3)(2 \times 10^3)}{(10 + 2)(10^3)} = \frac{20 \times 10^6}{12 \times 10^3} = 1.67K$$

With the values from Table 6–5:

$$A_{iE} = \frac{-110}{(3.25 \times 10^{-5})(1.67 \times 10^3) + 1}$$

$$= \frac{-110}{1.054} = -104$$

Voltage Gain

By definition, the voltage gain is the ratio of a-c output voltage to a-c input voltage:

$$A_{vG} = \frac{v_{OG}}{v_{IG}} \qquad (6\text{-}12)$$

Equation (6–10), the output loop equation, may be used to derive an expression for V_{OG}. However, unlike the current gain derivation, it is now desirable to replace all current terms with the appropriate voltage terms. From Ohm's law:

$$i_O = \frac{v_{OG}}{R_{L(\text{a-c})}} \qquad (6\text{-}11a)$$

The input current may be rewritten in terms of v_{IG} by considering the voltage equation for the input loop (Fig. 6–5):

$$v_{IG} = h_{iG}i_I + h_{rG}v_{OG} \qquad (6\text{-}13)$$

or:

$$i_I = \frac{v_{IG} - h_{rG}v_{OG}}{h_{iG}} \qquad (6\text{-}13a)$$

When Eqs. (6–13a) and (6–11a) are substituted into Eq. (6–10), the following is obtained:

$$\frac{h_{fG}(v_{IG} - h_{rG}v_{OG})}{h_{iG}} + h_{oG}v_{OG} + \frac{v_{OG}}{R_{L(\text{a-c})}} = 0 \qquad (6\text{-}10c)$$

or:

$$v_{OG}\left[\frac{-h_{fG}h_{rG}}{h_{iG}} + h_{oG} + \frac{1}{R_{L(\text{a-c})}}\right] = \frac{-h_{fG}v_{IG}}{h_{iG}} \qquad (6\text{-}10d)$$

This is an inconvenient form, but yields:

$$A_{vG} = \frac{-h_{fG}}{h_{iG}}\left[\frac{1}{(-h_{fG}h_{rG}/h_{iG}) + h_{oG} + (1/R_{L(\text{a-c})})}\right] \qquad (6\text{-}12a)$$

when the ratio v_{OG}/v_{IG} is substituted into Eq. (6–12). The common denominator for the bracketed term yields:

$$A_{vG} = \frac{-h_{fG}}{h_{iG}}\left[\frac{h_{iG}R_{L(\text{a-c})}}{-h_{fG}h_{rG}R_{L(\text{a-c})} + h_{oG}h_{iG}R_{L(\text{a-c})} + h_{iG}}\right] \qquad (6\text{-}12b)$$

or:

$$A_{vG} = \frac{-h_{fG}R_{L(\text{a-c})}}{(h_{iG}h_{oG} - h_{fG}h_{rG})R_{L(\text{a-c})} + h_{iG}} \tag{6-12c}$$

The parenthetical quantity $(h_{iG}h_{oG} - h_{fG}h_{rG})$ appears in several of the design equations, and for convenience, has been assigned a special symbol:

$$\Delta h_G = h_{iG}h_{oG} - h_{fG}h_{rG} \tag{6-14}$$

which, when substituted into Eq. (6-12c), yields:

$$A_{vG} = \frac{-h_{fG}R_{L(\text{a-c})}}{\Delta h_G R_{L(\text{a-c})} + h_{iG}} \tag{6-12d}$$

Example 6-8.   Calculate the voltage gain for a common base amplifier using the transistor described in Example 6-6. Transformer coupling is used to feed a device with an equivalent resistance of 1K. The turns ratio is 2:1.

Solution.   The voltage gain for the CB amplifier is given by:

$$A_{vB} = \frac{-h_{fB}R_{L(\text{a-c})}}{\Delta h_B R_{L(\text{a-c})} + h_{iB}}$$

The quantity Δh_B is given by:

$$\Delta h_B = h_{iB}h_{oB} - h_{fB}h_{rB}$$

Using the values in Example 6-6 (for the common base configuration):

$$\Delta h_B = 40(5 \times 10^{-7}) - (-0.98)(4.5 \times 10^{-4})$$
$$= (0.21 + 4.4)(10^{-4}) = 4.61 \times 10^{-4}$$

The a-c load is:

$$R_{L(\text{a-c})} = \left(\frac{N_1}{N_2}\right)^2 R_S = 2^2(1 \times 10^3) = 4\text{K}$$

which leads to a voltage gain of:

$$A_{vB} = \frac{-(-0.98)(4 \times 10^3)}{(4.61 \times 10^{-4})(4 \times 10^3) + 40}$$
$$= \frac{3.92 \times 10^3}{41.8} = 94$$

Power Gain

Amplifier power gain is defined by the ratio of output power to input power:

$$A_{pG} = \frac{i_o v_{OG}}{i_I v_{IG}} = A_{iG} A_{vG} \tag{6-15}$$

Substituting Eqs. (6–9a) and (6–12d) yields:

$$A_{pG} = \frac{h_{fG}^2 R_{L(a-c)}}{(h_{oG} R_{L(a-c)} + 1)(\Delta h_G R_{L(a-c)} + h_{iG})} \tag{6-15a}$$

Example 6-9. What is the power gain of the amplifier in Example 6–7?

Solution. The power gain is given by Eq. (6–15a), or simply by the product of the voltage and current gains. Since the current gain is available in Example 6–7, the latter approach is preferred:

$$A_{vE} = \frac{-h_{fE} R_{L(a-c)}}{\Delta h_E R_{L(a-c)} + h_{iE}}$$

where:

$$\begin{aligned}
\Delta h_E &= h_{iE} h_{oE} - h_{fE} h_{rE} \\
&= 2410(3.25 \times 10^{-5}) - (110)(3.79 \times 10^{-4}) \\
&= (7.84 - 4.17)(10^{-2}) = 3.67 \times 10^{-2} \\
A_{vE} &= \frac{-110(1.67 \times 10^3)}{(3.67 \times 10^{-2})(1.67 \times 10^3) + 2410} \\
&= \frac{-(1.84 \times 10^5)}{2471} = -74.5
\end{aligned}$$

The power gain is:

$$A_{pE} = A_{iE} A_{vE} = (-104)(-74.5) = 7750$$

Input Resistance

The input resistance is the equivalent resistance at the terminals *I-G*, as shown in Fig. 6–8, Part A and can be used to replace the entire transistor, as loaded by $R_{L(a-c)}$ (Part B of the figure). By definition, then:

$$r_{iG} = \frac{v_{IG}}{i_I} \tag{6-16}$$

Equation (6–13) can be solved for v_{IG}/i_I directly:

$$\frac{v_{IG}}{i_I} = h_{iG} + \frac{h_{rG} v_{OG}}{i_I} \tag{6-16a}$$

It is necessary to obtain an expression for v_{OG}/i_I in terms of the *h*-parameters and $R_{L(a-c)}$. The output loop equation [(6–10)] can be manipulated to yield such a result. To begin with, Eq. (6–11a) is substituted for i_o and

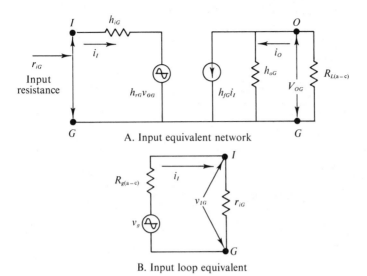

A. Input equivalent network

B. Input loop equivalent

Figure 6-8.   *Amplifier Input Resistance*

v_{OG} is factored out of the expression:

$$h_{fG}i_I + \left(h_{oG} + \frac{1}{R_{L(a-c)}}\right)v_{OG} = 0 \qquad \text{(6-10e)}$$

or:

$$\frac{v_{OG}}{i_I} = \frac{-h_{fG}}{h_{oG} + (1/R_{L(a-c)})} \qquad \text{(6-10f)}$$

When the last equation is substituted into Eq. (6–16a):

$$r_{iG} = h_{iG} - \frac{h_{fG}h_{rG}}{h_{oG} + (1/R_{L(a-c)})} \qquad \text{(6-16b)}$$

If the two terms in the denominator are placed over a common denominator, $R_{L(a-c)}$, and, then, if the entire right side of the equation is placed over the common denominator, $h_{oG}R_{L(a-c)} + 1$, the numerator may be factored in such a manner that the equation will simplify to:

$$r_{iG} = \frac{h_{iG} + \Delta h_G R_{L(a-c)}}{h_{oG}R_{L(a-c)} + 1} \qquad \text{(6-16c)}$$

Example 6-10.   Calculate the input resistance for a common collector amplifier using the transistor described in Table 6–5. The equivalent a-c load on the amplifier is 80K.

Solution.   The input resistance is given by:

$$r_{iC} = \frac{h_{iC} + \Delta h_C R_{L(a-c)}}{h_{oC} R_{L(a-c)} + 1}$$

where (with values from Table 6–5):

$$\Delta h_C = h_{iC} h_{oC} - h_{fC} h_{rC} = 2410(3.25 \times 10^{-5}) - (-111)(1) = 111$$

$$r_{iC} = \frac{2410 + (111)(8 \times 10^4)}{(3.25 \times 10^{-5})(8 \times 10^4) + 1} = \frac{8.88 \times 10^4}{3.6} = 2.46\text{M}$$

Output Resistance

The output resistance is the equivalent resistance at the terminals
O-G, as shown in Fig. 6–9, Part A, and can be used to replace the entire
transistor, with $R_{g(a-c)}$ in the input loop (Part B of the figure). By definition,
then:

$$r_{oG} = \frac{v_{oG}}{i_o} \tag{6-17}$$

Deriving the ratio v_{oG}/i_o in terms of the loop equations for Fig. 6–5 requires
considerable manipulation of the circuit, using Thevenin's voltage generator theorem and the superposition theorem. A more direct approach
consists of using the general a-c equations [(7–1b) and (7–2b)] along with

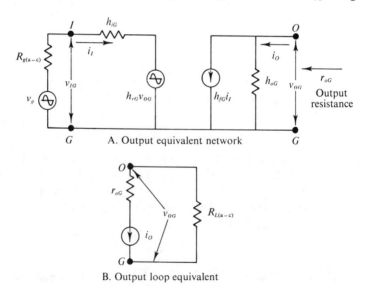

A. Output equivalent network

B. Output loop equivalent

Figure 6-9.   *Amplifier Output Resistance*

the relationship:

$$v_{IG} = -i_I R_{g(\text{a-c})} \tag{6-18}$$

obtained from Fig. 6–5. Substituting Eq. (6–18) into Eq. (6–2b) yields:

$$-i_I R_{g(\text{a-c})} = h_{iG} i_I + h_{rG} v_{OG} \tag{6-2c}$$

or:

$$-h_{rG} v_{OG} = (h_{iG} + R_{g(\text{a-c})}) i_I \tag{6-2d}$$

or:

$$i_I = \frac{-h_{rG} v_{OG}}{h_{iG} + R_{g(\text{a-c})}} \tag{6-2e}$$

Substituting Eq. (6–2e) into Eq. (6–1b) yields:

$$i_O = \frac{-h_{fG} h_{rG} v_{OG}}{h_{iG} + R_{g(\text{a-c})}} \tag{6-1c}$$

or:

$$i_O = \left[\frac{-h_{fG} h_{rG}}{h_{iG} + R_{g(\text{a-c})}} + h_{oG} \right] v_{OG} \tag{6-1d}$$

from which the ratio v_{OG}/i_O can be obtained and substituted into Eq. (6–17):

$$r_{oG} = \frac{1}{\{-h_{fG} h_{rG}/(R_{g(\text{a-c})} + h_{iG})\} + h_{oG}} \tag{6-17a}$$

This equation can be manipulated by finding a succession of common denominators, factoring, and substituting, to yield:

$$r_{oG} = \frac{R_{g(\text{a-c})} + h_{iG}}{\Delta h_G + h_{oG} R_{g(\text{a-c})}} \tag{6-17b}$$

which is the final "simplified" expression.

Example 6-11. What is the output resistance of the amplifier described in Example 6–8 if the source resistance is 500 ohms and the input biasing resistor is 80K?

Solution. The output resistance is given by:

$$r_{oB} = \frac{R_{g(\text{a-c})} + h_{iB}}{\Delta h_B + h_{oB} R_{g(\text{a-c})}}$$

The a-c source resistance is the parallel combination of 500 ohms and 80K or, approximately, 500 ohms. The value for Δh_B can be obtained from Example 6–8:

$$r_{oB} = \frac{500 + 40}{(4.61 \times 10^{-4}) + (5 \times 10^{-7})(5 \times 10^{2})}$$

$$= \frac{540}{7.11 \times 10^{-4}} = 760\text{K}$$

Design Comparisons and Approximations

The general design equations are summarized in Table 6–6. By consulting Table 6–3, the h-parameters for specific configurations can be obtained. Substituting these into the general equations yields the three sets of design equations required for specific amplifier design, as listed in Table 6–7. Although a great deal of insight toward understanding amplifier operation is gained by using the graphical analyses of Chap. 5, an even greater appreciation of amplifier performance ranges can be obtained by plotting the equations in Table 6–7 as $R_{L(\text{a-c})}$ and $R_{g(\text{a-c})}$ are varied. This is accomplished in Figs. 6–10 through 6–14 for a transistor having the h-parameter values listed in Table 6–5.

TABLE 6-6

Generalized Hybrid Design Equations

Design Characteristic	Design Equation
A_{iG}	$\dfrac{-h_{fG}}{h_{oG}R_{L(\text{a-c})} + 1}$
A_{vG}	$\dfrac{-h_{fG}R_{L(\text{a-c})}}{\Delta h_G R_{L(\text{a-c})} + h_{iG}}$
A_{pG}	$\dfrac{h_{fG}^2 R_{L(\text{a-c})}}{(h_{oG}R_{L(\text{a-c})} + 1)(\Delta h_G R_{L(\text{a-c})} + h_{iG})}$
r_{iG}	$\dfrac{h_{iG} + \Delta h_G R_{L(\text{a-c})}}{h_{oG}R_{L(\text{a-c})} + 1}$
r_{oG}	$\dfrac{R_{g(\text{a-c})} + h_{iG}}{\Delta h_G + h_{oG}R_{g(\text{a-c})}}$

$\Delta h_G = h_{iG}h_{oG} - h_{fG}h_{rG}$

The current gain for the CB configuration remains constant (at h_{fG}) until extremely high load resistances are attached (Fig. 6–10). The CE and CC configurations are much more sensitive to load variations—but even these current gains remain constant over a wide range of practical resistance values. Hence, the approximation:

$$A_{iG} \approx -h_{fG} \qquad \textbf{(6-19)}$$

In Fig. 6–11, it can be seen that the CC voltage gain is one for all practical load resistance values, since high loads are always used with this circuit. Furthermore, over most of the practical CE and CB load

TABLE 6-7

Hybrid Design Equations for the Three Transistor Amplifier Configurations

Design Equations

Design Characteristics	Common Base	Common Emitter	Common Collector
Current Gain	$\dfrac{-h_{fB}}{h_{oB}R_{L(a\text{-}c)}+1}$	$\dfrac{-h_{fE}}{h_{oE}R_{L(a\text{-}c)}+1}$	$\dfrac{-h_{fC}}{h_{oC}R_{L(a\text{-}c)}+1}$
Voltage Gain	$\dfrac{-h_{fB}R_{L(a\text{-}c)}}{\Delta h_B R_{L(a\text{-}c)}+h_{iB}}$	$\dfrac{-h_{fE}R_{L(a\text{-}c)}}{\Delta h_E R_{L(a\text{-}c)}+h_{iE}}$	$\dfrac{-h_{fC}R_{L(a\text{-}c)}}{\Delta h_C R_{L(a\text{-}c)}+h_{iC}}$
Power Gain	$\dfrac{h_{fB}^2 R_{L(a\text{-}c)}}{(h_{oB}R_{L(a\text{-}c)}+1)(\Delta h_B R_{L(a\text{-}c)}+h_{iB})}$	$\dfrac{h_{fE}^2 R_{L(a\text{-}c)}}{(h_{oE}R_{L(a\text{-}c)}+1)(\Delta h_E R_{L(a\text{-}c)}+h_{iE})}$	$\dfrac{h_{fC}^2 R_{L(a\text{-}c)}}{(h_{oC}R_{L(a\text{-}c)}+1)(\Delta h_C R_{L(a\text{-}c)}+h_{iC})}$
Input Resistance	$\dfrac{h_{iB}+\Delta h_B R_{L(a\text{-}c)}}{h_{oB}R_{L(a\text{-}c)}+1}$	$\dfrac{h_{iE}+\Delta h_E R_{L(a\text{-}c)}}{h_{oE}R_{L(a\text{-}c)}+1}$	$\dfrac{h_{iC}+\Delta h_C R_{L(a\text{-}c)}}{h_{oC}R_{L(a\text{-}c)}+1}$
Output Resistance	$\dfrac{R_{g(a\text{-}c)}+h_{iB}}{\Delta h_B + h_{oB}R_{g(a\text{-}c)}}$	$\dfrac{R_{g(a\text{-}c)}+h_{iE}}{\Delta h_E + h_{oE}R_{g(a\text{-}c)}}$	$\dfrac{R_{g(a\text{-}c)}+h_{iC}}{\Delta h_C + h_{oC}R_{g(a\text{-}c)}}$
	$\Delta h_B = h_{iB}h_{oB} - h_{fB}h_{rB}$	$\Delta h_E = h_{iE}h_{oE} - h_{fE}h_{rE}$	$\Delta h_C = h_{iC}h_{oC} - h_{fC}h_{rC}$

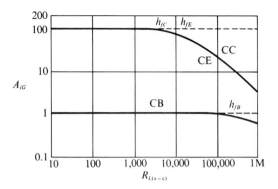

Figure 6-10.   *Current Gain Variation* (John F. Pierce, *Transistor Circuit Theory and Design*, 1963. Courtesy Charles E. Merrill.)

values, the voltage gain can be approximated by:

$$A_{vG} \approx \frac{-h_{fG}R_{L(a\text{-}c)}}{h_{iG}} \qquad (6\text{-}20)$$

The power gain curves follow the parabolic curves shown in Fig. 6-12. There is no good approximation for CC power gain. The CE and CB power gain may be approximated by:

$$A_{pG} \approx \frac{h_{fG}^2 R_{L(a\text{-}c)}}{h_{iG}} \qquad (6\text{-}21)$$

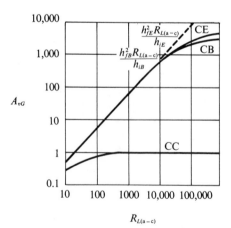

Figure 6-11.   *Voltage Gain Variation* (John F. Pierce, *Transistor Circuit Theory and Design*, 1963. Courtesy Charles E. Merrill.)

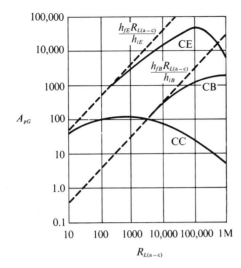

Figure 6-12.   *Power Gain Variation* (John F. Pierce, *Transistor Circuit Theory and Design*, 1963. Courtesy Charles E. Merrill.)

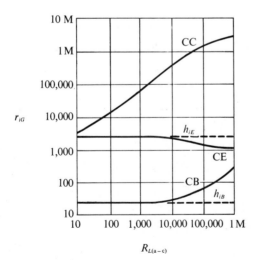

Figure 6-13.   *Input Resistance Variation* (John F. Pierce, *Transistor Circuit Theory and Design*, 1963. Courtesy Charles E. Merrill.)

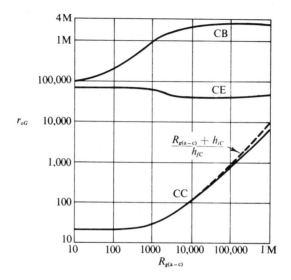

Figure 6-14.   *Output Resistance Variation* (John F. Pierce, *Transistor Circuit Theory and Design*, 1963. Courtesy Charles E. Merrill.)

TABLE 6-8

Approximate Hybrid Design Equations for the Three Transistor Amplifier Configurations

Design Characteristic	Approximate Design Equations		
	Common Base	*Common Emitter*	*Common Collector*
Current Gain	$-h_{fB}$	$-h_{fE}$	$-h_{fC}$
Voltage Gain	$\dfrac{-h_{fB}R_{L(\text{a-c})}}{h_{iB}}$	$\dfrac{-h_{fE}R_{L(\text{a-c})}}{h_{iE}}$	1
Power Gain	$\dfrac{h_{fB}^2 R_{L(\text{a-c})}}{h_{iB}}$	$\dfrac{h_{fE}^2 R_{L(\text{a-c})}}{h_{iE}}$	None
Input Resistance	h_{iB}	h_{iE}	None
Output Resistance	None	None	$\dfrac{R_{g(\text{a-c})} + h_{iC}}{-h_{fC}}$

However, this approximation fits the CB configuration better than the CE cofiguration.

The input resistance for CB and CE configurations may be approximated by:

$$r_{iG} \approx h_{iG} \tag{6-22}$$

as shown in Fig. 6–13. No good approximation exists for the CC configuration. The variability in output resistance (Fig. 6–14) is sufficient to preclude any good approximations, except for the CC configuration:

$$r_{oC} \approx \frac{R_{g(\text{a-c})} + h_{iC}}{-h_{fC}} \tag{6-23}$$

Table 6–8 summarizes the approximate design equations. These approximations must be used with considerable caution, since they are valid only over certain ranges of $R_{L(\text{a-c})}$ and $R_{g(\text{a-c})}$. These approximations compare very well with the approximations indicated early in Chap. 5.

Example 6-12. Calculate the desired quantities for Examples 6–7, 6–8, and 6–9, using the approximate equations of Table 6–8. Compare results.

Solution. For Example 6–7:

$$A_{iE} \approx -h_{fE} = -110 \qquad [-104]$$

For Example 6–8:

$$A_{vB} \approx \frac{-h_{fB}R_{L(\text{a-c})}}{h_{iB}} = \frac{-(-0.98)(4 \times 10^3)}{40}$$

$$= \frac{3.92 \times 10^3}{40} = 97.2 \qquad [94]$$

For Example 6–9:

$$A_{pE} \approx \frac{h_{fE}^2 R_{L(\text{a-c})}}{h_{iE}} = \frac{(-110)^2(1.67 \times 10^3)}{2410}$$

$$= \frac{2.02 \times 10^7}{2410} = 8390 \qquad [7750]$$

The bracketed quantities indicate answers obtained in the previous examples. It can be seen that the approximations can only be used as a rough estimate. However, since transistors vary considerably from their specified *h*-parameters in any case, these rough approximations are adequate in many instances and save considerable computation.

6.4 Maximum Power Transfer Conditions

The conditions for maximum power transfer are discussed in Chap. 5 [Fig. 5–41, Eqs. (5–53), (5–54), and associated text]. Under matched conditions (with $R_{g(\text{a-c})}$ equal to r_{iG} and $R_{L(\text{a-c})}$ equal to r_{oG}), an amplifier will achieve its maximum possible power gain. The necessary values for $R_{g(\text{a-c})}$ and $R_{L(\text{a-c})}$ can be derived in terms of the transistor h-parameters only.

The general expression for r_{iG} is given by Eq. (6–16c). However, if the amplifier is matched, r_{oG} can be substituted for $R_{L(\text{a-c})}$ in the equation, and Eq. (6–17b) can be substituted for r_{oG}. This results in a rather complex expression containing only $R_{g(\text{a-c})}$ and the transistor h-parameters. With considerable algebraic manipulation and some appropriate approximations, the expression:

$$R_{g(\text{a-c})} = h_{iG}\sqrt{1 - \frac{h_{fG}h_{rG}}{h_{iG}h_{oG}}} \qquad (6\text{--}24)$$

can be obtained. A similar approach can be taken in order to develop an expression for $R_{L(\text{a-c})}$, which must be equal to r_{oG}. In its final form, this is given by:

$$R_{L(\text{a-c})} = \frac{1}{h_{oG}\sqrt{1 - \dfrac{h_{fG}h_{rG}}{h_{iG}h_{oG}}}} \qquad (6\text{--}25)$$

Notice that the expression under the radical sign is the same in both equations. Equations (6–24) and (6–25) specify the $R_{g(\text{a-c})}$- and $R_{L(\text{a-c})}$-values that *must be used if a transistor amplifier is to be a matched amplifier.* They do not, however, assure that such values can be achieved in a particular amplifier design. Distortion, coupling network arrangement, and actual source resistance, R_g, must be taken into consideration. In general, it is easier to obtain matched conditions with transformer coupling (by selecting the proper turns ratio) than with any other coupling arrangement.

If the matched conditions *can be achieved in a practical amplifier design,* the maximum possible power gain for the amplifier is obtained:

$$A_{pG(\text{max})} = \frac{h_{fG}^2}{h_{iG}h_{oG}\left[1 + \sqrt{1 - \dfrac{h_{fG}h_{rG}}{h_{iG}h_{oG}}}\,\right]^2} \qquad (6\text{--}26)$$

The penalty suffered by *not being able to match* can be obtained by comparing the value of Eq. (6–26) (for the transistor in question) with the actual power gain that is predicted for the unmatched condition [Eq. (6–15a) or its approximate form].

Equations (6–24), (6–25), and (6–26) are perfectly general. They can be made to apply to the specific amplifier configurations simply by substituting the specific h-parameters for the general parameters (from Table 6-3).

Example 6-13. What a-c load and source resistances must be used in Example 6-9 in order to achieve matching? What power gain will be achieved if matching is accomplished?

Soltuion. The necessary a-c source resistance is:

$$R_{g\text{(a-c)}} = h_{iE}\sqrt{1 - \frac{h_{fE}h_{rE}}{h_{iE}h_{oE}}} = 2410\sqrt{1 - \frac{110(3.79 \times 10^{-4})}{2410(3.25 \times 10^{-5})}}$$

$$= 2410\sqrt{1 - 0.533} = 2410\sqrt{0.467} = 2410(0.684)$$

$$= 1650 \text{ ohms}$$

The necessary a-c load resistance is:

$$R_{L\text{(a-c)}} = \frac{1}{h_{oE}\sqrt{1 - \dfrac{h_{fE}h_{rE}}{h_{iE}h_{oE}}}} = \frac{1}{(3.25 \times 10^{-5})(0.684)}$$

$$= \frac{1}{2.22 \times 10^{-5}} = 45\text{K}$$

With such a design, the power gain will be an absolute maximum value, given by:

$$A_{pE\text{(max)}} = \frac{h_{fE}^2}{h_{iE}h_{oE}\left[1 + \sqrt{1 - \dfrac{h_{fE}h_{rE}}{h_{iE}h_{oE}}}\right]^2}$$

$$= \frac{(110)^2}{2410(3.25 \times 10^{-5})[1 + 0.684]^2} = \frac{1.21 \times 10^4}{2.23 \times 10^{-1}}$$

$$= 54,300$$

The gain achieved in Example 6-9 is 7750. However, the a-c load resistance is only 1.67K, compared to the required 45K. The price of this major mismatch is obvious. However, other considerations such as operating point, distortion, etc. may prevent matching. Even the design of the circuit itself may prevent matching.

6.5 Variation of Parameters

The h-parameters are assumed to be constant within the basic definition of the hybrid equivalent circuit. The condition that this method of analysis be employed only for small-signal amplifiers assures that this constancy will be reasonably maintained. Since the transistor characteris-

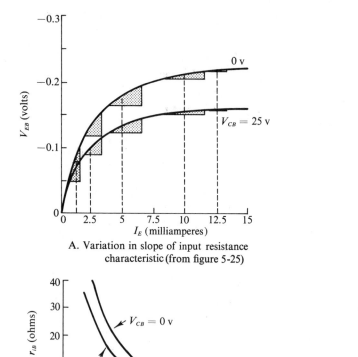

A. Variation in slope of input resistance characteristic (from figure 5-25)

B. Parameter variation

Figure 6-15.   *Variation of Input Resistance Parameter in* CB *Configuration*

tics (Figs. 5–23, 5–24, and 5–25) are not all linear over the entire range of operation, the *h*-parameters *cannot be true constants.* Figure 6–15, Part A illustrates this fact by presenting the slope at several points along a CB input resistance characteristic. If the incremental values, ΔI_E and ΔV_{EB}, are made very small, and the slope is determined at a large number of points, a continuous curve for h_{iB} versus I_E (or V_{EB}) can be obtained (Part B of the figure). Since the input resistance characteristic changes as V_{CB} changes (see Fig. 5–23, Part C), h_{iB} also must change as a function of V_{CB}. Once the variation of a parameter has been obtained for one configuration, it can be determined for the other configurations by using the relationships in Table 6–4.

Curves for *h*-parameter variation can, in general, be obtained from the manufacturer. A typical set is shown in Fig. 6–16. These curves are

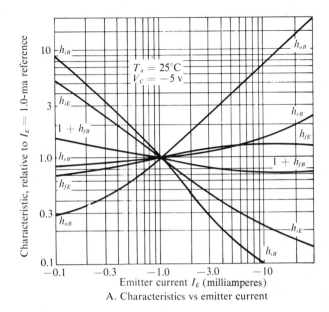

A. Characteristics vs emitter current

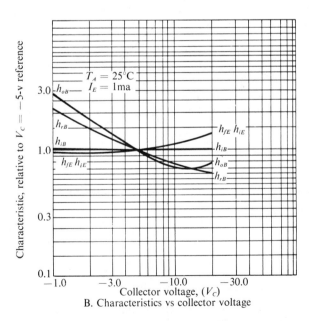

B. Characteristics vs collector voltage

Figure 6-16. *Variation of Hybrid Parameters with Operating (Bias) Conditions (GE Transistor Manual,* 1964. Courtesy General Electric, Semiconductor Products Department)

normalized; that is, they are specified with respect to the *h*-parameter values *at a particular operating point* ($I_E = 1$ ma with collector voltage variable and $V_C = 5$ volts with emitter current variable). Hence, the actual *h*-parameter values associated with this point must be specified separately. The reference point is usually chosen as the one most commonly used (or the manufacturer's recommended use) with the subject transistor, however, and is the point where the specified *h*-parameters would be measured. Notice, also, that the temperature is specified in Fig. 6–16. At other temperatures, the *h*-parameter variation (and absolute values) would be entirely different. This is to be expected, in view of the temperature-sensitive microscopic phenomena described in previous chapters.

Access to the *h*-parameter variation curves assist the circuit designer in two ways: they provide a means of calculating the *h*-parameter values at an operating point other than the one recommended by the manufacturer; and they provide an indication of how large the "small-signal" may be before serious changes in the *h*-parameter values will occur.

Example 6-14.   With I_E established at 1 milliampere, what are the *h*-parameters for the transistor illustrated in Fig. 6–16 when the collector voltage is -10 volts? Assume that the reference values are as specified in Example 6–6.

Solution.   The actual parameter value is given by:

actual value = normalized value × reference value

From Example 6–6, the reference values are:

$$h_{iE} = 2000 \text{ ohms}$$
$$h_{fE} = 49$$
$$h_{rE} = 5.5 \times 10^{-4}$$
$$h_{oE} = 2.5 \times 10^{-5} \text{ mho}$$

From Fig. 6–16, Part B, the normalized values are:

$$h_{iE} = 1.1$$
$$h_{fE} = 1.1$$
$$h_{rE} = 0.78$$
$$h_{oE} = 0.75$$

The actual values at the new operating point are:

$$h_{iE} = 2000(1.1) = 2200 \text{ ohms}$$
$$h_{fE} = 49(1.1) = 54$$
$$h_{rE} = (5.5 \times 10^{-4})(0.78) = 4.3 \times 10^{-4}$$
$$h_{oE} = (2.5 \times 10^{-5})(0.75) = 1.88 \times 10^{-5} \text{ mho}$$

6.6 Frequency Response Analysis

If all components of the transistor equivalent circuit were truly pure resistances and if the coupling networks contained no reactive elements, the voltage gain, current gain, and power gain of an amplifier *would not vary with signal frequency*. However, the junctions of a transistor display a capacitive effect (as does the junction diode in Chap. 4), and none of the coupling networks (Fig. 5–36) consist of resistors only. Hence, it becomes necessary to introduce techniques for calculating the variation of gain with frequency. The variation of response with frequency is not, in itself, an undesirable characteristic. In many applications, amplifiers are designed to operate over a specific band of frequencies with a high degree of discrimination against frequencies outside this band. For such applications, the ideal response would appear as shown in Fig. 6–17, Part A, where the gain is constant over the desired bandwidth, given by:

$$B = f_H - f_L \approx f_H \qquad (6\text{-}27)$$

where f_H is the desired *upper cutoff frequency* and f_L is the desired *lower*

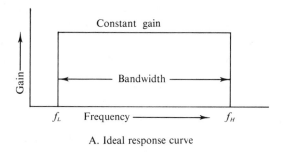

A. Ideal response curve

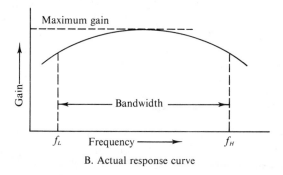

B. Actual response curve

Figure 6-17.   *Amplifier Frequency Response*

cutoff frequency. The approximation in Eq. (6–27) is valid when f_L is much less than f_H. For the ideal *bandpass amplifier*, the response to signals higher in frequency than f_H and lower in frequency than f_L *would be zero.* No amplifier displays this characteristic exactly. Rather, the response drops off gradually at both ends, as shown in Part B of the figure.

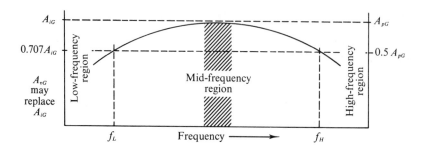

Figure 6-18. *Cutoff Frequency Definitions and the Response Regions*

For convenience of analysis, the response curve is divided into three regions, as shown in Fig. 6–18. Over the mid-frequency range, where gain is almost constant, all circuit components *can* be approximated by pure resistances. Hence, *the hybrid design equations are valid for establishing the mid-frequency response values.* Over the low-frequency range, the gain is degraded by series capacitors (RC coupling) or inductive reactances (impedance and transformer coupling). Over the high-frequency range, the degradation is brought about by leakage reactances (impedance and transformer coupling) or transistor limitations. Notice, in Fig. 6–18, that f_L and f_H occur at the point where current gain (and voltage gain) drops to 0.707 times the mid-frequency value. This is true *by definition.* Notice, also, that f_L and f_H occur at the point where power gain drops to 0.5 times the mid-frequency value. This is true (also by definition) since the power curve represents the product of the current and voltage gain curves $(0.707A_{iG} \times 0.707A_{vG} = 0.5A_{pG})$. Other definitions may be found, but the "half-power" bandwidth will be used throughout this text.

Transistor Frequency Characteristics

Two phenomena contribute to making the transistor characteristics dependent upon frequency: the junction capacitances, and the nonuniform transfer of carriers across the base region. The collector-to-base and emitter-to-base capacitances (see Fig. 6–19) are shunted across the input and output terminals of the transistor. The input and output capacitances,

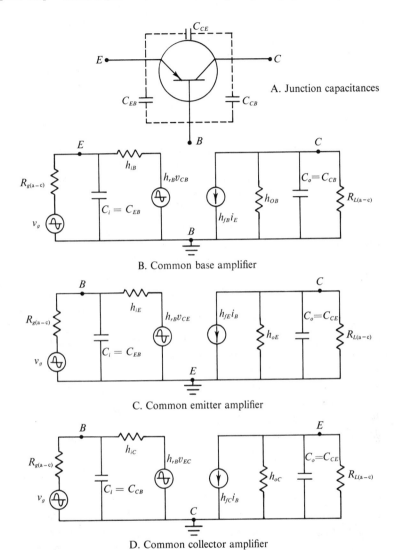

A. Junction capacitances

B. Common base amplifier

C. Common emitter amplifier

D. Common collector amplifier

Figure 6-19.   *Junction Capacitances and Placement in the Amplifier Configurations*

of course, depend on the configuration arrangement. The collector-to-base capacitance typically ranges between two and fifty picofarads. The emitter-to-base capacitance is very high (greater than one thousand picofarads) because the junction is forward biased. (The variation of capacitance with bias voltage, or depletion region width, is discussed in Chap. 4.) The third capacitance (collector-to-emitter) ranges from two to ten times the collector-to-base capacitance value. The actual values are usually specified by the manufacturer. Since capacitive reactance is inversely related to frequency and capacitance, the junction capacitances, at high frequencies, approach short circuit conditions. However, because of the order of magnitude associated with the capacitances (picofarads), this condition occurs at frequencies that are too high to be of concern in audio-amplifier design.

The transfer of carriers from emitter to collector does not occur instantaneously. The time required to cross the base region, *the transit time*, depends on the base width and the carrier diffusion constants. Furthermore, all carriers do not travel at the same velocity and, hence, all do not arrive at the collector at the same time. (The carrier velocities follow the Maxwell-Boltzmann distribution discussed in Appendix B.) Since the carriers arrive at the collector at different times, when their movement is in response to an a-c signal, there must be a phase difference between the signal components represented by each carrier. For this reason, some of the carriers contribute strongly to the total a-c current, while others act as interference and cancel a portion of the signal. This cancellation becomes more pronounced at high frequencies, since the lower-velocity carriers cannot respond to the rapid fluctuations. As a result, they are drawn even more out-of-phase as frequency increases. This increased interference, along with the junction capacitance effects, causes α (or h_{fB}) to decrease as frequency increases. The frequency at which h_{fB} has decreased to 0.707 times its low-frequency value is called the *alpha cutoff frequency*, f_α.

The alpha cutoff frequency is related to base width and carrier diffusion constant:

$$f_\alpha = \frac{D}{W^2} \qquad (6\text{-}28)$$

where D is the diffusion constant in meters²/volt·second, and W is the base width in meters. Obviously, changing the base width changes f_α in an inverse manner. Furthermore, f_α is quite sensitive to base width, which is squared in Eq. (6–28). Very high-frequency transistors have very narrow base widths. A check of the electron and hole diffusion constants (Table 4–3) will show that NPN transistors (with electrons as the majority carrier) inherently have better frequency characteristics than do PNP transistors (with holes as the majority carrier). This check will also show that germanium transistors will respond to higher frequencies than will silicon transistors (for the same base width), since either carrier has a higher diffusion constant in germanium. Normally, for the junction transistor, f_α is in the megacycle range. Hence, for audio-frequency amplifiers in the common base configuration, the transistor does not present a frequency response problem.

Since the forward current transfer parameter for the CE and CC configurations is dependent upon h_{fB} (Table 6-4), these parameters must also be frequency dependent. The table shows that h_{fE} and h_{fC} have approximately the same value, and the same relationship to h_{fB}. Hence, they must follow a similar variation with frequency. However, the cutoff frequency for these two configurations is *much lower* than that for the CB configuration. The frequency at which h_{fE} (or β) reaches 0.707 times its low-frequency value is called the *beta cutoff frequency*. It is related to the alpha cutoff frequency by:

$$f_\beta = (1 - |h_{fB}|)f_\alpha \qquad (6\text{-}29)$$

and the CC cutoff frequency is almost identical. For most audio-frequency transistor amplifiers in the CE and CC configurations, the upper cutoff frequency of the amplifier, f_H, is established by f_β.

The alpha and beta cutoff frequencies are not the only factors considered for the frequency response analysis. The frequency at which the maximum power gain, $A_{pG(\max)}$ [from Eq. (6-26)] is reduced to one is also of interest, and is denoted by $f_{\max}$. When specified by the manufacturer, the value will, in general, apply to the CB configuration. The product:

$$GBW = f_{\max}A_{pB(\max)} \qquad (6\text{-}30)$$

is called the *gain-bandwidth product*. This is a useful figure for comparing transistors, since it expresses the ideal gain and frequency capabilities of the device when used in a matched common base amplifier.

It is possible to construct reactive a-c equivalent circuits which permit the direct derivation of frequency-sensitive amplifier performance equations. However, this becomes a tedious process of parameter conversions and calculations. For this reason, throughout this text, the a-c equivalent circuit will be retained as a purely resistive network, with the transistor cutoff frequencies invoked when analyzing the high-frequency region of an amplifier's response. This approach yields adequate accuracy for most practical applications.

Example 6-15. For a base width of 6×10^{-4} meter, compare the alpha cutoff frequencies for silicon and germanium PNP and NPN transistors. (Use the diffusion data in Table 4-3.)

Solution. The alpha cutoff frequency is given by:

$$f_\alpha = \frac{D}{W^2}$$

For the NPN transistor, the majority carriers are electrons. For silicon (from Table 4–3):

$$f_\alpha = \frac{3.04 \times 10^{-1}}{(6 \times 10^{-4})^2} = \frac{3.04 \times 10^{-1}}{3.6 \times 10^{-7}} = 485 \, kc$$

and for germanium:

$$f_\alpha = \frac{7.28 \times 10^{-1}}{3.6 \times 10^{-7}} = 2.02 \, mc$$

For the PNP transistor, the majority carriers are holes. For silicon:

$$f_\alpha = \frac{1.01 \times 10^{-1}}{3.6 \times 10^{-7}} = 281 \, kc$$

and for germanium:

$$f_\alpha = \frac{3.64 \times 10^{-1}}{3.6 \times 10^{-7}} = 1.01 \, mc$$

These figures support the fact that (for a given base width) NPN transistors have a higher cutoff frequency than do PNP transistors and that germanium transistors have a higher cutoff frequency than do silicon transistors.

Example 6-16. If h_{fE} for the transistors in Example 6–15 is 85, what is the beta cutoff frequency for each?

Solution. The beta cutoff frequency is given by:

$$f_\beta = (1 - |h_{fB}|)f_\alpha$$

The alpha cutoff frequencies are calculated in Example 6–15. The value for h_{fE} is known and must be used to determine h_{fB}. From Table 6–4:

$$h_{fB} = \frac{-h_{fE}}{1 + h_{fE}} = \frac{-85}{1 + 85} = \frac{-85}{86} = -0.989$$

For the silicon NPN transistor:

$$f_\beta = (1 - 0.989)(845 \times 10^3) = (0.011)(845 \times 10^3) = 8.55 \, kc$$

For the germanium NPN transistor:

$$f_\beta = (0.011)(2.02 \times 10^6) = 20.4 \, kc$$

For the silicon PNP transistor:

$$f_\beta = (0.011)(281 \times 10^3) = 2.84 \, kc$$

For the germanium PNP transistor:

$$f_\beta = (0.011)(1.01 \times 10^6) = 10.2 \, kc$$

These figures represent a considerable reduction in cutoff frequency over the common base values.

RC Coupling Response

The response of the RC coupled amplifier (Fig. 6–20) is best analyzed by considering the three frequency ranges indicated in Fig. 6–17. The value of the coupling capacitor, C_C, is such that, in the mid-frequency range, it is essentially a short circuit (to the a-c signals). This leads to the mid-frequency equivalent circuit shown in Fig. 6–21, Part A. Since this is a

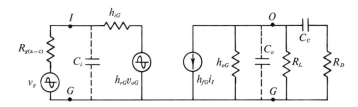

Figure 6-20. *Hybrid Equivalent RC Coupled Amplifier*

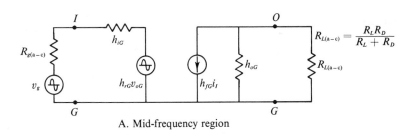

A. Mid-frequency region

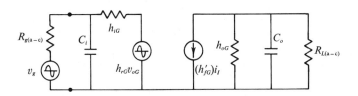

B. High-frequency region

Figure 6-21. *Mid- and High-Frequency RC Coupled Equivalent Amplifier Circuits*

purely resistive circuit, the a-c performance equations (Table 6–7 or 6–8, as appropriate) apply. At higher frequencies, the equivalent circuit is as shown in Part B of the figure. The output and input capacitances are shown (the coupling capacitor is still an a-c short). These capacitances will be given by C_{BE}, C_{CB}, or C_{CE}—depending upon the circuit configuration (Fig. 6-19). The effect of these capacitances and the transit time of the carriers dictate that the high-frequency response be determined solely by the transistor cutoff frequencies:

$$f_H = f_g \qquad (6\text{-}31)$$

where f_g is f_α (CB configuration) and f_β (CE and CC configurations).

Since all of the gain equations (Table 6–7) are proportional to h_{fB} (or h_{fB}^2, in the case of power gain), and because h_{fB}, h_{fE}, and h_{fC} all follow a similar variation, it is possible to construct a universal high-frequency response curve for the RC coupled amplifier. This curve is presented in Fig. 6–22. A_{iG} and A_{vG} refer to the calculated mid-frequency gains; A_i, A_v, and A_p refer to the gains at any frequency, f; f_H refers to f_α or f_β, as the configuration demands, and θ is the phase shift.

Figure 6–23 represents the low-frequency equivalent circuit. Here, the reactance of the coupling capacitor must be considered. At low frequencies, this reactance increases, reducing the current flow from the amplifier and dropping part of the output voltage, thus decreasing the voltage applied to the driven device, R_D. The coupling capacitor acts as a part of a voltage divider network (Fig. 6–24). A detailed circuit analysis will show that current and voltage gain drop to 0.707 times the mid-frequency value (and

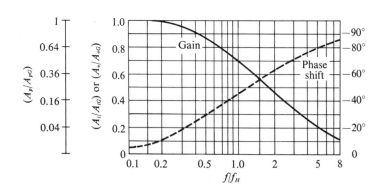

Figure 6-22.   *Universal High-Frequency Response for RC Coupled Amplifier*

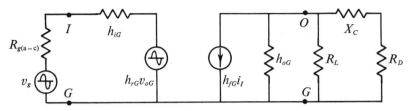

Figure 6-23.   *Low-Frequency RC Coupled Equivalent Amplifier Circuit*

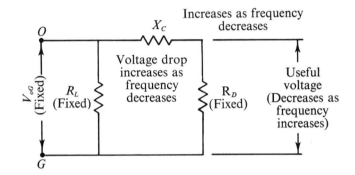

Figure 6-24.   *Voltage Divider Action of Coupling Capacitor at Low Frequencies*

power gain drops to 0.5 times the mid-frequency value), when:

$$f = f_L = \frac{1}{2\pi C_C (R_{L(\text{d-c})} + R_D)} \tag{6-32}$$

when r_{oG} is ten (or more) times greater than $R_{L(\text{d-c})}$. When r_{oG} is less than ten times $R_{L(\text{d-c})}$, the equation becomes:

$$f = f_L = \frac{1}{2\pi C_C \left\{ \left[\dfrac{r_{oG} R_{L(\text{d-c})}}{r_{oG} + R_{L(\text{d-c})}} \right] + R_D \right\}} \tag{6-32a}$$

which establishes the lower cutoff frequency for the amplifier. When designing an amplifier, Eqs. (6–32) or (6–32a) can be solved for C_C in order to obtain the coupling capacitor value necessary to achieve a desired lower cutoff frequency. It is not difficult to get very low-frequency response in most transistor amplifiers. The gain for the low-frequency equivalent circuit is given by the universal low-frequency response curve shown in Fig. 6–25.

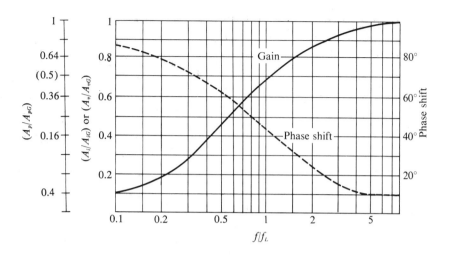

Figure 6-25.   *Universal Low-Frequency Response for* RC *Coupled Amplifier*

Example 6-17. The coupling capacitor used in Example 6–7 is 5 microfarads. The transistor has an alpha cutoff frequency of 10 mc. Determine the upper and lower cutoff frequencies. Plot the current gain response as a function of frequency. (The a-c source resistance is 500 ohms.)

Solution. For the CE amplifier, the upper cutoff frequency is given by the beta cutoff frequency:

$$f_H = f_\beta = (1 - |h_{fB}|)f_\alpha$$

h_{fB} must be determined from the relationship in Table 6–4 and the h_{fE}-value in Example 6–7. (However, since the conversions for this transistor have been performed and are listed in Table 6–5, the h_{fB}-value can be obtained from this table.)

$$f_H = (1 - 0.991)(10 \times 10^6) = 90 \text{ kc}$$

The relationship for determining the lower cutoff frequency depends on the relative values of r_{oE} and $R_{L(\text{a-c})}$. From Table 6–7:

$$r_{oE} = \frac{R_{g(\text{a-c})} + h_{iE}}{\Delta h_E + h_{oE}R_{g(\text{a-c})}} = \frac{500 + 2410}{(3.67 \times 10^{-2}) + (3.25 \times 10^{-5})(500)}$$

$$= \frac{2910}{1.99 \times 10^{-2}} = 146 \text{ K}$$

(The value for Δh_E is determined in Example 6–9.) Since r_{oE} is more than ten times $R_{L(\text{a-c})}$ (which is 1.67K), the lower cutoff frequency is:

$$f_L = \frac{1}{2\pi C_C(R_{L(\text{d-c})} + R_D)}$$
$$= \frac{1}{2\pi(5 \times 10^{-6})[(10 \times 10^{3}) + (2 \times 10^{3})]}$$
$$= \frac{1}{\pi(0.12)} = 0.029 \text{ cps}$$

which is essentially d-c. The mid-frequency current gain is -104, as calculated in Example 6–7. Using Fig. 6–22 for the high-frequency response, the following data are obtained:

f/f_H	f	A_i/A_{iE}	A_i
0.1	9 kc	1.0	−104
0.2	18 kc	0.99	−103
0.5	45 kc	0.79	−82
1.0	90 kc	0.707	−73.5
2.0	180 kc	0.45	−46.8
5.0	450 kc	0.2	−20.8
8.0	420 kc	0.12	−12.5

Using Fig. 6–25, it can be seen that the low-frequency gain is given by the mid-frequency gain at eight times f_L or, for this example, at 0.232 cps. This is essentially d-c. Hence, the amplifier current gain will stay flat at -104 almost all the way down to d-c. The complete current gain response curve is shown in Fig. E6–17.

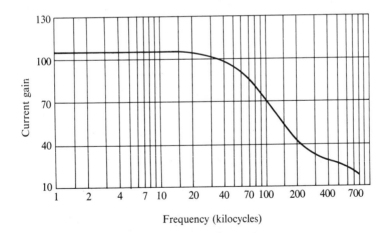

Figure E6-17

Transformer Coupling Response

Transformer coupling is more difficult to analyze and predict accurately than is RC coupling. The most convenient approach, however, is to consider the equivalent circuits for each of the response regions. The transformer coupled amplifier and its mid-frequency equivalent are shown in Fig. 6–26. The mid-frequency circuit is purely resistive, yielding to analysis by the a-c design equations of Tables 6–7 and 6–8. The bandwidth of a transformer coupled amplifier is generally less than the bandwidth that can be obtained with RC coupling.

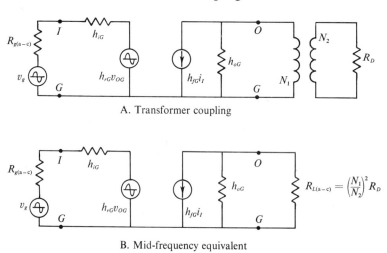

A. Transformer coupling

B. Mid-frequency equivalent

Figure 6-26.   *Transformer Coupled Amplifier and Hybrid Equivalents*

An equivalent circuit for the transformer can be constructed in much the same manner as the transistor equivalent. The procedure is more direct since the transformer is a *passive* device, resulting in the circuit of Fig. 6–27, Part A. R_P and R_S are primary and secondary winding resistances, respectively, and are so small, in most cases, that they may be neglected. L_P is the primary inductance, while L_{LP} and L_{LS} are the primary and secondary *leakage inductances* (produced by the primary flux that is *not coupled* to the secondary, and vice versa). The turns ratio, N_1/N_2, is used to reflect all values from the secondary *into the primary*. C_P and C_S are the winding capacitances (distributed between each turn of wire), and C_{PS} is the capacitance between the two windings. An additional physical component, the *core loss*, may be represented by a resistor across L_P. However, this is usually quite large with respect to $R_{L(a\text{-c})}$, so that very little current is shunted from the load.

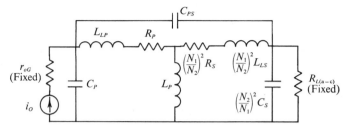

A. Complete equivalent circuit

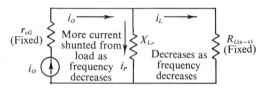

B. Low-frequency equivalent

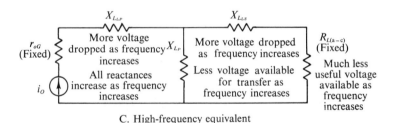

C. High-frequency equivalent

Figure 6-27.   *Transformer Equivalent Circuits*

At low frequencies, the reactances of L_{LP} and L_{LS} are so small that the voltage loss due to this component is negligible. However, the reactance of L_P also decreases with decreasing frequency, so that less voltage is available across the primary for transfer into the secondary. (In the equivalent circuit for the transformer, the decreasing reactance of the primary may be considered to shunt current away from the load as shown in Fig. 6–27, Part B.) The low-frequency response will be down to the cutoff value when:

$$f = f_L = 2\pi L_P R_{L(a\text{-}c)} \qquad (6\text{-}33)$$

when r_{oG} is ten (or more) times greater than $R_{L(a\text{-}c)}$, and when r_{oG} is less than ten times $R_{L(a\text{-}c)}$:

$$f = f_L = 2\pi L_P \left[\frac{r_{oG} R_{L(a\text{-}c)}}{r_{oG} + R_{L(a\text{-}c)}} \right] \tag{6-33a}$$

At high frequencies, the leakage reactance values increase to the point where the voltage losses become appreciable. This results in less voltage across L_P to be transferred into the secondary, and in a smaller portion of the secondary voltage being applied to the load. Ignoring the capacitances, the gain will be down to the cutoff value when:

$$f = f_H = \frac{r_{oG} + R_{L(a\text{-}c)}}{2\pi[L_{LP} + (N_1/N_2)^2 L_{LS}]} \tag{6-34}$$

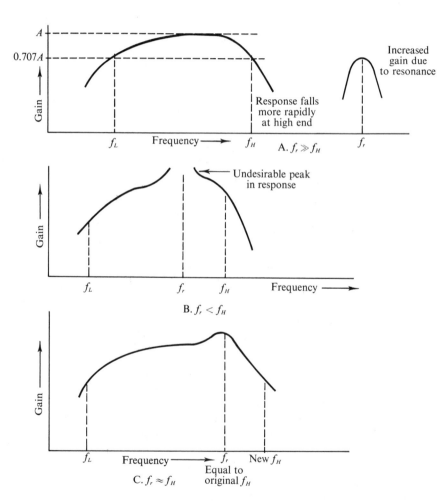

Figure 6-28. *Effect of Transformer Resonance on Frequency Response*

The variety of LC combinations in the high-frequency equivalent circuit leads to an unusual response characteristic for the transformer coupled amplifier in this frequency range. There is a parallel resonance frequency given by:

$$f_r = \frac{1}{2\pi\sqrt{L_P C_0}} \tag{6-35}$$

where C_0 is the total transistor output capacitance. If f_r is larger than f_H, a response curve similar to the one in Fig. 6–28, Part A will be obtained. If f_r is less than f_H, the curve in Part B will result. Often, L_P is chosen so that f_r and f_H are very nearly equal, resulting in the response curve of Part C. Such an arrangement has the advantage of extending the upper cutoff frequency (as shown), but results in a *nonuniform* gain across the amplifier bandwidth. If L_P has been chosen to meet a specific low-frequency requirement [from Eq. (6–33) or (6–33a)], the proper resonance frequency may still be obtained by deliberately placing a capacitor across the primary, or by adding capacitance in series with the primary.

Example 6-18. The amplifier in Example 6–9 must have a lower cutoff frequency not greater than 100 cps. The a-c source resistance is 500 ohms. What is the minimum value of primary inductance that can be tolerated in the transformer?

Solution. The lower cutoff frequency relationship depends on the relative values of r_{oB} and $R_{L(a\text{-}c)}$. (The value of r_{oB} is calculated in Example 6–11, and is 760K.) Since r_{oB} is more than ten times $R_{L(a\text{-}c)}$ (which is 4K):

$$f_L = 2\pi L_p R_{L(a\text{-}c)}$$

Solving for L_p:

$$L_p = \frac{f_L}{2\pi R_{L(a\text{-}c)}} = \frac{100}{2\pi(4 \times 10^3)} = 3.98 \text{ millihenries}$$

Impedance Coupling Response

Impedance coupling (Fig. 6–29) is similar to transformer coupling, in many respects. The lower cutoff frequency can be approximated by Eqs. (6–33) and (6–33a), as appropriate. However, the coupling capacitor will be quite large with respect to other capacitances in the circuit. Since C_C also may degrade response (as in the RC coupled amplifier), it is necessary to consider an equation similar to Eq. (6–32):

$$f_L = \frac{1}{2\pi C_C R_D} \tag{6-36}$$

The higher value [Eq. (6–36) or (6–33)] approximates the lower cutoff frequency of the amplifier. The parallel resonance frequency is given by:

$$f_r = \frac{1}{2\pi\sqrt{LC_c}} \qquad (6\text{-}37)$$

The coupling capacitor, in general, will be quite large with respect to other capacitances in the circuit. These equations are useful only for making gross approximations. Impedance coupling is seldom used, as it involves much trial and error in order to achieve specific results.

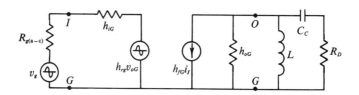

Figure 6-29.   *Hybrid Equivalent Impedance Coupled Amplifier*

6.7 Multistage Considerations

Despite the inherent high gains associated with the single-stage transistor amplifier in the CE configuration, most practical amplifiers require that several stages be connected in series, or *cascade*. This simply means that the device driven by each stage (represented by R_D in all previous discussions) is *another amplifier stage*—complete with biasing networks and coupling network—until the final stage, which is loaded by the device being "operated" by the amplifier. Although, from a physical standpoint, there is no limit to the number of stages that can be connected together, from an operational standpoint, three or four stages are usually sufficient. Furthermore, although the gain of a *multistage amplifier* is much greater than the gain of any individual stage, *frequency response is degraded.* In practice, it is the bandwidth limitations that finally determine how many stages may be utilized.

With the amplified signals of each stage serving as the input signal to the next stage, care must be exercised in selecting operating point, maximum dissipation power, and the transistor, itself, for each of the stages, in order to prevent excessive distortion and overdriving in the final stages of the cascade. Figure 6–30 illustrates the design criteria that must be observed. The small signal applied to the first stage permits it to operate in a

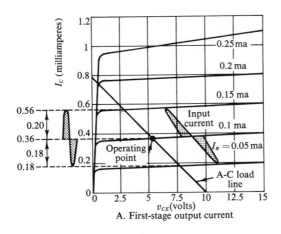

A. First-stage output current

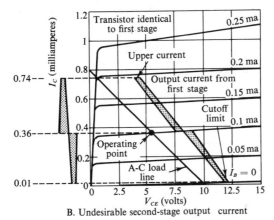

B. Undesirable second-stage output current

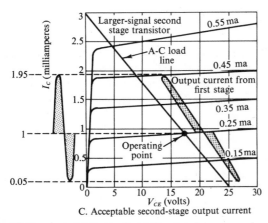

C. Acceptable second-stage output current

Figure 6-30. *Graphical Considerations for Compatable Multistage Amplifiers*

303

linear region (Part A). However, the output voltage applied to the input of the second stage is so large that it is overdriven if the same transistor is used (Part B). The selection of a transistor with a higher signal capability (Part C) will eliminate the problem. As must be expected, the final stages of the cascade are faced with more severe distortion considerations than are the initial stages. The best way to handle the graphical design of a multistage amplifier is to *start at the final stage*, and design backward toward the source.

Multistage amplifiers are not limited to the CE-configured stages. The three configurations can be cascaded in any desired manner. However, the reduced gains of the CB and CC configurations make them less desirable—*unless they are to be used as matching stages*. From Figs. 6–13 and 6–14, it can be seen that CB amplifiers have a *low input resistance* and a *high output resistance*, and that these resistances remain constant over a wide range of load resistance values. Conversely, the CC amplifier has a *high input resistance* and a *low output resistance*, also constant over a wide range of load values. This makes such configurations ideally suited as input stages (the first stage) and output stages (the last stage) of a multistage amplifier when it becomes necessary to match high- and low-resistance values.

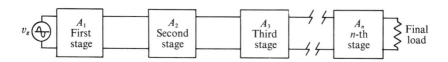

Figure 6-31.   *Generalized Cascade Arrangement*

A generalized cascade is shown in Fig. 6–31. Since the amplified output voltage, $A_{v1}v_g$, of the first stage serves as the input signal to the second stage, the output of the second stage must be given by the product $A_{v1}A_{v2}v_g$. This process is repeated through all stages, so that the multistage voltage gain is:

$$A_{vn} = A_{vG_1}A_{vG_2}A_{vG_3} \cdots A_{vG_n} \tag{6-38}$$

where n denotes the total number of stages in the cascade. The same is true of the current and power gains:

$$A_{in} = A_{iG_1}A_{iG_2}A_{iG_3} \cdots A_{iG_n} \tag{6-39}$$

$$A_{pn} = A_{pG_1}A_{pG_2}A_{pG_3} \cdots A_{pG_n} \tag{6-40}$$

Since the *overall gain* is the product of the individual stage gains, it must be realized that this figure builds up very rapidly.

Power gain is usually of more importance to the practical amplifier design than are the current and voltage gains. Since the overall power gain is the product of the individual stage gains, it becomes necessary to talk in terms of very large numbers when absolute power gain, p_{out}/p_{in}, is specified. For this reason, a special power gain unit, *the decibel*, has been adopted. This unit is defined by:

$$A_{pG}(db) = 10 \log_{10} \left(\frac{p_{out}}{p_{in}}\right) \tag{6-41}$$

$$= 10 \log_{10} A_{pG}$$

The use of this unit is illustrated by Fig. 6–32, which is a plot of the gains indicated in Fig. 6–12 *in terms of decibels*. To achieve this plot, the gain values at several points along the curves in Fig. 6–12 are substituted for A_{pG} in Eq. (6–41). A comparison of both sets of curves will point out certain significant characteristics of the decibel notation:

1. Any three-decibel increase (+3 db) in gain is equivalent to *doubling* the absolute power gain, and, conversely,
2. Any three-decibel decrease (−3 db) in gain is equivalent to cutting the absolute power gain in *half*.

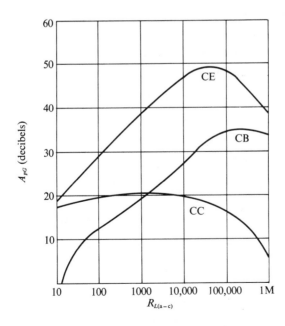

Figure 6-32.   *Power Gain Variation in Decibels (from* Fig. 6–12)

Within the definition of the logarithmic function, *unity power gain must be associated with zero decibels* (this is a standard reference point). These items make the decibel notation a very convenient system of gain units once the reader becomes familiar with the new concept. *Negative decibels* (not shown in the figure) indicate a power gain *less than one.*

Multistage amplifiers are especially suited to the decibel notation. Since the overall power gain is the product of the individual stage power gains, and since the product is simply the sum of the factors' logarithms:

$$A_{pn}(\text{db}) = A_{pG_1}(\text{db}) + A_{pG_2}(\text{db}) + A_{pG_3}(\text{db}) \tag{6-42}$$
$$+ \cdots + A_{pG_n}(\text{db})$$

which is simply Eq. (6–40) expressed in the decibel system.

Example 6-19. The amplifier in Example 6–7 uses a 10-volt battery in the output loop as a bias supply. The forward bias current, I_B, is 0.1 milliampere. An input signal with a peak-to-peak value of 0.12 volt is applied to this amplifier. If the characteristic curves for this transistor are the ones given in Fig. 6–30, can an identical second stage design be used?

Solution. It is necessary to determine whether the transistor can accept the output signal from the first stage without producing a considerable amount of distortion (overdriving). The first-stage operation must be determined by plotting a d-c load line, establishing the operating point, and then plotting the a-c load line. All of these procedures are described in Chap. 5. The results are shown in Fig. E6–19, Part A. In order to establish the minimum and maximum input current values, the input resistance to the amplifier must be known. Since the a-c load is small (1.67K), the approximation (from Table 6–8) can be used:

$$r_{iE} \approx h_{iE} = 2410 \text{ ohms}$$

The peak-to-peak input current is:

$$i_{I(\text{p-p})} = \frac{v_{I(\text{p-p})}}{r_{iE}} = \frac{0.12}{2.41 \times 10^3} = 0.05 \text{ milliampere}$$

Since I_B is 0.1 milliampere:

$$i_{B(\text{max})} = I_B + \frac{i_{I(\text{p-p})}}{2} = (0.1 \times 10^{-3}) + \frac{(0.05 \times 10^{-3})}{2}$$
$$= 0.125 \text{ milliampere}$$

and:

$$i_{B(\text{min})} = I_B - \frac{i_{I(\text{p-p})}}{2} = (0.1 \times 10^{-3}) - (0.025 \times 10^{-3})$$
$$= 0.075 \text{ milliampere}$$

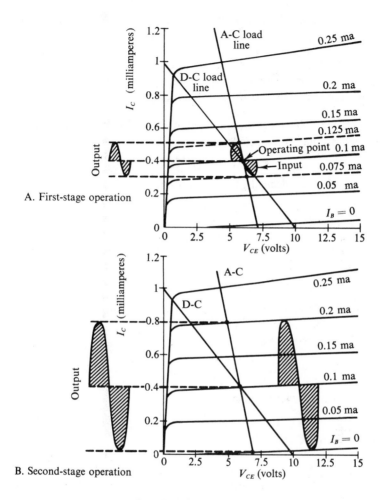

A. First-stage operation

B. Second-stage operation

Figure E6-19

The input signal current is shown in Fig. E6–19, Part A, along with the interpolated characteristics for I_B equal to 0.125 milliampere and I_B equal to 0.075 milliampere. These characteristics intersect with the a-c load line to establish the operating limits for the first stage. The associated output current is also shown. If the second stage is identical to the first stage, the same d-c load line, operating point, and a-c load line apply. This is shown in Fig. E6–19, Part B, along with the input signal current (the output signal current from the first stage). As shown, the transistor can accept this signal without being overdriven. Some distortion is shown, however. Whether this is tolerable depends on the particular application, and is subject to further analysis by the harmonic analysis techniques described in Chap. 5.

Example 6-20. If the amplifier stage described in Example 6–7 can be used to form a two-stage cascade, what is the multistage power gain (see Example 6–9, also) in absolute gain units and in decibels?

Solution. The single-stage power gain is 7750 (from Example 6–9). The absolute power gain is:

$$A_{p2} = A_{pE_1} A_{pE_2} = (7.75 \times 10^3)^2 = 6 \times 10^7$$

The multistage decibel gain is given by:

$$A_{p2}(\text{db}) = A_{pE_1}(\text{db}) + A_{pE_2}(\text{db})$$

Since the two stages are identical:

$$A_{pE}(\text{db}) = 10 \log_{10} A_{pE} = 10 \log_{10}(7750) = 10(3.89) = 38.9 \text{ db}$$

and:

$$A_{p2}(\text{db}) = 2(38.9) = 77.8 \text{ db}$$

It is interesting to check the $A_{p2}(\text{db})$-value against the absolute gain value to assure their agreement. The conversion from decibels to absolute gain units is:

$$A_{p2} = \text{antilog}\left[\frac{A_{p2}(\text{db})}{10}\right] = \text{antilog}\,(7.78) = 6.04 \times 10^7$$

which is well within reason.

Mid-Frequency Gains

Calculation of the mid-frequency gain values for a multistage amplifier is accomplished by using the a-c design equations (Tables 6–7 and 6–8)

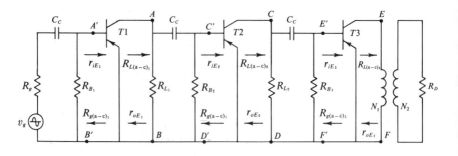

Figure 6-33.   *Simplified Three-Stage Cascade*

on a stage-by-stage basis, then combining these values to produce the overall mid-frequency response. Figure 6–33 represents a generalized three-stage cascade. The first two stages are RC coupled; the final load, R_D, is coupled to the last stage by a transformer. (All stages could be coupled in the same manner. The combination of couplings in the figure has been chosen in order to demonstrate the generality of the analysis techniques.) Aside from the *h*-parameter values, the only quantity needed to calculate the mid-frequency current, voltage, and power gains is the a-c load resistance, $R_{L(a-c)}$, for each stage. The equivalent a-c loads on each stage in Fig. 6–33 are shown in Fig. 6–34. *With the exception of the last stage, the* a-c *load contains the input resistance of an amplifier stage,* as shown. This input resistance, itself, is dependent only upon the transistor parameters and the stage load. From the figure, it becomes apparent why the response of a multistage amplifier *must be started at the last stage and worked backward* (toward the source).

The output resistance of the stages is not needed unless it is desirable

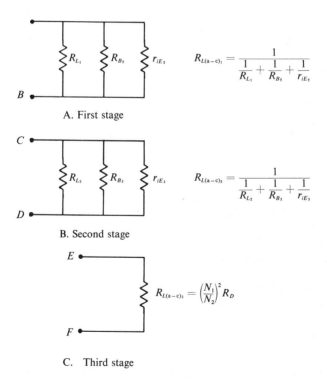

A. First stage

$$R_{L(a-c)_1} = \frac{1}{\dfrac{1}{R_{L_1}} + \dfrac{1}{R_{B_2}} + \dfrac{1}{r_{iE_2}}}$$

B. Second stage

$$R_{L(a-c)_2} = \frac{1}{\dfrac{1}{R_{L_2}} + \dfrac{1}{R_{B_3}} + \dfrac{1}{r_{iE_3}}}$$

C. Third stage

$$R_{L(a-c)_3} = \left(\frac{N_1}{N_2}\right)^2 R_D$$

Figure 6-34.   *Equivalent A-C Loads (Mid-Frequency Range)*

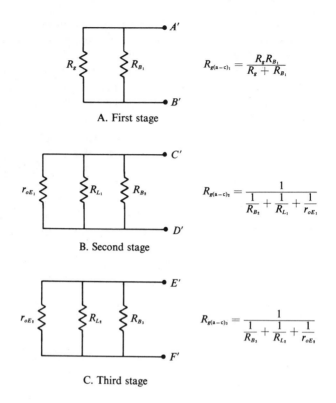

A. First stage

$$R_{g(a-c)_1} = \frac{R_g R_{B_1}}{R_g + R_{B_1}}$$

B. Second stage

$$R_{g(a-c)_2} = \frac{1}{\dfrac{1}{R_{B_2}} + \dfrac{1}{R_{L_1}} + \dfrac{1}{r_{oE_1}}}$$

C. Third stage

$$R_{g(a-c)_3} = \frac{1}{\dfrac{1}{R_{B_3}} + \dfrac{1}{R_{L_2}} + \dfrac{1}{r_{oE_2}}}$$

Figure 6-35.   *Equivalent Source Resistances (Mid-Frequency Range)*

to design a matched amplifier, or to determine whether an existing amplifier is matched. Since the output resistance of each stage is dependent upon the equivalent a-c source resistance, $R_{g(a-c)}$, it must be determined by starting at the first stage and working forward toward the final stage. Figure 6–35 illustrates the equivalent a-c source resistances for each stage of the amplifier in Fig. 6-33.

The bilateral nature of the transistor accounts for the tedious process of analysis that has been described. Indirectly, the load on each stage affects the gains (and input resistances) of *all of the preceding stages*. Conversely, each of the input loop networks affects the output resistance of *all of the successive stages*. Even the source resistance, R_g, is indirectly contained in each of the r_{oG}-calculations.

Example 6-21.   The multistage amplifier in Fig. E6–21 uses transistors with the *h*-parameters listed in Example 6–6. What is the overall voltage gain of the amplifier?

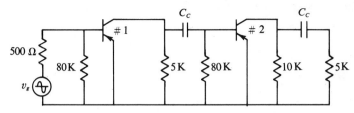

A. Two-stage, RC coupled amplifier

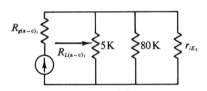

B. Second-stage equivalent

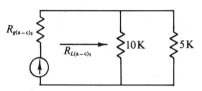

C. First-stage equivalent

Figure E6-21

Solution. The equivalent second stage is shown in Fig. E6–21, Part B. The voltage gain is given by (from Table 6–7):

$$A_{vE_2} = \frac{-h_{fE}R_{L(a\text{-}c)_2}}{\Delta h_E R_{L(a\text{-}c)_2} + h_{iE}}$$

where:

$$R_{L(a\text{-}c)_2} = \frac{(10 \times 10^3)(5 \times 10^3)}{(10 + 5)(10^3)} = \frac{50 \times 10^6}{15 \times 10^3} = 3.34K$$

and:

$$\Delta h_E = h_{iE}h_{oE} - h_{fE}h_{rE}$$
$$= (2 \times 10^3)(2.5 \times 10^{-5}) - 49(5.5 \times 10^{-4})$$
$$= (5 \times 10^{-2}) - (2.7 \times 10^{-2}) = 2.3 \times 10^{-2}$$

Hence:

$$A_{vE_2} = \frac{-(49)(3.34 \times 10^3)}{(2.3 \times 10^{-2})(3.34 \times 10^3) + (2 \times 10^3)}$$
$$= \frac{-(1.64 \times 10^5)}{2.08 \times 10^3} = -79$$

The first-stage equivalent is shown in Fig. E6–21, Part C. The voltage gain is:

$$A_{vE_1} = \frac{-h_{fE}R_{L(a\text{-}c)_1}}{\Delta h_E R_{L(a\text{-}c)_1} + h_{iE}}.$$

where:

$$R_{L(a\text{-}c)_1} = \frac{1}{1/(5 \times 10^3) + 1/(80 \times 10^3) + 1/r_{iE_2}}$$

The input resistance to the second stage is (from Table 6–7):

$$r_{iE_2} = \frac{h_{iE} + \Delta h_E R_{L(a\text{-}c)_2}}{h_{oE}R_{L(a\text{-}c)} + 1} = \frac{2000 + 76.9}{(2.5 \times 10^{-5})(3.34 \times 10^3) + 1}$$
$$= \frac{2.08 \times 10^3}{1.08} = 1.93K$$

Since the resistor of 80K is very large in comparison to the other two resistors, the a-c load on the first stage simplifies to:

$$R_{L(a\text{-}c)_1} = \frac{(5 \times 10^3)(1.93 \times 10^3)}{(5 + 1.93)(10^3)} = \frac{9.65 \times 10^6}{6.93 \times 10^3} = 1.39K$$

Hence:

$$A_{vE_1} = \frac{-(49)(1.39 \times 10^3)}{(2.3 \times 10^{-2})(1.39 \times 10^3) + (2 \times 10^3)}$$
$$= \frac{-(6.82 \times 10^4)}{(2.03 \times 10^3)} = -33.6$$

The multistage voltage gain is:

$$A_{v2} = (-79)(-33.6) = 2650$$

Notice that the multistage gain has a positive sign, indicating that the final output is in phase with the original input signal. The first stage produces a 180° phase shift. The second stage produces an additional 180° phase shift—a total of 360°, or one complete cycle.

Frequency Response (Identical Cutoff Frequencies)

The frequency response of a multistage amplifier must also be constructed on a stage-by-stage basis. Individually, the upper and lower cutoff frequencies, f_L and f_H, must be determined in the manner described for RC coupled, transformer coupled, and impedance coupled amplifiers in previous sections. Figure 6–36 illustrates the power gain versus frequency curves for each of the amplifier stages (Part A). These stages have *identical frequency characteristics*, f_L and f_H, although the gain magnitudes are different. Part B illustrates the overall two-stage power gain response, obtained by adding the curves in Part A.

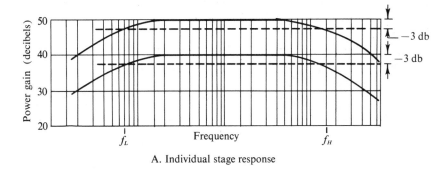

A. Individual stage response

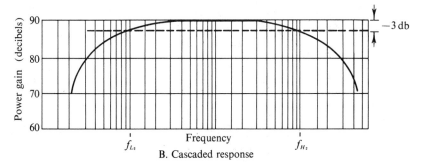

B. Cascaded response

Figure 6-36.   *Effect of Cascading Stages with Identical Frequency Characteristics*

Notice that the f_L- and f_H-values for the individual stages correspond to a power gain that is three decibels below the mid-frequency gain. A loss of 3 db, remember, is equivalent to cutting the power gain in half. Hence, these cutoff frequencies are consistent with the previous definitions, as they represent the frequency where the power gain is down to 0.5 times the mid-frequency value. *The cutoff frequencies for the multistage amplifier must also follow this definition.* The -3-db points are indicated in Part B. The corresponding upper and lower cutoff frequencies, f_{Ln} and f_{Hn}, are also indicated. These values *fall inside* the individual stage values, indicating that the multistage amplifier bandwidth is less than the individual stage bandwidth. The inverse relationship between bandwidth and gain is universal: a change in one cannot be accomplished without an inverse change in the other. The universal response curves can be applied to the multistage RC coupled amplifier as well as the single-stage amplifier. However, in order to do this, the $|A_{iG}|$, $|A_{vG}|$, and $|A_{pG}|$ indicated in the figures must be replaced with $|A_{in}|$, $|A_{vn}|$, and $|A_{pn}|$—the n-stage values. The ratios (f/f_H), in Fig. 6–22 and (f_L/f), in Fig. 6–25, must be replaced by (f/f_{Hn}) and (f_{Ln}/f), respectively, where f_{Hn} and f_{Ln} refer to the n-stage values. If f_L and f_H for the individual stages are the same, f_{Ln} and f_{Hn} can be derived directly:

$$f_{Ln} = \frac{f_L}{\sqrt{2^{1/n} - 1}} \tag{6-43}$$

$$f_{Hn} = f_H \sqrt{2^{1/n} - 1} \tag{6-44}$$

where n is the number of cascaded stages. It must be remembered that f_{Ln} and f_{Hn} refer to the multistage (cascade) amplifier and f_L and f_H refer to the individual stages. The *bandwidth* of the multistage amplifier degenerates very rapidly as the number of stages increases because of the large *decrease* in f_{Hn} and the large *increase* in f_{Ln}. In order to design a multistage amplifier with a specific bandwidth, the individual stages must be designed with an even larger bandwidth. The necessary cutoff frequencies for the individual stages are determined from Eqs. (6–43) and (6–44), solved for f_L and f_H:

$$f_L = f_{Ln} \sqrt{2^{1/n} - 1} \tag{6-43a}$$

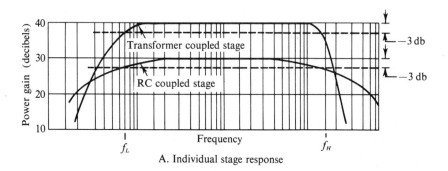

A. Individual stage response

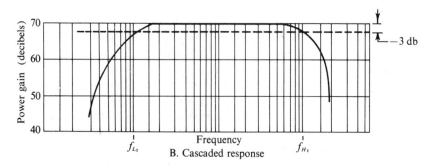

B. Cascaded response

Figure 6-37. *Effect of Cascading Unsymmetrical Stages with Identical Frequency Characteristics*

$$f_H = \frac{f_{Hn}}{\sqrt{2^{1/n} - 1}} \tag{6-44a}$$

Equations (6–43), (6–44), (6–43a), and (6–44a) can be used to approximate the cutoff frequency relationships for any set of stages having identical single-stage f_L- and f_H-values. However, since transformer and impedance coupled response curves are not symmetrical, a considerable error can be introduced (see Fig. 6–37).

The phase shift for a multistage amplifier is simply the summation of the individual stage phase shifts:

$$\theta_n = \theta_1 + \theta_2 + \cdots + \theta_k \tag{6-45}$$

Example 6-22. If the amplifier stage in Example 6–17 is used to form a three-stage cascade with each stage having identical upper and lower cutoff frequencies, what are the final multistage amplifier cutoff frequencies? Plot the current gain response versus frequency.

Solution. The lower cutoff frequency for the multistage amplifier is:

$$f_{L3} = \frac{f_L}{\sqrt{2^{1/3} - 1}} = \frac{2.9 \times 10^{-2}}{\sqrt{0.26}} = 5.8 \times 10^{-2} \text{ cps}$$

which is still essentially d-c. The upper cutoff frequency is:

$$f_{H3} = f_H\sqrt{2^{1/3} - 1} = (90 \times 10^3)(\sqrt{0.26}) = 46 \text{ kc}$$

The mid-frequency current gain for the cascade is:

$$A_{i3} = A_{iE_1}A_{iE_2}A_{iE_3} = (-104)(-104)(-104) = -(1.12 \times 10^6)$$

with the negative sign indicating phase reversal of the final output signal. The low-frequency region need not be considered since the gain will remain flat. Using Fig. 6–22, however, the high-frequency data are obtained:

f/f_{H3}	f	A_i/A_{i3}	A_i
0.1	4.6 kc	1.0	$-(1.12 \times 10^6)$
0.2	9.2 kc	0.99	$-(1.11 \times 10^6)$
0.5	23.0 kc	0.79	$-(8.85 \times 10^5)$
1.0	46.0 kc	0.707	$-(7.9 \times 10^5)$
2.0	92.0 kc	0.45	$-(5.04 \times 10^5)$
5.0	230.0 kc	0.2	$-(2.24 \times 10^5)$
8.0	368.0 kc	0.12	$-(1.34 \times 10^5)$

The resulting response curve is shown in Fig. E6–22.

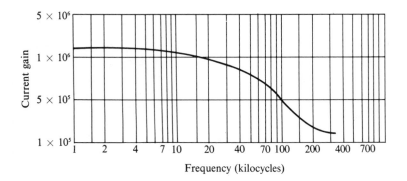

Figure E6-22

Example 6-23. A two-stage cascade, made of stages with identical cutoff frequencies, must have an overall upper cutoff frequency of 20 kc and an overall lower cutoff frequency of 16 cps. What must the individual stage cutoff frequencies be?

Solution. The individual stage lower cutoff frequency must be:

$$f_L = f_{L2}\sqrt{2^{1/2} - 1} = 16\sqrt{0.414} = 10 \text{ cps}$$

and the individual upper cutoff frequency must be:

$$f_H = \frac{f_{H3}}{\sqrt{0.414}} = \frac{20 \text{ kc}}{0.644} = 31 \text{ kc}$$

Frequency Response (Dissimilar Cutoff Frequencies)

Figure 6–38 illustrates the power gain versus frequency curves for each of two amplifier stages (Part A) which have *dissimilar frequency characteristics*. Part B represents the overall two-stage power gain response. Notice that f_{Hn} is less than f_{H_1} and f_{H_2}, and that f_{Ln} is larger than f_{L_1} and f_{L_2}. Just as in the "identical stage" case, the bandwidth is reduced to less than the individual stage bandwidths. However, the relative reduction in this case is *even greater than it would be if the two stages were identical*. Since the individual stage cutoff frequency values are not equal, there are no relationships between f_{Hn} or f_{Ln}, and f_H or f_L.

In view of the preceding discussion, if the dissimilar stages are RC coupled, the universal curves in Figs. 6–22 and 6–25 can be applied to the individual stages and combined to obtain the multistage curve. This con-

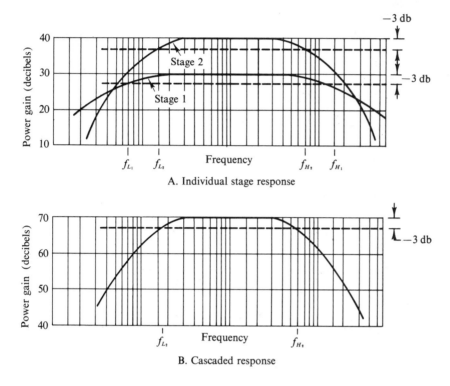

Figure 6-38. *Effect of Cascading Stages with Dissimilar Cutoff Frequencies*

sists of multiplying the curves, point-by-point, when the voltage, current, and power gains are expressed in absolute terms. The cutoff frequencies are then determined graphically from the points where the multistage gain drops to $0.707A_{in}$, $0.707A_{vn}$, or $0.5\ A_{pn}$. If the power gain is expressed in decibels, the curves are added, and the cutoff frequencies are associated with the points where the gain is 3 db less than $A_{pn}(db)$. (This technique is used in Fig. 6–38.)

The combination of RC coupled and transformer (or impedance) coupled stages is best handled graphically in all cases. However, the procedure can be simplified if several "identical" RC coupled stages are in cascade with one (or more) dissimilar stages. In this case, an analytical-graphical technique can be followed. First, the combined identical stage response can be obtained from the equations of the preceding section and the universal response curves, resulting in a curve similar to the one shown in Fig. 6–39, Part A. The dissimilar stage, or stages, are determined next

(Part B, for example). Finally, the curves are combined (Part C), and the cutoff frequencies are identified.

In all cases, the phase shifts of the individual stages *add* to produce the multistage phase characteristics.

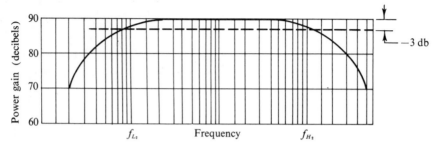

A. Two-stage RC coupled cascade

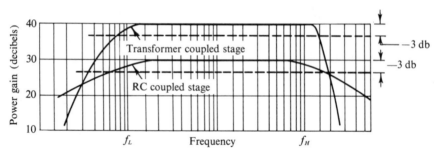

B. Additional stages

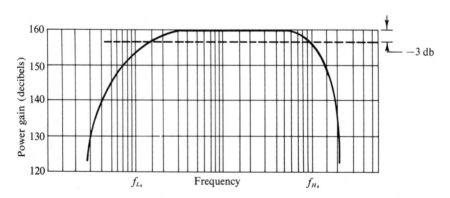

C. Composite cascade response

Figure 6-39.   *Construction of Complex Response Characteristics*

Multistage Matching

A multistage amplifier will attain its maximum power gain if all of the stages are matched; that is, the input resistance of each stage must be equal to the equivalent a-c source resistance, $R_{g(\text{a-c})}$, that feeds the stage, and the output resistance of each stage must be equal to the equivalent a-c load, $R_{L(\text{a-c})}$, that is fed by the stage. This requires a determination of the necessary $R_{g(\text{a-c})}$- and $R_{L(\text{a-c})}$-values [from Eqs. (6–24) and (6–25)] *for each of the transistors.*

Establishing the values for $R_{g(\text{a-c})}$ and $R_{L(\text{a-c})}$ to achieve matching does not, in itself, assure that matching can be achieved. It does not even assure that matching is desirable from a standpoint of distortion and operating point considerations. It is best to place the a-c load line on the transistor output characteristics and examine the operation that can be achieved. The a-c line can be moved about the curves until a good place-ment is achieved from visual judgement. If several promising positions are observed, a more detailed analysis may be obtained by constructing the dynamic transfer curve for each alternative. A more accurate judge-ment can be obtained from this process. Furthermore, this process can be used to select an optimum operating point, specify the d-c load, specify source voltages, and make a detailed distortion calculation. These graph-ical design techniques are discussed in Chap. 5.

The matched amplifier stages must be designed individually, starting with the last stage a-c load (the device being driven by the amplifier). Transformer coupling presents the most straightforward method of achieving a match. The necessary turns ratio is selected from:

$$\frac{N_1}{N_2} = \sqrt{\frac{R_{L(\text{a-c})n}}{R_D}} \tag{6-46}$$

where $R_{L(\text{a-c})}$ is determined from Eq. (6–25) for the transistor that will be used in the last stage (denoted by the subscript n). The next step is to match the input of the last stage to the output of the stage preceding it. This is accomplished by choosing the turns ratio from:

$$\frac{N_1}{N_2} = \sqrt{\frac{R_{L(\text{a-c})n-1}}{R_{g(\text{a-c})n}}} \tag{6-47}$$

where $R_{g(\text{a-c})n}$ is determined from Eq. (6–24) for the last-stage transistor, and $R_{L(\text{a-c})n-1}$ is determined from Eq. (6–25) for the transistor preceding the last stage (denoted by the subscript, $n-1$). If several more stages are involved, the turns ratio is determined from Eq. (6–47) with the subscripts decreasing by one as the design moves toward the front end of the ampli-fier; i.e., in the next stage the radical would contain the ratio $R_{L(\text{a-c})n-2}/R_{g(\text{a-c})n-1}$; the next, $R_{L(\text{a-c})n-3}/R_{g(\text{a-c})n-2}$; etc. Eventually, the design will reach the point where the first-stage input must be matched to the signal source. The turns ratio for this match is given by:

$$\frac{N_1}{N_2} = \sqrt{\frac{R_g}{R_{g(a-c)_0}}} \tag{6-48}$$

where R_g is the source resistance and $R_{g(a-c)_0}$ is determined from Eq. (6-24) for the first-stage transistor (denoted by the subscript, $n - n = 0$). It must be pointed out that a *fractional turns ratio* indicates that the *secondary contains more turns than the primary*. Notice that r_{oG} and r_{iG} are not mentioned directly during this analysis. However, since matching has been achieved, all output resistances "automatically" become equal to their associated $R_{L(a-c)}$-values, and all input resistances "automatically" become equal to their associated $R_{g(a-c)}$-values.

Matching RC coupled stages is a much more tedious process (not in concept, but in calculation) since several parallel resistors are usually involved in each $R_{L(a-c)}$- and each $R_{g(a-c)}$-determination. In fact, it is difficult, and in many cases, impossible, to achieve matching directly with RC coupled stages of the same configuration. Usually, it is more practical to obtain matching only at the front end (source resistance to first-stage input resistance) and back end (final-stage a-c load to final-stage output resistance) of the amplifier. The stages in between are left unmatched. This may require that an additional stage be used over the number required with complete matching, but is a practical design. Higher gain may be obtained for the same number of stages by using CB or CC (or both) stages as input and output matching devices with CE stages in between. The usual range of input resistance for the CE configuration is from 1K to 2K. Many source resistances fall in this same category. In this event, direct input matching is not too difficult to achieve. The output resistance of the CE configuration is usually in the 100K to 300K range. Most a-c loads are not this high. The CC congfiguration, however, has a high input resistance (several hundred thousand ohms) and a low output resistance (a few thousand ohms). Hence, the CC configuration is an excellent output matching device in many applications. In the event that the source resistance is large, the CC configuration can also serve as an input matching device. If the source resistance is only 100 or 200 ohms, the CB configuration may be used for matching. Its input resistance *can* be made a few hundred ohms or less. The output resistance of the CB configuration, however, is generally in the hundreds of thousands of ohms—far too high to match to the CE input resistance. In some instances, then, a CB first stage and a CC second stage, followed by one or more CE stages may be used for high gain. Some of these various arrangements are shown in Fig. 6-40. It is difficult to describe an adequate analysis procedure, as each

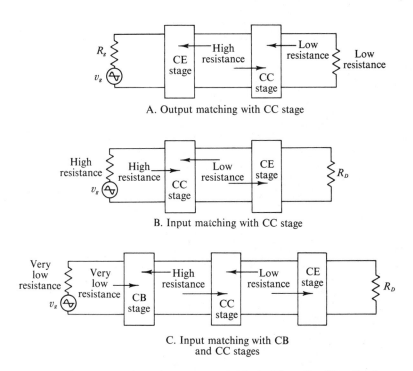

A. Output matching with CC stage

B. Input matching with CC stage

C. Input matching with CB
and CC stages

Figure 6-40.   *Matching Arrangements with the Three Amplifier Configurations*

situation may demand a slight variation in technique. However, the various pieces of general analysis presented in this chapter are more than adequate to perform these analyses.

Example 6-24.   The amplifier in Example 6–22 is to be redesigned with transformer coupling in order to achieve matched conditions for maximum power gain. The resulting circuit is shown in Fig. E6–24. Select the proper turns ratio for each transformer. Determine the overall mid-frequency power gain and compare this to the power gain for the unmatched (RC coupled) version. (Single-stage matching for this transistor is described in Example 6–13. Unmatched single-stage operation is described in Examples 6–7 and 6–9.)

Solution.   The output of the third stage is shown in Fig. E6–24, Part B. The turns ratio for matching this portion of the circuit is:

$$\left(\frac{N_1}{N_2}\right)_3 = \sqrt{\frac{R_{L(\text{a-c})_3}}{R_D}}$$

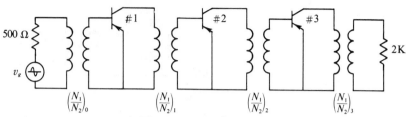

A. Three-stage, transformer coupled
amplifier

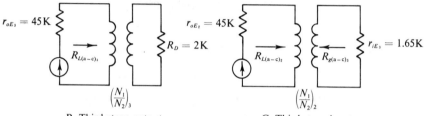

B. Third-stage output   C. Third-stage input

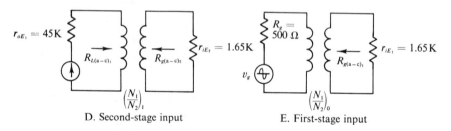

D. Second-stage input   E. First-stage input

Figure E6-24

where the value of $R_{L(\text{a-c})_3}$ for matching is 45K (determined in Example 6–13). Hence:

$$\left(\frac{N_1}{N_2}\right)_3 = \sqrt{\frac{45 \times 10^3}{2 \times 10^3}} = \sqrt{27.5} = 5.25:1$$

The input of the third stage is shown in Fig. E6–24, Part C. The turns ratio for matching this portion of the circuit is:

$$\left(\frac{N_1}{N_2}\right)_2 = \sqrt{\frac{R_{L(\text{a-c})_2}}{R_{g(\text{a-c})_3}}}$$

Since the transistors are identical, the required values for $R_{L(\text{a-c})_2}$ and $R_{L(\text{a-c})_3}$ are the same. The value of $R_{g(\text{a-c})_3}$ for matching is 1.65K (also determined in Example 6–13). Hence:

$$\left(\frac{N_1}{N_2}\right)_2 = \sqrt{\frac{45 \times 10^3}{1.65 \times 10^3}} = \sqrt{27.3} = 5.25:1$$

Satisfying the input matching condition for the third stage simultaneously satisfies the output matching conditions for the second stage. The input of the second stage is shown in Fig. E6–24, Part D. The turns ratio for matching this portion of the circuit is:

$$\left(\frac{N_1}{N_2}\right)_1 = \sqrt{\frac{R_{L(a-c)_1}}{R_{g(a-c)_2}}}$$

However, since the transistors are identical, $R_{L(a-c)_1}$ is the same as $R_{L(a-c)_2}$ and $R_{L(a-c)_3}$. Furthermore, $R_{g(a-c)_2}$ is equal to $R_{g(a-c)_3}$. For these reasons:

$$\left(\frac{N_1}{N_2}\right)_1 \approx 5.25:1$$

The output matching conditions for the first stage are simultaneously satisfied. The input of the first stage is shown in Fig. E6–24, Part E. The turns ratio for matching this portion of the circuit is:

$$\left(\frac{N_1}{N_2}\right)_0 = \sqrt{\frac{R_g}{R_{g(a-c)_1}}}$$

where $R_{g(a-c)_1}$ is equal to $R_{g(a-c)_2}$ and $R_{g(a-c)_3}$:

$$\left(\frac{N_1}{N_2}\right)_0 = \sqrt{\frac{5 \times 10^2}{1.65 \times 10^3}} = \sqrt{0.303} = 0.55:1$$

This indicates that the initial input transformer must have fewer turns in the primary than in the secondary (0.55 : 1 is the same as 1 : 1.82). The single-stage power gain in the matched condition is 5.43×10^4 (from Example 6–13). For the three-stage matched amplifier:

$$A_{p3} = A_{pE_1} A_{pE_2} A_{pE_3} = (5.43 \times 10^4)^3 = 1.6 \times 10^{14}$$

or, in decibels:

$$A_{p3}(db) = 10 \log_{10} A_{p3} = 10(14.2) = 142 \text{ db}$$

For the unmatched amplifier, the power gain is 7.75×10^3 (from Example 6–9). For the three-stage unmatched amplifier:

$$A_{p3} = (7.75 \times 10^3)^3 = 4.65 \times 10^{11}$$

or, in decibels:

$$A_{p3}(db) = 10(11.678) = 116.78 \text{ db}$$

This indicates that the unmatched power gain is only 0.29 per cent of the matched gain. This could also be expressed by saying that the unmatched amplifier is down 25 db (-25 db) from the matched amplifier.

6.8 Negative Feedback Amplifiers

The variability of transistor characteristics is discussed in Chap. 5. Since the characteristics vary widely between one transistor and another (even when both are selected from the same lot!), and since the h-parameters represent the characteristic slopes, the h-parameters must undergo a similar wide variation. The values of a specific transistor may deviate by 50 *per cent or more* from the indicated values. This makes it extremely difficult to place a high degree of confidence in an amplifier design, whether the design is obtained through graphical or mathematical methods, and makes the actual construction of an amplifier a trial-and-error process. Furthermore, once an amplifier is built and adjusted to meet the desired criteria, a completely different set of operating characteristics will be obtained when the transistor becomes faulty and must be replaced. Such inconsistencies cannot be tolerated in most amplifier applications. Fortunately, most amplifiers contain *negative feedback* paths which tend to stabilize gain and make it *somewhat independent of the transistor parameters*. Negative feedback requires the application of a new input voltage component 180° out of phase with the input terminal voltage and proportional to the output current or voltage (Fig. 6–41). Hence, negative feedback constitutes an *out-of-phase coupling between the output and input loops*.

An *in-phase* coupling between output and input loops produces *posi-*

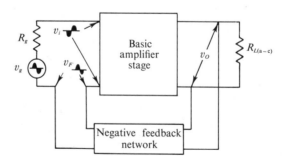

Figure 6-41.   *General Negative Feedback Arrangement*

tive feedback which *decreases* amplifier stability and, ultimately, results in oscillation rather than amplification. This form of feedback is discussed in Chap. 10. It is mentioned here in order to stress the care that must be taken to assure the proper phase relationships when designing negative feedback paths. Furthermore, feedback may occur accidentally, through stray magnetic field or electric field coupling, and may be either negative or positive in such cases. This requires special care in shielding and wiring in order to avoid such detrimental and unpredictable effects.

The deliberate use of negative feedback makes it possible to predict amplifier operation with a high degree of confidence through analytical techniques. Without negative feedback, it would be impossible to construct precision amplifiers or calibrated instrumentation with semiconductor devices. (The same is true, to a lesser degree, of vacuum tubes.) Not only does the feedback compensate for variations in transistor characteristics, it compensates for inaccuracies in component (resistor, capacitor, inductor) values as well. As stated previously, such values may vary as much as 20 per cent from the indicated values. Other desirable effects are also obtained: *increased bandwidth, decreased distortion*, and *decreased noise*. These desirable qualities, however, are not achieved without any losses. *Gain is always reduced by negative feedback.* Hence, the design of practical amplifiers requires a compromise of gain, with an associated increase in the number of cascaded stages, against obtaining more desirable frequency, noise, distortion, and stability characteristics.

Negative feedback is also known as *degenerative* or *inverse* feedback. Regardless of the name, the concepts and results are the same.

Single-Stage Series Feedback

Figure 6–42 illustrates a generalized single-stage amplifier equivalent circuit with *series feedback*. The feedback voltage is developed across the resistor R_F, which is a *series component* in both the input and output loops. Since the output current, i_o, predominates in determining the voltage across R_F (in most cases, $i_o \gg i_I$) the feedback voltage is *proportional to the output current*. For this reason, the term *current feedback* is often used for this arrangement.

It would be possible, using the circuit in Fig. 6–42, to derive a completely new set of *feedback design equations* in terms of the transistor h-parameters, $R_{L(a-c)}$ and R_F. However, it is more convenient to use the existing set (Tables 6–6 and 6–7), and to express the feedback amplifier gains, input resistance, and output resistance in terms of the non-feedback values and a *feedback factor*. In order to do this, it is necessary to inves-

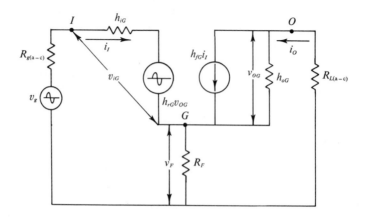

Figure 6-42.   *Hybrid Equivalent with Series Feedback*

tigate the *change* in v_{IG}, v_{OG}, i_o, and i_I that is brought about by the feedback path.

A comparison of Figs. 6–42 and 6–9 shows that the presence of R_F in the output loop does not affect the Kirchoff current equation [Eq. (6–10)]. It does, however, affect Eq. (6–11), which becomes:

$$v_{OG} = i_o[R_{L(a-c)} + R_F] \tag{6-11b}$$

If the procedure for the derivation of non-feedback current gain is followed, with Eq. (6–11b) substituted for Eq. (6–11), the current gain with feedback is given by:

$$A_{iG(F)} = \frac{-h_{fG}}{h_{oG}[R_{L(a-c)} + R_F] + 1} \tag{6-49}$$

Because of the small value of h_{oG}, $A_{iG(F)}$ will not differ greatly from A_{iG}. As a matter of fact, in view of the small variation of A_{iG} with $R_{L(a-c)}$ (Fig. 6–10) until extremely high load values are present, the approximation for A_{iG} [Eq. (6–19)] applies equally well to $A_{iG(F)}$. Hence, it is practical to say that series current feedback does not affect amplifier current gain:

$$A_{iG(F)} = A_{iG} \tag{6-49a}$$

By definition, the voltage gain of an amplifier is given by the ratio of output to input voltages. In the non-feedback case, v_{IG} is equal to v_g (neglecting the source resistance), as shown in Fig. 6–43, Part A. *With feedback*, the value of v_{IG} *must be increased*, since:

$$v_{IG} = v_g + v_F \tag{6-50}$$

as shown in Part B of the figure. An increase in v_{IG} with no change in v_{OG} effectively produces *a lower voltage gain* for the amplifier:

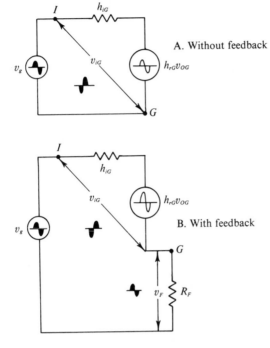

Figure 6-43. *Comparison of Input Loop Equivalents*

$$A_{vG(F)} = \frac{v_{OG}}{v_{IG} + v_F} < A_{vG} \tag{6-51}$$

The value of v_F can be found from the equivalent circuit in Fig. 6–44. It is a fraction of the total output voltage, given by:

$$v_F = v_{OG}\left[\frac{R_F}{R_{L(a\text{-}c)} + R_F}\right] \tag{6-52}$$

Since v_{OG} is equal to $|A_{vG}|v_{IG}$, where $|A_{vG}|$ is the magnitude of the voltage gain without feedback, the equality in Eq. (6–50) can be written as:

$$A_{vG(F)} = \frac{|A_{vG}|v_{IG}}{v_{IG} + |A_{vG}|v_{IG}[R_F/(R_{L(a\text{-}c)} + R_F)]} \tag{6-53}$$

$$= \frac{|A_{vG}|}{1 + |A_{vG}|B_v}$$

where B_v is termed the *voltage feedback factor:*

$$B_v = \frac{R_F}{R_{L(a\text{-}c)} + R_F} \tag{6-54}$$

Since the denominator of Eq. (6–53) will *always be greater than the*

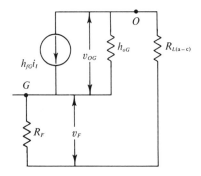

Figure 6-44.   *Output Loop Equivalent*

numerator, the previous indication that voltage gain with feedback is less than voltage gain without feedback [Eq. (6–51)] is further supported.

Power gain is the product of voltage and current gain. The reduced voltage gain associated with series feedback, then, must be accompanied by a reduction in power gain:

$$A_{pG(F)} = A_{iG}A_{vG(F)} = A_{iG}\left[\frac{|A_{vG}|}{1+|A_{vG}|\,B_v}\right] \tag{6-55}$$

$$= \frac{A_{pG}}{1+|A_{vG}|\,B_v}$$

A_{iG} is substituted directly for $A_{iG(F)}$ because of the approximation presented in Eq. (6–49a).

Example 6-25.   A resistance of 100 ohms is placed in the emitter branch of the amplifier in Examples 6–7 and 6–9 to form a series feedback component. What are the gains associated with this feedback amplifier?

Solution.   The current gain is not affected:

$$A_{iE(F)} = A_{iE} = -104$$

The voltage gain with feedback is:

$$A_{vE(F)} = \frac{A_{vE}}{1+|A_{vE}|\,B_v}$$

where:

$$B_v = \frac{R_F}{R_{L(a-c)}+R_F} = \frac{1\times 10^2}{(1.67\times 10^3)+(0.1\times 10^3)}$$

$$= \frac{1\times 10^2}{1.77\times 10^3} = 0.0565$$

Hence:

$$A_{vE(F)} = \frac{-74.5}{1 + (74.5)(5.65 \times 10^{-2})} = \frac{-74.5}{5.21} = -14.3$$

The power gain with feedback is:

$$A_{pE(F)} = \frac{A_{pE}}{1 + |A_{vE}| B_v} = \frac{7750}{5.21} = 1488$$

The power gain may also be determined from:

$$A_{pE(F)} = A_{iE(F)} A_{vE(F)} = (-104)(-14.3) = 1488$$

It can be seen that even a small amount of feedback can result in a considerable gain reduction.

Single-Stage Shunt Feedback

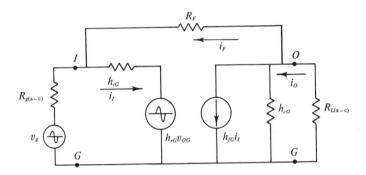

Figure 6-45.   *Hybrid Equivalent with Shunt Feedback*

Figure 6–45 illustrates a generalized single-stage amplifier equivalent circuit with *shunt feedback*. This circuit is frequently used in transistor amplifiers as a biasing network (Chap. 5). The path permits the "injection" of a new a-c current component, i_F, into the input loop, along with the d-c biasing current. Since the magnitude of this current is *proportional to the output voltage*, the term *voltage feedback* is often used for this arrangement. The addition of a new current component must result in a higher current in the input loop:

$$i_{I(F)} = i_I + i_F \tag{6-56}$$

and, since current gain is expressed by the ratio of output current to input current, *must result in a reduced current gain*. The feedback current gain is given by:

$$A_{iG(F)} = \frac{i_o}{i_I + i_F} < A_{iG} \qquad (6\text{-}57)$$

The value for i_F can be found from a consideration of voltage divider principles, resulting in the approximation:

$$i_F = i_o \left[\frac{R_{L(\text{a-c})}}{R_F} \right] \qquad (6\text{-}58)$$

as shown in the figure. Since i_o is equal to $A_{iG}i_I$, where A_{iG} is the magnitude of the current gain without feedback, the equality in Eq. (6–57) can be written as:

$$A_{iG(F)} = \frac{|A_{iG}|}{1 + |A_{iG}| B_i} \qquad (6\text{-}59)$$

where B_i is termed the *current feedback factor*:

$$B_i = \frac{R_{L(\text{a-c})}}{R_F} \qquad (6\text{-}60)$$

Since the denominator of Eq. (6–59) will *always be greater than the numerator*, the reduction of current gain with shunt feedback indicated previously [Eq. (6–57)] is further supported.

No additional voltage components are introduced in series with the voltage components of the amplifier without feedback, leading to the fact that *voltage gain is not affected by shunt feedback*:

$$A_{vG(F)} = A_{vG} \qquad (6\text{-}61)$$

Power gain *is* affected, however, since it is the product of voltage and current gains:

$$A_{pG(F)} = \frac{A_{pG}}{1 + |A_{iG}| B_i} \qquad (6\text{-}62)$$

which is derived in a manner similar to that presented for series feedback [Eq. (6–55)].

Example 6-26. The amplifier described in Examples 6-7 and 6-9 is to use a single-source supply in the output loop and is to be biased with the feedback network shown in Fig. 5–51. The feedback resistance must be 80K in order to obtain the desired biasing current. What effect does this arrangement have on the gains associated with the amplifier?

Solution. The feedback biasing network in Fig. 5–51 is a shunt feedback component, as can be determined by examining Fig. 6–45. The current gain with shunt feedback is:

$$A_{iE(F)} = \frac{A_{iE}}{1 + |A_{iE}| B_i}$$

where:

$$B_i = \frac{R_{L(a\text{-}c)}}{R_F} = \frac{1.67 \times 10^3}{8 \times 10^4} = 0.021$$

Hence:

$$A_{iE(F)} = \frac{-104}{1 + (104)(2.1 \times 10^{-2})} = \frac{-104}{3.18} = -32.8$$

The voltage gain is not affected:

$$A_{vE(F)} = A_{vE} = -74.5$$

The power gain with shunt feedback is:

$$A_{pE(F)} = A_{iE(F)}A_{vE(F)} = (-32.8)(-74.5) = 2440$$

Single-Stage Series/Shunt Feedback

Most practical amplifier circuits contain *some degree* of series *and* shunt feedback, operating simultaneously. When both are present, the voltage and current gains can be analyzed separately, using Eqs. (6–53) and (6–59). As the product of these two gains, the power gain is affected most:

$$A_{pG(F)} = \frac{A_{pG}}{1 + A_{pG}B_iB_v + |A_{iG}|B_i + |A_{vG}|B_v} \tag{6-63}$$

Equations (6–55), (6–62), and (6–63) are plotted in Fig. 6–46 and provide an indication of the rapid reduction in gain as the feedback factor increases. The power gain undergoes the most rapid reduction for the series/shunt feedback combination, since the current gain and voltage gain are *both* reduced.

Example 6-27.   The amplifier described in Examples 6–7 and 6–9 is to use shunt feedback biasing (as described in Example 6–26) and a series feedback component (as described in Example 6–25). What is the power gain for this amplifier?

Solution.   The power gain is given by:

$$A_{pE(F)} = \frac{A_{pE}}{1 + |A_{pE}|B_iB_v + |A_{iE}|B_i + |A_{vE}|B_v}$$
$$= \frac{7.75 \times 10^3}{16.5} = 470$$

The same result can be obtained by considering the feedback current and voltage gains. The voltage gain is reduced to -14.3 by the

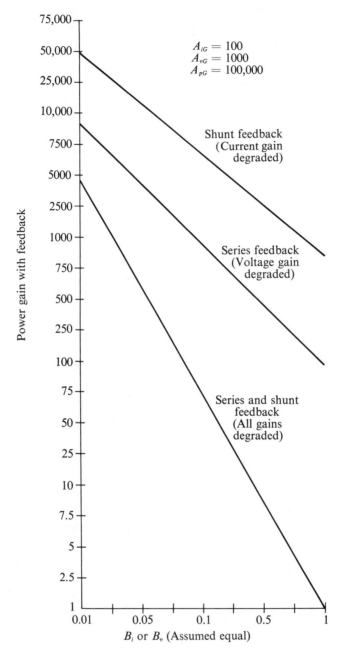

$$A_{iG} = 100$$
$$A_{vG} = 1000$$
$$A_{pG} = 100,000$$

Shunt feedback
(Current gain
degraded)

Series feedback
(Voltage gain
degraded)

Series and shunt
feedback
(All gains
degraded)

Power gain with feedback

B_i or B_v (Assumed equal)

Figure 6-46. *Effect of Negative Feedback on Power Gain*

series feedback while the current gain is reduced to -33.7 by the shunt feedback:

$$A_{pE(F)} = A_{iE(F)}A_{vE(F)} = (-14.3)(-32.8) = 470$$

Gain Stability and Distortion

If the gain of an amplifier without feedback changes by an amount ΔA, the change in gain if feedback is present is given by:

$$\Delta A_F = \frac{\Delta A}{1 + |A| B_F} \tag{6-64}$$

where the changes are expressed in terms of percentages. A may be current gain, voltage gain, or power gain; and B_F may be B_i, B_v, or B_iB_v, as appropriate.

From Eqs. (6–53), (6–55), (6–59), (6–62), and (6–63), it can be seen that if $|A| B_F$ becomes much greater than one, the equations can be approximated by:

$$A_F \approx \frac{1}{B_F} \tag{6-65}$$

where, again, B_F is a generalized feedback factor. From Eq. (6–65), it can be seen that the use of negative feedback may make the amplifier gain (voltage gain for series feedback; current gain for shunt feedback) essentially *independent of the transistor h-parameters*.

The change in distortion brought about by negative feedback is not easy to accept (and understand) on an intuitive basis. Figure 6–47 illustrates a nonlinear dynamic transfer characteristic with a sinusoidal input current and nonsinusoidal output current (Part A). Part B of the figure illustrates the resultant input current when negative feedback is applied. Notice that this resultant input current is now a *nonsinusoidal signal, but is distorted inversely with respect to the distortion introduced by the transfer characteristic.* This permits a degree of compensation for the nonlinearity of the characteristic so that the output signal becomes more nearly sinusoidal (Part C). Mathematically, the decrease in distortion is expressed by:

$$D_F = \frac{D}{1 + |A| B_F} \tag{6-66}$$

where D_F and D must be expressed in percentages. (The value for D may be determined graphically by the procedure described in Chap. 5.)

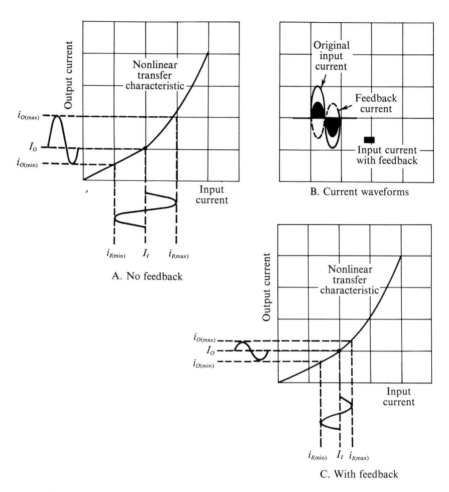

Figure 6-47. *Graphical Illustration of Distortion Reduction with Negative Feedback*

Example 6-28. The amplifier described in Examples 6–7 and 6–9 uses a transistor with a specified h_{fE}-value of 110. This is an average value and any particular transistor selected from the batch may vary considerably. What per cent change in power gain is experienced by this amplifier if the transistor selected has an h_{fE}-value 30 per cent less than the specified value? What per cent change in power gain is experienced if the shunt feedback circuit of Example 6–26 is used?

Solution. A 30-per cent decrease in the specified h_{fE}-value produces:

$$h'_{fE} = (1 - 0.3)h_{fE} = 0.7h_{fE} = 0.7(110) = 77$$

The power gain with this transistor is (from Table 6-7):

$$A'_{pE} = \frac{(h'_{fE})^2 R_{L(a-c)}}{(h_{oE} R_{L(a-c)} + 1)(\Delta h'_E R_{L(a-c)} + h_{iE})}$$

where:

$$\Delta h'_E = h_{iE} h_{oE} - h'_{fE} h_{rE} = 2410(3.25 \times 10^{-5}) - 77(3.79 \times 10^{-4})$$
$$= 4.92 \times 10^{-2}$$

Hence:

$$A'_{pE} = \frac{(77)^2(1.67 \times 10^3)}{[(3.25 \times 10^{-5})(1.67 \times 10^3) + 1][(4.92 \times 10^{-2})(1.67 \times 10^3) + 2410]}$$
$$= \frac{9.9 \times 10^6}{1.054(2.49 \times 10^3)} = 3770$$

This represents a decrease in gain of:

$$\frac{7750 - 3770}{7750} \times 100 \text{ per cent} = \frac{3980}{7750} \times 100 \text{ per cent} = 51.4 \text{ per cent}$$

If the shunt feedback of Example 6–26 is used, the per cent change in gain will be:

$$\Delta A_F = \frac{\Delta A}{1 + |A| B_F}$$

Where $|A|$ must be the current gain without feedback which, from Example 6–7, is 104. B_F is the shunt feedback factor (0.021, from Example 6–26), so that:

$$\Delta A_F = \frac{51.4 \text{ per cent}}{1 + (104)(2.1 \times 10^{-2})} = \frac{51.4 \text{ per cent}}{3.18} = 16 \text{ per cent}$$

This would indicate that from a gain stabilization viewpoint, an even greater amount of feedback may be desirable, since 16 per cent is still a fairly large variation. Of course, the feedback change is now measured with respect to the feedback power gain which, from Example 6–26, is 2440. This means that the use of the degraded transistor in the non-feedback amplifier reduces the power gain from 7750 to 3770 (a decrease of 51.4 per cent), while its use in the feedback amplifier reduces the power gain from 2440 to 16 per cent less than this value, or 1960. This represents a considerable reduction in gain over the non-feedback case. However, the value of 2440 is much more stable. That is, the substitution of another transistor with an h_{fE}-value different from 110 would not change the power gain nearly as much as it would in the non-feedback amplifier.

Example 6-29. If the application for which the amplifier in Example 6–28 is designed requires a minimum power gain of 7000, what can be done to provide a gain-stable amplifier to meet this requirement?

Solution. A multistage amplifier with stabilizing feedback in each stage can be designed to meet the minimum gain requirement. The necessary gain for each stage of a two-stage cascade would be:

$$\sqrt{7000} = 83.6$$

However, since even the best stabilization circuit will experience some degree of gain reduction if a transistor with degraded characteristics is used, it is necessary to include a "safety factor" in the design. Let each stage power gain be arbitrarily established at 100. This will provide a two-stage power gain of 10,000 (beyond the minimum requirement) when no degradation is present.

The non-feedback amplifier has a power gain of 7750. If the stabilized amplifier is to have a gain of 100 per stage, each stage must include a feedback factor of:

$$B_i = \frac{A_{pE} - A_{pE(F)}}{A_{pE(F)} |A_{iE}|} = \frac{7750 - 100}{100(104)} = 0.735$$

It is of interest to check the effect of a degraded transistor in this amplifier. If the transistor in Example 6–28 (with an h_{fE} of 77, rather than 110) were placed in one stage of the cascade, the reduction in power gain for this stage would be:

$$\Delta A_F = \frac{\Delta A}{1 + |A_{iE}| B_F} = \frac{51.4 \text{ per cent}}{1 + (104)(0.735)} = 6.63 \text{ per cent}$$

which means that the power gain for this stage will be approximately 94. The power gain of the second stage will remain at 100. Hence, the overall power gain for the cascade is 9400—well above the minimum requirement. If, by chance, the degraded transistor were placed in both stages, the power gain of both stages would be reduced to 94. This results in a cascade gain of approximately 8850—still more than adequate for the application. From this, it can be seen that the transistor characteristics could be degraded considerably, while still maintaining satisfactory operation for the amplifier. This is an important advantage of negative feedback amplifiers. In fact, transistor amplifiers would be very unpredictable if it were not for the negative feedback that is almost always present in one form or another.

Example 6-30. In Example 5–15, a total harmonic distortion of 6.75 per cent is calculated for a particular amplifier. This is quite high for most audio applications. In Example 5–17, a current gain of 38, voltage gain of 241, and power gain of 9150 are calculated for the same amplifier. How much negative feedback must be designed into the circuit in order to achieve only 1 per cent total harmonic distortion with a minimum reduction in power gain?

Solution.   The per cent distortion with feedback is:

$$D_F = \frac{D}{1 + |A| B_F}$$

Rearranging for B_F:

$$B_F = \frac{D - D_F}{|A| D_F}$$

If series feedback is used, only the voltage gain is affected:

$$B_v = \frac{6.75 \text{ per cent} - 1 \text{ per cent}}{241(1 \text{ per cent})} = \frac{0.0675 - 0.01}{241(0.01)} = \frac{0.0575}{2.41} = 0.0238$$

This will result in a voltage gain of:

$$A_{vE(F)} = \frac{A_{vE}}{1 + |A_{vE}| B_F} = \frac{241}{1 + (241)(2.38 \times 10^{-2})}$$

$$= \frac{241}{6.75} = 35.7$$

and a power gain of:

$$A_{pE(F)} = A_{iE(F)} A_{vE(F)} = 38(35.7) = 1360$$

If shunt feedback is used, only the current gain is affected:

$$B_i = \frac{0.0675 - 0.01}{38(0.01)} = \frac{0.0575}{0.38} = 0.151$$

This will result in a current gain of:

$$A_{iE(F)} = \frac{A_{iE}}{1 + |A_{iE}| B_i} = \frac{38}{1 + (38)(0.151)} = \frac{38}{6.75} = 5.64$$

and a power gain of:

$$A_{pE(F)} = A_{iE(F)} A_{vE(F)} = 5.64(241) = 1360$$

Hence, the specific reduction of distortion does not depend on the type feedback employed. The feedback power gain reduction will always be the same. Shunt feedback would probably be used because single-supply biasing can be achieved with the same network. If the shunt feedback resistor cannot be selected to provide a feedback factor of 0.151 because of bias current considerations, a combination of series and shunt feedback may be in order. The appropriate reduction in distortion can still be achieved with the same reduction in power gain.

Cutoff Frequencies and Bandwidth

Since the series and shunt feedback components discussed thus far have been purely resistive, no new frequency-dependent characteristics are introduced by the feedback paths. Hence, for the audio amplifier, the feedback gain equations apply across the entire frequency response spectrum (low-, mid-, and high-frequency regions). Furthermore, the phase-shift characteristics are not affected. Figure 6–48 presents a plot of power gain for an RC coupled amplifier without feedback (taken from Fig. 6–36 for a single stage). The power gain *for the same amplifier* with different series (or shunt) feedback factor values is also shown in the figure. Notice that the power gain curves *with feedback* reach 0.5 times the mid-frequency value *at a higher frequency than f_H and at a lower frequency than f_L*. Hence, Fig. 6–48 provides a graphical illustration of the fact that *bandwidth is increased through the use of negative feedback*. In view of the inverse relationship between gain and bandwidth discussed previously (on the basis of energy conservation), this should not come as a surprise. The upper and lower cutoff frequencies for the feedback stage are given by:

$$f_{H(F)} = f_H(1 + |A|B_F)$$

(6-67)

and:

$$f_{L(F)} = \frac{f_L}{1 + |A|B_F}$$

(6-68)

This increase in upper cutoff frequency and decrease in lower cutoff frequency can also be reasoned from Eq. (6-64), if it is rewritten as:

$$\Delta A = [1 + |A|B_F]\Delta A_F$$

(6-64a)

When going from the mid-frequency gain value to the cutoff frequency gain value, ΔA_F must be equal to 29.3 per cent (by definition). Since the bracketed term is greater than one, the corresponding change in gain for the non-feedback amplifier (ΔA) must be greater than 29.3 per cent. This occurs only at a frequency higher than f_H and lower than f_L.

In many practical amplifier circuits, the feedback component is *not purely resistive*. In such instances, the feedback factor, itself, is frequency dependent and the simple graphical relationship illustrated in Fig. 6–48 does not hold true. Since the phase of the feedback voltage (or current) varies with frequency in this instance, pure negative feedback (a 180° phase inversion) will not be maintained across the amplifier frequency

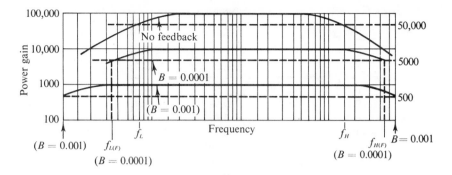

Figure 6-48.   *Variation of Gain and Cutoff Frequencies for Amplifiers with Negative Feedback*

band. In fact, over some frequency ranges the feedback *may become positive*, producing undesirable oscillations, or instability. This is particularly noticeable at the high and low ends of the response curves. Trial-and-error adjustments are called for when this occurs.

Example 6-31.   The amplifier described in Examples 6–7 and 6–9 has a power gain of 7750. The frequency response with a particular RC coupling network is described in Example 6–17. Shunt feedback is used to achieve single-supply biasing for this amplifier. The feedback factor is 0.008. What are the upper and lower cutoff frequencies for the feedback amplifier? Plot the power gain (in decibels) as a function of frequency.

Solution.   From Example 6–17, the upper cutoff frequency is 90 kc and the low-frequency response is essentially d-c. With feedback, the upper cutoff frequency is:

$$f_{H(F)} = f_H(1 + |A| \, B_F) = f_H(1 + |A_{iE}| \, B_i)$$
$$= (90 \times 10^3)[1 + (104)(8 \times 10^{-3})] = (90 \times 10^3)(1.832)$$
$$= 165 \text{ kc}$$

Since negative feedback tends to decrease the lower cutoff frequency, and since this is already near d-c, the feedback effect need not be considered. The mid-frequency power gain with feedback is:

$$A_{pE(F)} = \frac{A_{pE}}{1 + |A_{iE}| \, B_i} = \frac{7750}{1.832} = 4100$$

Using Fig. 6–22 for the high-frequency response, the following data are obtained:

$f/f_{H(F)}$	f	$A_{p(F)}/A_{pE(F)}$	$A_{p(F)}$	$A_{p(F)}$(db)
0.1	16.5 kc	1.0	4100	36.13
0.2	33.0 kc	0.98	4020	36.04
0.5	82.5 kc	0.625	2560	34.08
1.0	165 kc	0.5	2050	33.13
2.0	330 kc	0.202	829	29.18
5.0	825 kc	0.04	164	22.14
8.0	1320 kc	0.144	59	17.71

These values are plotted in Fig. E6–31.

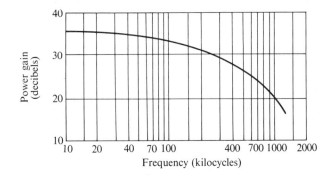

Figure E6-31

Input and Output Resistances

The presence of negative feedback also alters the a-c input and output resistances of the amplifier. Series feedback always causes an increase:

$$r_{iG(F)} = r_{iG}(1 + |A_{vG}| B_v) \qquad (6\text{-}69)$$
$$r_{oG(F)} = r_{oG} + R_F(1 + |A_{vG}| B_v) \qquad (6\text{-}70)$$

and for shunt feedback:

$$r_{iG(F)} = r_{iG}(1 + |A_{iG}| B_i) \qquad (6\text{-}71)$$
$$r_{oG(F)} = \frac{r_{oG}}{1 + |A_{iG}| B_i} \qquad (6\text{-}72)$$

Matching

Even with feedback, a maximum possible power gain for a given transistor amplifier will be obtained only under matched conditions ($r_{iG(F)} = R_{g(a-c)}$; $r_{oG(F)} = R_{L(a-c)}$). However, the value of maximum possible power gain will be less with feedback than the value that can be achieved without feedback [Eq. (6–26)]. The maximum possible power gain with feedback is determined from Eq. (6–55), (6–62), or (6–63), as appropriate, with $A_{pG(max)}$ replacing A_{pG}. Under the feedback condition, Eq. (6–24) and Eq. (6–25) are no longer valid. The matching process becomes more of a trial-and-error analysis, but the change in r_{iG} and r_{oG} (previous section) can be controlled by varying the feedback factor. The use of negative feedback is the most practical way to achieve matching in the RC coupled amplifier circuit.

Cascade Arrangements

If the individual stages of a multistage amplifier have their own series, shunt, or combination feedback arrangements (Fig. 6–49), the design procedure follows a pattern similar to that described for the multistage amplifier without feedback. However, the feedback gains, resistances, and cutoff frequencies must be substituted for the non-feedback values in

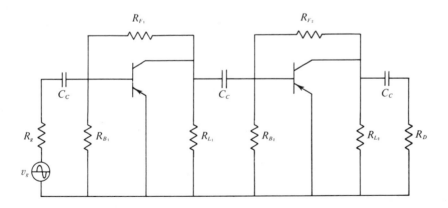

Figure 6-49.   *Two-Stage Cascaded Amplifier with Shunt Feedback in Each Stage*

the design equations. With these substitutions, the equations developed for the non-feedback amplifier cascade apply equally well to the feedback case.

Example 6-32. The amplifier described in Example 6–26 is to be used in a three-stage cascade, with each stage having the same amount of shunt feedback. Plot the current gain for the multistage amplifier as a function of frequency if the RC coupling network described in Example 6–17 is used.

Solution. From Example 6–26, the mid-frequency current gain with feedback is −32.8. For the three-stage cascade with identical feedback in each stage:

$$A_{i3(F)} = A_{iE(F)_1}A_{iE(F)_2}A_{iE(F)_3} = (-32.8)^3 = -(3.52 \times 10^4)$$

From Example 6–17, the upper cutoff frequency is 90 kc and the lower cutoff frequency is essentially d-c. Negative feedback reduces the lower cutoff frequency and need not be considered. The upper cutoff frequency for each stage is:

$$f_{H(F)} = f_H(1 + |A_{iE}|B_i) = (90 \times 10^3)[1 + (104)(2.1 \times 10^{-2})]$$
$$= (90 \times 10^3)(3.18) = 286 \text{ kc}$$

However, with three stages in cascade, the upper cutoff frequency is:

$$f_{H(F)3} = f_{H(F)}\sqrt{2^{1/3} - 1} = (286 \times 10^3)\sqrt{0.73} = 244 \text{ kc}$$

With data from Fig. 6–22 (as in Examples 6–17, 6–22, and 6–31), the current response curve in Fig. E6–32 can be obtained.

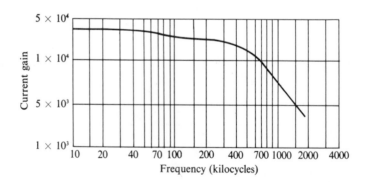

Figure E6-32

Multistage Feedback

Figure 6–50 illustrates an amplifier with multistage feedback; that is, the feedback path runs between one stage and another. As shown, the feedback is from the final stage to the first stage. If it were from the final stage to the second stage, or from the second stage to the first, the process would still be termed multistage feedback. The feedback analysis equations still apply. However, the non-feedback gains for the individual stages must be replaced by the product of the gains of the stages enclosed by the feedback path. In essence, this is equivalent to replacing the stages enclosed by the feedback loop by a single stage having the non-feedback cascaded properties of the enclosed stages. This technique generally results in higher feedback gains than would be achieved by a cascaded arrangement with feedback in each stage. Since most distortion occurs in the final stages of

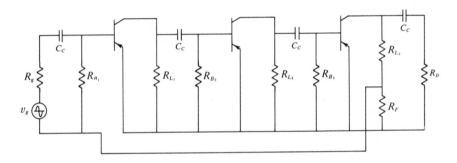

Figure 6-50.   *Three-Stage Cascaded Amplifier with Multistage Series Feedback from Last Stage to First Stage*

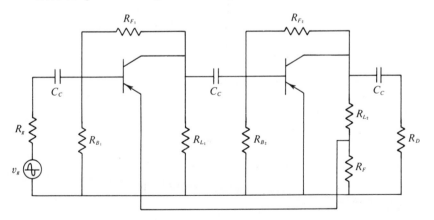

Figure 6-51.   *Two-Stage Cascaded Amplifier with Shunt Feedback in Each Stage and Multistage Feedback*

a cascade (where the signal excursions may become quite large), it is very practical to enclose the last stage and its preceding stages with a feedback loop. Because of the large value of the final output signal, the distortion can be corrected by very small feedback factors. This will inherently result in higher feedback gains, since the gain of *all* the stages is not affected.

Multistage and single-stage feedback may both be present in an amplifier arrangement (Fig. 6–51). In order to analyze this circuit, the individual stages must be treated first. Once this is accomplished, the multistage feedback effects may be considered. With all of these interactions, the cascaded gains will be much lower than could be achieved with no feedback. However, the stability, bandwidth, and distortion characteristics are greatly enhanced.

Example 6-33. Series feedback is to be applied from the third stage to the first stage in the multistage amplifier described in Example 6–32. (This will result in a circuit similar to that illustrated in Fig. 6–51, with an additional stage.) How much feedback must be applied in order to obtain the 286-kc upper cutoff frequency that is available in the individual stages? What happens to the power gain in the process?

Solution. The upper cutoff frequency is given by:

$$f'_{H(F)3} = f_{H(F)3}(1 + |A_{vE}|B_v)$$

Rearranging for B_v:

$$B_v = \frac{f'_{H(F)3} - f_{H(F)3}}{|A_{vE}|f_{H(F)3}} = \frac{(286 - 244)(10^3)}{(74.5)(2.44 \times 10^5)} = 2.31 \times 10^{-3}$$

This will not affect the current gain, so that the multistage current gain remains at $-(3.52 \times 10^4)$. The voltage gain for the cascade will be reduced. This gain, before the multistage feedback is applied, is given by:

$$A_{v3} = A_{vE_1}A_{vE_2}A_{vE_3} = (-74.5)^3 = -(4.14 \times 10^5)$$

With the series feedback this is reduced to:

$$A_{v3(F)} = \frac{A_{v3}}{1 + |A_{v3}|B_v} = \frac{-(4.14 \times 10^5)}{1 + (4.14 \times 10^5)(2.31 \times 10^{-3})}$$

$$= \frac{-(4.14 \times 10^5)}{9.57 \times 10^2} = -433$$

This results in a power gain of:

$$A_{p3(F)} = A_{i3(F)}A_{v3(F)} = -(3.52 \times 10^4)(-433) = 1.52 \times 10^7$$

which, in decibels, is:

$$A_{p3(F)}(\text{db}) = 10\log_{10}A_{p3(F)} = 10\log_{10}(1.52 \times 10^7) = 718 \text{ db}$$

PROBLEMS

1. The h-parameters specified for a particular transistor are: $h_{iB} = 22$ ohms, $h_{rB} = 8 \times 10^{-4}$, $h_{fB} = -0.97$, and $h_{oB} = 2 \times 10^{-6}$ mho. Determine the h-parameters for the remaining configurations.
2. The h-parameters specified for a particular transistor are: $h_{iB} = 55$ ohms, $h_{rB} = 5 \times 10^{-4}$, $h_{fE} = 45$, and $h_{oB} = 1 \times 10^{-6}$ mho. Determine the remaining eight h-parameter values.
3. The transistor in Problem 1 is used in a common base amplifier with a source resistance of 800 ohms and an a-c load resistance of 50K. Determine the current, voltage, and power gains for this amplifier.
4. The transistor in Problem 1 is used in a common emitter amplifier with a source resistance of 300 ohms. The d-c load resistance is 8K. The amplifier is RC coupled to a device having an equivalent resistance of 3K. A signal current with an rms value of 5 microamperes is applied. What is the output power?
5. The transistor in Problem 2 is used in a common emitter amplifier with an equivalent a-c load of 15K. Compute the current gain by the "exact" and the "approximate" methods. Compare the results.
6. The transistor in Problem 2 is used in a common collector amplifier that has transformer coupling in both the input and output loops. The input transformer has a 3:1 turns ratio and the output transformer has a 10:1 turns ratio. The signal source resistance is 500 ohms. The amplifier feeds a device with an equivalent resistance of 2K. Determine the input and output resistances for this amplifier.
7. The amplifier in Problem 3 uses a biasing resistor of 8K in the input loop. Determine the output resistance for this amplifier.
8. What is the input resistance of the amplifier in Problem 4?
9. What a-c source and load resistance values must be used with the transistor in Problem 1 if maximum power gain is to be achieved with a common emitter amplifier?
10. What is the maximum power gain that can be obtained with the transistor in Problem 2 in each of the three configurations?
11. Using the input and output characteristics of transistor B in Appendix D, determine the variation in the input resistance parameter and output conductance parameter as I_C varies. Use enough points to plot a set of normalized curves with I_C equal to 6 milliamperes as a reference point. The collector-to-emitter voltage is to be maintained constant at 2.5 volts.
12. Using the output characteristics of transistor E in Appendix D, determine the variation in the associated h-parameter as I_B varies. Use enough points to plot a set of normalized curves with I_B equal

to 90 microamperes as a reference point. The collector-to-emitter voltage is to be maintained constant at 5 volts.

13. Assume that the curves in Fig. 6–16 apply to the transistor in Problem 2 and that the *h*-parameter values listed in Problem 2 are the reference-point values. What are the values of the common emitter and common collector *h*-parameters when the collector voltage is −5 volts and the emitter current is 6 milliamperes?

14. If the curves in Fig. 6–16 apply to the transistor in Problem 1 and the *h*-parameters listed in Problem 1 apply when I_E is 1 milliampere and the collector voltage is −2 volts, what are the reference *h*-parameter values for the common base configuration?

15. The alpha cutoff frequency for the transistor in Problem 1 is 5 megacycles per second. What is the beta cutoff frequency?

16. The alpha cutoff frequency for the transistor in Problem 2 is 8 megacycles per second. The transistor is to be used in an RC coupled common emitter amplifier which must have an upper cutoff frequency equal to or greater than 20 kilocycles per second. Can the transistor be used?

17. What must the alpha cutoff frequency be in Problem 16 if the upper cutoff frequency for the common emitter amplifier is to be exactly 20 kilocycles per second?

18. The amplifier in Problem 3 uses a biasing resistor of 8K in the input loop. What is the lower cutoff frequency for this amplifier when RC coupled by a 2-microfarad capacitor?

19. The amplifier in Problem 4 uses a biasing resistor of 80K in the input loop. The lower cutoff frequency for this amplifier must be 80 cycles per second. What coupling capacitance value must be used?

20. The transistor in Problem 2 is used in a common emitter amplifier that has transformer coupling in the output loop. The transformer has a turns ratio of 5:1, a primary inductance of 150 millihenries, and leakage inductances of 6 millihenries in the primary and 1 millihenry in the secondary. The a-c source resistance is 300 ohms, and the amplifier feeds a device with an equivalent resistance of 2K. Determine the upper and lower cutoff frequencies for the amplifier.

21. The transistor in Problem 1 is to be used in a transformer coupled common base amplifier with maximum power gain. The amplifier is to feed a device with an equivalent resistance of 2K. Assume that the primary leakage inductance is (N_1/N_2) times the secondary leakage inductance. Determine the primary inductance and both leakage inductances if the lower cutoff frequency cannot be greater than 30 cycles per second and the upper cutoff frequency cannot be less than 15 kilocycles per second. (Hint: The turns ratio necessary to achieve matching must be determined first.)

22. Transistor *B* in Appendix D is to be used for two identical common emitter stages in a cascaded RC coupled amplifier. The operating point is defined by I_B equal to 40 microamperes, V_{CE} equal to -4 volts, and I_C equal to -5 milliamperes. The equivalent a-c load resistance on both stages is 500 ohms. An input current of 5 milliamperes is to be applied to the first stage. Can this be done without overdriving the second stage?

23. Transistor *C* in Appendix D is to be used for two common emitter stages in a cascaded amplifier. Each stage is to have an identical operating point defined by I_B equal to 8 milliamperes, V_{CE} equal to 10 volts, and I_C equal to 0.3 ampere. The a-c load resistance for the second stage is 30 ohms. The a-c load resistance on the first stage is 125 ohms. The input resistance to the first stage is 1K. What is the maximum peak-to-peak input voltage that can be applied to the first stage without overdriving either stage?

24. A particular amplifier stage has a current gain of -70 and a voltage gain of -54. Three of these stages are cascaded. What is the power gain of the cascade (in decibels)?

25. A cascaded amplifier with two identical stages has a power gain of 80 decibels. The current gain for each stage is -45. What is the voltage gain for each stage?

26. The common collector amplifier stage in Problem 6 is to be placed in cascade with the common emitter stage in Problem 4. What is the current, voltage, and power gain of the cascade?

27. Three of the amplifier stages described in Problem 4 are to be RC coupled into a cascaded amplifier. What are the current, voltage, and power gains of the cascade?

28. A particular transistor with the following *h*-parameters:

$$h_{iB} = 39 \text{ ohms} \qquad h_{fB} = -0.98$$
$$h_{rB} = 380 \times 10^{-6} \qquad h_{oB} = 4.9 \times 10^{-7} \text{ mho}$$

is to be used in a three-stage common emitter RC coupled amplifier. The signal source has an a-c resistance of 1K and the cascade is to feed a device with an equivalent a-c resistance of 20K. A biasing resistor of 80K is used in the input loop of each stage. The d-c load resistor in each stage is 15K. What is the power gain (in decibels) of the cascade?

29. A particular transistor with the following *h*-parameters:

$$h_{iE} = 3000 \text{ ohms} \qquad h_{fE} = 50$$
$$h_{oE} = 20 \times 10^{-6} \text{ mho} \qquad h_{rE} = 1 \times 10^{-3}$$

is to be used in a two-stage, common emitter transformer coupled amplifier with maximum power gain. The signal source is transformer coupled to the first stage and has an a-c resistance of 450 ohms. The cascade feeds a device with an equivalent resistance of 15K. Select the proper turns ratio for each of the three transformers and determine the power gain of the cascade (in decibels).

30. A three-stage cascade is made of individual stages with identical lower cutoff frequencies (100 cycles per second) and upper cutoff frequencies (35 kilocycles per second). What is the lower cutoff frequency and upper cutoff frequency for the cascade?

31. A two-stage cascade is to have a lower cutoff frequency of 20 cycles per second and an upper cutoff frequency of 20 kilocycles per second. If each of the stages has identical cutoff frequencies, what are these frequencies?

32. A two-stage RC coupled cascade is made of identical transistors in the common emitter configuration. The cascade must have an upper cutoff frequency not less than 80 kilocycles per second. What is the minimum alpha cutoff frequency that can be associated with the transistor?

33. Each stage of the amplifier in Problem 32 has a current gain of -55. Plot the current gain of the cascade as a function of frequency in the high-frequency region.

34. The coupling capacitor between each of the stages in Problem 27 is 3 microfarads. The biasing resistor in the input loop of each stage is 50K. The transistor has an alpha cutoff frequency of 8 megacycles per second. Determine the lower and upper cutoff frequencies of the cascade and plot the power gain (in decibels) as a function of frequency.

35. The transistor in Problem 2 has an alpha cutoff frequency of 8 megacycles per second. It is used (in the common emitter configuration) with an RC coupled common base amplifier as a second stage. The second stage uses the transistor in Problem 1, which has an alpha cutoff frequency of 5 megacycles per second. The biasing resistor in the input loop of the first stage is 50K and in the second stage, 80K. The signal source has an equivalent resistance of 600 ohms. The cascade is used to feed a device with an equivalent resistance of 100K. Coupling capacitors of 2 microfarads are used throughout. Determine the upper and lower cutoff frequencies for the cascade and plot the power gain (in decibels) as a function of frequency.

36. The transistor in Problem 28 has an alpha cutoff frequency of 10 megacycles per second. Determine the upper cutoff frequency for the cascade and plot the power gain (in decibels) for the high-frequency region.

37. What value coupling capacitor must be used in each stage of the cascade in Problem 28 if each stage is to have an identical lower cutoff frequency and the cascade is to have a lower cutoff frequency of 80 cycles per second?

38. The total harmonic distortion in a particular amplifier is 5 per cent. The gain, without feedback, is 300. How much feedback must be applied if the distortion is to be reduced to 1 per cent?

39. The transistor in Problem 1 is such that its forward current transfer parameter will degrade by 5 per cent over a period of time. How much feedback must be used in the amplifier of Problem 4 if its current gain cannot degrade by more than 1 per cent over the same time interval?

40. The amplifier in Problem 3 is biased with a shunt feedback resistor of 200K. What are the mid-frequency current, voltage, and power gains for this amplifier?

41. A single-stage amplifier has an upper cutoff frequency of 30 kilocycles per second. How much feedback must be used to double the upper cutoff frequency?

42. What is the mid-frequency power gain of the amplifier in Problem 4 if a 50-ohm resistor is placed in the emitter branch?

43. The amplifier in Problem 5 is biased with a shunt feedback resistor of 100K and has a 40-ohm resistor placed in the emitter branch. What are the mid-frequency current, voltage, and power gains for this amplifier?

44. The amplifier in Problem 20 is biased with a shunt feedback resistor of 150K. What is the mid-frequency power gain of this amplifier and what are the upper and lower cutoff frequencies?

45. What are the input and output resistances of the amplifier in Problem 40?

46. What are the input and output resistances of the amplifier in Problem 42?

47. What is the maximum power gain that can be achieved with the transistor in Problem 1 if it is used in a common base amplifier with a feedback factor of 0.003?

48. What is the maximum power gain that can be achieved with the transistor in Problem 2 if it is used in a common emitter amplifier with a feedback factor of 0.05?

49. Shunt feedback is used to bias each of the stages in Problem 27. A feedback factor of 0.04 results. What are the current, voltage, and power gains of the cascade?

50. The transistor used in the cascade of Problem 28 has an alpha cutoff frequency of 10 megacycles per second. What is the upper cutoff

frequency of the cascade if a feedback factor of 0.02 is introduced in each stage? Plot the feedback power gain (in decibels) as a function of frequency.

51. A feedback factor of 0.003 is introduced between the last and the first stages in Problem 24. What is the power gain (in decibels)?

52. If the feedback factor in Problem 51 is introduced between the last and the second stages in the cascade of Problem 24, what is the power gain (in decibels)?

53. An additional feedback factor of 0.0005 is introduced between the last and the first stages in Problem 50 in order to overcome distortion in the amplifier. What is the upper cutoff frequency of the cascade? Plot the feedback power gain (in decibels) as a function of frequency.

54. The transistor used in the cascade of Problem 28 has an alpha cutoff frequency of 10 megacycles per second. The upper cutoff frequency of the cascade must be doubled for a particular application. However, a minimum reduction in the mid-frequency power gain of the cascade is desired. Should an equal amount of feedback be used in each stage, or should multistage feedback from the last stage to the first stage be used? Support your answer with the appropriate design changes.

Further Reading

"Basic Theory and Applications of Transistors," TM 11—690. Washington, D. C.: U. S. Government Printing Office, 1959.

Martin, T. L., Jr., *Electronic Circuits.* Englewood Cliffs, N. J.: Prentice-Hall, Inc., 1955.

Pierce, J. F., *Transistor Circuit Theory and Design.* Columbus, Ohio: Charles E. Merrill, 1963.

Ryder, J. D., *Electronic Fundamentals and Applications.* Englewood Cliffs, N. J.: Prentice-Hall, Inc., 1959.

Seidman, A. H. and S. L. Marshall, *Semiconductor Fundamentals.* New York: John Wiley and Sons, Inc., 1963.

Surina, T. and C. Herrick, *Semiconductor Electronics.* New York: Holt, Rinehart, and Winston, Inc., 1964.

7

High-Frequency
Amplifiers

High-frequency amplifiers fall into two categories: those that have a very narrow bandwidth and those that have an extremely wide bandwidth. *Narrowband*, or *selective*, amplifiers are used to amplify a specific set of frequencies while "rejecting" all others. Such amplifiers are used, for example, in radio receiver circuits to select one frequency (station) in the midst of many nearby frequencies. These amplifiers use a parallel-resonant load that is "tuned" to a specific frequency. *Broadband* amplifiers are used to amplify nonsinusoidal signals, such as the coded pulses associated with television picture transmission. Such amplifiers utilize negative feedback and special *frequency compensating* circuits that may be of a resonant nature. These amplifiers are, in general, Class *A* linear amplifiers so that the hybrid equivalent design equations can be used. However, the a-c loads are considerably different in behavior, introducing special frequency-response considerations. Phase shift, as a function of frequency, becomes a critical item in most broadband applications where, for audio amplifiers, it is usually not considered. High-frequency operation also requires a careful consideration of inherent feedback characteristics (such as junction capacitances). Although of little concern at audio frequencies, such characteristics are a basic cause of instability at higher frequencies. External circuit arrangements, known as *neutralization* circuits and *unilateralization* circuits, are used to compensate for internal transistor feedback.

7.1 Selective Amplifiers

In general, selective amplifiers use a parallel-resonant circuit as an a-c load. These circuits are "tuned" to a desirable *center frequency*. At this frequency the amplifier experiences a maximum gain. Depending upon the quality of the load components (in particular, the resistive components), the gain may fall gradually on either side of the center frequency, or it may fall very sharply. However, the selective amplifier does not have a "flat" mid-frequency response in all instances, as does the audio-frequency amplifier. Because of this, the selective amplifier is used to discriminate between signals on a basis of signal frequency. The degree of discrimination, or *selectivity*, of the amplifier depends on the narrowness of the amplifier bandwidth. Ideally, it would be most desirable to achieve frequency selection with an amplifier response similar to that illustrated in Fig. 7-1, Part A. However, realistic response curves

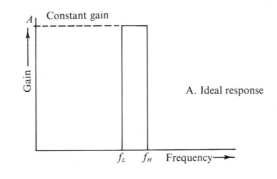

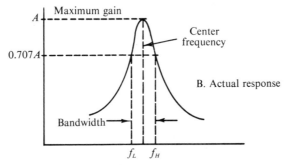

Figure 7-1.   *Narrowband (Selective) Amplifier Response Characteristics*

follow the tendencies shown in Part B. Notice that the response begins to degrade *immediately* on either side of the center, or resonant, frequency. Unlike the ideal response, which would reject all frequencies outside the amplifier bandwidth, the practical amplifier merely attenuates frequencies outside the band. Hence, an especially strong signal outside the band may still be amplified to a high enough amplitide to cause undesirable outputs.

The inductive component of the parallel-resonant load is usually the primary of a transformer—with the secondary serving to transfer the signal to a subsequent stage, or to the device being driven by the signal. Because of this, the selective amplifier is useful from another standpoint: it can be used as an impedance matching device, resulting in maximum possible power gain for a given transistor.

In order to design a selective amplifier, it is necessary to understand the current-voltage-impedance relationships associated with parallel-resonant circuits. The behavior is similar to the parallel-tuned circuit of general electrical network theory and applications. However, because the "tank" is coupled to another device through the transformer secondary, there is an additional "loading" effect that is not associated with general tuned networks. This loading effect tends to degrade amplifier selectivity (broaden the bandwidth) and may, in some instances, cause a shift in the center frequency.

Unloaded Parallel-Resonant Circuits

When the impedance of the inductor-capacitor parallel combination (Fig. 7–2) becomes *purely resistive*, parallel resonance has occurred. This condition is also known as *antiresonance* in order to distinguish it from the resonant condition associated with a series inductor-capacitor combination. This distinction is not merely a matter of terminology—the resistance of an antiresonant circuit is extremely high; the resistance of a

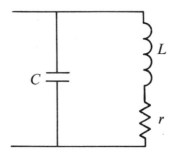

Figure 7-2. *Parallel-Resonant Circuit*

series resonant (or simply, "resonant") circuit is very low. Since both are used as amplifier loads, it is necessary to keep this distinction in mind in order to avoid considerable confusion. Both types are analyzed in detail in standard electrical network texts. Only those relationships of importance to selective amplifier design will be considered here.

The inductive component of the parallel-resonant circuit is an energy storage device with a winding resistance as an energy dissipating device. This inherent resistance, r, can be represented as an equivalent series resistance (Fig. 7–2). The *quality factor* of the coil, a measure of the energy storage and energy dissipation characteristics, is given by:

$$Q = \frac{2\pi f L}{r} = \frac{\omega L}{r} \tag{7-1}$$

Since Q is *frequency dependent*, the specification of Q without an associated frequency is of little value. However, once Q and a corresponding frequency (Q_1 and f_1) are known, the Q at any other frequency can be determined directly:

$$Q_2 = Q_1\left(\frac{f_2}{f_1}\right) \tag{7-2}$$

where f_2 may be less than, or greater than, f_1. For parallel-resonant circuit design, the Q at the antiresonant frequency, denoted Q_{ar}, is of primary importance:

$$Q_{ar} = Q_1\left(\frac{f_{ar}}{f_1}\right) \tag{7-2a}$$

At antiresonance, the impedance of the parallel-resonant circuit is *purely resistive*, and is given by:

$$Z_{ar} = (1 + Q_{ar}^2)r \approx Q_{ar}^2 r \tag{7-3}$$

Through various definitions and algebraic manipulations, it is also possible to relate Z_{ar} to the inductive and capacitive components of the circuit:

$$Z_{ar} = \frac{Q_{ar}}{\omega_{ar}C} = Q_{ar}\omega_{ar}L \tag{7-3a}$$

for values of Q_{ar} greater than ten. The angular frequency, ω, is defined as always:

$$\omega_{ar} = 2\pi f_{ar} \tag{7-4}$$

where the antiresonant frequency is given by:

$$f_{ar} = \frac{1}{2\pi}\sqrt{\frac{1}{LC}} \cdot \sqrt{1 - \left(\frac{1}{Q_{ar}^2}\right)} \tag{7-5}$$

For Q_{ar} greater than ten:

$$f_{ar} = \frac{1}{2\pi}\sqrt{\frac{1}{LC}} \tag{7-5a}$$

The variation of the parallel-resonant circuit impedance as a function of frequency is given by:

$$Z = \frac{Q^2 r(1 + \delta)^2}{1 + jQ\delta(1 + \delta)(2 + \delta)} \tag{7-6}$$

where δ is a frequency ratio, to be defined. The only assumption associated with Eq. (7–6) is that Q must be greater than ten. Hence, the equation is a valid expression for Z at any frequency if the antiresonant frequency is specified, since, by definition:

$$\delta = \frac{f - f_{ar}}{f_{ar}} = \left(\frac{f}{f_{ar}}\right) - 1 \tag{7-7}$$

Notice that δ equal to zero is the condition for antiresonance ($f = f_{ar}$). Under this condition, Eq. (7–6) reduces to the approximate form of Eq. (7–3) and is purely resistive since the imaginary term becomes zero. When δ is positive ($f > f_{ar}$), the j-term in the denominator is positive, leading to a negative reactance for Z (division by j yields a $-j$). Thus, the impedance is capacitive in nature above the antiresonant frequency. For negative δ-values ($f < f_{ar}$), the inverse is true: the j-term in the denominator is negative, leading to a positive reactance for Z. Hence, for frequencies below the antiresonant frequency, the impedance is inductive in nature.

When δ is restricted to values much less than one, Eq. (7–6) can be approximated by:

$$Z = \frac{Q_{ar}^2 r}{1 + j2Q_{ar}\delta} = |Z| \underline{/\theta} \tag{7-6a}$$

which has a magnitude:

$$|Z| = \frac{Q_{ar}^2 r}{1 + 4(Q_{ar}\delta)^2} \tag{7-6b}$$

and a phase angle:

$$\theta = \arctan\left[-2(Q_{ar}\delta)\right] \tag{7-6c}$$

Based on Eqs. (7–6b) and (7–6c), it is possible to develop a *universal antiresonant impedance characteristic*, as shown in Fig. 7–3. The impedance axis has been converted to the ratio:

$$\left|\frac{Z}{Z_{ar}}\right| \approx \frac{1}{1 + 4(Q_{ar}\delta)^2} \tag{7-6d}$$

since [from Eq. (7–3)] Z_{ar} and $Q_{ar}^2 r$ are equivalent. This is a most convenient form for the impedance characteristic and lends itself directly to the determination of selective amplifier response.

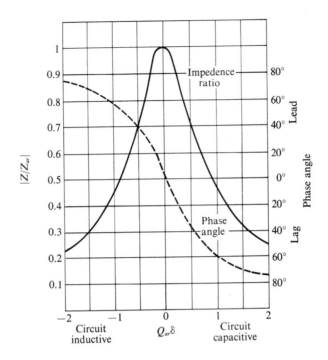

Figure 7-3.   *Universal Antiresonant Impedance Characteristic*

Based on an examination of the phase angle in Fig. 7–3, the impedance of the combination may be inductive or capacitive, as discussed previously. This dependency is only a function of frequency [δ in Eq. (7–6c)].

Example 7-1.   A coil with an inductance of 50 millihenries has a Q of 200 at a frequency of 1000 cycles per second. What is the winding resistance of the coil?

Solution.   The Q of the coil is defined by:

$$Q = \frac{2\pi f L}{r}$$

Rearranging for the coil resistance:

$$r = \frac{2\pi f L}{Q} = \frac{2\pi(1 \times 10^3)(5 \times 10^{-2})}{200} = 1.57 \text{ ohms}$$

Example 7-2.   The coil in Example 7–1 is to be used in an antiresonant circuit tuned to 50 kilocycles per second. What is the antiresonant resistance of the circuit? What value capacitance must be used in the circuit?

Solution. The antiresonant resistance is given by:

$$Z_{ar} = Q_{ar}\omega_{ar}L$$

where:

$$Q_{ar} = Q_1\left(\frac{f_{ar}}{f_1}\right) = 200\left[\frac{5 \times 10^4}{1 \times 10^3}\right] = 10,000$$

with the values for Q_1 and f_1 obtained from Example 7-1. Hence:

$$Z_{ar} = (1 \times 10^4)2\pi(5 \times 10^4)(5 \times 10^{-2}) = 157M$$

It is interesting to check this against the approximation:

$$Z_{ar} \approx Q_{ar}^2 r = (1 \times 10^4)^2(1.57) = 157M$$

showing that this approximation is valid. The antiresonant frequency is given by:

$$f_{ar} = \frac{1}{2\pi}\sqrt{\frac{1}{LC}}$$

when Q_{ar} is greater than ten. Rearranging:

$$C = \frac{1}{(2\pi f_{ar})^2 L} = \frac{1}{4\pi^2(5 \times 10^4)^2(5 \times 10^{-2})}$$
$$= 0.001 \text{ microfarad}$$

Example 7-3. A particular antiresonant circuit has an antiresonant Q of 200 and an antiresonant frequency of 100 kilocycles per second. The antiresonant impedance is 3 megohms. What is the circuit impedance at 99 kilocycles per second? At 99.5 kilocycles per second? At 100.25 kilocycles per second? At 102 kilocycles per second?

Solution. If the quantity Q_{ar} δ is restricted to values between -2 and $+2$, the impedances can be obtained from Fig. 8–3. The δ-values are given by:

$$\delta = \left(\frac{f}{f_{ar}}\right) - 1$$

For the frequencies of interest:

f	f/f_{ar}	δ	$Q_{ar}\delta$	$|Z/Z_{ar}|$	$|Z|$	θ
9.9×10^4	0.99	-0.01	-2	0.25	750K	76°
9.95×10^4	0.995	-0.005	-1	0.45	1.35M	62°
1.0025×10^5	1.0025	0.0025	0.5	0.7	2.1M	$-42°$
1.02×10^5	1.02	0.02	4	—	—	—

The product $Q_{ar}\delta$ is beyond the range of Fig. 7-3 when the frequency is 102 kilocycles per second. However, the impedance magnitude is given by:

$$|Z| = \frac{Q_{ar}^2 r}{1 + 4(Q_{ar}\delta)^2} = \frac{Z_{ar}}{1 + 4(Q_{ar}\delta)^2}$$
$$= \frac{3 \times 10^6}{1 + 4(4)^2} = \frac{3 \times 10^6}{65} = 46.1K$$

and the phase angle is given by:

$$\theta = \arctan[-2(Q_{ar}\delta)] = \arctan[-2(4)] = \arctan(-8)$$
$$= -83°$$

Loaded Parallel-Resonant Circuits

When the parallel-resonant circuit is used as an amplifier load impedance, the inductive component is the primary of a transformer. The secondary of the transformer serves to "couple" the signal from the selective amplifier to the next stage, or to some driven device. This is illustrated in Fig. 7-4, Part A. The secondary of the transformer also reflects the secondary resistance (R_D in Fig. 7-4), into the primary (and into the parallel-resonant combination), as indicated in Part B of the figure:

$$R_L = \left(\frac{N_1}{N_2}\right)^2 R_D \tag{7-8}$$

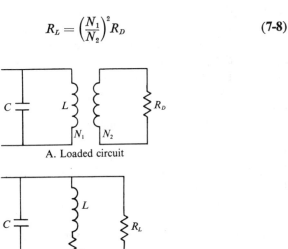

A. Loaded circuit

B. Equivalent circuit

Figure 7-4.   *Loaded Parallel-Resonant Circuit*

Because of this, the parallel-resonant circuit behaves as though it were experiencing additional losses beyond those associated with the winding resistance, r. This effect is known as "loading" the parallel-resonant circuit, resulting in a *loaded Q:*

$$Q_L = \left(\frac{R_L}{Z_{ar} + R_L}\right)Q_U \tag{7-9}$$

where Q_U is the unloaded Q, and Z_{ar} is defined by Eqs. (7–3) and (7–3a). Since the denominator of the parenthetical expression is greater than the numerator, Eq. (7–9) indicates that, regardless of the value of Q, the loaded Q, Q_L, will always be less than the unloaded Q, Q_U. Equations (7–1) through (7–7) are associated with the *unloaded* circuit. It is most convenient to work in terms of the unloaded circuit first, then to make the necessary adjustments to convert to the loaded circuit. All of the equations derived in the previous section are valid for the loaded circuit if Q and Q_{ar} are replaced by Q_L and $Q_{ar(L)}$, which can be derived on the basis of Eq. (7–9).

The *loaded resonant impedance* of the parallel-resonant circuit is given by the same conversion factor:

$$Z_{ar(L)} = \left(\frac{R_L}{Z_{ar} + R_L}\right)Z_{ar} \tag{7-10}$$

so that Eq. (7–6) and all derivatives can be easily rewritten by substituting $Z_{ar(L)}$ for Z_{ar}. For this reason, the curves in Fig. 7–3 are truly universal: they apply to the loaded and unloaded circuits. For the loaded circuit, $Z_{ar(L)}$- and $Q_{ar(L)}$-values must be used in the place of Z_{ar} and Q_{ar}. The definition of δ remains unchanged. Examination of Eq. (7–10) will show that the loaded antiresonant impedance is simply the parallel combination of Z_{ar} and R_L.

As long as $Q_{ar(L)}$ is greater than ten, Eq. (7–5a) may be used to approximate f_{ar}. Under this condition, f_{ar} will not be altered by the loading. However, if $Q_{ar(L)}$ is less than ten, the value of f_{ar} will be decreased by the loading, and the value may be obtained by substituting $Q_{ar(L)}$ in Eq. (7–5). Hence, loading can cause a shift in the antiresonant frequency under extreme circumstances. A decrease in f_{ar} produces an increase in δ for any given frequency [f in Eq. (7–7)]. This produces a pronounced change in the impedance variation: the change in $|Z|$ and θ is more gradual over a specific frequency variation. The effect *can be compensated for in advance* by deliberately designing the unloaded circuit to a higher value of f_{ar}, permitting the loading to shift the value to the desired center frequency. However, because of other inherent degradations associated with loading, it is more practical to select a transformer whose primary has an unloaded Q high enough to maintain the loaded Q well above 10.

Example 7-4.   The antiresonant circuit in Example 7–2 is coupled to a resistance of 15K through a transformer having a turns ratio of 4:1. What effect does this have on the antiresonant Q and the antiresonant impedance of the circuit?

Solution.   The loaded antiresonant Q is given by:

$$Q_{ar(L)} = \left[\frac{R_L}{Z_{ar} + R_L}\right] Q_{ar(U)}$$

where:

$$R_L = \left(\frac{N_1}{N_2}\right)^2 R_D = 4^2(15 \times 10^3) = 240\text{K}$$

Hence:

$$Q_{ar(L)} = \left[\frac{2.4 \times 10^5}{(157 + 0.24)(10^6)}\right](1 \times 10^4)$$

$$= \left[\frac{2.4 \times 10^5}{1.572 \times 10^8}\right](1 \times 10^4)$$

$$= (1.53 \times 10^{-3})(1 \times 10^4) = 15.3$$

The loaded antiresonant impedance is:

$$Z_{ar(L)} = \left[\frac{R_L}{Z_{ar} + R_L}\right] Z_{ar} = (1.53 \times 10^{-3})(1.57 \times 10^8)$$

$$= 240\text{K}$$

From this, it is apparent that loading can have a drastic effect on antiresonant circuit operation and cannot, therefore, be ignored.

Singly-Tuned Selective Amplifiers

The parallel-resonant circuits discussed thus far are *singly-tuned circuits.* That is, only the primary of the transformer contains a significant parallel capacitive component, resulting in a single antiresonant frequency. (It is also possible to use a parallel capacitive component *in the secondary,* resulting in an entirely different type response to be discussed in the next section.)

The selective amplifiers used in the majority of transistor high-frequency, small-signal applications are operated Class A and simply have the RC coupling or standard transformer coupling networks replaced by a loaded, singly-tuned, parallel-resonant circuit. Since the amplifiers are operated Class A, they satisfy the conditions prescribed for linear, small-signal amplifiers and can be adequately described by the hybrid parameters and the associated design equations. With this in mind, selective amplifier design is simply a matter of combining the parallel-resonant equations presented in this chapter with the amplifier design equations of Chap. 6. For the most part, this consists of using the loaded antiresonant resistance, $Z_{ar(L)}$, as the a-c load for the circuit:

$$R_{L(a\text{-}c)} = Z_{ar(L)} \tag{7-11}$$

in all of the mid-frequency design equations (Tables 6–7 and 6–8). In general, the total capacitance in the antiresonant circuits consists of the parallel combination of C, the actual capacitor, and C_{oG}, the output junction capacitance.

The frequency response for the singly-tuned selective amplifier must be based on the impedance variations of Eqs. (7–6) and Fig. 7–3, rather than on the audio-frequency concepts of Chap. 6. However, the principles of the derivation are similar. If Z_L, the generalized loaded impedance, given by:

$$Z_L = \frac{Z_{ar(L)}}{1 + j2Q_{ar(L)}\delta} \tag{7-12}$$

[from Eq. (7–6a) in the loaded condition] is substituted for $R_{L(a\text{-}c)}$ in the equations of Table 6–7 or 6–8, the magnitude and phase variations associated with current, voltage, and power gain can be obtained. If the results are expressed in terms of general gain, A, and "mid-frequency" gain (the gain at the antiresonant frequency, A_{ar}), a curve such as that shown in Fig. 7–5 is obtained. This may be used as a general response curve for singly-tuned selective amplifiers. From this curve, it is apparent that the bandwidth of the selective amplifier is a function of $Q_{ar(L)}$. It can be shown, from any of the response equations or from Eq. (7–12), that, by the basic definition of bandwidth, the selective amplifier bandwidth is:

$$B_L = \frac{f_{ar(L)}}{Q_{ar(L)}} \tag{7-13}$$

Although the loaded values are indicated in Eq. (7–13), the equation itself is perfectly general. The L-subscripts are used to remind the reader that, for amplifier design, any change in conditions brought about by loading must be considered. Since the selective amplifier response is symmetrical about the antiresonant frequency, the cutoff frequencies are specified by:

$$f_L = f_{ar} - \frac{B_L}{2} \tag{7-14}$$

$$f_H = f_{ar} + \frac{B_L}{2} \tag{7-15}$$

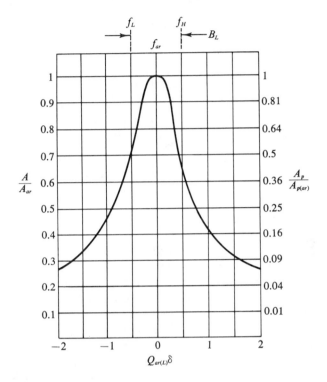

Figure 7-5.   *Relative Gain Characteristics for Singly-Tuned Amplifier*

[In Eq. (7–14), f_L refers to the lower cutoff frequency. In Eq. (7–15), f_H refers to the upper cutoff frequency. In both equations, B_L refers to the loaded bandwidth.] When more than one singly-tuned selective stage is placed in cascade, the gain of the cascade is still given by the products of the individual stage gains *if* $f_{ar(L)}$ *is the same for all stages.* Within this condition the bandwidth of the cascade is given by:

$$B_{L(n)} = B_L\sqrt{2^{1/n} - 1} \tag{7-16}$$

where n is the number of identical selective stages. In view of Eq. (7–16), *the selectivity of the amplifier is increased by cascading stages,* since the bandwidth is reduced. The lower and upper cutoff frequencies are specified by Eqs. (7–14) and (7–15), with $B_{L(n)}$ replacing B_L.

Cascaded selective amplifiers with different antiresonant frequencies will result in an undesirable response curve as illustrated in Fig. 7–6. Since such a response defeats the selective nature of the singly-tuned amplifier, it becomes apparent that *indentical stages are critical for cascaded*

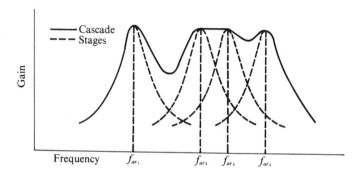

Figure 7-6. *Unsymmetrical Cascading*

selective amplifiers. For this reason, all transistors in the cascade should be identical and the input and output impedances of all stages must be matched. Impedance matching assures uniform loading, resulting in the same $Q_{ar(L)}$, $Z_{ar(L)}$, f_{ar}, and B_L for all stages. The transformer coupling associated with the singly-tuned amplifier, fortunately, lends itself to impedance matching. The design is achieved by selecting an appropriate turns ratio for the transformer, as discussed in Chap. 6. Because of the nature of the parallel-resonant circuit, it might appear that the loaded antiresonant impedance would introduce additional complexities. However, E. Wolfendall has shown that, for maximum amplifier power gain and fixed bandwidth, $r_{oG(n-1)}$ must be matched to $r_{iG(n)}$, *regardless of the value of Z_{ar}.* Hence:

$$\frac{N_1}{N_2} = \sqrt{\frac{r_{oG(n-1)}}{r_{iG(n)}}} \tag{7-17}$$

For a particular transistor, Eqs. (6–24) through (6–26) will apply to matched operation.

Matching conditions and the input-output impedance relationships discussed thus far apply *only at the antiresonant frequency.* At any other frequency, $r_{oG(n-1)}$ and $r_{iG(n)}$ must be replaced by $z_{oG(n-1)}$ and $z_{iG(n)}$—leading to an unmatched situation. Fortunately, within the narrow band of most selective amplifiers, the variation from purely resistive components is not sufficient to cause a major mismatch. Outside the band, where the mismatch becomes more pronounced, the degradation in gain is an advantage, providing further discrimination against unwanted signals. A typical variation of input impedance as a function of frequency is shown in Fig. 7-7. Similarly, the variation in output impedance is shown in Fig. 7-8. These curves are obtained by substituting Eq. (7–12) for $R_{L(a-c)}$ in the design equations for r_{oG} and r_{iG} (Tables 6–7 and 6–8).

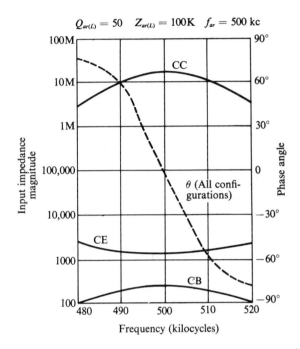

Figure 7-7. *Input Impedance Variation with Antiresonant Load*

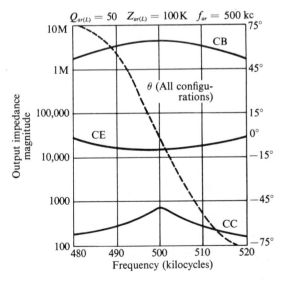

Figure 7-8. *Output Impedance Variation When Amplifier is Driven by a Source with Antiresonant Characteristics*

In many practical selective amplifier designs, matching is best achieved by tapping into the transformer primary, rather than by using the full primary winding. This is illustrated in Fig. 7–9. *Tapping into the transformer does not affect the antiresonant frequency of the parallel-resonant circuit.* However, the effective turns ratio is determined only by that part of the primary that is connected across the amplifier output terminals, as indicated in the figure. This approach is taken whenever a small turns ratio is desired along with an extremely high unloaded Q. Many alternate arrangements using split capacitors and tapped secondary windings may also be used. The reader is referred to standard radio engineering handbooks for such circuit arrangements.

Selective amplifiers frequently employ series or shunt (or both) feedback networks in their design. The effect of negative feedback on amplifier gain and bandwidth is the same as that discussed in Chap. 6. However, because of the reactive nature of the input and output impedances for the selective amplifier, care must be exercised to assure that feedback is, in fact, negative in nature. If the design is arranged so that negative feedback occurs at antiresonance, the same feedback factors may be used across the amplifier bandwidth, as a reasonable approximation, if the

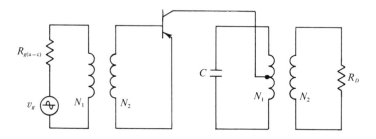

Figure 7-9.   *Selective Amplifier with "Tapped" Primary*

bandwidth is very narrow. However, frequencies outside the band must be checked to assure that the feedback *never becomes positive.* Such feedback will result in amplifier instability (oscillations).

Example 7-5.   What is the impedance of the loaded antiresonant circuit in Example 7–4 at 45 kilocycles per second? At 57.5 kilocycles per second?

Solution. If the product $Q_{ar(L)}\delta$ is restricted to values between -2 and $+2$, the loaded impedance can be obtained from Fig. 7–3 (substituting $Q_{ar(L)}\delta$ for $Q_{ar}\delta$ and reading $|Z_L/Z_{ar(L)}|$ on the vertical axis). For the frequencies of interest:

f	f/f_{ar}	δ	$Q_{ar(L)}\delta$	$|Z_L/Z_{ar(L)}|$	$|Z_L|$	θ
4.5×10^4	0.9	-0.1	-1.53	0.3	72K	65°
5.75×10^4	1.15	0.15	2.3	—	—	—

The product $Q_{ar(L)}\delta$ is beyond the range of Fig. 7-3 when the frequency is 57.5 kilocycles per second. However, the loaded impedance magnitude is:

$$Z_L = \frac{Q_{ar(L)}^2 r}{1 + 4(Q_{ar}\delta)^2} = \frac{Z_{ar(L)}}{1 + 4(Q_{ar}\delta)^2}$$

$$= \frac{2.4 \times 10^5}{1 + 4(2.3)^2} = \frac{2.4 \times 10^5}{22.2} = 10.8K$$

and the phase angle is given by:

$$\theta = \arctan[-2(Q_{ar(L)}\delta)] = \arctan[-2(2.3)]$$
$$= \arctan(-4.6) = -78°$$

Example 7-6. The transistor listed in Table 6-5 is used in a common emitter, singly-tuned amplifier with the loaded antiresonant circuit in Example 7-4. The value of C_{CE} (the output junction capacitance) is not large enough to affect the antiresonant frequency. What are the current, voltage, and power gains for this amplifier at antiresonance? (Express power gain in decibels.)

Solution. The current gain is (from Table 6-7):

$$A_{iE(ar)} = \frac{-h_{fE}}{h_{oE}Z_{ar(L)} + 1} = \frac{-110}{(3.25 \times 10^{-5})(2.4 \times 10^5) + 1}$$

$$= \frac{-110}{8.8} = -12.5$$

The voltage gain is:

$$A_{vE(ar)} = \frac{-h_{fE}Z_{ar(L)}}{\Delta h_E Z_{ar(L)} + h_{iE}}$$

where:

$$\Delta h_E = h_{iE}h_{oE} - h_{fE}h_{rE}$$
$$= (2.41 \times 10^3)(3.25 \times 10^{-5}) - 110(3.79 \times 10^{-4})$$
$$= 3.67 \times 10^{-2}$$

Hence:

$$A_{vE(ar)} = \frac{-110(2.4 \times 10^5)}{(3.67 \times 10^{-2})(2.4 \times 10^5) + (2.41 \times 10^3)}$$

$$= \frac{-(2.64 \times 10^7)}{1.121 \times 10^4} = -2350$$

The power gain is:

$$A_{pE(ar)} = A_{iE(ar)} A_{vE(ar)} = (-12.5)(-2350) = 29,400$$

which, expressed in decibels, is:

$$A_{pE(ar)}(\text{db}) = 10 \log_{10}(A_{pE(ar)}) = 10 \log_{10}(29,400) = 44.68 \text{ db}$$

Example 7-7. Determine the lower and upper cutoff frequencies of the amplifier in Example 7-6. Plot the power gain (in decibels) as a function of frequency.

Solution. The lower cutoff frequency is given by:

$$f_L = f_{ar} - (B_L/2)$$

where the loaded bandwidth is:

$$B_L = \frac{f_{ar(L)}}{Q_{ar(L)}} = \frac{5 \times 10^4}{15.3} = 3.72 \text{ kc}$$

Hence:

$$f_L = (50 \times 10^3) - \frac{3.27 \times 10^3}{2} = (50 - 1.635)(10^3) = 48.365 \text{ kc}$$

The upper cutoff frequency is:

$$f_H = f_{ar} + (B_L/2) = (50 + 1.635)(10^3) = 51.635 \text{ kc}$$

The data to plot the power response curve must be obtained from Fig. 7-5. (The antiresonant power gain is 29,400, or 44.68 db, from Example 7-6.)

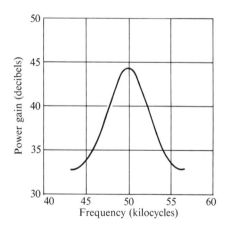

Figure E7-7

$Q_{ar(L)}\delta$	δ	f/f_{ar}	f	$A_p/A_{p(ar)}$	A_p	$A_p(db)$
-2	-0.131	0.869	43.45 kc	0.0625	1,840	32.65
-1	-0.0654	0.9346	46.65 kc	0.2025	5,950	37.40
-0.5	-0.0327	0.9673	48.4 kc	0.5	14,700	41.68
0	0	1	50 kc	1	29,400	44.68
0.5	0.0327	1.0327	51.6 kc	0.5	14,700	41.68
1	0.0654	1.0654	53.35 kc	0.2025	5,950	37.40
2	0.131	1.131	56.55 kc	0.0625	1,840	32.65

These data are plotted in Fig. E7-7.

Example 7-8. Three of the stages in Example 7-7 are placed in cascade. What is the power gain (in decibels) at antiresonance for the cascade and what are the lower and upper cutoff frequencies?

Solution. The power gain is given by:

$$A_{p3(ar)}(db) = A_{p(ar)_1}(db) + A_{p(ar)_2}(db) + A_{p(ar)_3}(db)$$
$$= 3(44.68) = 134.04 \text{ db}$$

The lower cutoff frequency is given by:

$$f_{L(3)} = f_{ar} - (B_{L(3)}/2)$$

where:

$$B_{L(3)} = B_L\sqrt{2^{1/n} - 1} = (3.27 \times 10^3)\sqrt{2^{1/3} - 1}$$
$$= (3.27 \times 10^3)\sqrt{0.26} = 1.67 \text{ kc}$$

Hence:

$$f_{L(3)} = (50 \times 10^3) - \frac{1.67 \times 10^3}{2} = (50 - 0.835)(10^3)$$
$$= 49.165 \text{ kc}$$

The upper cutoff frequency is:

$$f_{H(3)} = f_{ar} + (B_{L(3)}/2) = (50 + 0.835)(10^3) = 50.835 \text{ kc}$$

Example 7-9. The transistor in Example 6-13 is to be used in both stages of a two-stage singly-tuned amplifier with maximum power gain. The cascade is tuned to 200 kilocycles per second and must have an operating bandwidth of 10 kilocycles per second. The signal source has an equivalent resistance that directly matches the input resistance to the first stage. The cascade feeds a device with an equivalent resistance of 2K. The output junction capacitance for the transistor is 50 picofarads. Specify the inductance and capacitance that must be used in each antiresonant circuit (see Fig. E7-9), the unloaded antiresonant Q, and the necessary turns ratio for each transformer.

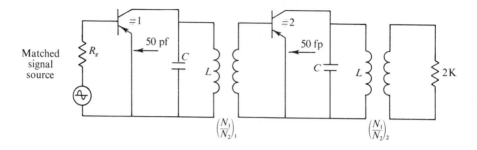

Figure E7-9

Solution. From Example 6–13, the a-c source resistance for each stage must be 1650 ohms and the a-c load resistance for each stage must be 45K. This means that the input resistance of the stage must be 1.65K and the output resistance of each stage must be 45K. In order for the last stage to be matched to the load:

$$\left(\frac{N_1}{N_2}\right)_2 = \sqrt{\frac{r_{oG_2}}{R_D}} = \sqrt{\frac{45 \times 10^3}{2 \times 10^3}} = 4.75 : 1$$

In order for the first stage to be matched to the second stage:

$$\left(\frac{N_1}{N_2}\right)_1 = \sqrt{\frac{r_{oG_1}}{r_{iG_2}}} = \sqrt{\frac{45 \times 10^3}{2 \times 10^3}} = 5.2 : 1$$

If the cascade is to have an operating (loaded) bandwidth of 10 kilocycles per second, each stage must have a bandwidth of:

$$B_L = \frac{B_{L(2)}}{\sqrt{2^{1/2} - 1}} = \frac{1 \times 10^4}{\sqrt{0.414}} = 15.6 \text{ kc}$$

This will require that each stage have a loaded antiresonant Q of:

$$Q_{ar(L)} = \frac{f_{ar(L)}}{B_L} = \frac{2 \times 10^5}{1.56 \times 10^4} = 12.8$$

The unloaded antiresonant Q is given by:

$$Q_{ar(U)} = Q_{ar(L)} \left[\frac{Z_{ar} + R_L}{R_L}\right]$$

The values of $Q_{ar(L)}$ and R_L are known. (R_L is the secondary resistance reflected into the primary. Since the turns ratio of each transformer has been calculated for matched conditions, this must be 45K in both stages.) The unloaded antiresonant impedance is not known. However, since it is related to the loaded antiresonant impedance by:

$$Z_{ar(L)} = \left[\frac{Z_{ar} + R_L}{R_L}\right]Z_{ar}$$

it may be determined. In view of the fact that maximum power gain is to be achieved and that $Z_{ar(L)}$ is the a-c load on each stage, $Z_{ar(L)}$ must be made equal to the output resistance of the amplifier stage—45K. This is the same as R_L. Since $Z_{ar(L)}$ is the parallel combination of R_L and Z_{ar}, if $Z_{ar(L)}$ and R_L are to be equal, Z_{ar} must be at least ten times greater than R_L. Selecting a factor of fifteen is reasonable unless further design problems are encountered. This would make the unloaded antiresonant resistance equal to:

$$Z_{ar} = 15R_L = 15(45 \times 10^3) = 675K$$

This would require that the unloaded antiresonant Q be:

$$Q_{ar(U)} = 12.8\left[\frac{(675 \times 10^3) + (45 \times 10^3)}{45 \times 10^3}\right]$$

$$= 12.8\left[\frac{7.2 \times 10^5}{4.5 \times 10^4}\right] = 205$$

In order to obtain the specified unloaded antiresonant impedance with the calculated unloaded antiresonant Q, the inductance must be:

$$L = \frac{Z_{ar}}{Q_{ar}\omega_{ar}} = \frac{6.75 \times 10^5}{205(2\pi)(2 \times 10^5)}$$

$$= \frac{6.75 \times 10^5}{8.2 \times 10^7} = 2.63 \text{ millihenries}$$

With such an inductance and the fact that the loaded antiresonant Q is greater than ten, the necessary capacitance to achieve antiresonance at 200 kilocycles per second is:

$$C = \frac{1}{(2\pi f_{ar})^2 L} = \frac{1}{4\pi^2(2 \times 10^5)^2(2.63 \times 10^{-3})}$$

$$= \frac{1}{4.15 \times 10^9} = 241 \text{ picofarads}$$

However, the output junction capacitance, in parallel with the actual capacitor in the antiresonant circuit, contributes a portion of this value. Because of this, the capacitor used in the antiresonant circuit must be:

$$(241 - 50)(10^{-12}) = 191 \text{ picofarads}$$

Example 7-10. Each of the stages in Example 7–9 are forward biased with a shunt feedback resistor of 200K. What is the feedback power gain at antiresonance for the two-stage cascade? Express the result in decibels.

Solution. The maximum power gain achieved by each of the stages in the cascade is 54,300 (from Example 6–13). The feedback factor is given by:

$$B_i = \frac{Z_{ar(L)}}{R_F} = \frac{45 \times 10^3}{200 \times 10^3} = 0.225$$

This feedback is present in each stage, leading to a single-stage power gain of:

$$A_{p(ar)(F)} = \frac{A_{p(ar)}}{1 + |A_{i(ar)}| B_i}$$

The antiresonant current gain is given by (from Table 6–7):

$$A_{i(ar)} = \frac{-h_{fE}}{h_{oE} Z_{ar(L)} + 1}$$

The *h*-parameters can be obtained from Example 6–13, so that:

$$A_{i(ar)} = \frac{-110}{(3.25 \times 10^{-5})(4.5 \times 10^4) + 1} = \frac{-110}{2.46} = -44.7$$

Hence:

$$A_{p(ar)(F)} = \frac{54,300}{1 + (44.7)(0.225)} = \frac{54,300}{11.06} = 4910$$

For the two-stage cascade:

$$A_{p(ar)2(F)} = A_{p(ar)_1} A_{p(ar)_2} = 2.41 \times 10^7$$

which, in decibels, is given by:

$$A_{p(ar)2(F)}(\text{db}) = 10 \log_{10}(A_{p(ar)2(F)}) = 10 \log_{10}(2.41 \times 10^7)$$
$$= 73.82 \text{ db}$$

Doubly-Tuned Amplifiers

When both the primary and secondary of the coupling network contain a parallel capacitive component such as in Fig. 7–10, the selective amplifier is *doubly-tuned*. Although such circuits are more difficult to design and to maintain in adjustment, they can have a "flatter" response across the bandwidth of the amplifier when certain critical design conditions are met. For some selective amplifier applications, a wider bandwidth is desirable. For singly-tuned amplifiers, wider bandwidths require a considerable reduction in Q. This results in a lower antiresonant impedance and a reduction in resonant gain. The doubly-tuned amplifier always has a greater bandwidth for a specific Q and a specific resonant gain. With proper design, the doubly-tuned amplifier bandwidth may be

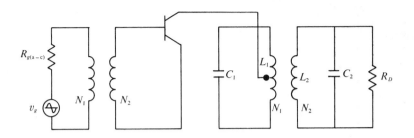

Figure 7-10. *Doubly-Tuned Selective Amplifier*

250 per cent greater than the singly-tuned bandwidth, for a given Q. However, such large increases in bandwidth are not achieved without disadvantages. As the bandwidth increases beyond 140 per cent of the associated singly-tuned bandwidth, the doubly-tuned response curves experience a loss of gain in the vicinity of the antiresonant frequency.

The antiresonant frequency for the primary and the secondary circuits can be determined separately by using Eq. (7–5) or (7–5a), as appropriate. In order to simplify the doubly-tuned analysis, it is assumed that both portions of the circuit are tuned to the same antiresonant frequency:

$$f_{ar_1} = f_{ar_2} \qquad (7\text{-}18)$$

and that the loaded Q of both portions is greater than ten. These are not unreasonable assumptions for practical amplifier designs.

In determining the antiresonant frequency, or in selecting a particular capacitance to provide a desired antiresonant frequency, it is necessary to consider the capacitance reflected from one side of the transformer to the other. Transformers reflect capacitances in proportion to the *inverse* of the turns ratio squared. Since N_1/N_2 is generally greater than one in order to achieve matching, the reflection of secondary capacitances into the primary is insignificant. (N_2/N_1 is a fraction, and squaring a fraction produces an even smaller number.) Such small capacitances produce antiresonance at frequencies far higher than the upper cutoff frequency of the amplifier. For this reason, secondary reflections into the primary will not be considered (and are not mentioned in conjunction with singly-tuned amplifiers). The reflection of primary capacitances into the secondary, as illustrated in Fig. 7–11, can be significant, however. The reflected value (C'_S) is given by:

$$C'_S = \left(\frac{N_1}{N_2}\right)^2 (C_p + C_{oG}) \qquad (7\text{-}19)$$

where C_{oG} is the output junction capacitance (in the primary portion of

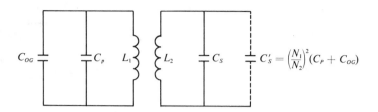

Figure 7-11.   *Reflection of Primary Capacitances into Secondary*

the circuit) and C_P is the primary capacitance used to tune the primary antiresonant circuit. The total secondary capacitance must be used in calculations for determining f_{ar_2} and is given by:

$$C = C_S' + C_S + C_{iG} \qquad (7\text{-}20)$$

where C_S is the physical capacitor placed in the secondary antiresonant circuit and C_{iG} is the input junction capacitance or other stray capacitances in the secondary circuit. (C_{iG} may be negligible in many cases.)

The loading effect of the secondary resistance reflected into the primary is discussed in conjunction with singly-tuned amplifiers and in the previous section on antiresonant circuit loading. For the doubly-tuned amplifier, *both portions are loaded*. Furthermore, there is a continuous interaction between the primary and secondary, as well as between the secondary and primary. These interactions are best described in terms of the transformer *coefficient of coupling*. This factor is a measure of the "goodness" of the energy transfer between the two coils. It is based on the amount of the total magnetic flux as compared to the flux that is lost (leakage) by not being coupled to both coils:

$$k = \frac{M}{\sqrt{L_1 L_2}} \qquad (7\text{-}21)$$

where M is the mutual inductance between the two coils. Because of this coupling effect, the antiresonant impedance of the circuit, and the peak gain value, vary. When Q_{ar_1} and Q_{ar_2} are equal, as k increases, so does the peak gain value—to a point. Once this point is reached, the antiresonant gain value begins to decrease even though k continues to increase. (The maximum value for k is one, since M cannot exceed $\sqrt{L_1 L_2}$.) The value of k associated with the maximum peak gain value is termed the *critical coupling coefficient*:

$$k_c = \frac{1}{\sqrt{Q_{ar_1} Q_{ar_2}}} \qquad (7\text{-}22)$$

The Q of each portion of the doubly-tuned circuit must be determined

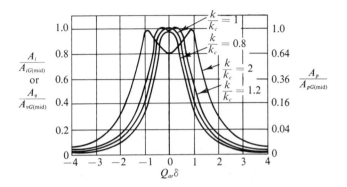

Figure 7-12.   *Doubly-Tuned Amplifier Response Characteristics* $(Q_{ar_1} = Q_{ar_2})$ (Glen M. Glasford, *Fundamentals of Television Engineering*, 1955. Courtesy McGraw-Hill Book Co., Inc.)

separately from Eq. (7–1), (7–2), or (7–2a) with the appropriate primary and secondary component values.

Figure 7–12 illustrates the voltage, current, and power gain curves for the doubly-tuned selective amplifier *when Q_{ar_1} is equal to Q_{ar_2}*. For values of k less than (or equal to) k_c, the doubly-tuned response is similar to the singly-tuned response, except that it is "broader" at any particular relative gain value. Values of k less than k_c denote the presence of *insufficient coupling*. Such values do not produce a maximum antiresonant gain value, but do have greater selectivity. The maximum antiresonant gain value is achieved when k and k_c are equal (critical coupling). Values of k greater than k_c denote the presence of *overcoupling*. Overcoupling produces a decrease in the antiresonant gain value and causes the maximum gain value to occur at *two frequencies*, equally spaced about the antiresonant frequency. When such a response does not seriously distort the amplified signals, overcoupling may be used to achieve a considerable increase in bandwidth. Notice that the ratio k/k_c equal to 1.2 yields a much better approximation to the ideal selective amplifier response (Fig. 7–1) than does the singly-tuned response curve (Fig. 7–5). The slight decrease in gain at the antiresonant frequency will not cause serious signal distortions. The factor δ used in Fig. 7–12 is defined by Eq. (7–7) when f_{ar_1} is substituted for f_{ar}. The "mid-frequency" gain values, A_{ar}, in the figures must be determined from the design equations (Tables 6–7 and 6–8) with $R_{L(a-c)}$ equal to the primary antiresonant impedance:

$$Z_{ar(L)_1} = 2\pi f_{ar_1}(1 - k^2)L_1 \qquad (7\text{-}23)$$

When Q_{ar_1} is considerably greater than Q_{ar_2}, an entirely different variation of antiresonant impedance and amplifier response is obtained.

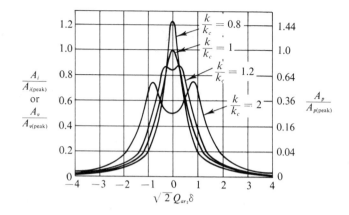

Figure 7-13.   *Doubly-Tuned Amplifier Response Characteristics* $(Q_{ar_1}$ $\gg Q_{ar_2})$ (Glen M. Glasford, *Fundamentals of Television Engineering*, 1955. Courtesy McGraw-Hill Book Co., Inc.)

This condition is illustrated in Fig. 7–13. Insufficient and critical coupling conditions still produce a singly-tuned type response. However, the maximum peak value is higher for insufficient coupling than it is for critical coupling—*the inverse of the variation associated with a circuit having Q_{ar_1} and Q_{ar_2} equal.* Overcoupling still produces less gain at antiresonance, with two peaks equally spaced about the antiresonant frequency. However, the gain is always less than the value obtained for the critical-coupled case. Amplifiers are not generally designed with Q_{ar_1} significantly greater than Q_{ar_2}, but can be useful in a limited number of applications.

Several variations of bandwidth measurement are associated with doubly-tuned selective amplifiers. For critical coupling, with Q_{ar_1} and Q_{ar_2} equal, the bandwidth (as defined by the 0.707 current and voltage gain frequencies, or the 0.5 power gain frequencies) is given by:

$$B = \frac{\sqrt{2}\, f_{ar}}{Q_{ar}} \qquad (7\text{-}24)$$

Equation (7–24) indicates that the bandwidth obtained with the most common doubly-tuned amplifier is 1.414 times the bandwidth associated with an equivalent singly-tuned amplifier. For the overcoupled case, the two peak frequencies are given by:

$$f_A = f_{ar_1}\left[1 - \frac{k_c}{2}\sqrt{\left(\frac{k}{k_c}\right)^2 - 1}\,\right] \qquad (7\text{-}25)$$

$$f_B = f_{ar_1}\left[1 + \frac{k_c}{2}\sqrt{\left(\frac{k}{k_c}\right)^2 - 1}\,\right] \qquad (7\text{-}26)$$

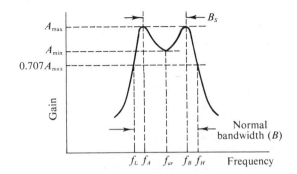

Figure 7-14.   *Doubly-Tuned Bandwidths for Overcoupled Circuits*

These frequencies are illustrated in Fig. 7–14 along with a specially defined bandwidth, determined by the lower and upper frequency values associated with $A_{\max}$:

$$B_S = \sqrt{2}\,(f_B - f_A) \tag{7-27}$$

An alternate method of defining the special bandwidth for an overcoupled circuit permits the direct determination of the peak-to-antiresonant gain ratio associated with a particular k/k_c-ratio. The gain ratio is given by:

$$\left|\frac{A_{(\text{peak})}}{A_{(ar)}}\right| = \Delta = \frac{(k/k_c)^2 + 1}{2(k/k_c)} \tag{7-28}$$

which leads to:

$$\frac{k}{k_c} = \Delta + \sqrt{\Delta^2 - 1} \tag{7-29}$$

With Eq. (7–29), (k/k_c) can be determined for any desired Δ-value (gain ratio). From Eqs. (7–25), (7–26), and (7–27), a new relationship for the special bandwidth is obtained:

$$B_S = \sqrt{2} f_{ar_1} k_c \sqrt{\left(\frac{k}{k_c}\right)^2 - 1} \tag{7-27a}$$

When Δ is equal to 1.414 (the gain ratio associated with the normal bandwidth definition), the ratio k/k_c must be equal to 2.032 [from Eq. (7–29)]. Under these conditions:

$$B = 2.5 f_{ar_1} \frac{1}{\sqrt{Q_{ar_1} Q_{ar_2}}} \tag{7-30}$$

indicating an increase on the order of 250 per cent for the overcoupled, doubly-tuned amplifier. However, it must be realized that under these conditions, the gain at the antiresonant frequency is also down to 0.707 times the peak gain value.

Regardless of the bandwidth definition, cascading doubly-tuned stages with identical antiresonant frequencies results in an overall bandwidth of:

$$B_n = B\sqrt[4]{2^{1/n} - 1} \tag{7-31}$$

A comparison of Eq. (7–31) and Eq. (7–16) shows that bandwidth losses occur much less rapidly for doubly-tuned stages placed in cascade than for singly-tuned cascades.

Doubly-tuned stages can be matched by satisfying the turns ratio of Eq. (7–17). Under such conditions, the maximum possible gain value will be achieved for a specific transistor, as specified by Eq. (6–26).

> **Example 7-11.** A doubly-tuned coupling network has a primary inductance of 180 millihenries, a secondary inductance of 40 millihenries, and a mutual inductance of 10 millihenries. The turns ratio is 2:1. The primary and secondary both have a loaded antiresonant Q of 17 and both must have an antiresonant frequency of 100 kilocycles per second. The output junction capacitance of the transistor in the primary circuit is 5 picofarads. The stray capacitance in the secondary is negligible. Determine the necessary capacitance that must be put into both antiresonant circuits.
>
> *Solution.* Since the loaded antiresonant Q of both circuits is greater than ten, the antiresonant frequency is given by:
>
> $$f_{ar} = \frac{1}{2\pi\sqrt{LC}}$$
>
> where L and C must refer to the total inductance and capacitance in each part of the circuit. Rearranging this equation for the primary portion:
>
> $$C = \frac{1}{(2\pi f_{ar_1})^2 L_1} = \frac{1}{4\pi^2(1 \times 10^5)^2(1.8 \times 10^{-1})}$$
>
> $$= \frac{1}{(5.82 \times 10^{10})} = 14.1 \text{ picofarads}$$
>
> Since the output junction capacitance is 5 picofarads, the primary capacitance must be:
>
> $$C_P = C - C_{oG} = (14.1 - 5)(10^{-12}) = 9.1 \text{ picofarads}$$
>
> For the secondary portion the necessary capacitance is:
>
> $$C = \frac{1}{(2\pi f_{ar_2})^2 L_2} = \frac{1}{4\pi^2(1 \times 10^5)^2(4 \times 10^{-2})}$$
>
> $$= \frac{1}{(3.16 \times 10^{10})} = 63.4 \text{ picofarads}$$

The total capacitance in the secondary is:

$$C = \left(\frac{N_1}{N_2}\right)^2 (C_p + C_{oG}) + C_s$$

Rearranging for the secondary capacitor value:

$$C_S = C - \left(\frac{N_1}{N_2}\right)^2 (C_p + C_{oG})$$
$$= (63.4 \times 10^{-12}) - 2^2(9.1 \times 10^{-12})$$
$$= (63.4 - 36.4)(10^{-12}) = 27 \text{ picofarads}$$

Example 7-12. The doubly-tuned coupling network in Example 7-11 is used with the transistor whose *h*-parameters are listed in Table 6–5. The amplifier is in the common emitter configuration. What is the power gain at antiresonance? Express the answer in decibels.

Solution. From Table 6–7, the power gain is:

$$A_{p(ar)} = \frac{h_{fE}^2 Z_{ar(L)_1}}{(h_{oE}Z_{ar(L)_1} + 1)(\Delta h_E Z_{ar(L)_1} + h_{iE})}$$

The loaded anitresonant impedance in the primary circuit is:

$$Z_{ar(L)_1} = 2\pi f_{ar}(1 - k^2)L_1$$

where:

$$k = \frac{M}{\sqrt{L_1 L_2}} = \frac{10 \times 10^{-3}}{\sqrt{(1.8 \times 10^{-1})(4 \times 10^{-2})}}$$
$$= \frac{10 \times 10^{-3}}{\sqrt{72 \times 10^{-4}}} = \frac{10 \times 10^{-3}}{8.49 \times 10^{-2}} = 0.118$$

Hence:

$$Z_{ar(L)_1} = 2\pi(1 \times 10^5)[1 - (0.118)^2](1.8 \times 10^{-1}) = 111.5\text{K}$$

and:

$$A_{p(ar)} = \frac{(110)^2(1.115 \times 10^5)}{[(3.25 \cdot 10^{-5})(1.115 \cdot 10^5) + 1][(3.67 \cdot 10^{-2})(1.115 \cdot 10^5) + (2.41 \cdot 10^3)]}$$
$$= \frac{1.35 \times 10}{4.62(6.5 \times 10^3)} = 4.48 \times 10^4$$

Converted to decibels:

$$A_{p(ar)}(\text{db}) = 10 \log_{10} A_{p(ar)} = 10 \log_{10} (4.48 \times 10^4) = 46.52 \text{ db}$$

Example 7-13. If the inductive components in Example 7–11 were changed (without changing the loaded antiresonant *Q*-values) in order to achieve critical coupling, what effects would be noticed on the power gain versus frequency characteristics?

Solution. Critical coupling, $k = k_c$, or $(k/k_c) = 1$, would result in a single peak response curve, as shown in Fig. 7-12. This would require a reduction in k (since k_c is 0.0589), which would result in a decrease in the loaded antiresonant impedance. However, this would probably have little effect on the peak power gain, since $Z_{ar(L)}$ appears in both the numerator and denominator (see Example 7-12). The exact variation can be obtained only by a new evaluation of $Z_{ar(L)}$ and $A_{p(ar)}$. Unlike the overcoupled circuit, the peak gain and antiresonant gain are the same. The bandwidth for this degree of coupling is:

$$B = \frac{\sqrt{2}f_{ar}}{Q_{ar}} = \frac{1.414(1 \times 10^5)}{17} = 8.34 \text{ kc}$$

Example 7-14. The amplifier in Example 7-12 is placed in cascade with another, identical, doubly-tuned stage. The input junction capacitance for the transistor is 2 picofarads. What is the bandwidth of the two-stage cascade? Is it necessary to make any changes in the design of the first stage?

Solution. The cascade bandwidth is:

$$B_2 = B\sqrt[4]{2^{1/2} - 1} = (19.68 \times 10^3)\sqrt[4]{0.414} = 15.8 \text{ kc}$$

The 2-picofarad input junction capacitance is in parallel with the secondary capacitance, C_S, and the reflected primary capacitance, C_S'. Since a total secondary capacitance must be 63.4 picofarads to obtain antiresonance at 100 kc (Example 7-11), the value of C_S may be reduced slightly:

$$C_S = (27 - 2)(10^{-12}) = 25 \text{ picofarads}$$

where the original C_S-value (27 picofarads) is also obtained from Example 7-11. Since 2 picofarads is within the design tolerances of most capacitors, and within the range of error associated with most of the calculations, in practice the change would probably not be necessary. In fact, the primary and secondary capacitors are often adjustable in order to correct for such inaccuracies. (In lieu of this, the inductances, or one of the inductors, may be adjustable.)

7.2 Broadband Amplifiers

Many applications of electronic amplifiers require that *nonsinusoidal signals,* such as pulses, sawtooth waveforms, and others, be amplified with a minimum amount of distortion. Such waveforms contain a large

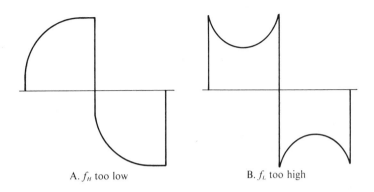

A. f_H too low   B. f_L too high

Figure 7-15. *Effects of Insufficient Bandwidth on Squarewave Amplification*

number of harmonic components (Appendix C). These components have specific amplitude and phase relationships that must be maintained in order to avoid distortion. The amplifier must be operated over a linear portion of the transistor characteristic in order to avoid the introduction of *unwanted harmonics.* However, linear operation, alone, will not assure undistorted reproduction. In addition, the bandwidth must be sufficient to pass all harmonics of the input signal (Fig. 7–15), the gain must be constant across the band to avoid changing the relative harmonic amplitudes (Fig. 7–16), and the phase shift must be constant across the band to

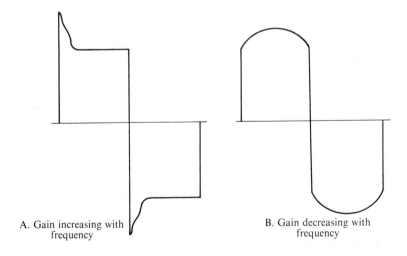

A. Gain increasing with   B. Gain decreasing with
  frequency   frequency

Figure 7-16. *Effects of Gain Variations on Squarewave Amplification*

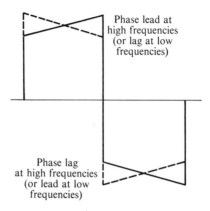

Figure 7-17.   *Effects of Phase Variations on Squarewave Amplification.*

avoid changing the relative harmonic phase relationships (Fig. 7–17). Amplifiers designed to satisfy these three conditions are termed *broadband*, or *video*, amplifiers. Of course, *some* compromise of the three conditions is tolerable and, in many instances, unavoidable. The amount of acceptable variation depends entirely upon the application. The fundamental frequency and the lower-frequency harmonics have the greatest amplitude. Hence, these are the components that must be maintained most critically. The higher-frequency harmonics are less critical and, in many instances, some of them may be neglected. If this were not true, useful nonsinusoidal amplifiers would not be practical.

The upper and lower cutoff frequencies required for a broadband amplifier can be related to the *period* of the nonsinusoidal signal that it is designed to handle. As an approximation:

$$f_L = \frac{1}{10T} \tag{7-32}$$

and:

$$f_H = \frac{10}{T} \tag{7-33}$$

where T is the period, in seconds. In general, this will provide an adequate bandwidth. If the response is made *maximally flat*, gain will be constant over almost all of the frequencies bounded by f_L and f_H. A maximally flat response is illustrated in Fig. 7–18. Unlike the gain variation associated with audio amplifiers, which falls gradually to the cutoff values (as described in Chap. 6), the maximally flat response maintains a constant value, then drops abruptly to the half-power values. *Phase shift* across

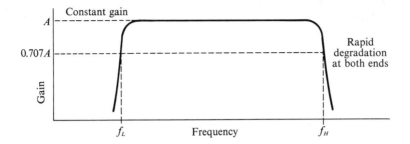

Figure 7-18.   *Maximally Flat Response Characteristics*

the band, defined by Eqs. (7–32) and (7–33), *is most critical.* It must remain constant—*or it must vary linearly with frequency*—to within a few degrees. Obviously, if phase shift is constant across the band, all components of the input signal will maintain the same relative phase in the output signal. Figure 7–19 illustrates why a *linear variation* in phase shift also permits the same relative phase to be maintained. The fundamental and second harmonic components are shown. The amount of phase shift is exaggerated for clarification. The phase shift at the fundamental frequency is 45°. Since the variation is linear, at twice this frequency the phase shift must be twice as great (90°). *However, since the period of the second harmonic is half the period of the fundamental, the two output components maintain the same relative phase.* This is also true of all higher harmonics: the third harmonic experiences three times the fundamental phase shift, but has only one-third the fundamental period; etc.

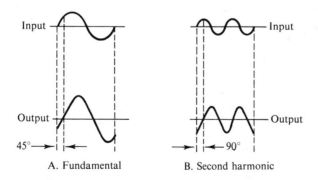

Figure 7-19.   *Maintenance of Relative Phase with Linear Phase Shift (as a Function of Frequency)*

Example 7-15. A triangular waveform with a period of 26×10^{-5} second is to be amplified. Determine the necessary upper and lower cutoff frequencies for the amplifier.

Solution. The upper cutoff frequency is:

$$f_H = \frac{10}{T} = \frac{10}{2.6 \times 10^{-4}} = 38.5 \text{ kc}$$

and the lower cutoff frequency is:

$$f_L = \frac{1}{10T} = \frac{1}{10(2.6 \times 10^{-4})} = 385 \text{ cps}$$

Stagger-Tuned Amplifiers

Figure 7–6 illustrates the unsymmetrical response obtained when singly-tuned amplifiers of unlike antiresonant frequencies are placed in cascade. However, such a response occurs only if the individual antiresonant frequencies are chosen in a haphazard fashion. If all stages have an identical antiresonant gain, but have appropriately staggered antiresonant frequencies and bandwidths (as listed in Table 7–1) a maximally flat, broadband response can be achieved. This is shown for the staggered double, staggered triple, and staggered quadruple in Fig. 7–20. The bandwidth indicated in Table 7–1 (B_o) may be determined from the lower and upper cutoff frequencies given by Eqs. (7–32) and (7–33):

$$B_o = f_H - f_L \tag{7-34}$$

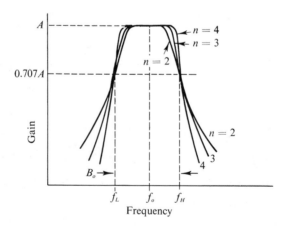

Figure 7-20. *Comparison of Response for Staggered Double, Triple, and Quadruple Designed to Achieve Same Bandwidth*

TABLE 7-1

Design Conditions for
Stagger-Tuned (Broadband) Amplifiers

Staggered . . .	Number of Stages	Stage Bandwidth	Stage Antiresonant Frequency
Double (or Pair)	2	$B_{L_1} = 0.71\,B_o$ $B_{L_2} = 0.71\,B_o$	$f_{ar_1} = f_o + 0.35\,B_o$ $f_{ar_2} = f_o - 0.35\,B_o$
Triple	3	$B_{L_1} = 0.5\,B_o$ $B_{L_2} = 0.5\,B_o$ $B_{L_3} = B_o$	$f_{ar_1} = f_o + 0.43\,B_o$ $f_{ar_2} = f_o - 0.43\,B_o$ $f_{ar_3} = f_o$
Quadruple	4	$B_{L_1} = 0.38\,B_o$ $B_{L_2} = 0.38\,B_o$ $B_{L_3} = 0.92\,B_o$ $B_{L_4} = 0.92\,B_o$	$f_{ar_1} = f_o + 0.46\,B_o$ $f_{ar_2} = f_o - 0.46\,B_o$ $f_{ar_3} = f_o + 0.19\,B_o$ $f_{ar_4} = f_o - 0.19\,B_o$
Quintuple	5	$B_{L_1} = 0.81\,B_o$ $B_{L_2} = 0.81\,B_o$ $B_{L_3} = 0.26\,B_o$ $B_{L_4} = 0.26\,B_o$ $B_{L_5} = B_o$	$f_{ar_1} = f_o + 0.29\,B_o$ $f_{ar_2} = f_o - 0.29\,B_o$ $f_{ar_3} = f_o + 0.48\,B_o$ $f_{ar_4} = f_o - 0.48\,B_o$ $f_{ar_5} = f_o$
Sextuple	6	$B_{L_1} = 0.26\,B_o$ $B_{L_2} = 0.26\,B_o$ $B_{L_3} = 0.71\,B_o$ $B_{L_4} = 0.71\,B_o$ $B_{L_5} = 0.97\,B_o$ $B_{L_6} = 0.97\,B_o$	$f_{ar_1} = f_o + 0.48\,B_o$ $f_{ar_2} = f_o - 0.48\,B_o$ $f_{ar_3} = f_o + 0.35\,B_o$ $f_{ar_4} = f_o - 0.35\,B_o$ $f_{ar_5} = f_o + 0.13\,B_o$ $f_{ar_6} = f_o - 0.13\,B_o$

As indicated by the L-subscripts in Table 7-1, the individual stage bandwidths are *loaded bandwidths*. The individual stage antiresonant frequencies are obtained from the staggered cascade center frequency, which is defined by:

$$f_o = \frac{f_H - f_L}{2} \qquad (7\text{-}35)$$

Once the antiresonant frequency and loaded bandwidth for each stage have been determined, each stage is designed in accordance with the singly-tuned relationships that have been described. This design process starts with a determination of the loaded Q_{ar}-value for each stage and is then based on obtaining equal antiresonant gains for all the stages.

Example 7-16. The triangular waveform in Example 7-15 is to be amplified by a staggered quadruple. Specify the antiresonant frequencies and bandwidths to be used for each stage of the amplifier.

Solution. The bandwidth necessary to achieve minimally distorted reproduction is:

$$B_o = f_H - f_L = (38.5 - 0.385)(10^3) = 38.1 \text{ kc}$$

and the cascade center frequency is:

$$f_o = \frac{B_o}{2} = \frac{38.1 \times 10^3}{2} = 19 \text{ kc}$$

From Table 7-1, the necessary antiresonant frequencies are:

$$f_{ar_1} = f_o + 0.46 \, B_o = (19 \times 10^3) + 0.46(38.1 \times 10^3) \approx 36.5 \text{ kc}$$
$$f_{ar_2} = f_o - 0.46 \, B_o = (19 \times 10^3) - 0.46(38.1 \times 10^3) \approx 1.5 \text{ kc}$$
$$f_{ar_3} = f_o + 0.19 \, B_o = (19 \times 10^3) + 0.19(38.1 \times 10^3) \approx 26.2 \text{ kc}$$
$$f_{ar_4} = f_o - 0.19 \, B_o = (19 \times 10^3) - 0.19(38.1 \times 10^3) \approx 11.8 \text{ kc}$$

and the necessary stage bandwidths are:

$$B_{L_1} = B_{L_2} = 0.38 \, B_o = 0.38(38.1 \times 10^3) = 14.5 \text{ kc}$$
$$B_{L_3} = B_{L_4} = 0.92 \, B_o = 0.92(38.1 \times 10^3) = 35 \text{ kc}$$

These requirements are indicative of the fact that the individual stages in a broadband stagger-tuned amplifier must, themselves, be broadband. This requires very low loaded Q-values for the coils used in the design. Such low values would probably have to be obtained by placing additional resistance in series with the coils in each of the antiresonant circuits. Amplifiers of this type are best designed for maximum power gain. The necessary loaded Q-values, transformer turns ratios, and other design requirements for each stage can be determined (on a stage-by-stage basis) by a procedure similar to that presented in Example 7-9. Because of the differences in the antiresonant frequency, bandwidth, and loading on each stage, the design would not have identical antiresonant circuit components in each stage.

High-Frequency Compensation

The bandwidth of an RC coupled amplifier, described for audio frequencies in Chap. 6, *can be extended to provide broadband amplification.* The technique of bandwidth extension is known as *frequency compensation.* Since compensation results in greater bandwidth, the audio-frequency amplifiers described in Chap. 6 are frequently termed *uncompensated amplifiers.* Compensation may be obtained indirectly by using significant amounts of negative feedback. This, of course, also results in a significant gain reduction. A more desirable alternative incorporates the addition of an inductive component to the RC coupling network. The inductor-capacitor combination serves as an energy-storage device (series- or parallel-resonant operation) and, therefore, does not produce the high degree of gain reduction associated with negative feedback circuits. Because of the nature of resonant circuits, this form of compensation is used to extend the *upper cutoff frequency* and is known as *high-frequency compensation*. The technique is hinted at in Chap. 6 (Fig. 6–28 and associated text) as a part of transformer bandwidth extension with the transformer's natural resonant condition. The special circuits to be described here are more flexible and much more useful in practical amplifier applications.

The simplest and most common form of high-frequency compensation is known as *shunt-peaking* and is illustrated in Fig. 7–21. The inductive component is placed in series with the amplifier load resistor, R_L, but is *in shunt* with the total equivalent capacitance:

$$C_T = C_o + \frac{C_c(C + C_i)}{C_o + C + C_i} \tag{7-36}$$

where C_o is the output capacitance of the circuit preceding the coupling network, C_i is the input capacitance of the circuit following the coupling network, and C is a separate capacitor that may be placed in the circuit if required by the design conditions. In many circuits, C_c is much greater than $C + C_i$ so that the equivalent capacitance of the series combination is approximated by $C + C_i$. In this event, C_T is simply the sum of C_o, C, and C_i. For d-c operation, the shunt-peaking network provides only an insignificant additional resistance (the inductor winding resistance) to R_L. Because of this, $R_{L(d-c)}$ is not changed. Over the low- and mid-frequency ranges, the additional impedance introduced by the inductor (ωL_1) is not great enough to significantly alter the value of $R_{L(a-c)}$ which is discussed is Chap. 6. Hence, the mid-frequency gain can be determined, as usual, for the uncompensated amplifier. In the high-frequency

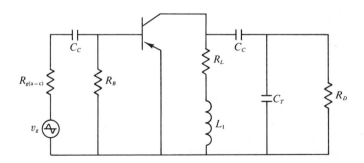

Figure 7-21. *RC Coupled Amplifier with Shunt-Peaking Circuit*

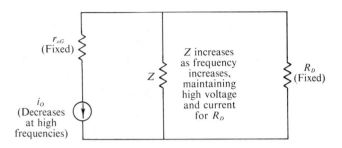

Figure 7-22.   *Equivalent Operation of Shunt-Peaking Circuit*

region, L_1 and C_T, in the compensated amplifier, form a parallel-resonant circuit.

For the uncompensated amplifier, higher frequencies near f_α or f_β cause the output capacitance to shunt a portion of the output current to ground. This results in less current to R_L and, subsequently, to the next stage, or to the device being driven by the amplifier (denoted by R_D in Fig. 7–21). Since the *useful* output signal is decreasing, this operation is equivalent to a reduction in amplifier gain. With the compensating network, frequencies that normally produce a shunting of current through C_o also produce an increasing impedance for the antiresonant circuit (L_1-C_T combination), if the circuit is properly designed. The equivalent circuit operation is indicated in Fig. 7–22. The increasing impedance, Z, maintains a high voltage across the transistor output terminals and across the next stage (or driven device) *despite* the fact that transistor output current decreases. The high voltage across R_D causes a high current through R_D. Hence, the overall result is to maintain a high useful voltage, current, and power—*compensating for the normal gain reduction that would be*

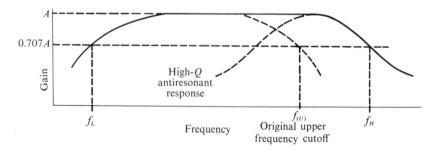

Figure 7-23.   *Equivalent Response for Ideal* RC *Coupled Amplifier with Shunt-Peaking Circuit*

experienced. Figure 7–23 illustrates the result in terms of the response curves for an uncompensated amplifier and an ideally designed shunt-peaking network. A useful component ratio is:

$$m_1 = \frac{L_1}{C_T R_L^2} \tag{7-37}$$

This permits universal response curves to be constructed, as shown in Fig. 7–24. From the 0.707 voltage (or current) gain point, or from the

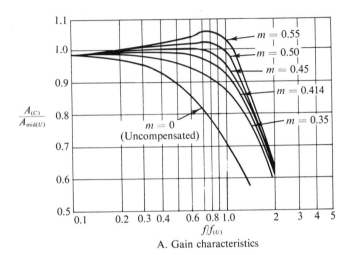

A. Gain characteristics

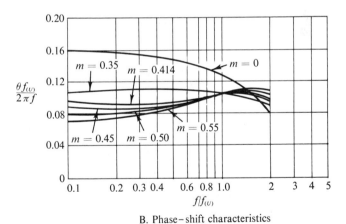

B. Phase–shift characteristics

Figure 7-24.   RC *Coupled Amplifier Response with Shunt-Peaking Circuit* (Glen M. Glasford, *Fundamentals of Television Engineering*, 1955. Courtesy McGraw-Hill Book Co., Inc.)

0.5 power gain point, it can be seen that shunt-peaking will raise the uncompensated upper cutoff frequency by a factor of approximately 1.8.

Maximal flatness is achieved with m_1 equal to 0.414. However, a slight amount of phase distortion will result from choosing this value. For this reason, it is sometimes more desirable to use m_1 equal to 0.35, sacrificing bandwidth and maximal flatness for a more constant phase characteristic. Values of m_1 greater than 0.414 produce a relative response greater than unity: $(|A_{(C)}/A_{\mathrm{mid}(U)}|) > 1$, or *overcompensation*. In most applications this is undesirable. However, in some instances, the overcompensation can be used to correct for other high-frequency degradations not associated with the amplifier itself. For example, a television transmission cable may have a reduced "gain" at high frequencies, as illustrated in Fig. 7–25. If the proper degree of overcompensation is employed in the amplifiers preceding (or following) the transmission line, the additional

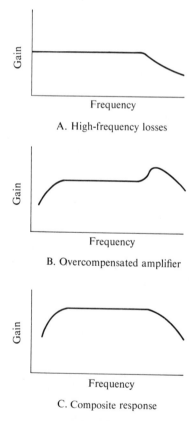

A. High-frequency losses

B. Overcompensated amplifier

C. Composite response

Figure 7-25.   *Use of Overcompensation to Achieve Response Equalization*

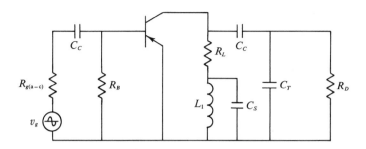

Figure 7-26.   *RC Coupled Amplifier with Modified Shunt-Peaking Circuit*

gain will correct for the line losses, resulting in a relatively constant *overall* gain. Such circuits may be used at radio or audio frequencies, and are termed *equalizer*, or *booster*, networks.

Figure 7–26 illustrates a *modified shunt-peaked amplifier* where:

$$C_S = k_1 C_T \tag{7-38}$$

Several of the response curves for this circuit are illustrated in Fig. 7–27. Comparing these responses with the simple shunt-peaked responses of Fig. 7–24, it can be seen that the modified circuit provides a somewhat more uniform gain characteristic as well as a more constant phase characteristic. Maximal flatness is achieved with m_1 equal to 0.414 and k_1 equal to 0.353. The best phase characteristic is achieved when m_1 is equal to 0.35 and k_1 is equal to 0.22. However, this results in a response that is less than maximally flat. In general, the modified shunt-peaking circuit increases the uncompensated upper cutoff frequency by a factor of about 1.9.

An entirely different compensating network is shown in Fig. 7–28. The inductive component is placed in series with the coupling capacitor— separating C_o and C_i. Component ratios are defined by:

$$m_2 = \frac{L_2}{C_T R_L^2} \tag{7-39}$$

and:

$$k_2 = \frac{C_T}{C_i} \tag{7-40}$$

For these equations, C_T is still defined by Eq. (7–36). The response curves are plotted in Fig. 7–29 for a constant value of k_2, and in Fig. 7–30 for various k_2-m_2 combinations. As shown, a considerable degree of over-compensation can be obtained with the series-peaked circuit. However, with the exception of the maximally flat gain achieved with m_2 equal to

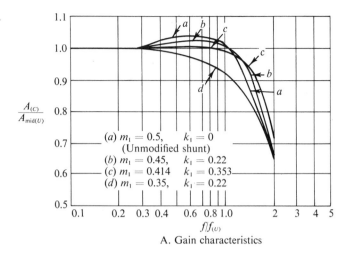

A. Gain characteristics

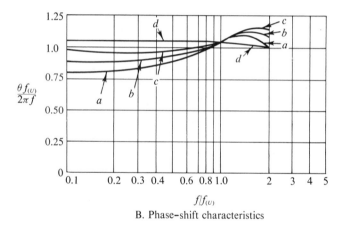

B. Phase–shift characteristics

Figure 7-27.   RC *Coupled Amplifier Response with Modified Shunt-Peaking Circuit* (Glen M. Glasford, *Fundamentals of Television Engineering*, 1955. Courtesy McGraw-Hill Book Co., Inc.)

0.75 and k_2 equal to 0.667 (Fig. 7–30), none of the responses are highly desirable. Even the conditions for maximally flat gain do not provide a constant phase shift across the entire bandwidth. In view of this, it may appear that the series-peaked amplifier does not offer a good solution to broadband amplifier requirements. Indeed, it does not, and is seldom used by itself. Rather, it is used *in combination* with shunt-peaking.

Figure 7–31 illustrates the combination series/shunt-peaked amplifier. Figure 7–32 provides the gain and phase characteristics for such an ampli-

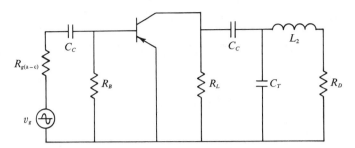

Figure 7-28. RC *Coupled Amplifier with Series-Peaking Circuit*

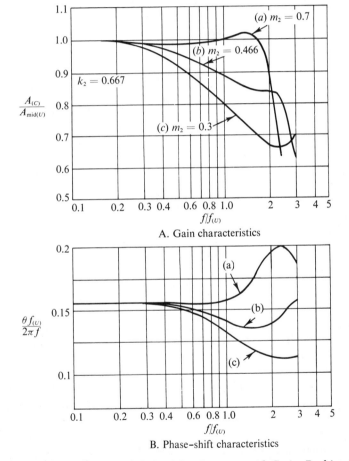

A. Gain characteristics

B. Phase-shift characteristics

Figure 7-29. RC *Coupled Amplifier Response with Series-Peaking Circuit (Fixed Capacitance Ratio)* (Glen M. Glasford, *Fundamentals of Television Engineering*, 1955. Courtesy McGraw-Hill Book Co., Inc.)

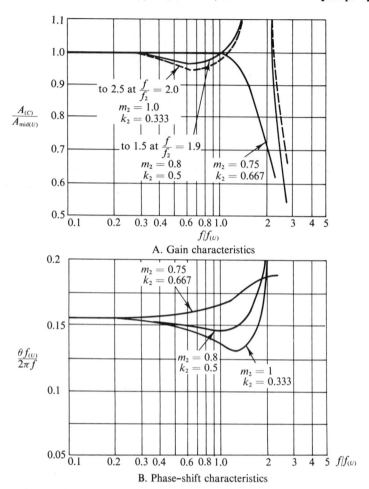

Figure 7-30. RC *Coupled Amplifier Response with Series-Peaking Circuit* (*Variable Capacitance Ratios*) (Glen M. Glasford, *Fundamentals of Television Engineering,* 1955. Courtesy McGraw-Hill Book Co., Inc.)

fier. Maximal flatness is achieved with m_1 equal to 0.147, m_2 equal to 0.604, and k_2 equal to 0.585. The associated phase characteristic, however, still experiences a rapid rise near the cutoff frequency. If these variations can be tolerated, the combination series/shunt-peaked network can be used to increase the uncompensated upper cutoff frequency by a factor on the order of 2.5 to 2.8. The best response is achieved if the *modified shunt-peaking* network is used in combination with the series-peaking network. Such a circuit appears in Fig. 7–33 with response characteristics in Fig. 7–34. Maximally flat gain is achieved with m_1 equal to 0.173, m_2 equal to

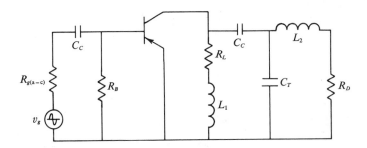

Figure 7-31.   RC *Coupled Amplifier with Series-Shunt-Peaking Circuits*

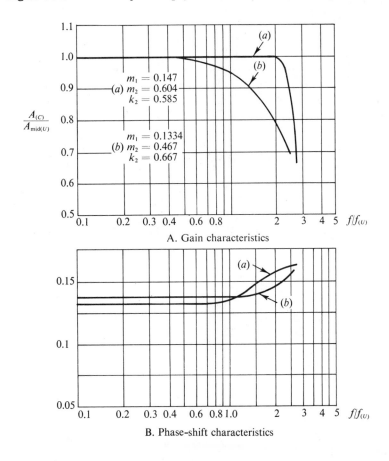

A. Gain characteristics

B. Phase-shift characteristics

Figure 7-32.   RC *Coupled Amplifier Response with Series- and Shunt-Peaking Circuits* (Glen M. Glasford, *Fundamentals of Television Engineering*, 1955. Courtesy McGraw-Hill Book Co., Inc.)

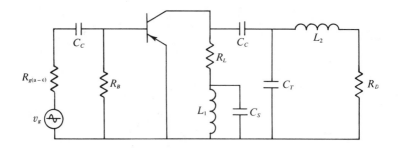

Figure 7-33. *RC Coupled Amplifier with Series- and Modified Shunt-Peaking Circuits*

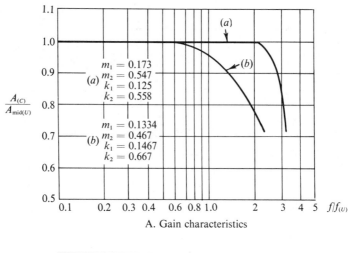

A. Gain characteristics

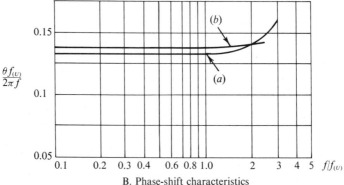

B. Phase-shift characteristics

Figure 7-34. *RC Coupled Amplifier Response with Series- and Modified Shunt-Peaking Circuits* (Glen M. Glasford, *Fundamentals of Television Engineering*, 1955. Courtesy McGraw-Hill Book Co., Inc.)

0.547, k_1 equal to 0.125, and k_2 equal to 0.558. *This circuit increases the uncompensated upper cutoff frequency by a factor of 3.25.* The phase characterisitc for this amplifier still experiences an increase that may not be desirable in all applications. When this variation cannot be tolerated, the second condition illustrated in Fig. 7–34 (or in Fig. 7–32) may be used, sacrificing bandwidth for a more constant phase characteristic.

Matching conditions for uncompensated amplifiers (Chap. 6) can be used for compensated amplifiers, as well. The effects of cascading compensated stages may also be treated by the relationships of Chap. 6. Such stages are generally designed to have the same upper cutoff frequency (all stages are identical in response characteristics).

Some degree of negative feedback is usually present in both compensated and uncompensated amplifiers. Thus, a degree of gain reduction is accepted in order to achieve even *greater bandwidth.* As long as the phase characteristic is fairly constant, no adverse instability will result. The effects of negative feedback: gain reduction, bandwidth enhancement, distortion reduction, etc., are treated by the same relationships provided in Chap. 6. *However, the determination of the upper cutoff frequency with compensation and feedback must be based on the higher (compensated) f_H-value, not the uncompensated f_H-value.*

Example 7-17. A particular common emitter, RC coupled, three-stage amplifier uses identical transistors with an upper cutoff frequency of 30 kilocycles per second. The triangular waveform in Example 7–15 is to be amplified by this cascade. The d-c load on each stage is 10K. The output junction capacitance for the transistor is 50 picofarads and the input junction capacitance is 20 picofarads. The coupling capacitance is 2 microfarads. Select an appropriate high-frequency compensation design to achieve the necessary upper cutoff frequency with a response that is maximally flat.

Solution. The upper cutoff frequency for the cascade must be 38.5 kilocyles per second. This means that each stage in the cascade must have an upper cutoff frequency of:

$$f_H = \frac{f_{H3}}{\sqrt{2^{1/3} - 1}} = \frac{38.5 \times 10^3}{\sqrt{0.26}} = 73.5 \text{ kc}$$

Since each stage has an inherent cutoff frequency of 30 kilocycles per second, this means that an extension on the order of 245 per cent is required. Such a large compensation can be obtained with either the series- and shunt-peaking combination (Figs. 7–31 and 7–32) or the combination series- and modified shunt-peaking combination (Figs. 7–33 and 7–34). The series- and shunt-peaking combination provides adequate extension capabilities and is selected because fewer circuit components are required.

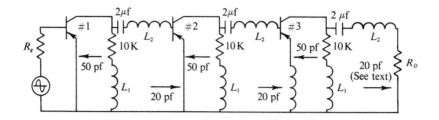

Figure E7-17

The resulting design is illustrated in Fig. E7–17. Notice that there is no indication of an additional capacitor placed in parallel with the inherent junction capacitances. There are two reasons for this. First, it is common design practice, whenever possible, to use only the junction capacitances, since this reduces the number of circuit components involved. Second, from Fig. 7–32, maximal flatness is obtained with:

$$m_1 = 0.147$$
$$m_2 = 0.604$$
$$k_2 = 0.585$$

The k_2-coefficient is defined by:

$$k_2 = \frac{C_i}{C_T}$$

where:

$$C_T = C_o + \frac{C_c(C + C_i)}{C_c + C + C_i}$$

Omitting the capacitance C and considering the fact that C_C is much greater than C_i reduces this equation to:

$$C_T = C_o + C_i = (50 + 20)(10^{-12}) = 70 \text{ picofarads}$$

Hence, the inherent capacitances in this design have a k_2-value of:

$$k_2 = \frac{20 \times 10^{-12}}{70 \times 10^{-12}} = 0.286$$

This is less than the condition for maximal flatness. Since k_2 is associated with the series-peaking portion of the circuit, it is necessary to examine Fig. 7–30 in order to determine the consequences of a reduced k_2-value. As shown in Fig. 7–30, a reduction in k_2 tends to degrade the high-frequency gain and to cause a very serious degradation in the phase-shift characteristic. However, since these are inherent junction capacitances, the design must tolerate this degradation. (Nothing can be done to alter the situation except to select other transistors with more appropriate junction capacitances.) Certainly, it is not desirable to add more parallel capacitance, since this would increase C_T and reduce k_2 even more. In conjunction with the shunt-peaking circuit, the degradation will not be as great as that indicated in Fig. 7–30. The necessary value for the series-peaking inductor for this circuit is:

$$L_2 = m_2 C_T R_L^2 = 0.604(70 \times 10^{-12})(10 \times 10^3)^2$$
$$= 4.23 \text{ millihenries}$$

and the shunt-peaking inductor is:

$$L_1 = m_1 C_T R_L^2 = 0.147(70 \times 10^{-12})(10 \times 10^3)^2$$
$$= 1.03 \text{ millihenries}$$

From Fig. 7–32, the upper cutoff frequency for this amplifier will be about 280 per cent of the uncompensated value:

$$f_H = (30 \times 10^3)(2.8) = 84 \text{ kc}$$

for each stage. Hence, the cascade cutoff frequency will be:

$$f_{H_3} = (84 \times 10^3)\sqrt{0.26} = 42.8 \text{ kc}$$

which is more than adequate for the application.

In order for the last stage to be properly compensated, the total equivalent input capacitance to the driven device must be 20 picofarads. If such a value is not present inherently, it must be placed in the circuit via an actual capacitor.

Example 7-18. A common emitter amplifier stage uses a transistor with a non-feedback current gain of -50 and an upper cutoff frequency of 20 kilocycles per second. Feedback biasing is used in the circuit, resulting in a shunt feedback factor of 0.021. The output capacitance of the transistor is 80 picofarads and the d-c load resistance is 5K. Specify the component values necessary to achieve maximally flat response with the modified shunt-peaking circuit and determine the upper cutoff frequency for the compensated amplifier.

Solution. The modified shunt-peaking circuit is shown in Fig. 7–26 and the response is shown in Fig. 7–27. For maximal flatness:

$$m_1 = 0.414$$
$$k_1 = 0.353$$

The necessary shunt-peaking inductance is:

$$L_1 = m_1 C_T R_L^2 = 0.414(80 \times 10^{-12})(5 \times 10^3)^2 = 828 \text{ microhenries}$$

if it is assumed that only the inherent junction capacitance is used in the circuit (see Example 7–16). The necessary shunt-peaking capacitance is:

$$C_S = k_1 C_T = 0.353(80 \times 10^{-12}) = 28.2 \text{ picofarads}$$

From Fig. 7–37, the compensated upper cutoff frequency is about 180 per cent of the uncompensated value. However, since feedback is present in the circuit, the uncompensated upper cutoff frequency is given by:

$$f_{H(F)} = f_H(1 + |A_{iE}| B_i) = (20 \times 10^3)[1 + (50)(2.1 \times 10^{-2})]$$
$$= (20 \times 10^3)(2.05) = 41 \text{ kc}$$

With the compensation that has been described, this will be extended to:

$$f_H = (41 \times 10^3)(1.8) = 73.8 \text{ kc}$$

Low-Frequency Compensation

As discussed in Chap. 6, the usual values of coupling capacitance, C_C, used in RC coupling networks is large enough to produce a lower cutoff frequency near d-c. However, additional capacitance networks, discussed in Chap. 9, may be present. Such circuits may tend to increase the value of f_L, regardless of the value of C_C. For this reason, it is occasionally necessary to use a *low-frequency compensating network* as illustrated in Fig. 7–35 in order to obtain the broadband amplifier f_L-value required by Eq. (7–32). The principle involved in low-frequency compensation is similar to the principle of high-frequency compensation: as less current is supplied to the load, the equivalent a-c load resistance is increased. This maintains a high output voltage and, therefore, maintains a high useful

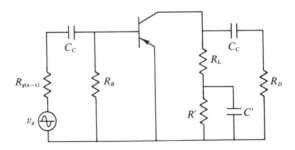

Figure 7-35. *RC Coupled Amplifier with Low-Frequency Compensation*

current to the driven device. The overall result is to maintain amplifier gain at lower frequencies. The value of the compensating capacitor, C', is such that at mid frequencies and at high frequencies, the compensating resistor, R', *is effectively bypassed* (the capacitive reactance is essentially zero, shunting R'). Hence, the circuit has no effect on the mid- and high-frequency response of the amplifier. However, at the lower frequencies, the capacitive reactance increases (Fig. 7–36) so that the impedance of the parallel combination R'-C' gradually increases, reaching a maximum value equal to R'. The best operation is obtained when:

$$C' = \frac{R_D C_C'(R_L + R')}{R_L R'} \tag{7-41}$$

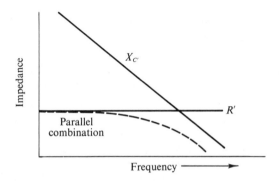

Figure 7-36.   *Variation of Low-Frequency Compensating Network Impedance*

where C_C' is the *effective coupling capacitance* associated with the lower cutoff frequency of the uncompensated amplifier *when a capacitance other than C_C is responsible for the cutoff value*. The value for C_C' is determined from:

$$C_C' = \frac{1}{2\pi f_{L(U)}(R_{L(d-c)} + R_D)} \tag{7-42}$$

where $f_{L(U)}$ is the lower cutoff frequency of the uncompensated amplifier. (The need for such an effective coupling capacitance is clarified in Chap. 9.)

Equation (7–41) is not adequate, by itself, to design the low-frequency compensating network, since R' would have to be chosen on an arbitrary basis. The *compensated* lower cutoff frequency is expressed by:

$$f_{L(C)} = \left[\frac{R_L}{R_L + R'}\right] f_{L(U)} \tag{7-43}$$

Hence, in order for an uncompensated amplifier with lower cutoff frequency, $f_{L(U)}$, to achieve a desired compensated lower cutoff frequency, $f_{L(C)}$, [determined from Eq. (7–32)], the value of R' must be:

$$R' = \left[\frac{f_{L(U)}}{f_{L(C)}} - 1\right]R_L \qquad (7\text{-}44)$$

This value of R' may be substituted in Eq. (7–41) to obtain the necessary value for C'.

Unlike the high-frequency compensating networks, the low-frequency compensating network *does* affect the d-c load resistance of the amplifier. Since the capacitor across R' is an open circuit to d-c current, the d-c load resistance is given by:

$$R_{L(d\text{-}c)} = R_L + R' \qquad (7\text{-}45)$$

Depending upon the relative values of $f_{L(U)}$, $f_{L(C)}$, and R_L, the value of R' may, in some instances, be so small that $R_{L(d\text{-}c)}$ does not change significantly.

The presence of negative feedback along with the low-frequency compensating network is treated with the relationships of Chap. 6. However, the compensated lower cutoff frequency, not the uncompensated value, must be used in determining the cutoff frequency with feedback.

Since the low-frequency compensating network is completely bypassed at high frequencies, and since the impedance of the high-frequency compensating network is insignificant at low frequencies, the two networks may be designed independently of each other. Hence, both types of compensating networks may be added to an uncompensated amplifier on the basis of their individual design characteristics. Figure 7–37 illustrates an

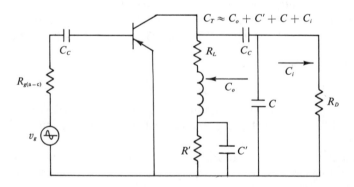

Figure 7-37. RC *Coupled Amplifier Using High-* (*Series/Shunt-Peaking*) *and Low-Frequency Compensation*

RC coupled broadband amplifier with both high- and low-frequency compensation. The high-frequency compensation is of the combination series/shunt-peaked type.

Example 7-19. A particular amplifier stage has a lower cutoff frequency of 500 cycles per second. This amplifier has a d-c load resistance of 10K and feeds a device with an equivalent resistance of 3K. It is to be used as an amplifier for the triangular waveform in Example 7-15. Design the low-frequency compensation network for this amplifier.

Solution. The low-frequency compensation network is illustrated in Fig. 7-35. From Example 7-15, a lower cutoff frequency of 385 cycles per second is needed for the specified triangular waveform. This will require a compensating resistor of:

$$R' = \left[\frac{f_{L(U)}}{f_{L(C)}} - 1\right]R_L = \left[\frac{500}{385} - 1\right](10 \times 10^3)$$
$$= 0.3(10 \times 10^3) = 3K$$

The necessary compensating capacitance is given by:

$$C' = \frac{R_D C'_C(R_L + R')}{R_L R'}$$

where C'_C is the equivalent coupling capacitance associated with the uncompensated lower cutoff frequency:

$$C'_C = \frac{1}{2\pi f_{L(U)}(R_{L(\text{d-c})} + R_D)}$$
$$= \frac{1}{2\pi(5 \times 10^2)[(10 + 3)(10^3)]}$$
$$= \frac{1}{4.09 \times 10^7} = 0.0245 \text{ microfarad}$$

Hence:

$$C' = \frac{(3 \times 10^3)(2.45 \times 10^{-8})(10 + 3)(10^3)}{(10 \times 10^3)(3 \times 10^3)}$$
$$= 73.5 \text{ microfarads}$$

Whether this compensation circuit could actually be used without adverse effects on operating point, power dissipation, and distortion is the subject of further graphical investigation (Chap. 5) since the use of R' alters the total d-c load resistance in the circuit. (The total d-c load resistance is 13K in the compensated circuit.)

Unsymmetrical Amplifier Response

The broadband and narrowband amplifiers that have been described in this chapter have symmetry about the center frequency. For most general applications, such a response is desirable and necessary—especially when high-frequency modulated signals or nonsinusoidal signals are to be amplified without distortion. Some special applications, however, may require that a specific frequency, or narrow range of frequencies, be rejected (attenuated), while frequencies *on either side must be amplified*. In order to obtain such a response (as illustrated in Fig. 7–38) the interstage

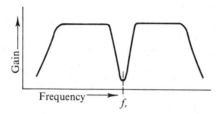

Figure 7-38.   *Unsymmetrical Response Characteristic*

coupling network must be a specially designed filter circuit, such as the one illustrated in Fig. 7–39. Such circuits are beyond the scope of this text, and may be obtained from standard electronic engineering handbooks or filter design texts.

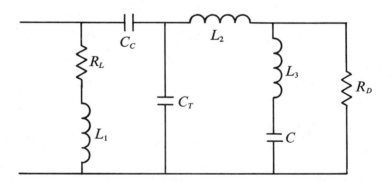

Figure 7-39.   *High-Frequency Compensating Circuits with Series-Resonant Circuit Bypassing Load*

7.3 Neutralization

In the derivation of the hybrid equivalent of the transistor, it has been shown that voltage variations in the output loop cause voltage variations in the input loop. Specifically, this feedback is expressed by the parameter, h_{rG} (Chap. 6). This feedback is *positive* in nature, that is, it is *in phase* with the input signal. Positive feedback induces instability in an amplifier, resulting in occasional or sustained oscillations. At audio frequencies, h_{rG} is so small that the induced instability may be ignored. However, at high frequencies—especially when tuned circuits are present—this instability can become appreciable. In order to avoid these instabilities, an equal amount of negative feedback must be applied through an external circuit branch. If this external negative feedback cancels both the resistive *and reactive* components of the internal feedback, the amplifier is said to be *unilateralized*. If only the reactive components are cancelled, the amplifier is said to be *neutralized*. In either case, the instability introduced by h_{rG} will be cancelled and oscillations will not occur.

PROBLEMS

1. A particular coil has an inductive reactance of 500 ohms at a frequency of 5 kilocycles per second. The winding resistance is 2 ohms. What is the Q of the coil at 5 kilocycles per second?

2. The Q of a coil is 2000 at 10 kilocycles per second. The inductance is 500 millihenries. What is the winding resistance?

3. What is the Q of the coil in Problem 2 at 18 kilocycles per second? At 6 kilocycles per second?

4. An antiresonant circuit has an antiresonant impedance of 200K at 50 kilocycles per second. The Q of the coil in the circuit is 200 at 10 kilocycles per second. What inductance is used in the circuit?

5. What capacitance must be used in Problem 4 in order to achieve antiresonance at 50 kilocycles per second?

6. The antiresonant circuit in Problems 4 and 5 is coupled to a load of 2K through a transformer with a 3:1 turns ratio. Determine the loaded Q at antiresonance, along with the loaded antiresonant impedance.

7. An inductance of 100 millihenries is used in an antiresonant circuit, coupled to a load of 10K, through a transformer with a 2:1 turns ratio. The unloaded Q of the coil is 500 at the antiresonant frequency of 100 kilocycles per second. What capacitance must be used to achieve

this frequency? What is the loaded antiresonant Q and impedance?

8. An unloaded antiresonant circuit has an antiresonant frequency of 80 kilocycles per second. If loading reduces the antiresonant Q of the coil to 5, how much frequency shift will be introduced?

9. A singly-tuned amplifier is to have an antiresonant frequency of 455 kilocycles per second and a loaded bandwidth of 15 kilocycles per second. The output resistance of the stage is 50K and the device being fed has an equivalent resistance of 2K. The output junction capacitance is 25 picofarads and the primary inductance is 500 microhenries. Specify the unloaded Q of the coil at antiresonance and the turns ratio necessary for matching.

10. A singly-tuned common emitter amplifier uses the transistor with h-parameters specified in Table 6–5. The antiresonant frequency is to be 200 kilocycles per second and the loaded bandwidth is to be 10 kilocycles per second. The output junction capacitance for this transistor is 50 picofarads. The primary inductance is 200 microhenries. The equivalent resistance of the device being fed is 10K and the signal source is matched to the input resistance of the stage. Specify the unloaded Q of the coil at antiresonance and the turns ratio necessary for matching in the output loop. Plot the power gain (decibels) as a function of frequency.

11. The transistor with h-parameters given in Problem 29 of Chap. 6 is used in a singly-tuned common emitter amplifier stage. The loaded Q of the antiresonant circuit is 25, the antiresonant frequency is 100 kilocycles per second, and the primary inductance of the circuit is 1 millihenry. A shunt feedback bias resistor of 200K is used in the circuit. Determine the feedback power gain and the loaded bandwidth of the amplifier.

12. A doubly-tuned common emitter amplifier stage has an antiresonant frequency of 455 kilocycles per second. The loaded Q of both coils is 25. The primary inductance is 150 microhenries. Critical coupling is used. Determine the antiresonant power gain of the stage, which uses the transistor with h-parameters listed in Table 6–5. What is the loaded bandwidth of the stage?

13. Three singly-tuned stages are placed in cascade. The loaded bandwidth of each stage is 18 kilocycles per second. What is the bandwidth of the cascade?

14. Two doubly-tuned stages are to be placed in cascade. The cascade must have a loaded bandwidth of 12 kilocycles per second. Determine the necessary loaded bandwidth for the two individual stages.

15. The reduction in gain at antiresonance for an overcoupled doubly-

tuned amplifier is not to exceed four-tenths of the peak gain value. What coupling coefficient must be used in the circuit, and what is the frequency separation of the gain peaks?

16. A doubly-tuned common emitter amplifier stage is overcoupled with an antiresonant power gain that is 75 per cent of the peak power gain. The loaded Q of both coils is 50. The primary inductance is 400 microhenries and antiresonance occurs at 300 kilocycles per second. The transistor in Problem 28 of Chap. 6 is used. The output junction capacitance is 40 picofarads. The device being fed has an equivalent capacitance of 20 picofarads. The turns ratio is 2:1. Plot the power gain as a function of frequency. Determine the necessary value of capacitance that must be placed in both the primary and secondary in order to achieve the specified antiresonant frequency.

17. A staggered double is to have an overall bandwidth of 50 kilocycles per second, centered at 100 kilocycles per second. Specify the antiresonant frequency and the bandwidth of each of the two stages.

18. A pulse waveform with a period of 2 microseconds is to be amplified by a staggered quintuple. Specify the necessary antiresonant frequency and bandwidth for each stage of the quintuple.

19. A staggered triple is to have an overall bandwidth of 60 kilocycles per second, centered at 120 kilocycles per second. The device being fed has an equivalent resistance of 5K. The transistor with h-parameters listed in Table 6–5 is to be used in a condition of maximum power gain in each stage. The signal source is matched to the input resistance of the first stage. Determine the turns ratio necessary to achieve matching in each stage, the unloaded antiresonant Q and primary inductance of each stage, and the overall antiresonant power gain. Plot the power gain (decibels) as a function of frequency.

20. The alpha cutoff frequency for the transistor in Problem 1 of Chap. 6 is 5 megacycles per second. The transistor is used in an RC coupled amplifier with a d-c load resistance of 8K and a coupling capacitor of 3 microfarads. The stage feeds a device with an equivalent resistance of 3K. A shunt-peaking compensation network is used to extend the upper cutoff frequency. Determine the compensated cutoff frequency for the stage and the necessary compensating circuit component values when the circuit is to have the most constant phase characteristic possible. Plot the power gain (decibels) as a function of frequency.

21. Repeat Problem 20 with the modified shunt-peaking compensation network.

22. Repeat Problem 20 with the series-peaking compensation network.

23. Repeat Problem 20 with the combination series- and shunt-peaking compensation network.

24. Repeat Problem 20 with the combination series- and modified shunt-peaking compensation network.

25. Repeat Problem 22 when the transistor uses a shunt feedback resistor of 150K in order to achieve self-biasing.

26. Repeat Problem 20 when the transistor uses a shunt feedback resistor of 200K for biasing, and three such stages are placed in cascade.

27. A three-stage RC coupled amplifier must have a lower cutoff frequency of 100 cps. The lower cutoff frequency for the individual stages is 300 cps. The d-c resistance on each stage is 8K. The output and input junction capacitances are 30 and 10 picofarads, respectively. The device being fed by the cascade has an equivalent resistance of 3K. Design the low-frequency compensating network for each stage.

28. Repeat Problem 27 when each stage uses a shunt feedback resistor of 300K to achieve biasing.

29. Assuming that the individual amplifier stages associated with Problems 20 and 27 are the same, plot the complete power gain response (decibels) as a function of frequency.

30. Repeat Problem 29 for the feedback described in Problem 28.

Further Reading

Glasford, G. M., *Fundamentals of Television Engineering*. New York: McGraw-Hill Book Co., Inc., 1955.

Martin, T. L., Jr., *Electronic Circuits*. Englewood Cliffs, N.J.: Prentice-Hall, Inc., 1955.

Pierce, J. F., *Transistor Circuit Theory and Design*. Columbus, Ohio: Charles E. Merrill Books, Inc., 1963.

Ryder, J. D., *Electronic Fundamentals and Applications*. Englewood Cliffs, N.J.: Prentice-Hall, Inc., 1959.

Surina, T. and C. Herrick, *Semiconductor Electronics*. New York: Holt, Rinehart and Winston, Inc., 1964.

8

Large-Signal Amplifiers

Eventually, in any medium- or high-power application, an amplifier stage, or stages, must be operated outside the constraints associated with small-signal, linear equivalent circuits. When this occurs, not only is it necessary to revert from a purely mathematical design analysis to a graphical analysis, but it is also necessary to pay special attention to power dissipation limits, breakdown limits, and distortion. Although most "power" amplifiers utilize silicon transistors because of their high ratings, in many applications even these transistors may be taxed to their design limits. The design analysis for large-signal amplifiers, then, is concerned primarily with distortion and transistor operating limits. The graphical determination of distortion is discussed in Chap. 5. The operating limitations include:

1. maximum power dissipation (see Chap. 5, constant power curves, temperature limitations, and deratings);
2. maximum collector voltage (see Chap. 5, reverse breakdown); and
3. maximum output current (or maximum input current), based on a consideration of distortion and an inherent transistor gain degradation.

The frequency response range must also be considered. Since most power amplifiers employ input or output transformers (or both), these stages usually provide the predominant bandwidth limitations associated with a complete amplifier arrangement. Frequency responses are considered in Chaps. 6 and 7. Since all of these factors have been considered in detail in previous portions of the text, their association with large-signal amplifiers will merely be indicated in this chapter, the bulk of which is devoted to the specific techniques required for large-signal design analysis, and to the special circuit arrangements that have been developed to circumvent the distortion and gain degradation problems.

Since the forward current amplification factor drops rapidly as high input-output currents are reached (see Fig. 6–16), in addition to increased distortion and an increased possibility of transistor destruction, the power amplifier faces an inherent degradation in gain. A special circuit arrangement, the *compound connection*, has been developed to circumvent this problem. Negative feedback may be used, to a degree, to reduce distortion. However, at the signal levels associated with these circuits, it is difficult to control feedback adequately. At audio frequencies, another circuit arrangement, the *push-pull connection*, is used to achieve low distortion and high operating efficiency. Both of these special circuits require *two transistors*, leading to additional complexity and cost. Furthermore, the push-pull arrangement requires "matched" transistors (two transistors with near-identical characteristics) in order to achieve the lowest possible distortion. This leads to even greater cost. However, unlike the vacuum tube push-pull amplifier, which always requires transformer coupling or *phase inversion* circuits, the transistor push-pull may be arranged in *complementary symmetry* fashion, eliminating the need for these additional restrictions. At radio frequencies, a load consisting of a parallel capacitor and inductor (the "tuned tank" of Chap. 7) is used to circumvent distortion problems. At the same time, since a tuned tank inherently produces a sinusoidal signal, it is possible to operate Class *C*, yielding the greatest possible efficiency as well as a minimal distortion. In effect, then, the radio-frequency power amplifier is used to provide periodic "pulses" to the tank which, because of its energy storage and resonant characteristics, reshapes the pulses into a continuous sinewave signal.

8.1 Single-Ended Amplifiers

When low-power, audio-frequency applications are considered, it may be possible to operate the power stage as a normal Class *A* amplifier. With a well-selected power transistor, serious distortion can be avoided even though large signals may be applied. It is important that power amplifier stages be operated in matched conditions ($R_{g(\text{a-c})} = r_{iG}$; $R_{L(\text{a-c})} = r_{oG}$) so that maximum power gain can be achieved whenever possible. For this reason, transformer coupling is commonly used in the input and output loops, with the proper turns ratio for matching. A typical common emitter stage is shown in Fig. 8-1, Part A, along with a graphical analysis of

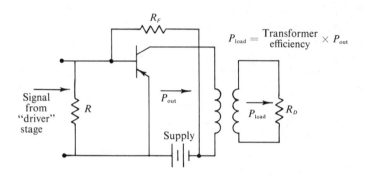

$$P_{\text{load}} = \frac{\text{Transformer}}{\text{efficiency}} \times P_{\text{out}}$$

A. Amplifier circuit

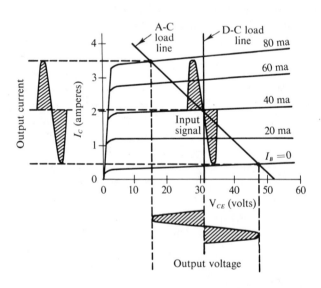

B. Amplifier operation

Figure 8-1.   *Single-Ended Class A Transformer Coupled Amplifier*

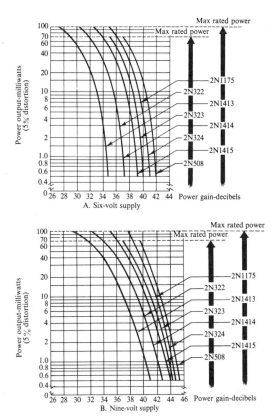

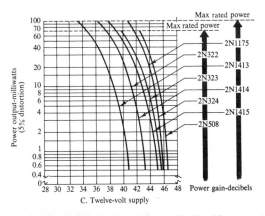

Figure 8-2.   *Single-Ended Design Charts* (J. F. Cleary, ed., *General Electric Transistor Manual*, 1964. Courtesy General Electric Company, Semiconductor Products Dept.)

operation (Part B). The details of graphical analysis are presented in Chap. 5, including distortion determinations. The frequency response for transformer coupled stages is discussed in Chap. 6. Such a circuit is referred to as a *single-ended amplifier* since a single transistor is used to feed a single output loop. Since transformer coupling is used, the theoretical efficiency of the single-ended, Class *A* amplifier is 50 per cent (Chap. 5). In practice, however, efficiencies somewhat lower than this will apply. The stages which "drive" the power stage will generally include cascaded RC coupled stages and are referred to as *preamplifiers*, or *drivers*. They are used to "boost" very small voltage (or current) signals to a high enough level to operate the power stage.

Transformer losses must be accounted for if an accurate design is to be achieved. They are generally accounted for in terms of *transformer efficiency*, the ratio of output (secondary) power to input (primary) power, specified by the transformer manufacturer (or measured directly). Because of these losses, it is always necessary to design a stage (driver, power, or any other) to produce an output terminal power that is greater than the desired (useful) output power delivered to the secondary load, as indicated in Fig. 8-1. Although it is necessary to perform a detailed graphical analysis to investigate all aspects of the stage's operation, manufacturer's design charts, such as those illustrated in Fig. 8-2, can be useful in selecting a transistor when a specific output power requirement is desired.

Example 8-1. The 2N322 transistor is used in a single-ended transformer coupled power stage with a 9-volt power supply. The transformer has an efficiency of 75 per cent. Using the design curves in Fig. 8-2, determine the maximum power gain (in decibels) for the amplifier if the useful output signal power must be 20 milliwatts and the distortion cannot exceed 5 per cent.

Solution. From Fig. 8-1:

$$P_{\text{load}} = (\text{Efficiency}) \times P_{\text{out}}$$

Rearranging for P_{out}:

$$P_{\text{out}} = \frac{P_{\text{load}}}{(\text{Efficiency})} = \frac{20 \times 10^{-3}}{0.75} = 25.33 \text{ milliwatts}$$

Using Fig. 8-2, Part B, for an output power of 25.33 milliwatts with 5 per cent distortion, the gain of the amplifier cannot exceed 36.5 decibels.

8.2 Push-Pull Amplifiers

Figure 8–3 shows a simplified version of a push-pull amplifier. The absence of forward bias in the input loop indicates that operation is Class *B*. Arranged in this fashion, each transistor conducts and amplifies one-half of the input cycle, resulting in higher output power than can be achieved with Class *A* operation. Part A of the figure illustrates circuit operation during the positive half of an input cycle. The base of transistor 1 is positive with respect to the emitter, while the base of transistor 2 is negative with respect to the emitter. For PNP transistors, this is equivalent to applying a reverse bias to the base-emitter junction of transistor 1 (preventing conduction) and a forward bias to the base-emitter junction of transistor 2 (causing conduction). The current flowing in the output loop of transistor 2 produces a secondary terminal polarity as indicated, producing a negative half-cycle across the load. (It has been assumed that primary and secondary windings are arranged in such a way that input and output polarities are the same. This is not always true. However, even when appropriate transformer inversions are considered, the general principles of push-pull operation are the same.) During the negative half of the input cycle (Part B), the base-emitter of transistor 1 is forward

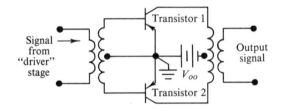

A. Amplifier circuit

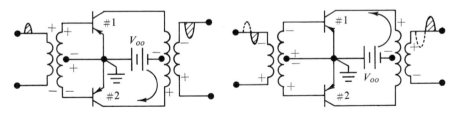

B. Positive input signal   C. Negative input signal

Figure 8-3.   *Basic Class B Push-Pull Amplifier and Operating Principles*

biased; the base-emitter of transistor 2 is reverse biased. This prevents conduction in transistor 2 and produces conduction in transistor 1. The current in the output loop of transistor 1 is such that a positive half-cycle is produced across the secondary load.

The center-tapped transformers in the input and output loops of the push-pull amplifier are used to produce the proper conduction and loading polarities. The push-pull amplifier utilizing two PNP or two NPN transistors *must have phase inversion* (two signals, 180° out of phase) *in order to operate*. With only a single signal available from the driver as shown, the center-tapped transformer and common emitter, grounded at the center-tap, produces an effect equivalent to phase inversion. The input transformer may be eliminated through the use of phase inversion amplifiers, which are driver stages designed to provide two signals 180° out of phase, or through the use of an NPN and PNP transistor in the push-pull amplifier, which eliminates the need for two input signals. Methods exist for eliminating the output transformer, also.

If well-matched transistors are used, no adverse distortion will be introduced by having two transistors develop separate halves of the output cycle. As a matter of fact, this operation can eliminate all even-harmonic distortion components. A new form of distortion, *crossover distortion*, is associated with Class *B* push-pull operation, however. In order to eliminate these components, it is necessary to operate the push-pull amplifier with a small forward bias. This leads to a Class *AB* push-pull amplifier which has both transistors conducting simultaneously during a part of the output cycle.

Phase Inverters

For reasons associated with cost, size, weight, and frequency response, it is not always desirable to have the driver stage feed the power stage through transformer coupling. Yet, it *is necessary* to have some form of circuit arrangement that produces two out-of-phase signals for the conventional Class *B*, push-pull amplifier. Driver stages that provide such an output are known as *phase inverters*. Phase inverters use one or more transistors; may be fed by another preamplifier stage, or stages; are operated Class *A*; and use RC coupling to feed the power stage.

Figure 8–4 is a simple, single-transistor phase inverter known as a *split-load inverter*. The output signals are produced across resistors R_1 and R_2, respectively. Each of these resistors is in parallel with the input resistance of one portion of the push-pull amplifier. The circuit is designed so that $V_{oG(1)}$ is equal to $V_{oG(2)}$. With this condition, the only difference

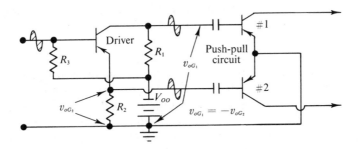

Figure 8-4. *Split-Load Phase Inverter*

between the output signals is the phase shift of 180°. Depending upon the particular application, a medium-range power transistor may be selected for use in the phase inverter. However, since Class *A*, linear operation is usually maintained, the circuit can be analyzed (or designed) by using the mathematical techniques (*h*-parameters) of Chap. 6.

A primary disadvantage of the split-load inverter is that it operates in two different configurations simultaneously. Furthermore, one of these stages operates with negative feedback while the other does not. These two conditions make it difficult to achieve and maintain the perfect balance required for $V_{oG(2)}$ to be equal.

In order to overcome the disadvantages and complexities associated with the split-load inverter, a two-transistor inverter may be used. Many two-stage inverters are available. The one illustrated in Fig. 8–5 utilizes two CE stages and, as such, is the most straightforward in design and analysis. Furthermore, it can be easily adjusted to maintain balanced output signal values and *has the additional advantage of providing current*

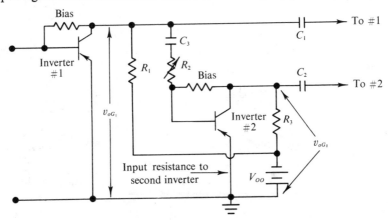

Figure 8-5. *Two-Stage Common Emitter Phase Inverter*

and voltage gains. Hence, although it may still be necessary to precede the inverter by one or more additional preamplifier stages, fewer such stages will be needed than for the split-load circuit.

The two bias resistors in Fig. 8–5 provide forward bias for the Class *A* operation of both transistors. They also produce negative feedback in the form of voltage feedback (see Fig. 6–45), but, because of the usual value of these resistors, it is a very small degree of feedback. In any event, the feedback for both stages *is equal* so that no unbalance occurs. The signal from transistor 1 feeds the top portion of the push-pull stage *and the second stage of the inverter.* Both signals are applied through RC coupling networks. Resistor R_3 is the d-c load for transistor 1 (capacitors C_1 and C_2 block the rest of the circuit). However, the equivalent a-c load on transistor 1 consists of R_1 in parallel with the series combination of R_2 and the input resistance of the second inverter stage, *all in parallel* with the input resistance of one of the power stages. This is shown in Fig. 8–6, Part A.

The CE amplifier inherently produces a 180° phase shift between input and output signals. Since the signal fed to the top stage of the push-pull amplifier is the same phase as the signal fed to the second inverter stage, the additional 180° phase shift through this stage assures that the bottom stage of the push-pull will always be fed a signal 180° out of phase with the top stage. This is indicated by a comparison of the various signals in

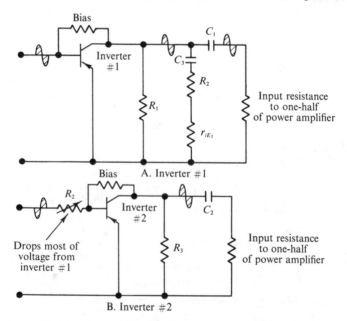

Figure 8-6.   *Equivalent Circuits for Inverter Stages in* **Fig. 8–5**

both parts of Fig. 8–6. In Part B is can be seen that the d-c load on the second inverter stage is simply R_3, while the a-c load is simply R_3 in parallel with the input resistance of one of the push-pull stages. Since both inverter stages produce voltage and current gain, it should be obvious that, unless a special arrangement is used, the output signal from the second inverter stage would be much larger than the output signal from the first inverter stage. This "special" arrangement consists of the *attenuating resistor*, R_2. The value of R_2 is such that much of the voltage output by the first inverter stage is dropped *before* the input to the second inverter stage. Hence, the proper adjustment of R_2 will assure that $V_{oG(1)}$ and $V_{oG(2)}$ are equal. With the same transistors used for both inverter stages, the design for equal output voltages generally forces the R_1-, R_2-, and R_3-values to be such that the output resistances of both inverter stages are about equal. This leads to the same equivalent source resistance for both push-pull stages, maintaining equal input currents also.

Example 8-2. Each of the two stages of the CE inverter in Fig. 8–5 has a voltage gain of -35 and an input resistance of 3K. Each half of the push-pull, Class *B* power amplifier fed by this inverter requires a peak driving current of 10 ma and has an input resistance of 2K. Specify the value of R_2 and the inverter input signal voltage necessary to achieve proper push-pull operation.

Solution. Since the input resistance for each half of the push-pull is 2K, an input peak current of 10 milliamperes requires that the push-pull input signal voltage have a peak value of 20 volts. Since the voltage gain of each inverter stage is -35, the peak input voltage to each must be:

$$v_{\text{in(peak)}} = \frac{v_{\text{out(peak)}}}{A_{vE}} = \frac{20}{35} = 0.572 \text{ volt}$$

However, since the first stage will have a peak output voltage of 20 volts, most of this must be dropped across R_2 (19.428 volts). Since the same current flows through R_2 and the input resistance to the second stage:

$$IR_2 = 19.428$$
$$Ir_{iE} = 0.572$$
$$\frac{19.428}{R_2} = \frac{0.572}{r_{iE}}$$
$$R_2 = \frac{19.428 r_{iE}}{0.572} = \frac{19.428(3 \times 10^3)}{0.572} = 102\text{K}$$

Complementary Symmetry

For transistor push-pull amplifiers, the entire problem of designing phase inversion circuits *can* be *avoided* with the use of a *complementary symmetry* push-pull amplifier. This amplifier utilizes an NPN and PNP push-pull connection, as shown in Fig. 8-7. The operation can be explained by the fact that, for an NPN transistor, the base must be positive with respect to the emitter in order to achieve conduction, while the reverse is true for the PNP transistor (see Chap. 5). During the positive half of the input cycle (Part A of the figure), the base-emitter junction of transistor 1 (PNP) is reverse biased so that it will not conduct. However, the base-emitter junction of the NPN transistor 2 is forward biased so that output current will flow, as shown. The center-tapped output transformer operation is the same as that discussed previously. During the negative half of the input cycle (Part B), transistor 2 becomes reverse biased (and stops conducting) while transistor 1 becomes forward biased (producing current flow, as shown). The resulting Class *B* push-pull operation is identical to that associated with the previous push-pull circuits, but *only one input signal is required.* As before, if well-matched transistors are used, no adverse distortion will be introduced by having the two halves of the output signal produced by separate transistors. However, it is more difficult to match the characteristics of an NPN and PNP transistor than it is to match the characteristics of two similar-type transistors. Obviously, then, a matched NPN/PNP pair must be more expensive to use and to

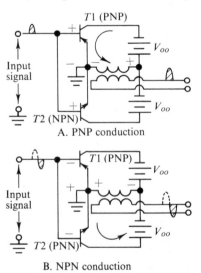

Figure 8-7.   *Complementary Symmetry Power Amplifier and Operation*

replace when a failure occurs. (The failure of one transistor in a matched pair requires the replacement of both by a new matched pair.)

Graphical Analysis

Regardless of whether the Class *B* push-pull amplifier uses two transistors of the same type, or the complementary symmetry arrangement, the voltage, current, and power gains can be determined through the graphical techniques of Chap. 5. Since it is assumed that matched transistors will always be used to avoid serious distortion, it is necessary to analyze only one of the stages in the push-pull arrangement. A typical analysis is shown in Fig. 8–8. The d-c load line is vertical, as is customary with transformer coupling, while the a-c load line is determined by:

$$R_{L(\text{a-c})} = \left(\frac{N_1}{2N_2}\right)^2 R_S \qquad (8\text{-}1)$$

where N_1 is the number of turns in the *full* primary winding, N_2 is the number of secondary turns, and R_S is the secondary resistance. Since only half the turns ratio is used for each transistor in the push-pull arrangement, the equivalent load on each transistor is only one-quarter

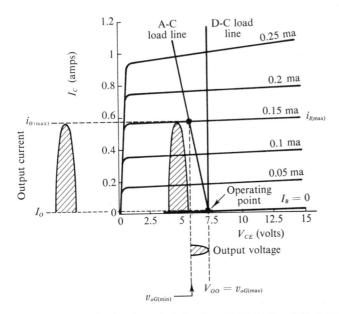

Figure 8-8.   *Graphical Analysis for One-Half of Class B Push-Pull Amplifier*

of the value associated with single-ended operation. (This fact alone assures that each push-pull stage will have a higher current gain than that obtainable from an equivalent single-ended power amplifier.) The fact that only half the output transformer turns ratio is used for each push-pull stage must also be considered when selecting a turns ratio for matching r_{oG} and $R_{L\text{(a-c)}}$:

$$\frac{N_1}{N_2} = 2\sqrt{\frac{r_{oG}}{R_S}} \tag{8-2}$$

where r_{oG} is the output resistance of *one push-pull* stage. Since r_{oG} and r_{iG} are not always readily available directly, these values may be approximated by the *h*-parameter equations (Chap. 6). However, it must be realized that these values will be in error. The degree of error will depend on the maximum current to which the power stages are driven.

With no forward bias, the minimum input current to a push-pull stage is zero. The minimum output current is always very nearly zero (Fig. 8–8). Because of this, the current gain for one stage of the push-pull is:

$$A_{iG} = \frac{i_{o\text{(max)}}}{i_{I\text{(max)}}} \tag{8-3}$$

Since this is based on *half the input and output cycle for the complete push-pull amplifier*, the current gain for the complete amplifier must also be given by Eq. (8–3). The minimum *input voltage* for one of the push-pull stages is also zero. The maximum output voltage is V_{oo} (Fig. 8–8). This leads to a voltage gain of:

$$A_{vG} = \frac{V_{oo} - v_{oG\text{(min)}}}{v_{I\text{(max)}}} \tag{8-4}$$

$$= \frac{V_{oo} - v_{oG\text{(min)}}}{(i_{I\text{(max)}})r_{iG}}$$

which is also the voltage gain for the complete push-pull amplifier. The output power for the complete amplifier is:

$$P_{\text{a-c}} = \frac{i_{o\text{(max)}}(V_{oo} - v_{oG\text{(min)}})}{2} \tag{8-5}$$

where $i_{o\text{(max)}}$ and $v_{oG\text{(min)}}$ are taken from the single-stage graphical analysis (Fig. 8–8).

Example 8-3.   Transistor C in Appendix D is used in both halves of a CE Class B, push-pull amplifier. The supply voltage is 20 volts. The output transformer turns ratio is 5:1. The push-pull feeds a device with an equivalent resistance of 6 ohms. Determine the output power when the peak input signal current is 8 milliamperes.

Solution. The output power is:

$$P_{\text{a-c}} = \frac{i_{O(\max)}(V_{OO} - v_{OE(\min)})}{2}$$

The values for $i_{O(\max)}$ and $v_{OE(\min)}$ must be obtained from a graphical analysis. The d-c load line and operating point are shown in Fig. E8-3. The a-c load is:

$$R_{L(\text{a-c})} = \left(\frac{N_1}{2N_2}\right)^2 R_S = \left(\frac{5}{2}\right)^2 (6) = 37.5 \text{ ohms}$$

This load line is also shown in Fig. E8-3. Hence:

$$P_{\text{a-c}} = \frac{0.31(20 - 8)}{2} = \frac{0.31(12)}{2} = 1.86 \text{ watts}$$

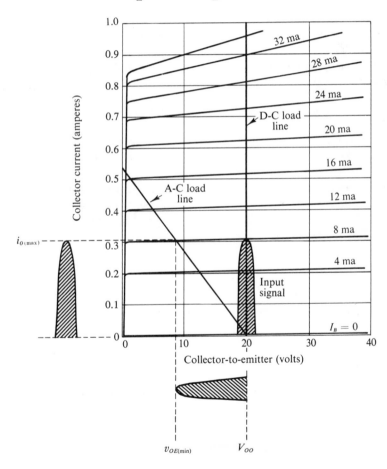

Figure E8-3

Operating Efficiency

Operating efficiency, in general, was discussed in Chap. 6. It was shown that the maximum theoretical efficiency for a Class A amplifier is 50 per cent when transformer coupling is used. It was indicated that the maximum theoretical Class B efficiency is 78.5 per cent. This value can be derived by considering the a-c and d-c power associated with the complete push-pull amplifier. Waveform analysis (Appendix C) indicates that, for a half-cycle sinusoid, as indicated in Fig. 8–8, the equivalent d-c current value is given by $i_{0(max)}/\pi$. Hence, the total d-c power for the push-pull amplifier is:

$$P_{\text{d-c}} = \frac{2V_{oo}(i_{0(max)})}{\pi} \tag{8-6}$$

The a-c power is given by Eq. (8–5). Since the operating efficiency is defined by the ratio of $P_{\text{a-c}}$ and $P_{\text{d-c}}$, and since, in the limit, $v_{oG(min)}$ will be zero (the maximum voltage excursion in Fig. 8–8 is from V_{oo} to zero), the maximum theoretical Class B push-pull amplifier efficiency is:

$$\eta_0 = \frac{\pi}{4} \times 100 \text{ per cent} = 78.5 \text{ per cent} \tag{8-7}$$

This derivation is based on a pure sinusoidal output signal. In practice, some degree of distortion will exist, raising the value of $I_{\text{d-c}}$ and, therefore, $P_{\text{d-c}}$. Furthermore, some degree of power loss will occur in the primary winding resistance, leading to a still higher d-c power drain from the bias battery. Both these quantities tend to decrease the operating efficiency. For a high-quality push-pull amplifier, however, efficiencies of 70 per cent or slightly higher can be achieved in practice.

Example 8-4. Specify the operating efficiency for the push-pull amplifier in Example 8–3.

Solution. The efficiency is given by:

$$\eta_0 = \frac{P_{\text{a-c}}}{P_{\text{d-c}}} \times 100 \text{ per cent}$$

From Example 8–3, $P_{\text{a-c}}$ is 1.86 watts. The d-c power is:

$$P_{\text{d-c}} = \frac{2V_{oo}(i_{0(max)})}{\pi} = \frac{2(20)(0.31)}{\pi} = 3.95 \text{ watts}$$

Hence:

$$\eta_0 = \frac{1.86}{3.95} \times 100 \text{ per cent} = 47 \text{ per cent}$$

which is considerably below the theoretical 78.5 per cent.

Distortion

The input currents for the two stages of the push-pull amplifier are expressed by:

$$i_{I(1)} = i_{I(\text{max})} \cos \omega t \tag{8-8a}$$

$$i_{I(1)} = i_{I(\text{max})} \cos (\omega t + \pi) \tag{8-8b}$$

indicating the 180° phase difference between the two signals. Since any waveform may be expressed as the sum of its harmonic components (Appendix C), the output currents for the two stages may be expressed by:

$$i_{O(1)} = I_{\text{d-c}} + i_{1(P)} \cos \omega t + i_{2(P)} \cos 2\omega t \tag{8-9a}$$
$$+ \cdots + i_{n(P)} \cos (n\omega t)$$

$$i_{O(2)} = I_{\text{d-c}} + i_{1(P)} \cos (\omega t + \pi) \tag{8-9b}$$
$$+ i_{2(P)} \cos 2(\omega t + \pi) + \cdots$$
$$+ i_{n(P)} \cos n(\omega t + \pi)$$

where $i_{n(P)}$ indicates the peak current for each harmonic component (and is related to $i_{I(\text{max})}$, and the transfer characteristic of the transistor in each stage). By *trigonometric identity*:

$$\cos (\omega t + \pi) = -\cos \omega t \tag{8-10a}$$

$$\cos 2(\omega t + \pi) = \cos \omega t \tag{8-10b}$$

$$\cos 3(\omega t + \pi) = -\cos \omega t \tag{8-10c}$$

$$\cos 4(\omega t + \pi) = \cos \omega t \tag{8-10d}$$

with this list continuing indefinitely, the same pattern repeating for odd and even harmonics. Hence, Eq. (8–9b) can be rewritten as:

$$i_{O(2)} = I_{\text{d-c}} - i_{1(P)} \cos \omega t + i_{2(P)} \cos 2\omega t \tag{8-9c}$$
$$- i_{3(P)} \cos 3\omega t + i_{4(P)} \cos 4\omega t - \cdots$$

From Fig. 8–3, it can be seen that the currents from the two transistors *subtract* in the center-tapped output transformer primary. Since the current in the secondary is proportional to the current in the primary:

$$i_S = (i_{O(1)} - i_{O(2)})K \tag{8-11}$$

where i_S is the secondary current and K is a *proportionality constant*. Substituting Eqs. (8–9a) and (8–9c) into Eq. (8–11) yields:

$$i_S = K(i_{1(P)} \cos \omega t + i_{3(P)} \cos 3\omega t \tag{8-11a}$$
$$+ i_{5(P)} \cos 5\omega t + \cdots)$$

indicating that the operation of a Class *B* push-pull amplifier *inherently eliminates all even-harmonic distortion* components. In order for this cancellation to occur, of course, the peak amplitudes of the harmonic

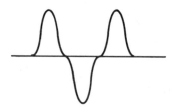

Figure 8-9. *Waveform with High Odd-Harmonic Content (Crossover Distortion)*

components must be equal for both transistors. This means that the peak input current values must be identical and that the two transistors must be *perfectly* matched in operating characteristics. Although these ideals will not occur in actual practice, the near-elimination of the even harmonics can be achieved.

Figure 8–9 illustrates the distorted waveform obtained when a fundamental sinewave is added to a third harmonic of a lower amplitude. This displays a general tendency for the waveform to "flatten" in the low amplitude regions. The inclusion of fifth, seventh, and other odd harmonics makes this general distortion even more apparent. This is known as *crossover distortion* because it is the result of nonlinearities introduced as conduction is transferred from one transistor to the other during Class *B,* push-pull operation. This can be seen graphically—and the amplitudes of the distortion components can be determined—if the *composite dynamic transfer characteristic* is constructed. Such a characteristic represents the i_I-i_O relationship for the complete push-pull amplifier. The dynamic transfer characteristic for one of the push-pull stages can be constructed as described in Chap. 5 and is shown in Fig. 8–10, Part A. Since the i_I-values and i_O-values for the second stage of the push-pull represent the *negative* portions of the input and output currents, respectively, if *matched transistors* are used, the dynamic transfer characteristic for one transistor will be the *mirror image* of the other. This is shown in Part B of the figure. Notice the extreme nonlinearity of the low-amplitude regions of both transistors. An input sinewave and resulting output signal is also shown in Part B. This is the crossover distortion (composed of odd harmonics) previously predicted on a purely mathematical basis. The output current values required to compute the d-c and harmonic amplitudes [Eqs. (5–63a) through (5–63e)] are indicated along the output current axis in Part B. In exercising such a graphical determination, very small amplitude values may be obtained for the d-c and even-harmonic amplitudes. This is the result of errors in constructing the two transfer curves as *exact*

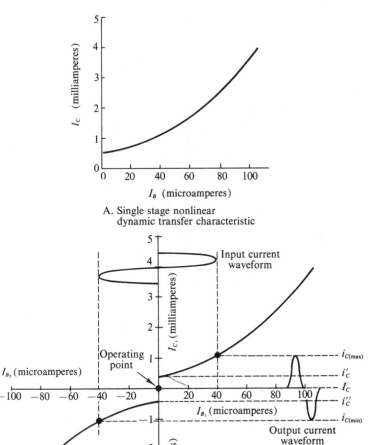

A. Single stage nonlinear
dynamic transfer characteristic

B. Composite dynamic transfer
characteristic for Class-B
push-pull operation (with
zero forward bias)

Figure 8-10. *Composite Graphical Analysis for Class B Push-Pull Operation*

mirror images, and in reading the appropriate values from the graphs. Obtaining an *exact* match of two transistors is impossible, however, so that some small value for the d-c and even-harmonic components will, in fact, exist during amplifier operation.

Class *AB* Operation

The problem of crossover distortion can be eliminated if the push-pull amplifier is operated Class *AB*. That is, each of the transistors is permitted to conduct *slightly more than half of the input cycle* so that both are operating *simultaneously* in the low-amplitude signal regions. Class *AB* operation is achieved by supplying a small forward bias to the transistors (see Chap. 5) by way of a voltage divider network such as the one illustrated in Fig. 8–11. The value of resistor R_1 (the bias resistor) is very much less than the value of R_2 (which serves to drop almost *all* of the supply voltage and to restrict bias current to the desired value).

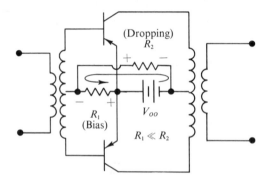

Figure 8-11.   *Class AB Push-Pull Amplifier*

Applying forward bias has the effect of "sliding" the input current axes of the two transfer characteristics in opposite directions, as shown in Fig. 8–12. Since the operating point for the two transistors must always be the same, the value of I_I, the forward bias current, must be the common point on both axes, as shown. Since the total output current is the difference of the two individual-stage output currents (see Fig. 8–3), the actual value of i_o, when both transistors are conducting, is:

$$i_o = i_{o(1)} - i_{o(2)} \qquad (8\text{-}12)$$

where $i_{o(1)}$ and $i_{o(2)}$ are obtained from the respective transfer characteristics for a particular value of i_I. When this is done, as in Fig. 8–12, Part B, the *equivalent composite transfer characteristic* is obtained. With the proper forward bias and well-matched transistors, the characteristic will be linear and crossover distortion will be eliminated. The only additional distortion will be the result of mismatched transistors or of driving the transistors into the high-current nonlinearities.

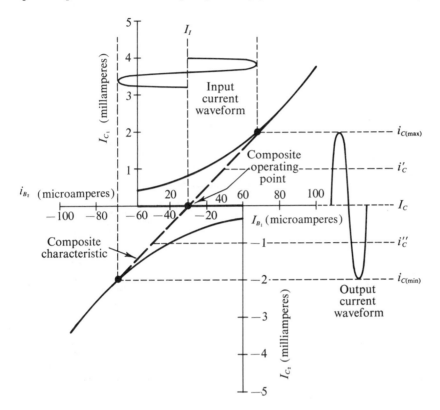

Figure 8-12.   *Composite Dynamic Transfer Characteristic for Class AB Push-Pull Amplifier*

The distortion components can be obtained from the data indicated in Fig. 8–12, using the techniques discussed in Chap. 5. Current gain can also be obtained from Fig. 8–12. However, a general amplifier analysis (current, voltage, and power gain) is best obtained from the usual output characteristic analysis (Fig. 8–13). *Only the complete half* of the waveform is used for the analysis. The current gain is given by:

$$A_{iG} = \frac{i_{O(\text{max})} - I_O}{i_{I(\text{max})} - I_I} \qquad (8\text{-}13)$$

Voltage gain is given by Eq. (8–4) and power gain is:

$$P_{\text{a-c}} = \frac{(i_{O(\text{max})} - I_O)(V_{OO} - v_{OG(\text{min})})}{2} \qquad (8\text{-}14)$$

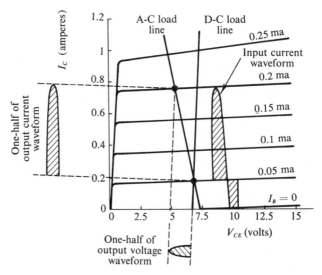

Figure 8-13.   *Graphical (Gain) Analysis for Class AB Push-Pull Amplifier*

Example 8-5.   Transistor A in Appendix D is operated in a Class AB push-pull amplifier with a 15-volt supply and an a-c load of 300 ohms seen in the transformer primary. The input bias current is 100 microamperes. Determine the a-c power output for the amplifier if the peak-to-peak input current is 800 microamperes. What voltage divider resistance must be used to achieve the necessary input bias current?

Solution.   The a-c and d-c load lines are shown in Fig. E8–5, along with the input signal, which has a peak current value of 400 microamperes (800/2). The maximum base current is:

$$i_{B(\text{max})} = I_B + i_{B(P)} = (100 + 400)(10^{-6}) = 500 \text{ microamperes}$$

The interpolated characteristic for 500 microamperes is also shown in Fig. E8–5, as are the various output signal values for determining the a-c power output:

$$P_{\text{a-c}} = \frac{(i_{O(\text{max})} - I_O)(V_{OO} - v_{OG(\text{min})})}{2}$$
$$= \frac{(24 - 7)(10^{-3})(15 - 10)}{2} = 42.5 \text{ milliwatts}$$

Notice that only the complete (top) half of the input cycle is considered in this determination. From Fig. 8–11, the input bias current can be established with a resistance of:

$$(R_2 + R_1) = \frac{15}{100 \times 10^{-6}} = 150\text{K}$$

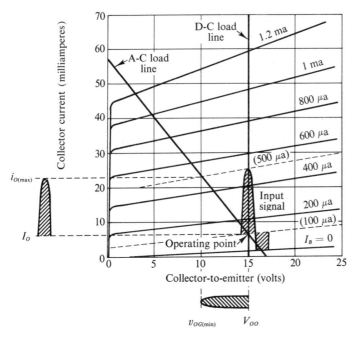

Figure E8-5

Resistor R_1 will be very small (5 or 10 ohms) so that R_2 may be made equal to 150K and the insignificant effect of R_1 may be neglected. However, R_1 must be in the circuit in order to establish the forward bias polarity essential to transistor operation.

Transformerless Push-Pull Amplifiers

The cost, weight, size, and frequency limitations associated with transformers has resulted in considerable investigation of "transformerless" amplifiers. It has been shown how the *input transformer* may be eliminated through the use of phase inverters or through the use of an NPN and PNP transistor in a complimentary symmetry arrangement. Figure 8–14 illustrates a method by which the operating load (in this case, a speaker) may be connected, with RC coupling, to a push-pull amplifier. The d-c load resistor is in parallel with the two transistors and has a small value so that the d-c load line will be approximately vertical (as with transformer coupling). However, the a-c load is also very small, resulting in essentially no voltage gain, a very high current gain, and a power gain considerably less than that obtained with transformer coupling. The two transistors in Fig. 8–14 are *in series with the supply battery* as far as d-c

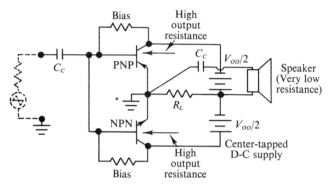

Figure 8-14.   CE *Transformerless Amplifier*

current flow is concerned. This means that a supply voltage *twice as large* as that needed for a comparable transformer coupled amplifier must be used. In the steady state, each transistor will drop half of the supply voltage from collector to emitter. A graphical analysis, then, must use $V_{oo}/2$ as the voltage-axis intercept.

The degradation in power gain associated with the circuit in Fig. 8-14 may also be considered to result from the extreme mismatch between the high transistor output resistance and the low a-c load resistance. If power gain is to be sacrificed for the sake of eliminating the transformer, it is often more practical to use the push-pull transistors in the CC configuration, rather than the CE configuration. This provides a low transistor output resistance to match (or more nearly match) the low a-c load resistance. This assures that *maximum power gain* will be achieved from the amplifier. In many instances, this value will be higher than that obtainable from the severely mismatched loading of the CE configuration. A typical amplifier arrangement is shown in Fig. 8-15.

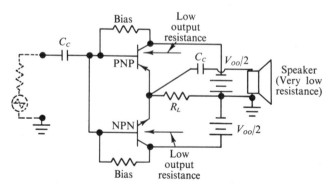

Figure 8-15.   CC *Transformerless Amplifier*

With the elimination of the transformer from the circuit, the push-pull amplifier can be made to operate well beyond the audio-frequency range. The upper cutoff frequency is now controlled by the transistor characteristics (the beta cutoff frequency for the CE and CC configuration) and the lower cutoff frequency is controlled by the various coupling capacitors. A complete discussion of frequency analysis appears in Chap. 6.

Example 8-6. The amplifier described in Example 8–3 is to be operated as a transformerless amplifier (Fig. 8–14), feeding the same load. The power supply value is changed to 60 volts and is center-tapped so that each transistor has a 30-volt supply value. Determine the a-c power output if the d-c load is made equal to 6 ohms.

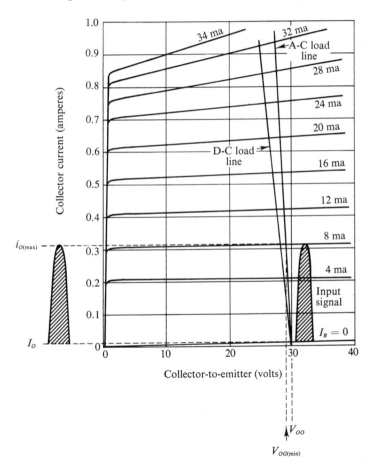

Figure E8-6

Solution. The a-c load for this amplifier is the parallel combination of the 6-ohm d-c load and the 6-ohm a-c load being fed by the amplifier, or 3 ohms. The d-c and a-c load lines are shown in Fig. E8–6, along with the various output signal values for determining the a-c power output:

$$P_{\text{a-c}} = \frac{i_{0(\text{max})}(V_{00} - v_{0G(\text{min})})}{2}$$

$$= \frac{0.3(30 - 29)}{2} = 0.15 \text{ watt}$$

Notice that a considerable reduction in output power is obtained, as compared to the transformer coupling of Example 8–3, despite the increase in supply voltage. This is due to the considerable mismatch between the CE output resistance and the 3-ohm a-c load resistance.

8.3 Compound-Connected Transistors

The variation of transistor operating characteristics as input current is increased can be seen by investigating the variation of the h-parameters (Fig. 6–16). Of particular interest is the decrease in h_{fa}, indicative of the fact that the unit output current per unit input current decreases as input current reaches higher values (the solid curve in Fig. 8–16). This degradation is responsible for less gain (decreased efficiency) and considerable distortion, thereby limiting the amount of driving current that can be

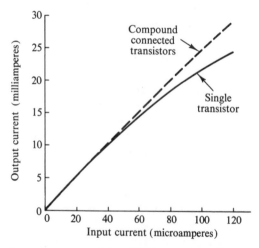

Figure 8-16.   *Variation of Output-Input Current Relationship*

applied to a particular transistor. By using two transistors in an arrangement known as the *compound connection,* this degradation can be postponed until higher driving current values are reached. This results in an essentially constant h_{fG} and linear operation (the dashed curve in Fig. 8-16) over a very wide range of input currents.

Equivalent h_{fG}

In the compound connection, as illustrated in Fig. 8-17, the two transistors can be considered to be *equivalent to one transistor* with an emitter, base, and collector terminal as marked in the figure. With this in mind, it must be possible to consider the entire arrangement within the dashed box as a generalized transistor (see Fig. 5-27) and it should be possible to construct a CB, CE, or CC amplifier from the basic arrangement. In Fig. 8-17 the amplifier is in the CB configuration.

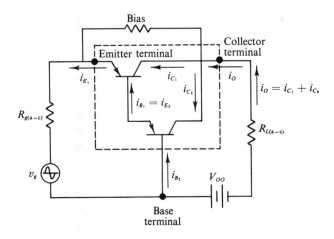

Figure 8-17. *Compound-Connected Transistor Amplifier (CB Configuration)*

Within the compound connection, itself, both transistors operate in the CB *configuration.* From Fig. 8-17, the collector current from transistor 1 is:

$$i_{C_1} = h_{fB_1} i_{E_1} \tag{8-15}$$

and the base current is:

$$i_{B_1} = (1 - h_{fB_1}) i_{E_1} = i_{E_2} \tag{8-16}$$

since the base current of transistor 1 is the emitter current for transistor 2. The collector current for transistor 2 is:

$$i_{C_2} = h_{fB_2} i_{E_2} \tag{8-17}$$

which, with the substitution of Eq. (8–16) yields:

$$i_{C_2} = h_{fB_2}(1 - h_{fB_1})i_{E_1} \tag{8-17a}$$

However, the total current to the load is the sum of i_{c_1} and i_{c_2} which, in terms of Eqs. (8–15) and (8–17a) is:

$$i_o = i_{E_1}[h_{fB_1} + h_{fB_2}(1 - h_{fB_1})] \tag{8-18}$$

The current i_{E_1} is the input current, i_I, for the compound connection. Since the forward current transfer factor is defined as the ratio of output to input current, it is possible to define an *equivalent forward current transfer factor* for the compound connection used in the CB configuration:

$$H_{fB} = \frac{i_o}{i_{E_1}} = -[|h_{fB_1}| + |h_{fB_2}|(1 - |h_{fB_1}|)] \tag{8-19}$$

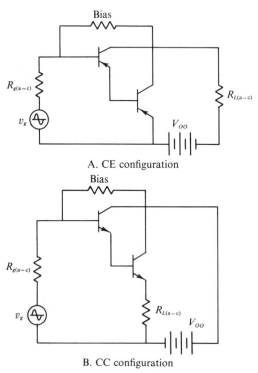

A. CE configuration

B. CC configuration

Figure 8-18. *Alternate Compound-Connected Amplifier Configurations*

In view of Eq. (8–19), H_{fB} must *always be greater than* h_{fB}—supporting the existence of the dashed line in Fig. 8–16. It must be pointed out that *only the magnitude* of h_{fB} is to be used in these equations. However, the algebraic sign introduced in Chap. 6, in order to account for signal phase relationships, must be associated with H_{fB}.

Since h_{fB} is on the order of 0.98 or 0.99, it can be seen that the value of H_{fB} will be *only slightly greater than* h_{fB_1}. However, the significance of this operation is the fact that as h_{fB} decreases the value of H_{fB} tends to remain constant. This is true over a range of significant decrease in h_{fB}. Further-more, when the compound connection is placed in the CE and CC con-figurations, as in Fig. 8–18, *the increase* in equivalent $h_{fE}(H_{fE})$ and $h_{fC}(H_{fC})$ is on the order of *several hundred*. H_{fE} and H_{fC} may be derived from H_{fB} by using the general h-parameter conversion equations in Table 6–4. Because of the "equivalent amplification effect" induced by the second transistor, a more constant value can be obtained for the H-parameters, and can be maintained over a wider range of input current values, especially if h_{fB_2} is slightly greater than h_{fB_1}.

Example 8-7. The value of h_{fB} for a particular PNP transistor is 0.97. This transistor is placed in a compound connection with an NPN transistor having an h_{fB}-value of 0.975. Determine the equiva-lent forward current transfer parameter for the arrangement when used as a CB, CE, and CC amplifier.

Solution. In the CB configuration, the equivalent forward current transfer parameter is:

$$H_{fB} = -[|h_{fB_1}| + |h_{fB_2}|(1 - |h_{fB_1}|)]$$
$$= -[0.97 + 0.975(1 - 0.97)] = -(0.97 + 0.029) = -0.999$$

The conversion equations for the CE and CC configurations are obtained from Table 6–4:

$$H_{fE} = \frac{H_{fB}}{1 + H_{fB}} = \frac{-(-0.999)}{1 - 0.999} = \frac{0.999}{0.001} = 999$$

$$H_{fC} = \frac{-1}{1 + H_{fB}} = \frac{-1}{0.001} = -1000$$

Equivalent Parameters

Since the compound connection is capable of maintaining *linear operation* over large-signal variations, the hybrid equivalent circuits can be substituted for the transistors. This is done in Fig. 8–19, Part A. How-ever, since the two transistors operate as an equivalent of one generalized

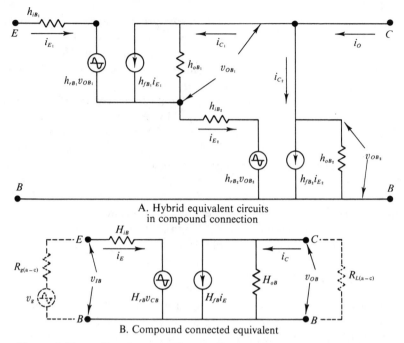

A. Hybrid equivalent circuits
in compound connection

B. Compound connected equivalent

Figure 8-19.   *Development of Hybrid Equivalent for Compound-Connected Amplifier*

device, it is possible to develop a *compound-connected equivalent*, such as in Part B of the figure. The value for H_{fB} has been derived. The remaining *H*-parameters can be derived also.

The reverse voltage feedback factor is generally very small (see Table 6–5). Its value is so small, in fact, that its addition to the output voltage of transistor 1 for subsequent feedback through transistor 1 is insignificant. Hence:

$$H_{rB} = h_{rB_1} \tag{8-20}$$

is a reasonable approximation.

From Figure 8–19, Part A, it can be seen that the input resistance parameters for the two transistors are in series:

$$H_{iB} = h_{iB_1} + h_{iB_2} \tag{8-21}$$

and the output conductance parameters are in parallel:

$$H_{oB} = h_{oB_1} + h_{oB_2} \tag{8-22}$$

The *H*-parameters for the CE and CC configurations can be derived from the CB-values using the conversion equations for Table 6–4. This does not apply to H_{rG}, which is always equal to h_{rG}. Using Eqs. (8–19) through

(8–22), the conversion equations in Table 6–4, and the typical CB *h*-parameter values of Table 6–5, the typical *H*-parameter values have been calculated and are presented in Table 8–1. These calculations assume that *both transistors are the same.*

TABLE 8-1

Example Values of Compound-Connected Hybrid
Parameters (from Transistor Listed in Table 6–5)

Common Base	Common Emitter	Common Collector
$H_{iB} = 43.4$	$H_{iE} = 4.34 \times 10^5$	$H_{iC} = 4.34 \times 10^5$
$H_{fB} = -0.9999$	$H_{fE} = 9999$	$H_{fC} = -10,000$
$H_{rB} = 3.25 \times 10^{-4}$	$H_{rE} = 3.79 \times 10^{-3}$	$H_{rC} = 1$
$H_{oB} = 5.84 \times 10^{-7}$	$H_{oE} = 5.84 \times 10^{-3}$	$H_{oC} = 5.84 \times 10^{-3}$

Class *A* Amplifier Analysis

The compound-connected arrangement can be used in any of the Class *A* amplifier circuits that have been described. It will operate with decreased distortion and will produce higher gains over an increased range of signal amplitudes. Under matched loading conditions, it will have an inherently higher maximum power gain. The definitions and design equations presented in Chaps. 6 and 7 may be used directly, simply by substituting the *H*-parameters for the *h*-parameters. Compound connections may be cascaded into multistage amplifiers through any of the coupling techniques that have been described. The frequency response equations of Chaps. 6 and 7 also apply, if an equivalent alpha cutoff frequency, f_{HB}, is substituted for f_α.

Because of the odd manner in which the second transistor compensates for changes in h_{fB} [Eq. (8–19)], not only will decreases due to current variation be corrected, but decreases due to frequency variation *will be corrected in a similar manner.* Hence, there is a tendency to hold h_{fB} constant even as frequency increases beyond f_{α_1} and f_{α_2}. For this reason, f_{HB} will be greater than either f_{α_1} or f_{α_2}, resulting in the fact that compound-connected amplifiers will have *inherently greater bandwidths* in all configurations. When the alpha cutoff frequency is the *same* for both transistors:

$$f_{HB} \approx 1.3 f_\alpha \qquad (8\text{-}23)$$

The determination of f_{HE} (which replaces f_β) can be made by substituting f_{HB} for f_α in Eq. (6–29). The CC cutoff frequency is approximated by f_{HE}.

Example 8-8. A particular NPN transistor has the following h-parameter values:

$$h_{iB} = 40 \text{ ohms} \qquad h_{rB} = 4.5 \times 10^{-4}$$
$$h_{fB} = -0.98 \qquad h_{oB} = 5 \times 10^{-7} \text{ mho}$$

This transistor is placed in a compound connection with another transistor having the same h-parameter values. The arrangement is used in a CE configuration and is RC coupled to a device with an equivalent resistance of 2K. The a-c load resistor for the amplifier is 10K. Determine the current and voltage gain for this amplifier.

Solution. The equivalent compound-connected CB parameters are:

$$H_{fB} = -[|h_{fB_1}| + |h_{fB_2}|(1 - |h_{fB_1}|)]$$
$$= -[0.98 + 0.98(1 - 0.98)] = (-0.98 + 0.0196) = -0.9996$$
$$H_{iB} = h_{iB_1} + h_{iB_2} = 40 + 40 = 80 \text{ ohms}$$
$$H_{rB} = h_{rB_1} = 4.5 \times 10^{-4}$$
$$H_{oB} = h_{oB_1} + h_{oB_2} = 1 \times 10^{-6} \text{ mho}$$

Using the conversion equations from Table 6–4 for the CE configuration:

$$H_{fE} = \frac{-H_{fB}}{1 + H_{fB}} = \frac{-(-0.9996)}{1 - 0.9996} = \frac{0.9996}{0.0004} = 2499$$

$$H_{iE} = \frac{H_{iB}}{1 + H_{fB}} = \frac{80}{0.0004} = 200\text{K}$$

$$H_{rE} = h_{rE_1} = \frac{h_{iB_1}h_{oB_1}}{1 + h_{fB}} - h_{rB} = \frac{40(5 \times 10^{-7})}{2 \times 10^{-2}} - (4.5 \times 10^{-4})$$
$$= (10 \times 10^{-4}) - (4.5 \times 10^{-4}) = 5.5 \times 10^{-4}$$

$$H_{oE} = \frac{H_{oB}}{1 + H_{fB}} = \frac{5.84 \times 10^{-7}}{4 \times 10^{-4}} = 1.46 \times 10^{-3} \text{ mho}$$

The current gain is given by (from Table 6–11):

$$A_{iE} = \frac{-H_{fE}}{H_{oE}R_{L(\text{a-c})} + 1}$$

where:

$$R_{L(\text{a-c})} = \frac{(10 \times 10^3)(2 \times 10^3)}{(10 + 2)(10^3)} = \frac{20 \times 10^6}{12 \times 10^3} = 1.67\text{K}$$

Hence:

$$A_{iE} = \frac{-2499}{(1.46 \times 10^{-3})(1.67 \times 10^3) + 1} = \frac{-2499}{3.44} = -728$$

The voltage gain is (from Table 6–11):

$$A_{vE} = \frac{-H_{fE}R_{L(a-c)}}{\Delta H_E R_{L(a-c)} + H_{iE}}$$

$$\Delta H_E = H_{iE}H_{oE} - H_{fE}H_{rE}$$
$$= (2 \times 10^5)(1.46 \times 10^{-3}) - (2.499 \times 10^3)(5.5 \times 10^{-4})$$
$$= 291$$

Hence:

$$A_{vE} = \frac{-(2.499 \times 10^3)(1.67 \times 10^3)}{291(1.67 \times 10^3) + (2 \times 10^5)} = \frac{-(4.17 \times 10^6)}{6.85 \times 10^5} = -6.08$$

Example 8-9. The alpha cutoff frequency for the two transistors used in Example 8–8 is 5 megacycles per second. What is the upper cutoff frequency for the compound connection?

Solution. The equivalent alpha cutoff frequency for the compound connection is:

$$f_{HB} = 1.3 f_\alpha = 1.3(5 \times 10^6) = 6.5 \text{ mc}$$

From the relationships in Chap. 6, the equivalent cutoff frequency in the CE configuration is given by:

$$f_{HE} = f_{HB}(1 - H_{fB}) = (6.5 \times 10^6)(1 - 0.9996)$$
$$= (6.5 \times 10^6)(4 \times 10^{-3}) = 26 \text{ kc}$$

Example 8-10. Determine the a-c source resistance and the a-c load resistance that must be used with the amplifier in Example 8–8 in order to achieve maximum power gain. Determine the maximum power gain.

Solution. From the relationships in Chap. 6:

$$R_{g(a-c)} = H_{iE}\sqrt{1 - \frac{H_{fE}H_{rE}}{H_{iE}H_{oE}}}$$

$$= (2 \times 10^5)\sqrt{1 - \frac{(2.499 \times 10^3)(5.5 \times 10^{-4})}{(2 \times 10^5)(1.46 \times 10^{-3})}}$$

$$\approx 200\text{K}$$

$$R_{L(a-c)} \approx \frac{1}{H_{oE}} = \frac{1}{1.46 \times 10^{-3}} = 685 \ \Omega$$

The maximum power gain that can be obtained by satisfying these conditions is:

$$A_{pE(\text{max})} \approx \frac{H_{fE}^2}{H_{iE}H_{oE}} = \frac{(2499)^2}{(2 \times 10^{-5})(1.46 \times 10^{-3})}$$

$$= \frac{6.25 \times 10^6}{2.91 \times 10^2} = 21,400$$

Push-Pull Amplifiers

Compound-connected transistors can be used in conventional Class *B* and Class *AB* transformer or RC coupled push-pull arrangements, as in Fig. 8–20. Since only PNP (or NPN) transistors are used in such an amplifier, the compound connection still requires two input signals, 180° out of phase. The Class *B* operation is still plagued by crossover distortion

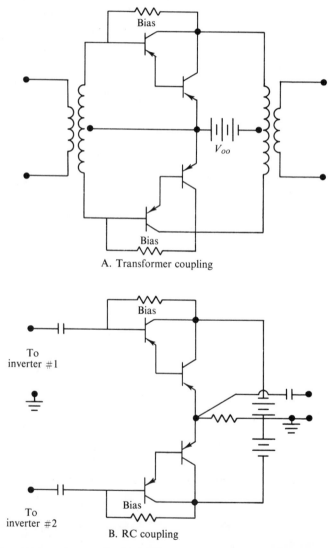

A. Transformer coupling

B. RC coupling

Figure 8-20.   *Compound-Connected Class AB Push-Pull Amplifiers*

(odd-harmonic components)—but to a lesser degree. Class AB operation eliminates this problem. Composite characteristic curves *can be constructed* for such a circuit in order to determine the amount of forward bias current necessary to eliminate crossover distortion. However, *two composite sets* must be constructed: one for the compound connection; another for the push-pull arrangement. Obviously, the proper biasing is best obtained by constructing a prototype circuit and using trial-and-error methods. Fortunately, due to the linearity associated with the compound connection, the Class A design equations can be used to approximate the Class B and Class AB push-pull amplifier design.

In order to eliminate the need for a phase inverter or a center-tapped input transformer, the *compound-connected complementary symmetry* arrangement in Fig. 8–21 may be used. As shown, this arrangement uses a PNP compound connection and an NPN compound connection, with the two joined in complementary symmetry. Such circuits are capable of providing very stable, high-power, low-distortion operation.

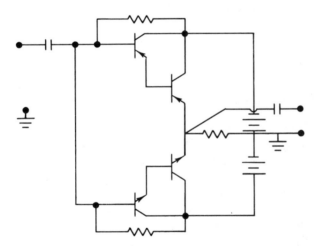

Figure 8-21. *Compound-Connected Complementary Symmetry Arrangement for Class AB Push-Pull Amplifier*

Example 8-11. The compound-connected CE amplifier described in Example 8–8 is used in a Class B push-pull arrangement. The d-c load resistor is 6 ohms and the amplifier is RC coupled (as in Fig. 8–20) to a device with an equivalent resistance of 6 ohms. Determine the output power for this arrangement when the input power is 50 milliwatts.

Solution. Because of the operation of the compound connection (described in Fig. 8–16 and associated text) the equivalent characteristics are considerably more linear than for a single-transistor configuration. For this reason, it is possible to analyze the compound-connected push-pull amplifier on the basis of its *H*-parameters, even through large-signal operating conditions are achieved. The power output is:

$$P_{\text{out}} = A_{pE} P_{\text{in}}$$

The power gain is (from Table 6–7):

$$A_{pE} = \frac{H_{fE}^2 R_{L(\text{a-c})}}{(H_{oE} R_{L(\text{a-c})} + 1)(\Delta H_E R_{L(\text{a-c})} + H_{iE})}$$

where $R_{L(\text{a-c})}$ is the parallel combination of two 6-ohm resistances, or 3 ohms. The values for H_{fE}, H_{oE}, H_E, and H_{iE} can be obtained from Example 8–8:

$$A_{pE} = \frac{(2.499 \times 10^3)^2(3)}{[(1.46 \times 10^{-3})(3) + 1][(291)(3) + (2 \times 10^5)]}$$

$$= \frac{1.87 \times 10^7}{2 \times 10^5} = 93.5$$

This leads to an output power of:

$$P_{\text{out}} = 93.5(0.05) = 4.68 \text{ watts}$$

8.4 Radio-Frequency Amplifiers

It has been indicated previously that, without transformer coupling, Class *B* and Class *AB* push-pull amplifiers can operate to frequencies of a few hundred thousand cycles per second. The use of compound-connected transistors will extend operation to still higher frequencies. Beyond several hundred kilocycles at best, however, it becomes essential to operate the large-signal amplifier *into a parallel resonant load*. Such amplifiers are narrowband, as discussed in Chap. 7, and are operated either Class *B* or Class *C*. Class *C* operation attains the highest possible efficiency and permits maximum input signal excursions along with the highest possible output power. Class *C* operation is not desirable when the load is resistive because of the associated distortion (see Chap. 5). However, a parallel resonant load inherently produces a sinusoidal signal—regardless of the form of the input energy. The suggested Class *C* operation, then, is equivalent to "pulsing" the resonant load with enough energy to produce a complete sinewave cycle, as shown in Fig. 8–22. In view of this, the operation may be regarded as a *damped oscillation*, with the damping overcome by periodic pulses of additional energy. Such operation is contrary to undamped, or *sustained oscillation*, which continues without

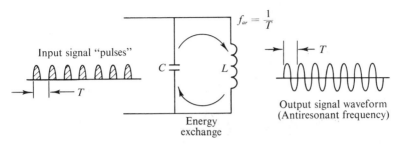

Figure 8-22. *Generation of Sinusoidal Signal from Energy Pulses in an Antiresonant Circuit*

additional excitation. The resonant load may also be regarded as a *filter* whose narrow band permits the fundamental (resonant) signal to pass unattenuated, but "rejects" all other harmonics in the pulse.

The Resonant Load

Parallel-resonant loads are discussed in detail in Chap. 7. All of the relationships and design equations included in that discussion apply equally well to large-signal applications. However, in Chap. 7, it was shown that special considerations must be made when the Q (loaded or unloaded) drops below 10. For large-signal applications the minimum value for Q_L has been determined to be 4π; large-signal designs should not be considered for values of Q_L lower than this.

Graphical Analysis

Class B and Class C operation can be analyzed graphically in a manner similar to that associated with a single stage of the Class B push-pull amplifier (Fig. 8–8). The d-c load line is approximated by a vertical line in most cases and the a-c load line is established by the loaded resonant resistance, $Z_{ar(L)}$, of the "tank." This analysis will permit an examination of the input and output current pulses and will assist in assuring that the maximum ratings of the transistor will not be exceeded. Operation of the transistor in a nonlinear region is not critical, since the resonant load will reject all harmonics and pass only the fundamental component. In fact, the Class C pulse, itself, contains such a multitude of harmonics that the introduction of additional nonlinearities is of little consequence.

A harmonic analysis can be performed on the Class C (or Class B) pulse. However, the graphical technique described in Chap. 5 no longer

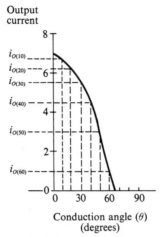

Output
current

Figure 8-23.   *Data for Class B and Class C Harmonic Analysis*

applies; it is valid only for signals that do not contain an extreme amount of distortion. Figure 8–23 illustrates the plot of a large-signal pulse arranged in the manner necessary for analysis. As shown, only half of the waveform is used. In general, any angular increment can be used to establish a number of points (i_o's) on the curve. A ten-degree interval is convenient and the following equations have been derived on the assumption that such an interval is used. The derivation of these equations is based on geometric approximations of calculus techniques used to determine the area enclosed by a general curve, such as the one shown. The d-c value associated with the waveform is:

$$I_{\text{d-c}} = \frac{1}{18}\left(\frac{i_{O(0)}}{2} + i_{O(10)} + i_{O(20)} + \cdots + i_{O(80)}\right) \qquad (8\text{-}24)$$

and the amplitude of the fundamental component is:

$$i_{1(P)} = \frac{1}{9}\left(\frac{i_{O(0)}}{2} + i'_{O(10)} + i'_{O(20)} + \cdots + i'_{O(80)}\right) \qquad (8\text{-}25)$$

where the parenthetical expressions must include all the points included on the waveform (Fig. 8–23). The 90° point is not included because the value at 90° will always be zero, even if the full "pulse" (Class *B* operation) is present. The primed values in Eq. (8–25) are defined by:

$$i'_{O(\theta)} = i_{O(\theta)} \cos\theta \qquad (8\text{-}26)$$

The remaining harmonic components are of no importance to the analysis.

Example 8-12. Transistor *A* in Appendix D is used in a radio-frequency power amplifier with an antiresonant load of 400 ohms.

A 20-volt supply is used. A peak input signal current of 1 milliampere is applied. What is the peak fundamental signal current obtained when the amplifier is operated Class *C* with only half of the peak input signal utilized?

Solution. Figure E8–12 illustrates Class *C* operation with only half of the peak input current used as a signal. The necessary output current values are:

$$i'_{O(10)} = i_{O(10)} \cos 10° = (16 \times 10^{-3})(0.98) = 15.7 \text{ ma}$$
$$i'_{O(20)} = i_{O(20)} \cos 20° = (12 \times 10^{-3})(0.94) = 11.3 \text{ ma}$$
$$i'_{O(30)} = i_{O(30)} \cos 30° = (8.5 \times 10^{-3})(0.87) = 7.4 \text{ ma}$$
$$i'_{O(40)} = i_{O(40)} \cos 40° = (4.5 \times 10^{-3})(0.77) = 3.46 \text{ ma}$$
$$i_{1(P)} = \frac{1}{9}\left[\frac{20(10^{-3})}{2} + 15.7(10^{-3}) + 11.3(10^{-3}) + 7.4(10^{-3}) \right.$$
$$\left. + 3.46(10^{-3})\right] = \frac{1}{9}(47.86)(10^{-3}) = 5.32 \text{ ma}$$

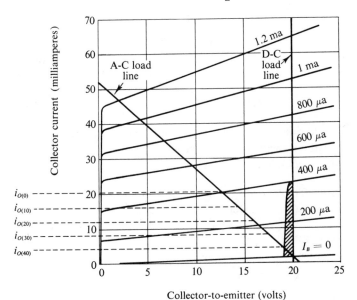

Figure E8-12

Efficiency

If the large-signal, resonant load amplifier is operated Class *B*, the maximum theoretical efficiency of the amplifier is 78.5 per cent—as derived previously for Class *B* operation. For Class *C* operation, since both the d-c power (related to $I_{d\text{-}c}$) and the a-c power (related to $i_{1(P)}$) depend on the degree of conduction that is present, no general derivation for efficiency, other than the basic definition, is possible. As the degree of conduction gets smaller and smaller, however, calculation of η_o from $I_{d\text{-}c}$, $i_{1(P)}$, and $Z_{ar(L)}$ will show the efficiency approaching 100 per cent. In practice, of course, 100 per cent would not be achieved because sinusodial operation would cease at some minimum value of $i_{1(P)}$.

The resonant load, itself, will result in additional losses not yet accounted for. This is the "insertion loss" discussed in Chap. 7. The insertion efficiency is given by:

$$\eta_L = \left(1 - \frac{Q_L}{Q_U}\right) \times 100 \text{ per cent} \tag{8-27}$$

The total efficiency of the amplifier is:

$$\eta_T = \eta_o \eta_L \tag{8-28}$$

Output Power

The useful output power, delivered to the secondary of the transformer in the tuned "tank," is given by:

$$P_O = \frac{\eta_L i_{1(P)}^2 Z_{ar(L)}}{2} \tag{8-29}$$

Because of the additional losses in the resonant load, it is necessary that the a-c power at the transistor output terminals, $i_{1(P)}^2 Z_{ar(L)}/2$, be greater than the useful power output of the amplifier.

Example 8-13.   The loaded Q of the circuit in Example 8–12 is 20 and the unloaded Q is 500. Determine the output power.

Solution.   The output power is:

$$P_O = \frac{\eta_L i_{1(P)}^2 Z_{ar(L)}}{2}$$

where:

$$\eta_L = \left(1 - \frac{Q_L}{Q_U}\right) \times 100 \text{ per cent} = \left(1 - \frac{20}{500}\right) \times 100 \text{ per cent}$$
$$= (1 - 0.04)100 \text{ per cent} = 96 \text{ per cent}$$

Hence:

$$P_O = \frac{0.96(5.32 \times 10^{-3})^2(400)}{2} = 10.85 \text{ milliwatts}$$

PROBLEMS

1. Transistor C in Appendix D is used as a single-ended, Class A power amplifier, transformer coupled to a device with an equivalent resistance of 12 ohms. The transformer turns ratio is 2 : 1. Single source biasing is obtained with a 30-volt supply and a shunt feedback resistor of 2.5K. A peak-to-peak input current of 16 milliamperes is applied. Determine the current, voltage, and power gains.

2. The 2N1175 (Fig. 8–2) is used in a single-ended, Class A amplifier with a 12-volt supply. The a-c load is selected to achieve a power gain of 42 decibels. The power applied to the load must be 40 milliwatts. What must the transformer efficiency be?

3. A particular power amplifier application requires that 60 milliwatts be delivered to the load. The transformer efficiency is 80 per cent and the amplifier power gain is 30,000. What input signal power must be applied?

4. Two transistors with characteristics listed in Table 6–5 are used in a two-stage common emitter phase inverter as is illustrated in Fig. 8–5. Each half of the push-pull amplifier has an input resistance of 2.6K and requires a peak input current of 40 milliamperes. R_1 and R_3 are both equal to 25K. Determine the value of R_2 required to produce equal amplitude currents for the two push-pull stages.

5. Transistor A in Appendix D is used in a Class B, push-pull amplifier arrangement (Fig. 8–3) with a 15-volt power supply. The secondary load has an equivalent resistance of 100 ohms. The transformer turns ratio is 4 : 1. Determine the output power if the peak-to-peak input current is 1.6 milliamperes.

6. Transistor C in Appendix D is to be used in a Class B, push-pull amplifier arrangement (Fig. 8–3) with a 30-volt supply. The secondary load has an equivalent resistance of 10 ohms. The transformer turns ratio is 3 : 1. Determine the current, voltage, and power gains for the amplifier when the peak input current is 12 milliamperes.

7. The characteristics for Transistor A in Appendix D are for an NPN transistor. A matched PNP transistor is used in a complimentary symmetry arrangement (Fig. 9–9). Class B operation is achieved with a 20-volt supply. The transformer turns ratio is 6 : 1 and the secondary load has an equivalent resistance of 30 ohms. Determine the current, voltage, and power gains for the amplifier when the peak-to-peak input current is 2 milliamperes.

8. Determine the efficiency of the amplifier in Problem 5.

9. Determine the efficiency of the amplifier in Problem 7.

10. Specify the voltage divider resistance that must be used in Problem

5 if the amplifier is to operate Class AB (Fig. 8–11) with an input bias current of 200 microamperes. Determine the output power for this operating condition.

11. A total voltage divider resistance of 6K is used to convert the amplifier in Problem 6 to Class AB operation (Fig. 8–11). Determine the voltage, current, and power gains for this operating condition.

12. Determine the compound-connected H-parameter values for a common base arrangement (Fig. 8–17) of two transistors having the following h-parameters:

$$h_{iB} = 39 \text{ ohms} \qquad h_{fB} = -0.98$$
$$h_{rB} = 380 \times 10^{-6} \qquad h_{oB} = 4.9 \times 10^{-7} \text{ mho}$$

13. Determine the compound-connected H-parameter values for a common emitter arrangement (Fig. 8–18) of two transistors having the following h-parameters:

$$h_{iE} = 3000 \text{ ohms} \qquad h_{oE} = 20 \times 10^{-6} \text{ mho}$$
$$h_{fE} = 50 \qquad h_{rE} = 1 \times 10^{-3}$$

14. The compound connection in Problem 12 is used in a common emitter amplifier (Fig. 8–18) with a source resistance of 800 ohms and an a-c load resistance of 50K. Determine the voltage, current, and power gains for this amplifier.

15. The compound connection in Problem 12 is used in a common emitter amplifier with a source resistance of 300 ohms. The d-c load resistance is 8K. The amplifier is RC coupled to a device having an equivalent resistance of 3K. A signal current with an rms value of 50 milliamperes is applied. What is the output power?

16. The compound connection in Problem 13 is used in a common collector amplifier that has transformer coupling in both the input and output loops. The input transformer has a 3 : 1 turns ratio and the output transformer has a 10 : 1 turns ratio. The signal source resistance is 500 ohms. The amplifier feeds a device with an equivalent resistance of 2K. Determine the input and output resistances for this amplifier.

17. What a-c source and load resistance values must be used with the compound connection in Problem 13 if maximum power gain is to be achieved in the common emitter configuration? What is the maximum power gain value that can be attained?

18. The alpha cutoff frequency for the transistors used in the compound connection of Problem 13 is 8 megacycles per second. What is the upper cutoff frequency of the compound connection when used in a common emitter configuration? Plot the power gain as a function

of frequency (in the high-frequency region) when the a-c load is 80K.

19. Two identical compound-connected stages, as described in Problem 15, are used in cascade. Determine the total power gain for the cascade.

20. The compound-connected amplifier in Problem 14 uses a single source supply with a shunt feedback resistor of 100K to establish forward bias. What is the voltage, current, and power gain for this amplifier?

21. The compound-connected arrangement in Problem 12 is used in a transformer coupled Class *B*, push-pull amplifier (Fig. 8–20). The secondary load is 3K and the transformer turns ratio is 6 : 1. Determine the output power when the peak-to-peak input signal current is 40 milliamperes.

22. Transistor *C* in Appendix D is used in a radio-frequency, Class *C* power amplifier with a 20-volt supply. The loaded antiresonant impedance is 30 ohms. What is the peak output current for this amplifier if a peak-to-peak input current of 32 milliamperes is applied?

23. Transistor *A* in Appendix D is used in a radio-frequency, Class *B* power amplifier with a 15-volt supply. The antiresonant circuit has an unloaded antiresonant impedance of 200K at 50 kilocycles per second and is coupled to a 200-ohm load through a transformer with a turns ratio of 3 : 1. The unloaded *Q* of the coil is 300 at 10 kilocycles per second. What is the output power of this amplifier if the peak input current is 200 microamperes?

Further Reading

"Basic Theory and Applications of Transistors," TM 11–690. Washington, D. C.: U. S. Government Printing Office, 1959.

Clearly, J. F., ed., *General Electric Transistor Manual*. Syracuse, N. Y.: General Electric Company, Semiconductor Products Department, 1964.

Pierce, J. F., *Transistor Circuit Theory and Design*. Columbus, Ohio: Charles E. Merrill Books, Inc., 1963.

Ryder, J. D., *Electronic Fundamentals and Applications*. Englewood Cliffs, N. J.: Prentice-Hall, Inc., 1959.

Seidman, A. H. and S. L. Marshall, *Semiconductor Fundamentals*. New York: John Wiley and Sons, Inc., 1963.

Surina, T. and C. Herrick, *Semiconductor Electronics*. New York: Holt, Rinehart, and Winston, 1964.

9

Bias Control, D-C
Amplifiers, and Noise

Although transistors are well-suited for direct current amplification by virtue of their microscopic structure, the characteristics of this structure also contribute directly to d-c instability. Not only does this instability produce design problems for d-c amplifiers; it creates inherent operating problems for *all transistor circuits* as well. As described in Chap. 5, d-c biasing networks are basically simple. The biasing level directly controls the mode (class) of operation. Hence, throughout all of the small- and large-signal amplifier designs that have been discussed, it has been assumed that the d-c operating point can be established *and maintained*. However, the circuitry associated with operating point maintenance has not been discussed. Changes in transistor characteristics with temperature fluctuations, supply voltage fluctuations, and collector voltage variations all contribute to d-c instability. This instability, in general, consists of *operating-point drift*. In view of the dependency of amplifier efficiency and distortion on the position of this point, the importance of not letting it drift should be obvious. *Bias stabilization* circuits must be incorporated into the basic amplifier designs in order to cancel (or, at least, to minimize) the instabilities. Most of the bias stabilization circuits utilize negative feedback to achieve stabilization. Because of this, some degree of amplifier gain may be sacrificed in order to achieve bias control. However, in some instances, the circuits may be designed or arranged so as to provide only d-c feedback—the a-c signals and, therefore, the a-c operation, are not affected. Other arrangements result in both d-c and a-c feedback, causing an associated degradation in amplifier gain.

Once d-c stabilization is achieved, practical direct coupled amplifiers may be built. Such amplifiers have a variety of applications in computer systems, laboratory instrumentation, medical electronic applications, or in any situation requiring the amplification of constant or very slowly varying signals. It is because of these applications that d-c stability is extremely critical: only the proper d-c "variations" must be amplified, *not the temperature and supply voltage variations.* Since there is no way to discriminate between the desirable and undesirable fluctuations, the instability must be eliminated or minimized to the point where it has a negligible effect on the output signal.

Every electrical signal is accompanied by unwanted *noise* signals: random disturbances that tend to distort the desirable signal. At low frequencies this noise may be heard (the hum in a loudspeaker), and at

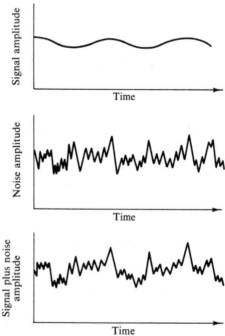

Figure 9-1.   *Effect of Noise on Signal Waveform*

high frequencies it may be visible (the "snow" on a TV screen). In terms of electrical signals, noise action is illustrated in Fig. 9-1. The desirable signal voltage (or, simply, the signal) and the noise voltage add directly to form the total signal-plus-noise waveform. As shown, it is possible for the actual signal shape to be completely lost in the presence of noise. This is especially true during the early stages of amplification, where signal amplitudes are very small. Noise is generally divided into two categories: *external* and *internal*. External noise is caused by atmospheric disturbances and by electromagnetic radiation from man-made devices (power lines, electric motors, etc.). This form of noise may be excluded by filtering and will not be discussed in this text. Internal noise, however, is caused within the microscopic structure of the circuit components—including the transistor. This noise source will be described, along with techniques for reducing its effects.

9.1 Factors Affecting Bias Stability

Once a particular operating point has been selected (through design analysis) and obtained in the actual amplifier circuitry, the operating-point values are still subject to variation. This variation is brought about by:

1. the nonuniformity of the transistor characteristics, brought about by mass production techniques, and particularly bothersome when replacing damaged or inoperative units;
2. *aging*, which is the process of gradual characteristic changes over the entire life period of the transistor;
3. the temperature dependency of the transistor characteristics and *h*-parameters (as discussed in Chaps. 5 and 6);
4. *creeping*, which is associated with temperature, but is a gradual change about the ambient conditions; and
5. the voltage fluctuations and internal resistance changes associated with the power supply.

Power supply variations can be countered by using voltage regulation circuits (Chaps. 3 and 4), or by replacing batteries before their characteristics degrade seriously. The effects of aging are combated, somewhat, by operating the transistor for a thousand hours or more before it is released by the manufacturer. In addition to providing better operating stability, this also permits the manufacturer to find faulty devices, since most failures that are due to inferior workmanship or materials will occur during the first few hundred hours of operation. The remaining changes brought about by further aging and by creeping phenomena are not serious in most amplifier applications. (D-C amplifiers are an exception.) The majority of the bias control circuits to be developed, then, are designed to minimize the temperature variations and to compensate for unit-to-unit nonuniformities.

Reverse Saturation Currents

The microscopic structure of the basic transistor currents is discussed in Chap. 5, along with the conventional (or macroscopic) equivalents (see Table 5-1). A review of this material will indicate that most of the basic currents, being composed of majority carriers, are not directly affected by temperature variations. The reverse saturation current, I_{co}, however, is composed of minority carriers flowing in <u>both</u> directions between the collector region and the base region. Since the number of minority carriers is highly sensitive to temperature (Chap. 2), I_{co} must experience a similar dependency. This is illustrated in Fig. 9-2, for both germanium and silicon. Because of the larger energy gap in silicon, its characteristics are always less sensitive to temperature variations.

In terms of the microscopic current components, the increase in I_{co} means that the number of electrons flowing from collector to base regions of a PNP transistor (or the number of holes, for an NPN transistor) has increased. This is indicated in Fig. 9-3, for the PNP transistor. The minority carrier flow from collector to base is accompanied by an equivalent minority carrier flow from base to collector, resulting in a composite increase in I_{co}. This is accompanied by several associated phenomena,

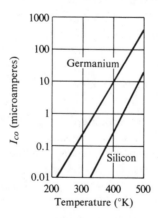

Figure 9-2.   *Variation of Reverse Current with Temperature*

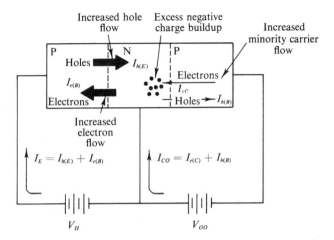

Figure 9-3.   *Carrier Phenomenon Associated with Increased Temperature*

also indicated in the figure. First, the additional electrons in the base region cause an accumulation of excess negative charge in this region, drawing more holes from the emitter to the base (increasing I_E). Because of the narrowness of the base region and the inertia of the carriers (see Chap. 5), however, *only a fractional part of the emitter current undergoes recombination in the base region*. Hence, in order to neutralize the increased number of minority carriers in the base, an even greater number of majority carriers must flow from the emitter. The fractional part of I_E that *does not recombine in the base*, αI_E, must flow into the collector region, *resulting in an increase in I_C beyond that associated with the initial increase in I_{CO}*. Because of these relationships, the increase in collector current is approximately equal to:

$$\Delta I_C \approx \left[\frac{\alpha}{1-\alpha}\right] \Delta I_{CO} = \beta(\Delta I_{CO}) \tag{9-1}$$

Figure 9–4 illustrates an immediate result associated with the increased collector current described by Eq. (9–1). The d-c load resistance does not change (significantly) over the indicated temperature variation. The base current, I_B, changes in accordance with the degree of temperature change. The net effect is a shift in operating point. This shift can be considerable for temperature increases that are well within reason for practical amplifier circuits. It may produce distortion, a change in operating class, or a change in operating efficiency.

Even in view of the detrimental effects of operating-point shift, if the transistor stabilizes at the new temperature conditions, the degradation may be tolerable. However, the degradation generally goes beyond a mere

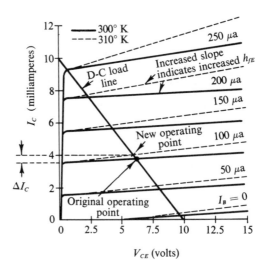

Figure 9-4.   *Composite Effect of Temperature Increases on Transistor Output Characteristics (CE Amplifier) and Operating Point*

operating-point shift. It has been assumed that the initial increase in I_{CO} results from an increase in ambient temperature. The associated increase in I_E and I_C is accompanied by increased power dissipation requirements. If this increase in power cannot be dissipated rapidly enough, the internal transistor temperatures will rise still higher, leading to a further increase in I_{CO} and a repeat of the entire cycle—*even though the ambient temperature may have stabilized.* This process of continued internal temperature rise, independent of ambient conditions, is known as *thermal runaway* and ultimately results in *transistor destruction.*

Base-to-Emitter Voltage

In the previous section, the increase in I_E resulting from increased I_{CO} is suggested on the basis of the attraction associated with the increased minority carriers in the base region. However, a greater insight into the bias control circuits can be obtained by examining the increased emitter current in terms of the temperature sensitivity of the base-to-emitter voltage. Considered alone, the emitter-to-base junction of the transistor behaves in a manner similar to that described for a forward biased junction diode (Chap. 4). Equations (4–19) and (4–20) indicate that there is a tendency for the junction potential to increase because of the direct relationship between V_j and V_T, and *to decrease* because of an inverse proportionality to the number of free minority carriers. A comparison of these two tendencies will show that the decreasing tendency predominates since the number of free minority carriers increases very rapidly with the increases in temperature, while V_T increases only slightly. For germanium, the decrease in junction potential is about 2.1 millivolts per °K increase in temperature. For silicon, the change is about 2.3 millivolts/°K.

The external forward bias voltage is used to overcome the junction potential and permit majority carriers to flow. For a given external bias voltage, decreases in the junction potential result in equal increases in the total base-to-emitter forward voltage, V_{BE}, *permitting more forward current (majority carriers) to flow.* In view of the fact that increased temperature reduces junction potential, it must also result in larger amounts of current flow from the emitter to the base. This explains why the increase in I_E can be greater than the increase in I_{co}. Although both are temperature dependent, I_E is the more sensitive of the two. Once the increase in I_E occurs through the reduction in junction potential, a portion of the increase, $(1 - \alpha)I_E$, goes into recombination with the increased minority carriers in the base. The balance of the increase, αI_E, passes on to the collector region, leading to an additional increase in I_C beyond that produced by the increase in I_{co} [Eq. (9–1)].

Forward Current Amplification Factor

So far, it has been assumed that the forward current amplification factor, α, or h_{fB} (although α is preferred for d-c discussions), remains unchanged as temperature varies. Examination of Eqs. (5–22b) and (5–22a)

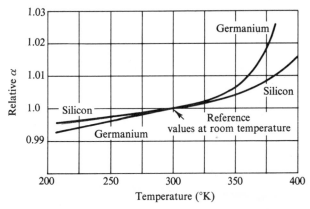

Figure 9-5.   *Typical Variation in Forward Amplification Factor with Temperature*

(the microscopic definitions of α) indicates that as I_{co} and the majority-carrier component of I_E increase, the value for α will also increase. A typical variation is shown in Fig. 9–5 for both germanium and silicon devices. Hence, the increase in I_C as temperature increases is even greater than that due to the increase in I_{co} and I_E alone [Eq. (9–1)]. In order to account for this increase, the higher value of α (or β, which is related to α) must be included in Eq. (9–1). Since the a-c parameters (h_{fB}, h_{fE}, and h_{fc}) are directly related to α, all of these quantities must increase as temperature increases. This is displayed, indirectly, in Fig. 9–4. Notice that the characteristic curves for the higher-temperature situation have a larger slope (larger h-parameters) than the lower-temperature characteristics.

Example 9-1. At room temperature, the forward current amplification factor for a particular germanium transistor is 0.98. The variation in forward current amplification factor as a function of temperature for this transistor is given by Fig. 9–5. The d-c base-to-emitter junction resistance is 100 ohms at room temperature. Determine the change in collector current that will occur when the temperature increases to 375°K.

Solution. The change in collector current produced by the α-variation and the change in reverse saturation current is given by:

$$\Delta I_c = \left[\frac{\alpha}{1 - \alpha} \right] \Delta I_{co}$$

The change in reverse saturation current can be determined from Fig. 9–2. For germanium:

$$\Delta I_{co} = (5 - 0.3)(10^{-6}) = 4.7 \text{ microamperes}$$

(The vertical axis in Fig. 9–2 is logarithmic in scale, and must be interpolated as such.) The value of α used in the equation must be determined at 375°K. From Fig. 9–5:

$$\frac{\alpha_{375°K}}{\alpha_{300°K}} = 1.018$$

Hence:

$$\alpha_{375°K} = 1.018 \, \alpha_{300°K} = 1.018(0.98) = 0.999$$

This leads to:

$$\Delta I_c = \left[\frac{0.999}{1 - 0.999} \right] (4.7 \times 10^{-6}) = 999(4.7 \times 10^{-6})$$
$$= 4.69 \text{ milliamperes}$$

The base-to-emitter potential increases at the rate of 2.1 millivolts per °K. At room temperature, the base-to-emitter voltage is on the order of 27 millivolts (Chap. 5). With a base-to-emitter resistance of 100 ohms, a base current of:

$$I_B = \frac{V_{BE}}{r_{BE}} = \frac{26 \times 10^{-3}}{1 \times 10^2} = 2.6 \text{ microamperes}$$

must flow. At 375°K the base-to-emitter potential is:

$$V_{BE_{375°K}} = (26 \times 10^{-3}) + (375 - 300)(2.1 \times 10^{-3})$$
$$= (26 + 157.5)(10^{-3}) = 183.5 \text{ millivolts}$$

The junction resistance decreases with temperature. However, it is difficult to determine the exact nature of this decrease without an investigation of the microscopic characteristics of the particular transistor in question. Hence, as an approximation:

$$I_{B_{375°K}} = \frac{183.5 \times 10^{-3}}{1 \times 10^2} = 18.35 \text{ microamperes}$$

This represents a change in base current given by:

$$\Delta I_B = (18.35 - 2.6)(10^{-6}) = 15.75 \text{ microamperes}$$

and a change in collector current of:

$$\Delta I_C = \alpha_{375°K} \Delta I_B = 0.999(15.75 \times 10^{-6}) = 15.7 \text{ microamperes}$$

From this, it can be seen that the change in collector current due to the change in base-to-emitter voltage is not significant when compared to the change due to the α-variation and the reverse saturation current. Hence, the total change in collector current is on the order of 5 milliamperes. Such a change, of course, is intolerable in most amplifier circuits. However, this represents the inherent change in the transistor, itself—not the change that would actually take place in an amplifier circuit.

9.2 Resistive Stabilizing Networks

The simplest techniques for achieving bias control, or stabilization, employ various resistive networks in the base, emitter, or collector branches of the amplifier. The design of these circuits assumes that there is a linear relationship between the collector current and I_{CO}, V_{BE}, and α. With this assumption *and an assumption that each of the temperature effects can be treated independently*, it is possible to express the change in collector current by a linear equation:

$$I_C = S_I(\Delta I_{CO}) + S_V(\Delta V_{BE}) + S_\alpha(\Delta \alpha) \tag{9-2}$$

where S_I, S_V, and S_α are *stability factors* for each of the temperature-sensitive effects. These stability factors are defined by:

$$S_I = \frac{\Delta I_C}{\Delta I_{CO}}\bigg|_{V_{BE},\ \alpha} \tag{9-3}$$

$$S_V = \frac{\Delta I_C}{\Delta V_{BE}}\bigg|_{I_{CO},\ \alpha} \tag{9-4}$$

$$S_\alpha = \frac{\Delta I_C}{\Delta \alpha}\bigg|_{I_{CO},\ V_{BE}} \tag{9-5}$$

The vertical line after each expression indicates that the quantities following the line must be maintained constant while the indicated variations are considered. (This is similar to the conditions placed on the determination of the h-parameters in Chap. 6. In fact, the stability factors are quite similar to the h-parameters in mathematical definition. Both quantities represent the slope of certain characteristics.) Equation (9-2) can be used to determine the *relative contribution* of each effect to the total change in I_C. This establishes the predominant effects in each circuit arrangement and serves as a guide in establishing the need for further stabilization networks or adjustments. The individual factors [Eqs. (9-3) through (9-5)] can be used to compare the stabilization merits of one circuit arrangement with another for each of the temperature-sensitive effects. In this sense, these factors are *relative figures of merit* and have little meaning as absolute quantities. In all cases, the circuit with the *smallest stability factor value* provides the least sensitivity to temperature variations.

Example 9-2.   The transistor in Example 9-1 is used in an amplifier arrangement that has a current stability factor of 4, a voltage stability factor of 5×10^{-5}, and an alpha stability factor of 8×10^{-6}. What change in collector current will occur at 375°K?

Solution.   The change in collector current for the amplifier is:

$$\Delta I_C = S_I(\Delta I_{CO}) + S_V(\Delta V_{BE}) + S_\alpha(\Delta \alpha)$$

From Example 9-1, the change in reverse saturation current is:

$$\Delta I_{CO} = 4.7 \text{ microamperes}$$

The change in base-to-emitter voltage is:

$$\Delta V_{BE} = V_{BE_{375°K}} - V_{BE_{300°K}} = (183.5 - 26)(10^{-3})$$
$$= 157.5 \text{ millivolts}$$

The change in alpha is:

$$\Delta \alpha = \alpha_{375°K} - \alpha_{300°K} = 0.999 - 0.98 = 0.019$$

Hence:

$$\Delta I_C = 4(4.7 \times 10^{-6}) + (5 \times 10^{-5})(157.5 \times 10^{-3})$$
$$+ (8 \times 10^{-6})(1.9 \times 10^{-2})$$
$$= (18.8 \times 10^{-6}) + (7.87 \times 10^{-6}) + (0.15 \times 10^{-6})$$
$$= 26.82 \text{ microamperes}$$

Since the collector currents for amplifiers range from several milliamperes to a few amperes, such a change will not significantly alter amplifier operation.

Fixed Biasing Networks

A general transistor amplifier with a fixed biasing arrangement (two supply sources) is shown in Fig. 9-6. In order to determine the stability factor expressions for this basic biasing arrangement, it is necessary to develop circuit equations containing I_C, I_{CO}, α, and V_{BE}. From the conventional current relationships in Table 5-1:

$$I_C = \alpha I_E + I_{CO} \tag{9-6}$$

From Fig. 9-6, it is possible to write:

$$I_C = I_E - I_B \tag{9-7}$$

and:

$$V_{BB} = R_E I_E + R_B I_B + V_{BE} \tag{9-8}$$

Solving Eq. (9-7) for I_B and substituting this expression in Eq. (9-8), it is possible to solve Eqs. (9-6) and (9-8) simultaneously (eliminating I_E) to obtain:

$$I_C = \frac{\alpha V_{BE} + \alpha V_{BB} + (R_E + R_B)I_{CO}}{R_E + R_B(1 - \alpha)} \tag{9-9}$$

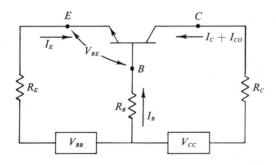

Figure 9-6.   *General Resistor Arrangement for Amplifier Circuit*

as a general relationship between I_C, I_{CO}, α, and V_{BE}. [V_{BB} appears in Eq. (9-9), but sensitivity to supply voltages will not be considered in this analysis.] In order to derive the sensitivity of I_C to changes in I_{CO}, the terms αV_{BE} and αV_{BB} need not be considered since they have no effect. Hence:

$$S_I = \frac{\Delta I_C}{\Delta I_{CO}} = \frac{(R_E + R_B)}{R_E + R_B(1 - \alpha)} \tag{9-10}$$

Since αV_{BB} and $(R_E + R_B)I_{CO}$ do not affect the sensitivity of I_C to changes in V_{BE}:

$$S_V = \frac{\Delta I_C}{\Delta V_{BE}} = \frac{\alpha}{R_E + R_B(1 - \alpha)} \tag{9-11}$$

Since Eq. (9-9) cannot be rearranged to obtain a single factor containing α, it is necessary to use the approximation:

$$S_\alpha = \frac{\Delta I_C}{\Delta \alpha} \approx \frac{V_{BB}}{R_E + R_B(1 - \Delta\alpha)} \tag{9-12}$$

In addition to maintaining α on the right side of the equation, V_{BE} has been dropped from the numerator, since it is much smaller than V_{BB}.

As stated previously, it is desirable to obtain the smallest values possible for the three stability factors. It is interesting to note that, since ΔI_C can never be less than ΔI_{CO}, the value for S_I can never be less than one. Similar limits cannot be placed on S_V and S_α. In most practical circuits, acceptable values for S_I range between 3 and 5 for germanium transistors and between 8 and 11 for silicon transistors.

TABLE 9-1

Stability Factors for the Basic Amplifier Configurations

Stability Factor	Amplifier Configuration		
	Common Base	Common Emitter	Common Collector
Current (S_I)	1	$\dfrac{1}{(1 - \alpha)}$	$\dfrac{R_E + R_B}{R_E + R_B(1 - \alpha)}$
Voltage (S_V)	$\dfrac{\alpha}{R_E}$	$\dfrac{\beta}{R_B}$	$\dfrac{\alpha}{R_E + R_B(1 - \alpha)}$
Alpha (S_α)	$\dfrac{V_{BB}}{R_E}$	$\dfrac{V_{BB}}{R_B(1 - \Delta\alpha)}$	$\dfrac{V_{BB}}{R_E + R_B(1 - \Delta\alpha)}$

Figure 9-7 presents the basic circuits for the CB, CE, and CC configurations. The circuits have been derived directly from Fig. 9-6 by permitting the indicated resistances to assume a value of zero. In view of this, Eqs.

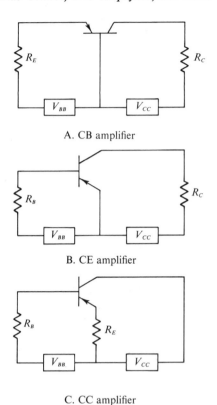

A. CB amplifier

B. CE amplifier

C. CC amplifier

Figure 9-7.   *General Resistor Arrangement for Basic Amplifier Configurations*

(9–10), (9–11), and (9–12) can be converted directly into the stability factors for each configuration by setting the appropriate resistance (R_E or R_B) to zero. These results are summarized in Table 9–1. Comparing these expressions, it can be seen that the basic CB amplifier has ideal current stability ($S_I = 1$) while the CE amplifier has very poor current stability. No general statement can be made regarding CC amplifier stability, since it depends on the relative values of R_E and R_B. The superiority of the basic CB amplifier current stability lies in the absence of a base lead resistor. This provides a path directly to ground for the excess minority carriers, preventing their accumulation in the base region. The CC amplifier has superior voltage stability, CB has fairly good voltage stability, and CE has the poorest voltage stability. The CC configuration has the best alpha stability while the CB and CE alpha stabilities may be very nearly equal.

Figure 9–8 illustrates the various degrees of current stability that can be achieved with a general amplifier, based on Eq. (9–10) The best stability

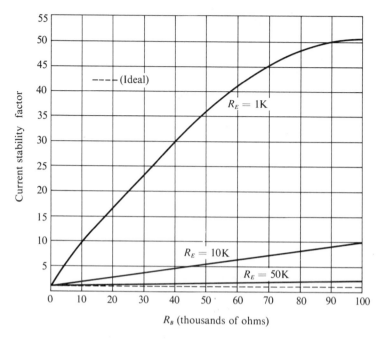

Figure 9-8. *General Variation of Current Stability Factor ($\alpha = 0.991$)*

is obtained with no base lead resistor ($R_B = 0$), so that S_I is equal to one. As stated, this can be achieved with the CB amplifier. For CE and CC amplifiers, this ideal condition can be obtained with transformer coupling of the input signal (Fig. 9–9). This arrangement also leads to less voltage and alpha stability since all the stability factors are now equivalent to those of the CB amplifier. Transformer coupling is well suited for matching purposes. However, frequency response will be degraded. In addition, R_E (which is now the biasing resistor) may have to be very large in order to achieve the proper value of forward bias current. This is of no particular consequence in the CB amplifier, since R_E may be arranged in parallel with r_{iE}. Hence, the a-c input resistance to the stage will always be approximately equal to r_{iE} (see Fig. 9–7, Part A). However, since R_E is the load resistor for the CC configuration and since r_{oc} is very low, a serious mismatch may occur for this arrangement. This can be overcome by selecting the input resistance to the next stage in such a way that $R_{L(a-c)}$ is made equal to r_{oc} (if such a selection is practical). For the CE amplifier, the presence of R_E produces series (current) feedback and causes a degradation in voltage gain (see Fig. 6–42 and associated text). This can be overcome by permitting R_E to be present as a d-c resistance, while being

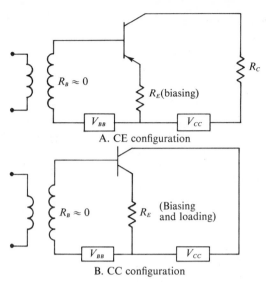

A. CE configuration

B. CC configuration

Figure 9-9.   *Use of Transformer Coupling to Achieve Good Bias Stability in Basic Amplifiers*

bypassed as an a-c resistance. Bypassing of the a-c signal is achieved by placing a capacitor in parallel with R_E as shown in Fig. 9–10. When it is desirable to have a high value of R_E for current stabilization *and a moderate*

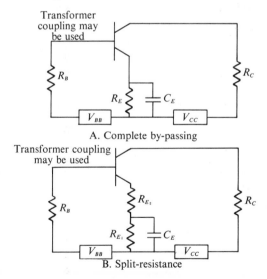

A. Complete by-passing

B. Split-resistance

Figure 9-10.   *Use of Emitter Bypass Capacitor to Achieve Current Stability with Decreased A-C Feedback*

degree of negative feedback (to enhance bandwidth or decrease distortion), two resistors may be used as shown in Part B of the figure. Only the unbypassed resistor contributes to negative feedback, but both resistors are present in the d-c biasing circuit.

Example 9-3. A common emitter amplifier (Fig. 9–7) has a base resistance of 100K and a d-c load resistance of 10K. The germanium transistor used in the amplifier has a forward current transfer factor of 0.96 and follows the variation shown in Fig. 9–5. Two bias supplies of 20 volts each are used in the circuit. Determine the current, voltage, and alpha stability factors for the amplifier at 350°K.

Solution. From Table 9–1:

$$S_I = \frac{1}{1 - \alpha} = \frac{1}{1 - 0.96} = \frac{1}{0.04} = 25$$

$$S_V = \frac{\beta}{R_E} = \left[\frac{\alpha}{1 - \alpha}\right]\frac{1}{R_B} = \left[\frac{0.96}{1 - 0.96}\right]\frac{1}{1 \times 10^5}$$
$$= 24(1 \times 10^{-5}) = 2.4 \times 10^{-4}$$

Since:

$$S_\alpha = \frac{V_{BB}}{R_B(1 - \Delta\alpha)}$$

and $\Delta\alpha$ is temperature dependent, the change in α must be obtained from Fig. 9–5:

$$\Delta\alpha = 0.006$$

Hence:

$$S_\alpha = \frac{20}{(1 \times 10^5)(1 - 0.006)} = \frac{20}{(1 \times 10^5)(9.94 \times 10^{-1})}$$
$$= 2.015 \times 10^{-4}$$

Example 9-4. Determine the emitter resistance value that must be placed in the amplifier of Example 9–3 if the current stability factor is to be reduced to 5. The a-c load on the amplifier is 3K and the voltage gain is −45. What effect will the emitter resistor have on amplifier operation?

Solution. The complete expression for current stability in the basic amplifier is:

$$S_I = \frac{R_E + R_B}{R_E + R_B(1 - \alpha)}$$

Rearranging for R_E:

$$R_E = \frac{R_B[1 - S_I(1 - \alpha)]}{S_I - 1} = \frac{(1 \times 10^5)[1 - 5(1 - 0.96)]}{5 - 1}$$

$$= \frac{(1 \times 10^5)(0.8)}{4} = 20\text{K}$$

This resistor represents a series feedback component with a feedback factor of (Chap. 6):

$$B_v = \frac{R_E}{R_E + R_{L(\text{a-c})}} = \frac{20 \times 10^3}{(20 + 3)(10^3)} = 0.87$$

This results in a voltage gain of:

$$A_{vE(F)} = \frac{A_{vE}}{1 + B_v|A_{vE}|} = \frac{-45}{1 + 0.87(45)} = \frac{-45}{40.2}$$

$$= -1.12$$

This is an intolerable gain reduction for most applications. The inclusion of R_E in the circuit will also reduce S_V and S_α. The reader is left to evaluate these and compare them to the stability factors in Example 9–3.

Example 9-5.   The emitter resistor in Example 9–4 is arranged as two resistors: one of 50 ohms and the other of 19.55K. The larger resistor is bypassed by a 2-microfarad capacitor (Fig. 9–10, Part B). Determine the voltage gain for this arrangement at 10 kilocycles per second.

Solution.   The capacitive reactance is:

$$X_{C_E} = \frac{1}{2\pi f C_E} = \frac{1}{2\pi(1 \times 10^4)(2 \times 10^{-6})} = \frac{1}{4\pi(10^{-2})}$$

$$= 8 \text{ ohms}$$

This reactance is in parallel with 19.55K, resulting in an equivalent impedance of 8 ohms. However, this is in series with the 50-ohm resistor so that the total emitter impedance is:

$$|Z_E| = 50.4 \text{ ohms}$$

The feedback factor is:

$$B_v = \frac{|Z_E|}{|Z_E| + R_{L(\text{a-c})}} = \frac{50.4}{(0.058 + 3)(10^3)}$$

$$= \frac{50.4}{3.058 \times 10^3} = 0.0165$$

The voltage gain is:

$$A_{vE(F)} = \frac{A_{vE}}{1 + B_v|A_{vE}|} = \frac{-45}{1 + (0.0165)(45)} = \frac{-45}{1.74}$$
$$= -25.8$$

Self-Biasing Networks

Figure 9–11 illustrates a general transistor amplifier with a shunt (voltage) feedback resistor which also serves as a self-biasing resistor. The biasing characteristics of this arrangement are discussed in Chap. 5 (see

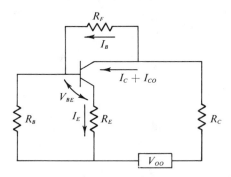

Figure 9-11. *General Resistor Arrangement for Amplifier Circuit with Shunt Feedback Biasing*

Fig. 5–51 and associated text). The feedback characteristics are discussed in Chap. 6 (see Fig. 6–45 and associated text). In order to determine the stability factor expressions for this commonly used self-biasing arrangement, it is necessary to develop circuit equations containing I_C, I_{CO}, α, and V_{BE}, as was done in the preceding section. Equations (9–6) and (9–7) (both of which are basic transistor amplifier equations) can be used to describe I_C for the circuit in Fig. 9–11. From Kirchoff's voltage equations:

$$V_{CC} = I_E(R_E + R_C) + I_B R_F \qquad (9\text{-}13)$$

If Eq. (9–6) is solved for I_E and Eq. (9–7) is solved for I_B, the new relationships may be substituted directly into Eq. (9–13):

$$V_{CC} = \frac{I_C[R_E + R_C + (1 - \alpha)R_F]}{\alpha}$$
$$- \frac{I_{CO}(R_E + R_C + R_F)}{\alpha} \qquad (9\text{-}13a)$$

When solved for I_C:

$$I_C = \frac{\alpha V_{CC} + I_{CO}(R_E + R_C + R_F)}{R_E + R_C + (1 - \alpha)R_F} \qquad (9\text{-}14)$$

This is a general relationship between I_C, I_{CO}, and α. V_{BE} does not appear in the equation, indicating that the feedback arrangement makes the d-c operation insensitive to changes in V_{BE}. [V_{CC} appears in Eq. (9–14), but sensitivity to supply voltages will not be considered in this analysis.] From Eq. (9–14), the current sensitivity is:

$$S_I = \frac{\Delta I_C}{\Delta I_{CO}} = \frac{R_E + R_C + R_F}{R_E + R_C + (1 - \alpha)R_F} \qquad (9\text{–}15)$$

The operation of this amplifier will be insensitive to changes in α if the condition:

$$R_E + R_C \geq 10(1 - \alpha)R_F \qquad (9\text{–}16)$$

is met, since the term $(1 - \alpha)R_F$ becomes insignificant and can be dropped from Eqs. (9–14) and (9–15). This condition is achieved in most practical amplifiers. The shunt feedback will degrade the current gain of the amplifier (Chap. 6). R_E will produce series feedback resulting in a reduction in voltage gain, also. This can be overcome, however, by bypassing R_E as in Fig. 9-10. Figure 9–12 illustrates the various degrees of current stability that can be achieved with the condition of Eq. (9–16) satisfied. Regardless of the value of $R_E + R_C$, smaller values of R_F cause S_I to approach one. However, since the voltage feedback factor for a-c signals

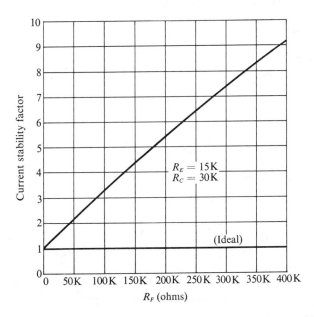

Figure 9-12.   *Variation of Current Stability Factor for Amplifier with Shunt Feedback Biasing*

is given by (R_C/R_F), lower values of R_F produce greater amounts of negative feedback. This causes greater reductions in current gain. Hence, there is a compromise to be reached in selecting the value of R_F.

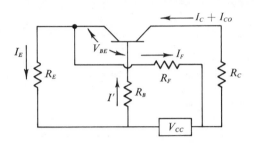

Figure 9-13. *General Resistor Arrangement for Amplifier Circuit with Voltage Divider Biasing*

Figure 9-13 illustrates another method of establishing self-biasing with a feedback resistor. This is similar to the arrangement in Fig. 9-10, *but the feedback resistor is connected directly to the supply, rather than to the collector.* Hence, R_F is in parallel with R_L in the d-c circuit, rather than in series. As in the previous current stability derivations, Eqs. (9-6) and (9-7) can be used to describe I_C. However, from Kirchoff's current equations, it is also necessary that:

$$I_B = I_F - I' \qquad (9\text{-}17)$$

From Kirchoff's voltage equations:

$$V_{CC} = I'R_B + I_FR_F \qquad (9\text{-}18)$$

and:

$$V_{BE} = I'R_B - I_ER_E \qquad (9\text{-}19)$$

Equation (9-6) may be solved for I_E; Eq. (9-7) for I_B; and Eq. (9-17) for I_F. Appropriate substitutions will yield:

$$I_F = I_C\left[\frac{(1-\alpha)}{\alpha}\right] - \frac{I_{CO}}{\alpha} + I' \qquad (9\text{-}20)$$

This expression may be substituted for I_F in Eq. (9-18) and the expression for I_E [from Eq. (9-6)] may be used in Eq. (9-19), leaving two equations with I' as the only unknown to be eliminated:

$$V_{CC} = I'(R_B + R_F) - I_{CO}R_F + \left[\frac{(1-\alpha)}{\alpha}\right]I_CR_F \qquad (9\text{-}18a)$$

$$V_{BE} = I'R_B - \left(\frac{I_C}{\alpha}\right)R_E + \left(\frac{I_{CO}}{\alpha}\right)R_F \qquad (9\text{-}19a)$$

These equations, solved simultaneously to eliminate I', and then solved for I_C, yield:

$$I_C = \frac{\alpha V_{CC}R_B + \alpha V_{BE}(R_B + R_F)}{R_E(R_B + R_F) + (1 - \alpha)R_F R_B} \qquad (9\text{-}21)$$

$$+ \frac{I_{CO}[R_F R_B + R_E(R_B + R_F)]}{R_E(R_B + R_F) + (1 - \alpha)R_F R_B}$$

as a general relationship between I_C, I_{CO}, α, and V_{BE}. [V_{CC} appears in Eq. (9–21), but sensitivity to supply voltages will not be considered in this analysis.] In order to derive the sensitivity of I_C to changes in I_{CO}, the terms $\alpha V_{CC}R_B$ and $\alpha V_{BE}(R_B + R_F)$ need not be considered since they have no effect. Hence:

$$S_I = \frac{\Delta I_C}{\Delta I_{CO}} = \frac{R_F R_B + R_E(R_B + R_F)}{R_E(R_B + R_F) + (1 - \alpha)R_F R_B} \qquad (9\text{-}22)$$

The sensitivity to changes in V_{BE} is given by:

$$S_V = \frac{\Delta I_C}{\Delta V_{BE}} = \frac{\alpha(R_B + R_F)}{R_E(R_B + R_F) + (1 - \alpha)R_F R_B} \qquad (9\text{-}23)$$

Since Eq. (9–21) cannot be solved explicitly for α, it is necessary to use an approximation [similar to Eq. (10–12)] for the alpha sensitivity:

$$S_\alpha = \frac{\Delta I_C}{\Delta \alpha} \approx \frac{V_{BE}(R_B + R_F)}{R_E(R_B + R_F) + (1 - \alpha)R_F R_B} \qquad (9\text{-}24)$$

All of these expressions can be made insensitive to changes in α if the condition:

$$R_E(R_B + R_F) \geq 10(1 - \alpha)R_F R_B \qquad (9\text{-}25)$$

is met. This causes the term $(1 - \alpha)R_F R_B$ to become insignificant, and it can be dropped from Eqs. (9–22) through (9–24). Since α is generally very

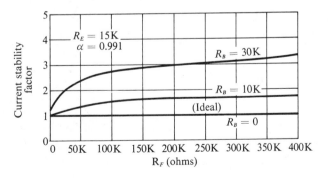

Figure 9-14.   *Variation of Current Stability Factor for Amplifier with Voltage Divider Biasing*

close to one, Eq. (9–23) may be further simplified to:

$$S_V \approx \frac{1}{R_E} \qquad (9\text{-}23a)$$

The current sensitivity for various resistance values is plotted in Fig. 9–14. As with the fixed biasing arrangement (Fig. 9–8), when R_B is zero (transformer coupling in the input) ideal current stability is achieved.

Example 9-6. The amplifier in Example 9–3 is to use single-source biasing. This is accomplished by removing the input loop source, and using a shunt feedback resistor with the available 20-volt output loop supply (as in Fig. 9–11). Determine the necessary value of R_F to maintain the same forward bias current. Evaluate the current stability factor with R_B retained in the circuit.

Solution. The forward bias current in Example 9–3 is:

$$I_E = \frac{V_{BB}}{R_B} = \frac{20}{1 \times 10^5} = 200 \text{ microamperes}$$

Since the output supply is also 20 volts, this value of I_E will be achieved with R_F equal to the R_B value:

$$R_F = R_B = 100\text{K}$$

(A detailed description of the R_F-analysis is presented in Chap. 5.)

The current stability factor is:

$$S_I = \frac{R_E + R_C + R_F}{R_E + R_C + (1 - \alpha)R_F}$$

indicating that R_B no longer affects current stability. (It is retained so that the equivalent input resistance of the amplifier, R_B in parallel with r_{iE}, will be approximately equal to r_{iE}.) Since there is no emitter resistor in the basic amplifier of Example 9–3, the current stability factor is:

$$S_I = \frac{R_C + R_F}{R_C + (1 - \alpha)R_F} = \frac{(10 + 100)(10^3)}{(10 \times 10^3) + (1 - 0.96)(1 \times 10^5)}$$

$$= \frac{1.1 \times 10^5}{1.4 \times 10^4} = 7.85$$

Example 9-7. Determine the current stability factor for the amplifier in Example 9–3 if the voltage divider arrangement (Fig. 9–13) is used instead of the shunt feedback arrangement described in Example 9–6.

Solution. The voltage divider resistance must be equal to the shunt feedback resistance if the same emitter current is to be obtained with the same output supply voltage (Chap. 5). Only the resistor connection is changed. Hence, from Example 9–6, the resistor value must be 100K. Since there is no emitter resistor in the amplifier of Example 9–3, the current stability factor is:

$$S_I = \frac{R_F R_B}{(1 - \alpha)R_F R_B} = \frac{1}{1 - \alpha} = \frac{1}{1 - 0.96}$$

$$= \frac{1}{0.04} = 25$$

9.3 Nonlinear Stabilizing Devices

The resistive bias control elements presented in the previous section achieve ideal current stability only when the base element resistance is near zero. If semiconductor devices (thermistors or junction diodes) are used as bias control elements, near-ideal current stability can be achieved, even with base-branch resistance present. In fact, some arrangements may produce *overcompensation*, where increases in I_C *are less than* increases in I_{co} ($S_I < 1$). This high degree of stability is accomplished by selecting semiconductor devices with the *same temperature sensitivity* as the transistor being controlled. If such a device is arranged so as to cause a reduction in I_C equivalent to the increase in I_{co}, ideal stabilization will be attained. Unfortunately, it is difficult (and in most cases, impossible) to get a perfect match over an extensive range of temperatures with a simple thermistor or junction diode arrangement. However, the use of more-complex diode arrangements or the use of *another transistor* can provide excellent stability, even beyond 425°K. These nonlinear devices will correct *only for ambient temperature changes*. Furthermore, careful circuit adjustments must be maintained at all times and cost may be increased by a factor of two or more. Hence, unless extreme precision is required (such as in laboratory instruments), the simple resistive circuits of the previous section are preferred. Even when nonlinear devices are used, certain of the resistive elements (especially the emitter resistor, R_E) are also included. This maintains control when the transistor junction temperatures are grossly different from the ambient temperatures, and compensates for *both internal and ambient temperature variations*.

The use of a voltage divider network to provide self-biasing for an amplifier is described in the previous section (Fig. 9–13). A second, *temperature-sensitive*, voltage divider may be added (as in Fig. 9–15) to provide a higher degree of stabilization. This second divider utilizes the bypassed (for a-c signals) emitter resistor and a thermistor to provide a variable d-c voltage in the base-emitter loop. Since R_B is in parallel with

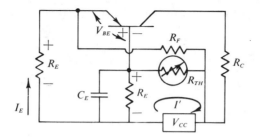

Figure 9-15. *Thermal Stabilization with Thermistor Control Circuit*

the combination base-emitter junction resistance and R_E, the voltage across R_B must be equal to the voltage across R_E plus V_{BE}. Hence, V_{BE} is the difference between the two resistive voltage drops.

R_F and R_B must be selected so that the voltage across R_B will always be greater than the voltage across R_E. This will assure that V_{BE} will always be an appropriate polarity for *forward biasing*. From the figure, it can be seen that the emitter voltage is used to cancel a part of the primary forward biasing voltage across R_B. The components are selected to produce the desired value of I_B at normal ambient temperature (usually, room temperature). If the ambient temperature increases, the thermistor resistance, R_{TH}, decreases, permitting I' to increase. From Eq. (9–26), an increase in I' produces a decrease in V_{BE}. Since the external bias voltage across the junction is decreased, I_B must also be decreased. This decreases I_C, tending to compensate for the increase in I_{CO} (brought about by the original increase in ambient temperature). For most transistors, a decrease of 2.5 millivolts/°K for V_{BE} will compensate for the normal increase in I_{CO} per unit temperature rise (Fig. 9–2). Hence, the thermistor resistance must decrease by a sufficient amount to produce a change of 2.5 millivolts/°K across R_E. A direct mathematical solution for ΔR_{TH} is not available. A trial-and-error method using a variable resistor in the place of R_{TH} (initially) is suggested. The voltage across R_B need not exceed the voltage across R_E by more than a few tenths of a volt. Once the nominal values for R_F, R_E, R_B, and R_{TH} are selected, the values of the variable resistor (representing R_{TH}) may be adjusted to find the ΔR-value needed to decrease the voltage across R_E by 2.5 millivolts. This is the resistance change per unit temperature change (ohms/°K) that the thermistor must have. The selection of R_F, R_E, and R_B can be somewhat rigorous, based on the equation in the preceding section.

Figure 9–16 illustrates a method by which a single junction diode may be used to provide a high degree of temperature stabilization in the voltage divider biasing arrangement. The diode is bypassed so that a-c signal

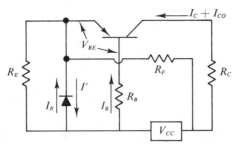

Figure 9-16.   *Thermal Stabilization with Single-Diode Control Circuit*

flow is not altered. The diode replaces R_B in the voltage divider network (see Fig. 9–13) and is forward biased. The forward resistance is low (R_B is small—approximately equal to the base-emitter junction resistance of the transistor). If any increase in I_{CO} is countered by an identical decrease in I', I_C will be insensitive to temperature variations of I_{CO}. I_{CO}, itself, is produced by the increased number of minority carriers flowing across the collector-to-emitter junction of the transistor. A similar minority carrier flow (denoted by I_R in Fig. 9–16) flows through the junction diode, *reducing the effective value of I'*. Hence, when an ambient temperature increase causes an increase in I_{CO}, it causes a similar increase in I_R (a similar *reduction* in I'). If the diode junction and transistor collector-to-emitter junction are identical, the increase in I_{CO} and the decrease in I' will be identical, resulting in perfect current stability ($S_I = 1$). Such operation can be maintained over a limited range of temperature variation.

A comparison of thermistor voltage divider stability and single junction diode stability is presented in Fig. 9–17. Thermistor stabilization circuits permit *some* fluctuation in collecter current, but provide a higher degree of stabilization than linear resistance circuits (see Figs. 9–8, 9–12, and 9–14) which, in most cases, merely reduce the rate at which I_C increases. However, thermistor stabilization breaks down below 400°K. Single diode stabilization offers near-perfect stability to about 350°K. The complexity associated with selecting R_{TH} and the proper ΔR_{TH}, as well as the superior precision of the diode circuit, leads to preference for diode stabilization. The breakdown in stability below 400°K is brought about by the significant temperature change in V_{BE} at temperatures beyond about 350°K. The thermistor network partially corrects for αV_{BE}, delaying its predominance. The single diode circuit offers no compensation for ΔV_{BE} beyond that provided by the linear resistors, R_E and R_F. Additional compensation may be obtained by using a more complex, *double-diode* stabilization circuit.

The double-diode stabilization circuit is illustrated in Fig. 9–18. The

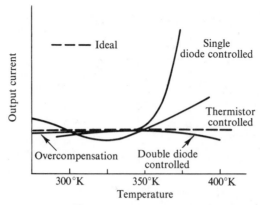

Figure 9-17.   *Comparison of Nonlinear Thermal Stabilization Circuits*

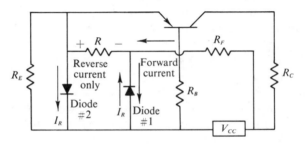

Figure 9-18.   *Thermal Stabilization with Double-Diode Control Circuit*

voltage across diode number 2 is equal to the difference in the voltages across R and diode number 1. Furthermore, R_F and R are selected so that the voltage across diode number 1 exceeds the voltage across R. This assures that V_{BE} will always be of the proper polarity for forward bias on the base-emitter junction. *It also assures that diode number 2 will always be reverse biased so that only the reverse saturation current will flow through it.* Below 350°K the second diode has little effect on circuit operation, although there is a tendency to provide overcompensation at low temperatures (see Fig. 9–17). As temperature increases, I_R (through both diodes) increases, causing the current through R (and the voltage across R) to increase. This effectively reduces the external base-to-emitter voltage, while the tendency of an increasing temperature is to increase V_{BE}. Hence, the two actions are compensating in nature. If the temperature continues to rise well beyond 400°K, the increased current through R can cause the voltage across R to exceed the voltage across diode number 1. This will cause the external emitter-to-base voltage to change polarity, *cutting the transistor off.*

9.4 Frequency Response Effects

Temperature stabilization is not achieved without producing changes in the a-c response of an amplifier. All self-biasing networks produce negative feedback. The effects of negative feedback on gain and frequency response are discussed in detail in Chap. 6. The effects on amplifier input and output resistance are also discussed in Chap. 6.

The importance of including an emitter resistor, R_E, in the d-c circuit has been emphasized throughout the preceding discussion of temperature stabilization. In general, higher values of R_E provide better stabilization. High values of R_E in the a-c circuit *cannot be tolerated*, however, because of the associated negative feedback. For this reason, "bypassing" of the emitter resistor is used, effectively removing R_E from the a-c circuit. (See Fig. 9–10.) The removal of R_E from the a-c circuit is not ideal, however. In fact, the addition of the bypass capacitor produces a feedback impedance, so that the feedback factor, B_v, becomes a complex function of frequency. Over the frequency range where R_E is ten (or more) times greater than $X_{C(E)}$, the bypassing of R_E is sufficient to ignore the feedback effects. Hence, C_E is generally chosen so that $X_{C(E)}$ will be about one-tenth of the R_E-value *at the center of the amplifier bandwidth*. Higher frequencies will reduce $X_{C(E)}$ so that the bypass capacitor has no effect on the upper cutoff frequency. At lower frequencies, however, $X_{C(E)}$ increases, causing an increase in the emitter impedance (and the negative feedback). As the frequency decreases farther, R_E will no longer be adequately bypassed and the negative feedback will cause a serious reduction in voltage gain. The gain will be reduced to 0.707 times its mid-frequency value when:

$$f_{L(E)} = \frac{(h_{fE} + 1)R_E + R_i + R_{g(\text{a-c})}}{2\pi C_E R_E (R_i + R_{g(\text{a-c})})} \tag{9-26}$$

where the quantities are defined as in Chap. 6 (and in Fig. 9–19, which is presented here for further clarification). Equation (9–26) considers only the degradation associated with having C_E and R_E in the circuit. The lower cutoff frequency for a coupling capacitor or a transformer must be deter-

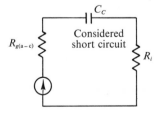

Figure 9-19.   *Equivalent Circuit Components for* Eq. (9–26)

mined separately, as described in Chap. 6. *The actual lower cutoff frequency for the amplifier will be the higher value between $f_{L(E)}$ and the coupling capacitor (or transformer) f_L-value.* In general, the emitter bypass capacitor will be the controlling component.

Example 9-8. The source feeding the amplifier in Example 9–5 has an equivalent resistance of 500 ohms. The amplifier has a d-c load resistance of 10K and is RC coupled to a device with an equivalent resistance of 2.3K. The output resistance for the amplifier is 80K. The coupling capacitor is 2 microfarads. Determine the lower cutoff frequency for the amplifier.

Solution. The lower cutoff frequency due to the bypass capacitor is:

$$f_{L(E)} = \frac{(h_{fE} + 1)R_E + R_i + R_{g(\text{a-c})}}{2\pi C_E R_E (R_i + R_{g(\text{a-c})})}$$

R_i (from Fig. 9–19) is the equivalent resistance following the coupling capacitor, or 2.3K in this example. $R_{g(\text{a-c})}$ (from Fig. 9–19) is the equivalent a-c source resistance feeding to the coupling capacitor. For the amplifier in this example, this is the parallel combination of the amplifier output resistance and the d-c load resistor:

$$R_{g(\text{a-c})} = \frac{(80 \times 10^3)(10 \times 10^3)}{(80 + 10)(10^3)} = \frac{800 \times 10^6}{90 \times 10^3} = 8.9\text{K}$$

(The unbypassed portion of the emitter resistor arrangement is in series with r_{oE}, but is not considered here since 50 ohms is insignificant with respect to 80K.) Hence:

$$f_{L(E)} = \frac{(24 + 1)(20 \times 10^3) + (2.3 \times 10^3) + (8.9 \times 10^3)}{2\pi(2 \times 10^{-6})(20 \times 10^3)[(2.3 \times 10^3) + (8.9 \times 10^3)]}$$

$$= \frac{5.11 \times 10^5}{8\pi(10^{-2})(11.2 \times 10^3)} = \frac{5.11 \times 10^5}{2.81 \times 10^3} = 182 \text{ cps}$$

The cutoff frequency associated with the coupling capacitor is:

$$f_L = \frac{1}{2\pi C_C \left\{ \left[\dfrac{r_{oE} R_{L(\text{d-c})}}{r_{oE} + R_{L(\text{a-c})}} \right] + R_D \right\}}$$

$$= \frac{1}{2\pi(2 \times 10^{-6}) \left\{ \left[\dfrac{(80 \times 10^3)(10 \times 10^3)}{(80 + 10)(10^3)} \right] + (2.3 \times 10^3) \right\}}$$

$$= \frac{1}{2\pi(2 \times 10^{-6})[(8.9 \times 10^3) + (2.3 \times 10^3)]}$$

$$= \frac{1}{8.16\pi(10^{-2})} = 4 \text{ cps}$$

Hence, the bypass capacitor predominates and the lower cutoff frequency for the amplifier is 182 cycles per second. However, the feedback produced by the emitter arrangement must be accounted for in order to determine the actual lower cutoff frequency:

$$f_{L(F)} = \frac{f_L}{1 + B_v |A_{vE}|} = \frac{182}{1 + 0.0165(45)} = \frac{182}{1.74} = 102 \text{ cps}$$

Example 9-9. Determine the value to be used for R_E in the circuit illustrated in Fig. E9–9 if the current stability factor is to be 5.

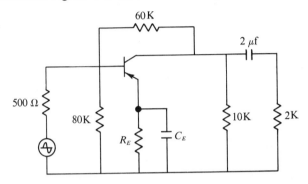

Figure E9-9

Solution. The current stability factor is given by:

$$S_I = \frac{R_E + R_C + R_F}{R_E + R_C + (1 - \alpha)R_F}$$

Rearranging for R_E:

$$\begin{aligned}
R_E &= \frac{S_I[R_C - (1 - \alpha)R_F]}{S_I - 1} \\
&= \frac{5[(1 \times 10^4) - (1 - 0.96)(6 \times 10^4)]}{5 - 1} \\
&= \frac{(1 - 0.24)(10^4)}{4} = \frac{7.6 \times 10^3}{4} = 1.9\text{K}
\end{aligned}$$

9.5 Direct-Coupled (D-C) Amplifiers

Throughout this text, the d-c voltages and currents for each amplifier stage are isolated from each other through the use of coupling capacitors, or transformers, designed to pass a-c signals while blocking d-c signals. This is required for most audio- and all high-frequency amplifiers. However, industrial, medical, and many defense applications have shown an in-

creasing requirement for the amplification of very slowly changing signals
(very low frequencies), even bordering on direct-current amplification
($f_L = 0$). Circuits conforming to such a response requirement cannot
contain coupling capacitors, bypass capacitors, or transformers. Rather,
each stage must be *directly coupled*. Since all signals are passed from one
amplifier stage to another, the temperature-sensitive variations must be
reduced to an absolute minimum. This means that such amplifiers must
be operated within a carefully controlled environment, or that *precise
stabilization circuits must be used.* Carefully regulated supply voltages are
almost universally used.

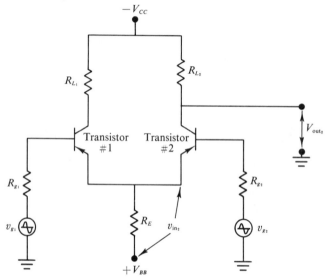

Figure 9-20.   *Basic Differential Amplifier*

A unique form of the d-c amplifier is the *differential amplifier*, illustrated
in Fig. 9–20. This amplifier provides an output signal equal to the difference of the two input signals:

$$v_{out_2} = A_{v(2)}(v_{g_1} - v_{g_2}) \qquad (9\text{-}27)$$

with a similar equation for output current. This is true because the useful
output signal for transistor number 1 appears across R_E and is applied
(180° out of phase) in series with v_{g_2} to the input of transistor number 2.
This means that (with respect to transistor number 2) transistor number 1
is operated in the CC configuration. Hence, v_{out_1} is approximately equal
to v_{g_1} and the useful input signal to transistor number 2 is approximately
equal to the difference:

$$v_{in_2} = v_{g_1} - v_{g_2} \qquad (9\text{-}28)$$

The second transistor is operating in the CE configuration with a gain of $A_{v(2)}$, justifying the validity of Eq. (9–27). Since temperature-sensitive variations in transistor number 2 are out of phase with the temperature-sensitive variations in transistor number 1, *there is a tendency for the cancellation of such variations.* In fact, if the two transistors are matched, the differential amplifier can achieve near-perfect temperature stability.

An additional set of amplifiers obtained through the use of direct coupling are termed *operational amplifiers.* These amplifiers use the normal d-c coupling arrangement with a considerable amount of negative feedback. Depending upon the feedback arrangement, the amplifier output signal is related to the source signal through specific mathematical operations (functions) such as division, multiplication, addition, and integration. The CE configuration is almost always used in order to obtain high amplifier gain.

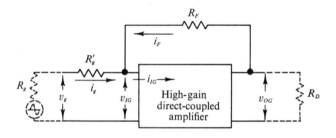

Figure 9-21.   *Basic Arrangement for Operational Amplifier*

The basic operational amplifier, consisting of a high gain d-c amplifier, a negative feedback path, and an external "source" resistance, is illustrated in Fig. 9–21. The input voltage and current (v_{iG} and i_{iG}) are negligible with respect to v_g, i_g, v_o, and i_F. Hence:

$$i_g + i_F = i_{iG} \approx 0 \tag{9-29}$$

and:

$$\frac{v_g}{R_G} + \frac{v_{oG}}{R_F} \approx 0 \tag{9-30}$$

where:

$$R_G = R_g + R_g' \tag{9-31}$$

with R_g as the inherent source resistance and R_g' as an additional (external) series resistance. From Eq. (9–30):

$$v_{oG} \approx -\left(\frac{R_F}{R_G}\right) v_g \tag{9-32}$$

indicating that the output voltage is related to the source voltage by a constant factor. (Phase reversal is indicated by the negative sign.) When R_F is greater than R_G, *multiplication by a constant greater than one is achieved.* When R_F is less than R_G, multiplication by a constant less than one (*equivalent to division*) is achieved. If several input terminals are provided in parallel (as in Fig. 9–22) *addition* can be achieved:

$$v_{oG} \approx -\left(\frac{R_F}{R_G}\right)(v_{g_1} + v_{g_2} + \cdots + v_{g_n})$$ (9-33)

when all R_G-values are equal and R_F is equal to R_G. If the equality is not maintained, a *weighted addition* is achieved:

$$v_{oG} \approx -R_F \left(\frac{v_{g_1}}{R_{G_1}} + \frac{v_{g_2}}{R_{G_2}} + \cdots + \frac{v_{g_n}}{R_{G_n}}\right)$$ (9-34)

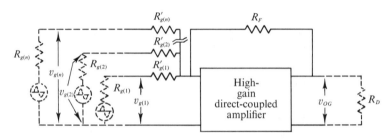

Figure 9-22.   *Operational Amplifier Arrangement for Addition of Input Voltages*

Other mathematical operations can be obtained with more-complex arrangements, including replacing R_F with feedback impedances of a capacitive or inductive nature.

The mathematical analysis of d-c amplifiers, which accounts for temperature stabilization and various feedback arrangements, is quite complex. D-C amplifiers provide sufficient subject matter for a complete text, and cannot be treated adequately here. The attempt here has been to introduce the existence of d-c amplifiers and to indicate some of the unusual applications associated with such amplifiers.

Example 9-10. An operational amplifier (Fig. 9–22) with three input signals: $v_{g_1} = 4$ volts, $v_{g_2} = 10$ volts, and $v_{g_3} = 5$ volts, must add half of v_{g_1} and one-third of v_{g_3} to v_{g_2}. Each voltage source has a resistance of 1K. A feedback resistance of 45K is used in the amplifier. Determine the value of the additional resistors that must be used in the input loops to achieve proper operation.

Solution.   The output voltage is given by:

$$v_{OG} = -R_F \left(\frac{v_{g_1}}{R_{G_1}} + \frac{v_{g_2}}{R_{G_2}} + \frac{v_{g_3}}{R_{G_3}} \right)$$

Since half of v_{g_1} is to appear in the output:

$$\frac{R_F}{R_{G_1}} = 0.5$$

$$R_{G_1} = \frac{R_F}{0.5} = \frac{45 \times 13^3}{0.5} = 90K$$

This means that R'_{g_1} must be:

$$R'_{g_1} = R_{G_1} - R_{g_1} = (90 - 1)(10^3) = 89K$$

The full value of v_{g_2} is to appear in the output:

$$R_{G_2} = \frac{R_F}{1} = R_F = 45K$$

$$R'_{g_2} = (45 - 1)(10^3) = 44K$$

One-third of v_{g_3} is to appear:

$$R_{G_3} = \frac{R_F}{0.33} = \frac{45 \times 10^3}{0.33} = 135K$$

$$R'_{g_3} = (135-1)(10^3) = 134K$$

9.6 Noise

As shown in Fig. 9–1, random noise generated outside an amplifier (and coupled into the circuit, either directly or indirectly), as well as inside the amplifier (by uncontrollable microscopic charge motion) tends to distort the desirable signal. In fact, random noise establishes a *lower limit* on the amplitude of the signals than can be usefully handled by any particular amplifier. External noise can be handled by shielding and filtering in most cases, or rejected by the bandwidth of the amplifier, itself. The internal noise cannot be excluded; it can, however, be reduced by proper circuit design and transistor selection. Since the noise is random, it cannot be expressed analytically as a function of time. That is, the instantaneous value of the noise voltage (or current) *cannot be predicted*. Fortunately, through considerable statistical analysis and experimentation, it has been possible to derive analytical expressions for the *average noise power* within the *amplifier bandwidth*. Although these derivations will not be pursued in detail, the general results will be applied. However, the reader is cautioned in the examination of noise characteristics. The techniques described must be used exactly within the *defining conditions*. They have no validity if this is overlooked.

In practice, the noise characteristics of a transistor are specified by the manufacturer in terms of total effect. The measure is called the transistor *noise factor*, defined by:

$$N_F = \frac{(S_i/N_i)}{(S_o/N_o)} \tag{9-35}$$

where the quantity (S_i/N_i) is the input *signal-to-noise ratio* and (S_o/N_o) is the *output signal-to-noise ratio*. Since these are power ratios, they are readily expressed in decibels (Chap. 6). When this is done, N_F is termed the *noise figure* of the transistor. Since the output signal power is simply the input signal power times the amplifier power gain ($S_o = A_{pG}S_i$), Eq. (9-35) reduces to:

$$N_F = \frac{N_o}{A_{pG}N_i} \tag{9-35a}$$

Since Eq. (9-35a) is in terms of noise powers and amplifier gain and is completely devoid of signal-level dependency, it is a more useful form for examining the technical nature of N_F. In fact, since the output noise power must include the *amplified input noise power* and any additional noise introduced by the transistor, itself ($N_o = A_{pG}N_i + N_s$, where N_s is the *semiconductor noise power*), Eq. (9-35a) reduces further to:

$$N_F = 1 + \frac{N_s}{A_{pG}N_i} \tag{9-35b}$$

This form of the definition for N_F clearly shows the two noise sources that must be considered: those in the input loop of the amplifier and those within the microscopic structure of the transistor material.

Input Noise

The random movement of charges, in response to photon captures and emissions, is discussed in Appendix B. It is shown that, since these motions follow the Maxwell-Boltzmann distribution, temperature is a primary influencing factor. In Chap. 2, the change in carrier motion under the influence of an electrical potential difference is described. Although this results in a net drift of carriers toward the higher potential (Fig. 2-11), there is still a high degree of randomness associated with the actual carrier motion. This randomness is the major source of noise in all electrical networks and is referred to as *thermal noise*. The discussion of photon emission and absorption in Appendix B indicates that the thermal energy (or power) is spread over a very broad band of frequencies, with a varying value across this band.

In order to avoid such a complex consideration, it has been convenient to define this noise as having an *equivalent uniform average value* over all frequencies (an infinite band). Such a noise characteristic is termed *white noise*. For practical amplifier considerations, only the equivalent value within the *amplifier bandwidth* is considered. Within these constraints, the input noise power is defined by:

$$N_i = \frac{2\pi k T r_i B}{R_{g(a\text{-}c)}} \qquad (9\text{-}36)$$

In this equation, k is the Boltzmann constant and T is the temperature in degrees Kelvin. The two resistances: the input resistance, r_i, to the amplifier and the equivalent a-c source resistance, $R_{g(a\text{-}c)}$, are the standard design resistances defined in Chap. 6. B is the amplifier bandwidth. Under matched conditions $R_{g(a\text{-}c)} = r_i$ and Eq. (9-36) reduces to:

$$N_i = 2\pi k T B \qquad (9\text{-}36a)$$

The definition in Eq. (9–36a) is used almost universally. The reader must realize, however, that it is valid *only under matched conditions*. Figure 9–23 illustrates the variation in N_i with temperature and $R_{g(a\text{-}c)}$. Obviously, considerable error can be introduced in the unmatched condition if Eq. (9–36a) is used without reservation.

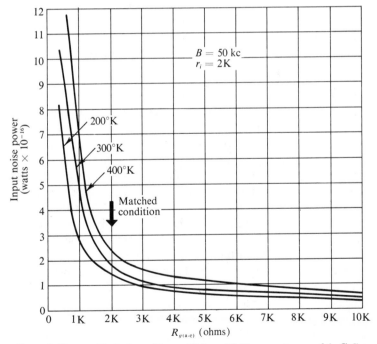

Figure 9-23.   *Variation of Input Noise with Temperature and* A-C *Source Resistance*

Semiconductor Noise

The source of semiconductor noise is not thoroughly understood. Experimental evidence indicates that it is related to recombination irregularities, crystal deformations, diffusion irregularities, minority carrier irregularities, and the ohmic contacts between conducting leads and the semiconductor material. This power varies inversely with frequency, so that it is more bothersome at low frequencies than at high frequencies. Although N_s follows the form:

$$N_s = \frac{KV_{OG}}{f^n} \qquad (9\text{-}37)$$

the value of K must be determined experimentally and varies from one material batch to another. The value of n may range from slightly less than one to slightly more than one. Hence, Eq. (9–37) is of little value, other than to demonstrate the general variability of N_s with V_{OG} and frequency. (As a better understanding of the phenomenon is achieved, K and n will undoubtedly be replaced by more definitive characteristic values.)

Noise Factor Variation

Care must be taken in considering the composite variation of N_F when Eqs. (9–36) and (9–37) are substituted into Eq. (9–35a). This is primarily a matter of interpretation. The resulting expression is given by:

$$N_F = 1 + \frac{K'V_{OG}R_{g(a\text{-}c)}}{f^n Tr_i BA_{pG}} \qquad (9\text{-}35c)$$

In this equation, all constants have been "lumped" into K'. In order to examine the basic variation of N_F with frequency, it is necessary to assume that V_{OG}, $R_{g(a\text{-}c)}$, T, and r_i are fixed. Hence, only f^n, B, and A_{pG} (all of which are frequency dependent) will be examined. This is shown in Fig. 9–24. At low frequencies, the equivalent bandwidth (Part A of the figure) is very small. However, the power gain is low. As frequency increases, A_{pG}, B, and f increase, causing a decrease in N_F. This is shown in Part B. At a particular frequency (denoted f' in the figure), the reduction in semiconductor noise power occurs at the same rate as the increase in thermal noise power, while A_{pG} is constant. At this point, N_F reaches a minimum value, where it remains until the amplifier gain begins to decrease. As A_{pG} decreases, N_F increases at about the same rate (by this time, the semiconductor noise power is reaching an insignificant value). This is shown in Part C of the figure.

With the basic N_F-variation in mind, it is possible to consider the other dependencies associated with Eq. (9–35c). Increases in V_{OG} cause all values

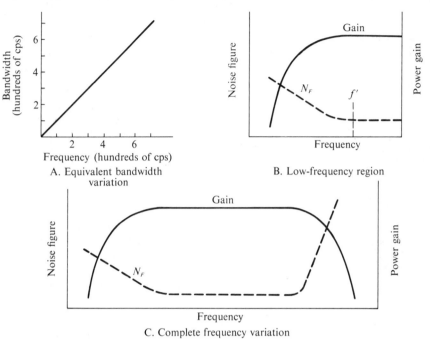

Figure 9-24.   *Variation of Noise Factor with Frequency*

in Fig. 9–24 to be higher. Values of $R_{g(a-c)}$ less than r_i tend to reduce the noise figure, while values of $R_{g(a-c)}$ greater than r_i tend to increase the noise figure. Although Eq. (9–35c) indicates that increases in temperature tend to *decrease* N_F, the opposite is true because of other temperature-dependent noise sources that have not been discussed. As long as T does not range too far above room temperature, these sources need not be considered. At higher temperatures, however, the equations must be modified somewhat.

The manufacturer's specification for N_F must carry specific conditions. It is usually defined for unit bandwidth ($B = 1$ cps), room temperature, fixed frequency (usually, 1000 cps), fixed V_{OG}, and a specific $R_{g(a-c)}$-value. In addition, since the temperature of the circuit resistors depends on the d-c current flow, a value will be specified for I_I (or I_0). Exceeding this current value will generally result in an appreciable increase in N_F.

Low-Noise Amplifiers

Because of the behavior of the noise factor, as described, certain design considerations can be followed, in addition to selecting a low-noise-factor transistor, to improve amplifier noise characteristics. V_{OG} and I_I should be maintained as low as possible. $R_{g(\text{a-c})}$ should also be maintained as low as possible. Unfortunately, all of these result in a lower amplifier gain. Hence, the actual selection of V_{OG}, I_1, and $R_{g(\text{a-c})}$ becomes a compromise between noise requirements and overall gain requirements. Fortunately, new developments in transistor fabrication continuously result in devices having lower noise figures.

Example 9-11. The transistor in Table 6–5 has a noise factor of 9. It is used in a common emitter amplifier with an equivalent a-c load of 5K and a shunt feedback factor of 0.004. The noise power into the amplifier is 10 microwatts. What is the mid-frequency output noise power?

Solution. The noise factor is defined by:

$$N_F = \frac{N_o}{A_{pE}N_i}$$

Rearranging for the output noise power:

$$N_o = N_F A_{pE} N_i$$

The mid-frequency power gain for the amplifier is (from Table 6–7):

$$A_{pE} = \frac{h_{fE}^2 R_{L(\text{a-c})}}{(h_{oE}R_{L(\text{a-c})} + 1)(\Delta h_E R_{L(\text{a-c})} + h_{iE})}$$

where:

$$\Delta h_E = 3.67 \times 10^{-2}$$

from Example 6–9. Hence:

$$A_{pE} = \frac{(1.1 \times 10^2)^2(5 \times 10^3)}{[(3.25 \times 5)(10^{-2}) + 1][(3.67 \times 5)(10) + (2.41 \times 10^3)]}$$

$$= \frac{5.5 \times 10^7}{1.1625(2.59 \times 10^3)} = 1.82 \times 10^4$$

However, shunt feedback is present. The power gain with feedback is:

$$A_{pE(F)} = \frac{A_{pE}}{1 + B_i|A_{iE}|}$$

where (from Table 6–7):

$$A_{iE} = \frac{-h_{fE}}{h_{oE}R_{L(\text{a-c})} + 1} = \frac{-110}{(3.25 \times 10^{-5})(5 \times 10^3) + 1}$$

$$= \frac{-110}{1.1625} = -94.8$$

Hence:

$$A_{pE(F)} = \frac{1.82 \times 10^4}{1 + (4 \times 10^{-3})(94.8)} = \frac{1.82 \times 10^4}{1.38} = 1.32 \times 10^4$$

and the output noise power is:

$$N_o = 9(1.32 \times 10^4)(1 \times 10^{-11}) = 1.19 \text{ microwatts}$$

PROBLEMS

1. A basic common base amplifier with an α of 0.97 uses two supply sources. It has a d-c load resistance of 5K and an emitter resistance of 10K. Determine the current stability factor.

2. A common emitter amplifier with an α of 0.98 uses shunt feedback to achieve a forward bias current of 0.4 milliampere with an output loop supply of 20 volts. The steady state collector-to-emitter voltage is 18 volts. The d-c load is 1K and there is no emitter resistance. The base resistance is 100K. Determine the current stability factor.

3. A transistor with characteristics as given in Table 6–5 is used in a common emitter amplifier with a voltage divider bias network. The voltage divider resistance is 18K, the base resistance is 5K, and the d-c load resistance is 2K. Determine the value of R_E necessary to produce a current stability factor of 8. What is the power gain of the amplifier if the emitter resistance is not bypassed?

4. A common emitter amplifier with an α of 0.96 has a transformer coupled output. It has a base resistance of 2K and a voltage divider (biasing) resistance of 50K. What is the current stability factor?

5. If the voltage divider resistance in Problem 4 is rearranged to produce shunt feedback biasing, what value must be used for R_E if the current stability factor is to be 4?

6. What is the voltage stability factor of the amplifier in Problem 3?

7. What is the voltage stability factor of the amplifier in Problem 4?

8. Determine the alpha stability of the amplifier in Problem 4 if the base-to-emitter voltage is 0.3 volt and the change in alpha is 0.05.

9. Transistor E in Appendix D is used in a common emitter amplifier with a 9-volt supply in the output loop. An operating point with a base current of 90 microamperes, a collector current of 5 milliamperes, and a collector-to-emitter potential of 5 volts is desired. Shunt feedback biasing is to be used. What value emitter resistance must be used if the current stability factor is to be 5?

10. The emitter resistor in Problem 9 is to be bypassed so that the series feedback is 0.005 at 15 kilocycles per second. What value bypass

capacitance must be used if the amplifier is RC coupled to a device with an equivalent resistance of 3K?

11. An amplifier using the transistor specified in Table 6–5 is fed by a source with an equivalent resistance of 1K. The amplifier has a d-c load resistance of 10K and is RC coupled to a device with an equivalent resistance of 1K. The coupling capacitance is 5 microfarads. An emitter resistance of 5K is used for current stabilization and is bypassed by a 3-microfarad capacitor. What is the lower cutoff frequency of the amplifier?

12. A transistor with an α of 0.98 is used in a common emitter amplifier with a d-c load resistance of 4K. The base resistance is 5K and a voltage divider resistance of 15K is used. The emitter branch contains two resistors: 200 ohms, unbypassed, and 3K, bypassed. What is the current stability factor?

13. The amplifier in Problem 12 is RC coupled to a device with an equivalent resistance of 5K. The coupling capacitance is 2 microfarads. The amplifier output resistance is 50K. Determine the bypass capacitor value if the lower cutoff frequency is to be 20 cycles per second.

14. A particular transistor with a noise figure of 5 decibels is used in an amplifier for a low noise application. The device being fed by the amplifier cannot function if the noise it receives exceeds 2 microwatts. The amplifier power gain is 55 decibels. What is the minimum value of input noise that can be tolerated for the amplifier?

15. What is the room temperature output noise power of the amplifier in Problem 14 if it has a bandwidth of 16 kilocycles per second, an input resistance of 2.5K, and is fed by a source with a resistance of 500 ohms?

Further Reading

"Basic Theory and Applications of Transistors," TM 11–690. Washington, D. C.: U. S. Government Printing Office, 1959.

Pierce, J. F., *Transistor Circuit Theory and Design.* Columbus, Ohio: Charles E. Merrill Books, Inc., 1963.

Seidman, A. H. and S. L. Marshall, *Semiconductor Fundamentals.* New York: John Wiley and Sons, Inc., 1963.

Surina, T. and C. Herrick, *Semiconductor Electronics.* New York: Holt, Rinehart, and Winston, 1964.

10

Sinewave Oscillators, Modulators, and Demodulators

Instability may be deliberately introduced into an amplifier circuit in order to achieve sustained oscillations. Such a circuit becomes, in effect, a *signal generator*, rather than a signal amplifier. If sustained sinusoidal oscillations are to be obtained, the instability must be carefully controlled. Such control is available through the use of *positive feedback;* that is, a portion of the output signal is returned to the transistor input in such a way that it is *in phase* with the "initiating" signal. For sustained oscillators, the initiating signal consists of the abrupt flow of forward bias current where previously there had been no current. Although this is a d-c current in its "steady state," the change from zero to the I_f-value is an a-c-like action that initiates a corresponding a-c-like change in the output loop (output current rises abruptly from zero to the I_o-value). This action is converted into a sinusoidal waveform of a specific frequency by a frequency-sensitive inductance-capacitance, resistance-capacitance, or crystal network.

In effect, the oscillator may be thought of as a lossless, highly selective, harmonic amplifier. In terms of harmonic analysis (Appendix C), the abrupt change in input current is similar to the leading edge of a square wave *and contains all possible sinusoidal frequencies*. These sinusoidal components, in turn, are amplified to produce the associated output current. The frequency-sentitive load is a filter. It selects *one* of the sinewave components and returns a portion of this component to the input terminals *in phase with the associated input component*. The filter network contains resistive elements which dissipate power—as do all passive electrical networks. When enough power is returned to the input to overcome the filter losses, an a-c signal is continuously passed from input to output (and vice versa). Hence, a sustained sinusoidal waveform is generated at the "filter" frequency. With appropriate coupling, a portion of this signal may be transferred to another device for further processing (usually, amplification) and eventual application.

It is frequently necessary to transmit signal waveforms from one place to another. It may be desirable to achieve the transfer with wires, coaxial cables, waveguides, or through free space. Since free space (or the atmosphere) attenuates low-frequency electromagnetic radiations very rapidly, it is desirable to use radio (and higher) frequencies for this application. However, in many instances, the signals to be transmitted contain only audio- or other low-frequency components. In order to transmit such low-frequency "information" at high frequencies, it is necessary to combine the low-frequency signals with a high-frequency *carrier signal*. This process is known as *modulation*. Modulation causes a characteristic (such as the amplitude or the frequency) of the carrier signal to vary in accordance with the information being transmitted. The modulated signal is nonsinusoidal and, therefore, is composed of specific harmonic components. If another set of information is transmitted on another carrier wave of a different frequency, the second modulated signal can contain an entirely different set of harmonic components. Hence, the two signals can be present simultaneously and a properly designed receiver *can distinguish between them on the basis of frequency selection*. The process of modulation is not restricted to transmitting low-frequency information at radio frequencies. It is commonly employed as a means of "separating" different transmissions, even though they may exist simultaneously—even at low frequencies.

In order to recover the transmitted information at some remote point, it is necessary to *demodulate* the modulated signal. This process converts the modulated characteristic (amplitude or frequency) back to the basic information and carrier signals, filters the carrier signal out, and passes the information for further processing and application.

Oscillators, modulators, and demodulators compose a set of electronic circuits that utilize techniques *directly in contrast with basic amplifier techniques*. The amplification process requires a high degree of stability and must be accomplished in a linear fashion in order to avoid distortion. Oscillators operate on the principal of *instability*. Modulators and demodulators *create new harmonic components* and, therefore, utilize *nonlinearities* as a basic operating characteristic.

10.1 Sinewave Oscillators

A very basic transistor oscillator circuit is given in Fig. 10–1. Resistors R_F and R_B provide forward bias (the voltage divider network described in Chap. 5) for the transistor. Resistor R_E is used for temperature stabilization. R_E and R_B are bypassed by capacitors C_E and C_B in order to avoid negative feedback (Chaps. 6 and 9). Negative feedback is intolerable, since it would tend to cancel a portion of the positive feedback required for oscillator operation. The positive feedback is achieved through the coupling between the primary coil and the "tickler coil." The coils are arranged so that the instantaneous polarities are as indicated. This assures positive feedback. (For the NPN transistor, all polarities would be reversed.) The secondary coil couples the oscillator signal to some other electronic device (usually an amplifier, since the oscillator signal may be quite small).

Normal Class *A* operating conditions are used to establish the transistor operating point. Oscillations begin when the power is applied (when d-c current begins to flow). The change in output current (from zero to I_0) is coupled from the primary to the tickler coil and causes an instan-

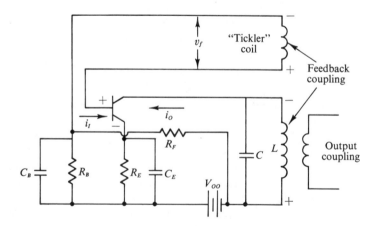

Figure 10-1.   *Simple Tickler-Coil Oscillator*

taneous surge in the secondary. The tickler-coil voltage is applied across the transistor input terminals, since R_B and R_E are bypassed. This causes an input a-c current component that is amplified, applied to the transformer primary, and coupled into the tickler coil. The additional current in the tickler coil raises the coil voltage (v_f in Fig. 10–1) and, therefore, the transistor input terminal voltage. This increase in input and output current (and voltage) continues until the transistor becomes *saturated*.

Saturation is illustrated in Fig. 10–2. For the oscillator circuit, $R_{L(d-c)}$ is essentially zero and produces a vertical load line. $R_{L(a-c)}$ is the loaded resonant resistance of the parallel-resonant (LC) circuit, as discussed in Chap. 7. The intersection of the a-c load line and the near-vertical portion of the characteristics is the *saturation point*. The output current *cannot exceed the indicated value*.

When the saturation point is reached, the changing nature of the primary current ceases for an instant. By the nature of transformer coupling, the tickler coil attempts to maintain a high current flow, but cannot. The instant the current in the tickler coil begins to decrease, so does the input terminal voltage. Since the transistor merely serves as an amplifier of the input terminal signal, the output current begins to decrease, also. When this happens, the primary coil again contains a changing current. This change is coupled to the tickler coil, which accentuates the already-decreasing current in this coil. Because of the positive feedback loop, all currents and voltages continue to decrease until the transistor is *cut off*.

Transistor cutoff is described in Chap. 5 and is illustrated in Fig. 10–2, Part B. The *cutoff point* is established by the intersection of the a-c load line and the characteristic curve for zero input current. The output current *cannot be less than the indicated value*. Hence, the cutoff point establishes a *lower limit* on oscillator operation.

When the cutoff point is reached, all changing conditions cease for an instant. However, there is a natural tendency for transistor operation to return to the *steady-state* (d-c operating) conditions. Because of the positive feedback, this return initiates the creation of the balance of the first cycle of operation and the first portion of the next cycle. Such a-c operation continues in a self-perpetuating manner. The rate at which the transition from saturation to cutoff (and vice versa) occurs is controlled by energy transfers between the primary coil and the parallel capacitor. Since the energy exchange is a sinusoidal function of time, the oscillator waveforms attain a sinewave shape within the first few cycles of operation.

Sustained oscillations may also be described in terms of power losses, power amplification, and feedback power. The simple tickler-coil oscillator, and any other positive feedback oscillator, may be represented by the "power blocks" shown in Fig. 10–3. The power gain of the amplifier is

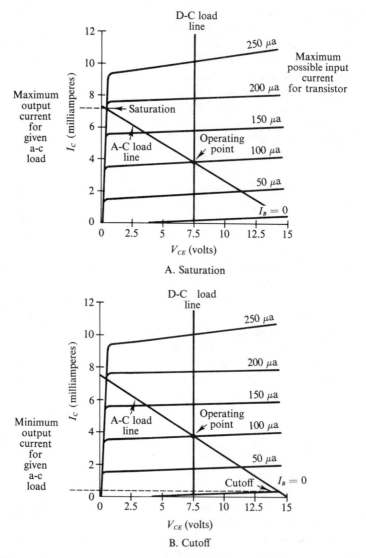

Figure 10-2.   *Determination of Saturation and Cutoff Conditions*

200, the transistor can handle an output power of 200 milliwatts between cutoff and saturation, and the power losses in the circuitry (the load and the feedback network) are 100 milliwatts. If the starting signal is 1 milliwatt, the first output cycle will be at a level equivalent to 200 milliwatts, with 100 milliwatts of this output power being lost. If 2 per cent

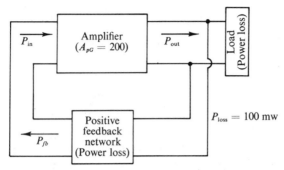

Figure 10-3. *Block Diagram of Oscillator Feedback Relationships*

of the useful 100 milliwatts of output power is fed back to the input, the next input cycle will be equivalent to 2 milliwatts. Hence, the next output cycle would be equivalent to 400 milliwatts, if it were not restricted to 200 milliwatts by saturation and cutoff limits. This means that sustained oscillation could be maintained with less feedback (1 per cent, in this example), since only enough power is needed to overcome the circuit losses and maintain operation between cutoff and saturation.

If less than an adequate amount of feedback is present, the amplifier may oscillate momentarily. Such an oscillation is *damped*, as shown in Fig. 10–4. In the example associated with Fig. 10–3, if the feedback factor is only 0.9 per cent, the feedback power (and input power) would only be 0.9 milliwatt. Hence, the second output cycle is equivalent to 180 milliwatts. After 100 milliwatts is lost, only 0.72 milliwatt (0.009×80 milliwatts) will be fed back for the third input cycle. This results in a third output cycle equivalent to 144 milliwatts. The fourth input cycle contains only 0.396 milliwatt, resulting in a fourth output cycle of 79.2 milliwatts. This power is *not sufficient to overcome the losses and provide additional feedback power.* Because of this, after the fourth cycle, the circuit will stabilize with only d-c signal flow. The decreasing power of each output cycle: 200, 180, 144, and 79.2 milliwatts, respectively, justifies the decreasing

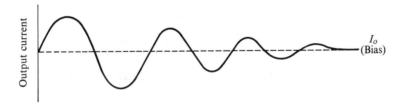

Figure 10-4. *Current Waveform for Damped Oscillation*

amplitude of each successive cycle in the damped waveform (Fig. 10–4).

Sustained oscillations may be generalized still further by using the basic mathematics of feedback operation (Chap. 6). For positive feedback, the basic feedback gain equation is given by:

$$A_{fb} = \frac{A}{1 - B|A|} \tag{10-1}$$

where A is the gain without feedback and B is the feedback factor (the fractional portion of the output signal fed back to the input). If the product, $B|A|$, is less than one, the denominator of Eq. (10–1) is less than one, leading to a feedback gain *greater than the gain without feedback*. This effect is directly opposite to the negative feedback effect.

When the condition:

$$B|A| = 1 \tag{10-2}$$

is met, the denominator of Eq. (10–1) is zero and the feedback gain is *infinite*, in theory. In practice, the feedback gain is limited by transistor cutoff and saturation. However, the condition of Eq. (10–2) *assures that sustained oscillation will occur*. The design of transistor oscillators is based on satisfying Eq. (10–2), which is known as the *Barkhausen criterion*. Each type feedback arrangement has *specific design equations relating the transistor parameters and the circuit component values in such a way that the Barkhausen criterion is met.*

Example 10-1.   A simple tickler-coil oscillator (Fig. 10-1) is built with Transistor B in Appendix D. The tickler coil to primary coupling is adjusted until sustained oscillations are obtained. A power supply of 6 volts is used and voltage divider biasing provides a base current of 20 microamperes. The output transformer has a 1:1 turns ratio and feeds a device with an equivalent resistance of 1K. What is the peak amplitude of the output current from the transistor?

Solution.   The d-c and a-c load lines are shown in Fig. E10–1. The amplifier will operate between cutoff and saturation. Saturation occurs at about 11 milliamperes. This permits an output current of the shape indicated in the figure, with its associated peak amplitude.

Example 10-2.   A particular amplifier has a power gain of 10,000. How much positive feedback must be added to the circuit in order to satisfy the Barkhausen criterion and cause sustained oscillations?

Solution.   The Barkhausen criterion is:

$$B|A| = 1$$

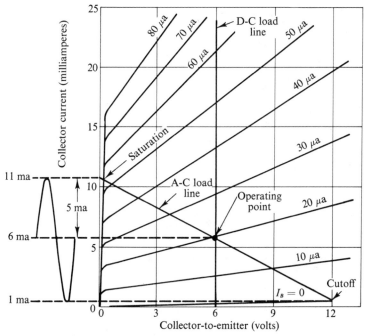

Figure E10-1

Hence:

$$B = \frac{1}{|A|} = \frac{1}{1 \times 10^4} = 0.0001$$

This is a very small amount of feedback and indicates why it is possible for stray feedback couplings to produce instabilities in amplifier operation.

Tuned-Circuit Oscillators

Two commonly used tuned-circuit oscillators are illustrated in Fig. 10–5. In both circuits, the antiresonant frequency determines the oscillation frequency. The CE configuration is used in order to achieve a high power gain through the transistors. All resistors that potentially provide negative feedback are bypassed with capacitors. The value of these capacitors is selected so that the capacitive reactance, at the oscillator frequency, is less than (or equal to) one-tenth of the associated resistor value. From Eq. (8–5a):

$$f = \frac{1}{2\pi\sqrt{LC}} \tag{10-3}$$

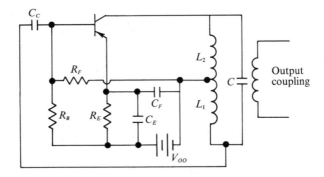

A. Hartley oscillator

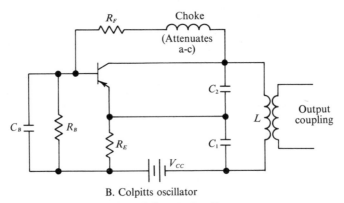

B. Colpitts oscillator

Figure 10-5.   *Common Tuned-Circuit Oscillators*

when the loaded antiresonant Q of the circuit is greater than 10 (which is almost always the case in a practical oscillator design). For the *Hartley oscillator*, both inductors are in series across the capacitor. Since series inductors add to produce a total inductance:

$$f = \frac{1}{2\pi\sqrt{(L_1 + L_2)C}} \qquad \text{[Hartley]} \qquad (10\text{-}3a)$$

For the *Colpitts oscillator*, the two capacitors are in series across the coil, leading to:

$$f = \frac{1}{2\pi\sqrt{L\left(\dfrac{C_1 C_2}{C_1 + C_2}\right)}} \qquad \text{[Colpitts]} \qquad (10\text{-}3b)$$

The feedback factor for the Hartley oscillator is a voltage feedback factor and is determined by the ratio of inductive reactance (X_{L_1}) to (X_{L_2}). This simplifies to:

$$B_v = \frac{L_1 + M}{L_2 + M} \tag{10-4}$$

where M is the mutual inductance between L_1 and L_2. The voltage gain equation is given in Tables 6–7 and 6–8. Satisfying the Barkhausen criterion ($B_v|A_v| = 1$), and solving for h_{fE}:

$$h_{fE} = \frac{L_2 h_{iE}}{L_1 R_{L(a\text{-}c)}} + \frac{\Delta h_E L_2}{L_1} \tag{10-5}$$

$R_{L(a\text{-}c)}$ is the antiresonant resistance of the parallel-resonant circuit. Even in the loaded condition, this resistance tends to be quite high with respect to h_{iE}. ($Q_{ar(L)}$ should be maintained above ten, as mentioned previously, and as explained in Chap. 7.) This tends to make the first term of Eq. (10–5) insignificant, leading to:

$$h_{fE} = \frac{\Delta h_E L_2}{L_1} \qquad \text{[Hartley]} \tag{10-5a}$$

This condition is the *minimum* for establishing sustained oscillations. *If h_{fE} is made greater than the right-hand side of* Eq. (10–5a), *oscillations will still be sustained:*

$$h_{fE} \geq \frac{\Delta h_E L_2}{L_1} \qquad \text{[Hartley]} \tag{10-5b}$$

Although this arrangement is less efficient (more feedback is present than is necessary), it is more practical to design for the "greater than" condition. Such a design permits the h_{fE}-value for the transistor to degrade (with age, or with a shift in operating conditions), while still maintaining oscillations.

The Colpitts oscillator feedback may be analyzed in a similar manner, leading to:

$$h_{fE} \geq \frac{\Delta h_E C_1}{C_2} \qquad \text{[Colpitts]} \tag{10-6}$$

where the "greater than" condition is, again, the more practical design condition.

Figure 10–6 presents a modified version of the Colpitts oscillator, known as the *Clapp oscillator*. Since the series combination of C_1 and C_2 is in parallel with C_3, the complete frequency equation is:

$$f = \frac{1}{2\pi \sqrt{L\left[\left(\dfrac{C_1 C_2}{C_1 + C_2}\right) + C_3\right]}} \tag{10-7}$$

The usual selection of component values tends to make the effects of C_1 and C_2 insignificant, so that oscillation frequency becomes dependent on

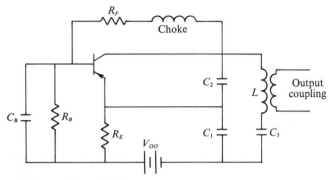

Figure 10-6. *Clapp Oscillator*

L and C_3 alone:

$$f = \frac{1}{2\pi\sqrt{LC_3}} \quad \text{[Clapp]} \tag{10-7a}$$

This is desirable from a practical design standpoint. If the oscillator is to be "tunable"; that is, of a variable frequency, only C_3 need be variable in the Clapp oscillator. In the Colpitts oscillator, tuning can be achieved only if C_1 and C_2 are "ganged" properly to maintain the condition in Eq. (10–6). For the Clapp oscillator, C_1 and C_2 can be fixed to satisfy Eq. (10–6), and changing C_3 will affect only the frequency of oscillation.

Tuned oscillators are used to achieve oscillation at high frequencies, since inductors and capacitors are, inherently, high-frequency components. The value of capacitance or inductance (or both) necessary to produce antiresonance at audio frequencies is prohibitively large. Such values can be achieved only with components of immense physical size.

Example 10-3. The transistor with characteristics listed in Table 6–5 is used in a Hartley oscillator (Fig. 10–5) with L_1 equal to 1×10^{-8} henry and C equal to 100 picofarads. Determine the value of L_2 that must be used to exactly satisfy the Barkhausen criterion and determine the associated oscillator frequency.

Solution. The Barkhausen criterion is:

$$h_{fE} = \frac{\Delta h_E L_2}{L_1}$$

Solving for L_2:

$$L_2 = \frac{L_1 h_{fE}}{\Delta h_E} = \frac{(1 \times 10^{-8})(1.1 \times 10^2)}{3.67 \times 10^{-2}} = \frac{1.1 \times 10^{-6}}{3.67 \times 10^{-2}}$$

$$= 30 \text{ microhenries}$$

The oscillator frequency is:

$$f = \frac{1}{2\pi\sqrt{(L_1 + L_2)C}} = \frac{1}{2\pi\sqrt{(0.01 + 30)(10^{-6})(1 \times 10^{-10})}}$$
$$= \frac{1}{2\pi\sqrt{30.01 \times 10^{-16}}} = \frac{1}{2\pi(5.48 \times 10^{-8})} = 2.91 \text{ mc}$$

L_2 could be made smaller. The Barkhausen criterion:

$$h_{fE} > \frac{\Delta h_E L_2}{L_1}$$

will be satisfied. However, since L_2 is in the denominator of the frequency expression, smaller values of L_2 will cause the oscillator to oscillate at higher frequencies. Hence, the frequency obtained when the Barkhausen criterion is exactly satisfied is the minimum frequency that can be achieved with any particular circuit.

Phase-Shift Oscillators

The appropriate feedback phase relationship for the tuned-circuit oscillator is obtained by appropriate terminal connections between the feedback component and the input terminals, while the oscillation frequency is controlled directly by the parallel-resonant circuit component values. The high selectivity of the parallel-resonant circuit severely attenuates all frequencies except the antiresonant frequency.

It is also possible to produce sustained oscillations by making the feedback factor a complex quantity—with both magnitude and phase angle varying as a function of frequency. Such a network must be designed so that when the Barkhausen criterion is satisfied in magnitude, the feedback phase angle is such as to provide positive feedback. The frequency that simultaneously satisfies the feedback phase and magnitude requirements will control the oscillation.

The RC circuit in Fig. 10–7 is a simple *phase-shifting network*. The current in the circuit and, therefore, the voltage across R, has a phase

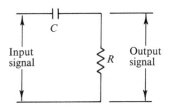

Figure 10-7.   *Phase-Shifting Network*

angle given by:

$$\theta = \tan^{-1}\left[\frac{1}{2\pi fCR}\right] \tag{10-8}$$

Because of the discontinuity associated with the tangent function, the shift provided by such a simple circuit is restricted to angles less than 90°. However, such RC "stages" may be cascaded. To produce greater total phase-shift values, the current from each stage "feeds" the next stage. Hence, the current shift of each stage adds successively. Such an RC *ladder* is used as the feedback network in the *phase-shift oscillator*.

A common phase-shift oscillator circuit is shown in Fig. 10-8, along with its hybrid equivalents (Parts B and C). The CE configuration is used because of its high gain and moderate input-output resistance values. Biasing and temperature stabilization resistors are bypassed, wherever possible, to minimize negative feedback. The RC stages are identical in order to simplify the design procedure. Notice, however, that in order for the last stage to be identical to the other stages, the positive feedback resistor must have a value:

$$R_F' = R - h_{iE} \tag{10-9}$$

since R_F', in series with h_{iE}, provides the total resistance in the last stage (Part C of the figure).

If each stage in the RC ladder is identical, the phase shift in each stage must be equal [Eq. (10-8)]. The CE configuration produces a 180° phase shift between output and input (Chap. 5). Hence, if the feedback is to be positive, the RC ladder must provide an additional 180° phase shift. With identical stages, the phase shift for each stage must be:

$$\theta_n = \frac{180°}{n} \tag{10-10}$$

In order to complete the oscillator design, it is nescesary to satisfy the magnitude of the Barkhausen criterion, as well as the phase shift. Developing the feedback factor for the equivalent circuit in Fig. 10-8, Part C requires the simultaneous solution of three current loop equations. Using this solution, and the voltage gain equation for the CE amplifier, it is possible to derive the Barkhausen criterion:

$$h_{fE} \geq 23 + \frac{29R}{R_L} + \frac{4R_L}{R} \tag{10-11}$$

Equation (10-11) applies only to the *three-stage* feedback ladder.

The d-c design of the phase-shift oscillator is the same as for a Class A amplifier, and must provide an appropriate operating point that will minimize distortion (see Chap. 5). This establishes the value of R_L. Temperature stabilization is achieved by techniques described in Chap. 9 and

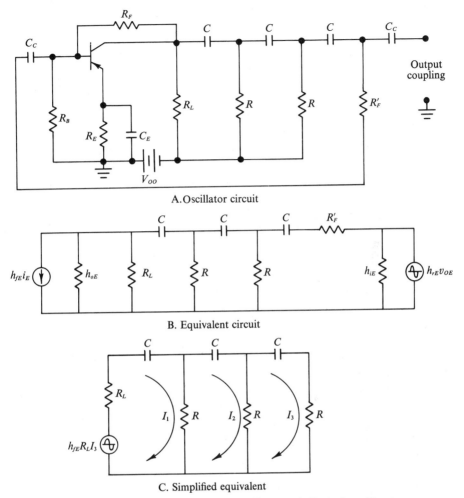

Figure 10-8.   *Typical Phase-Shift Oscillator with Equivalent Circuits*

all negative-feedback resistors are bypassed, if possible. In order to design the three-stage ladder for use with a particular transistor, R may be determined from Eq. (10–11). Each stage must shift the signal by $60°$; that is, $180°/3$. With the value of R and θ_n known, Eq. (10–8) can be used to approximate C for any desired oscillator frequency. However, Eq. (10–8) only *approximates* the relationship between R, C, f, and θ when the RC stages *are placed in the amplifier circuit*. To be exact, the loading effect must be taken into account. For the three-stage ladder, the proper feedback phase angle will occur when:

$$f = \frac{1}{2\pi C \sqrt{4RR_L + 6R^2}} \tag{10-12}$$

This equation can be used to determine C when R, R_L, and f are known. R'_F is determined from Eq. (10–9).

Although Eq. (10–8) may be used to approximate any number of RC stages, the lack of convenient equivalents to Eqs. (10–11) and (10–12) for four or more stages makes the design of other phase-shift oscillators a more difficult, trial-and-error process. Fortunately, the three-stage ladder is used most commonly, and is adequate enough to preclude any significant need for a greater number of stages. The phase-shift oscillator is used to produce frequencies in the audio range, since higher frequencies would require extremely small component values.

Example 10-4. The transistor with characteristics listed in Table 6–5 is to be used in a phase-shift oscillator with a frequency of 10 kilocycles per second. A three-stage RC ladder (Fig. 10–8) is used. The d-c load resistor must be 2K is order to obtain an undistorted output signal. Determine the necessary value for R and C.

Solution.   The Barkhausen criterion is given by:

$$h_{fE} = 23 + \frac{29R}{R_L} + \frac{4R_L}{R}$$

This equation could be solved for R, resulting in a quadratic expression. However, h_{fE} for this transistor is quite high (110), so that a wide range of values will satisfy the "greater than" condition. Since the input resistance to the transistor serves as a part of one of the R-components (the series combination of R'_F and r_{iE}), R must be greater than r_{iE}. Using the approximate expression for r_{iE}, it is found that r_{iE} is on the order of 2.41K. If an R-value of 3K is selected:

$$23 + \frac{29(3 \times 10^3)}{(2 \times 10^3)} + \frac{4(2 \times 10^3)}{(3 \times 10^3)}$$
$$= 23 + 43.5 + 2.66 = 69.16$$

indicating that the Barkhausen criterion is satisfied. The oscillator frequency is given by:

$$f = \frac{1}{2\pi C \sqrt{4RR_L + 6R^2}}$$

Rearranging for C:

$$C = \frac{1}{2\pi f \sqrt{4RR_L + 6R^2}}$$

$$= \frac{1}{2\pi(1 \times 10^4)\sqrt{4(3 \times 10^3)(2 \times 10^3) + 6(3 \times 10^3)^2}}$$

$$= \frac{1}{2\pi(1 \times 10^4)\sqrt{(24 \times 10^6) + (54 \times 10^6)}}$$

$$= \frac{1}{2\pi(1 \times 10^4)\sqrt{78 \times 10^6}} = \frac{1}{2\pi(1 \times 10^4)(8.84 \times 10^3)}$$

$$= 0.18 \text{ microfarad}$$

In the last RC stage, R'_F must be:

$$R'_F = R - r_{iE} = (3 - 2.41)(10^3) = 590 \text{ ohms}$$

Frequency Stability

The *frequency stability* of an oscillator refers to how well it maintains oscillation at the desired frequency. For the tuned circuit, the first step in achieving frequency stability consists of using an extremely high-Q circuit, even in the loaded condition. This makes the circuit very selective and also prevents any shift in antiresonant frequency under a changing load (see Chap. 7). The RC phase-shift oscillator frequency is also sensitive to loading, as indicated by Eq. (10–12). Both circuits are sensitive to temperature variations. Because of this, precision oscillators must be operated in a carefully controlled environment. Supply voltage variations also produce fluctuations in oscillator frequency. These can be avoided by careful use of voltage regulation circuits (Chap. 5).

An excellent frequency-stabilizing element is the *piezoelectric crystal*. Such a crystal (quartz is commonly used) is of a nature such that, when a voltage is applied across opposite faces, the crystal vibrates (physically) at a certain frequency. This vibration produces electrical oscillations on the crystal surface. These oscillations are picked up by the electrodes supplying the initial (d-c) voltage. These are then fed back to the transistor input and are amplified. A portion of this a-c signal is applied to the crystal, leading to further enhancement of the phenomenon.

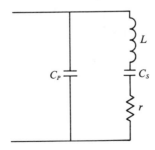

Figure 10-9.   *Crystal Equivalent Circuit*

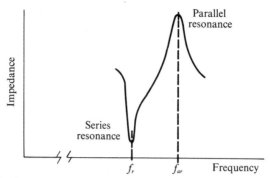

Figure 10-10.   *Impedance Variation for Piezoelectric Crystal*

Electrically, the crystal has an equivalent circuit as shown in Fig. 10–9. Because of the arrangement of the equivalent components, the crystal has two natural frequencies: a series resonant frequency, and an antiresonant frequency. This is indicated in Fig. 10–10. Either may be used to control oscillator frequency. The selection is based on whether it is desirable for the circuit to have a low (series-resonant) or high (parallel-resonant) impedance, for matching purposes. The stability of the crystal is derived from its high Q (20,000 or more) in the unloaded condition. Because of its temperature sensitivity, however, the crystal must be maintained under a constant temperature. A typical crystal-controlled oscillator is shown in Fig. 10–11. This is the basic Colpitts oscillator, with the crystal replacing the coil in the frequency-control circuit.

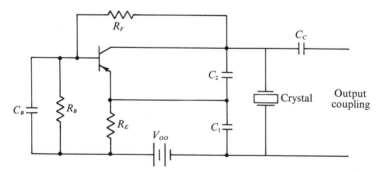

Figure 10-11.   *Colpitts Oscillator with Crystal Frequency Stabilization*

10.2 Modulation and Modulators

Modulation is the process of "coding" one electrical signal with another. A very basic form of modulation is employed in telegraphy, even in its crudest form, where a d-c signal is turned "on" and "off" in a prearranged manner to represent the letters of the alphabet. In a more modern sense, the radiotelegraph utilizes a high-frequency sinewave that is turned "on" and "off" according to the same code, in a process known as continuous-wave *keying*.

The more useful forms of modulation are more sophisticated than this "on"-"off" technique, which is a slow-transmission process. The direct transmission of music, speech, television images, remote sensor readings, etc., requires extremely high transmission rates. These rates are obtained by "superimposing" the desired signals directly onto one of the characteristics of a high-frequency *carrier signal* which is sinusoidal in shape. The carrier signal is given by:

$$i_c = i_{c(P)} \sin 2\pi f_c t \qquad (10\text{-}13)$$

where $i_{c(P)}$ is the peak carrier amplitude and f_c is the carrier frequency— the two characteristics that can be "coded." When the *carrier amplitude* is altered, the process is termed *amplitude modulation*. When the *frequency* is altered, the process is termed *frequency modulation*. Each modulation type has particular advantages and disadvantages. The selection of one over the other depends entirely on the desired result, and the degree of circuit sophistication that is permitted. Prior to discussing the manner of achieving modulation within a transistor amplifier or oscillator, it is essential that the reader develop an understanding of the modulation process, itself. A single-frequency sinewave, called the *modulating signal*, given by:

$$i_m = i_{m(P)} \sin 2\pi f_m t \qquad (10\text{-}14)$$

will be used initially, where $i_{m(P)}$ is the peak modulating signal amplitude and f_m is the modulating frequency. A generalization will then be made to include all signal waveforms.

In the unmodulated condition, the carrier signal appears as in Fig. 10-12, Part A. The peak amplitude and frequency are constant. The modulating signal is shown in Part B of the figure. In its simplest form, it, too, has a constant peak amplitude and frequency. The process of amplitude modulation (AM) requires that the carrier amplitude peak *vary about its unmodulated value* by an amount that is *proportional* to the instantaneous modulating signal amplitude, at a rate equal to the modulating frequency.

In Fig. 10-13, two signal processes are illustrated. The first (in Part A) represents the *addition* of the two signals in Fig. 10-12. The second (in Part B) represents the *multiplication* of the two signals in Fig. 10-12. In the multiplication process, the amplitude of the carrier signal varies in proportion to the modulating signal amplitude, at a rate equal to the

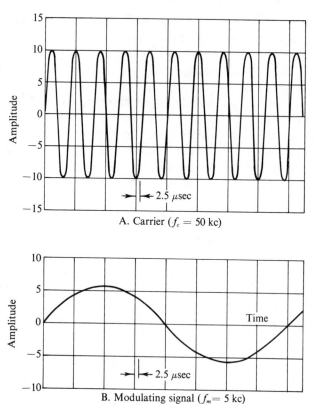

Figure 10-12.   *Typical Carrier and Modulating Signals*

modulating frequency—*the process of amplitude modulation has been accomplished.* Notice that the basic carrier signal frequency is still present. That is, f_c has not been changed by the modulation process. The modulating signal frequency is present *only in the variation of the carrier peak amplitude.* The modulating signal amplitude is also present *only in the variation of the carrier peak amplitude.* Hence, the modulating signal has not been lost—it has merely been "coded" onto the carrier amplitude characteristic.

Mathematically, the amplitude modulated signal is given by:

$$i_{c(AM)} = i_{c(P)} \sin 2\pi f_c t + i_{m(P)} \sin 2\pi f_m t \sin 2\pi f_c t \qquad \textbf{(10-15)}$$

indicating that the basic carrier signal is still present, but that an additional, more complex signal component is also present. *The amplitude modulated signal is not a sinusoidal signal.* Hence, there *must be* a series of sinusoidal components present that were not in either the original sinusoidal carrier or modulating signals. The product-term on the right-hand side of Eq. (10–15) expresses these new components. When properly

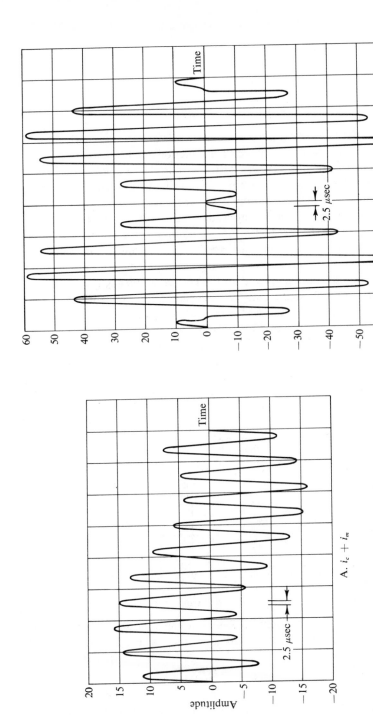

Figure 10-13. *Addition and Multiplication of Carrier and Modulating Signals*

513

expanded, Eq. (10–15) becomes:

$$i_{c(AM)} = i_{c(P)} \sin 2\pi f_c t + \frac{i_{m(P)}}{2} \cos 2\pi (f_c - f_m)t \qquad (10\text{-}15a)$$

$$- \frac{i_{m(P)}}{2} \cos 2\pi (f_c + f_m)t$$

indicating that two new sinusoidal components are created by the amplitude modulation process. The cosine functions indicate that the new components are 90° out of phase with the modulating and carrier signal components. The minus sign on the last term indicates that, with respect to each other, the two new components are out of phase by 180°. Both new components have a peak amplitude that is half the amplitude of the modulating signal. The frequency of one component is less than the carrier frequency by an amount equal to the modulating signal frequency. This component is referred to as the *difference signal*. The frequency of the other component is greater than the carrier frequency by an amount equal to the modulating signal frequency. This component is the *sum signal*. The *spectrum* for the AM signal; that is, the plot of component amplitude versus component frequency (Appendix C), is shown in Fig. 10–14. The difference signal is also known as the *lower side frequency;* the sum signal, as the *upper side frequency.* Although Eq. (10–15a) indicates a phase reversal between lower and upper side frequencies, it is common practice to show magnitudes only, as in Fig. 10–14. This practice will be adhered to throughout this text.

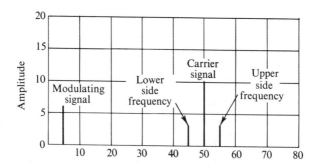

Figure 10-14.   *Amplitude Modulated Signal Spectrum*

The degree of proportionality between the modulating signal peak amplitude and the carrier signal peak amplitude is specified by the *amplitude modulation index:*

$$k_{AM} = \frac{i_{m(P)}}{i_{c(P)}} \qquad (10\text{-}16)$$

Fig. 10–15 illustrates the AM signal for various modulation index values.

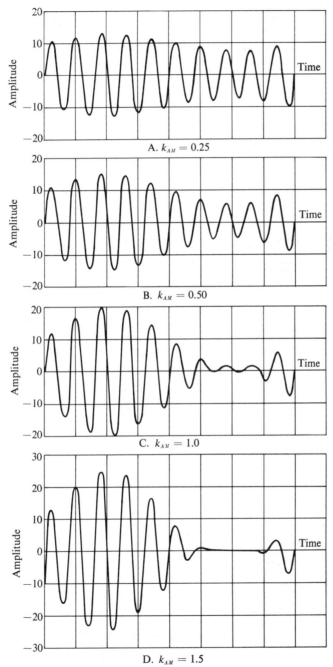

Figure 10-15.   *Effect of Modulating Index on AM Signal Waveform*

Obviously, when k_{AM} exceeds one (when $i_{m(P)}$ is greater than $i_{c(P)}$), as in Part D of the figure, a drastic amount of distortion has been introduced. In fact, the carrier amplitude variation no longer reflects the characteristics of the modulating signal—*some of the original information has been lost.*

It is now possible to generalize the amplitude modulation process. *Each modulating signal component creates an upper and lower side frequency component with an amplitude equal to half the original modulating amplitude. The carrier signal component is not altered by the process.* This is illustrated, with several modulating signals, in Fig. 10–16. The set of upper side frequencies is called the *upper sideband;* the set of lower side frequencies, the *lower sideband.* The process is *not restricted to sinusoidal modulating signals.* This is illustrated, for a sawtooth waveform, in Fig. 10–17. Part A illustrates the actual waveform. Parts B and C illustrate the associated spectrum when the sawtooth is presented in terms of its harmonic components.

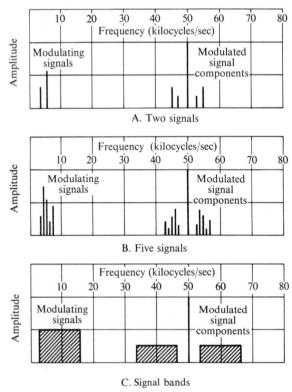

A. Two signals

B. Five signals

C. Signal bands

Figure 10-16.   *Build-Up and Generalization of Amplitude Modulated Signal Spectrum*

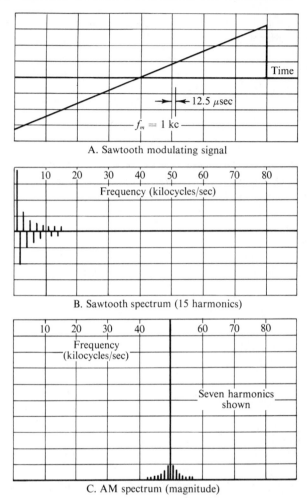

A. Sawtooth modulating signal

B. Sawtooth spectrum (15 harmonics)

C. AM spectrum (magnitude)

Figure 10-17.   *Amplitude Modulation with Sawtooth Waveform*

The process of frequency modulation requires that the carrier frequency *vary about its unmodulated value* by an amount that is *proportional* to the modulating signal amplitude, at a rate equal to the modulating frequency. Since the two quantities are proportional, the multiplication process is indicated—as with the AM technique. The original carrier frequency is present only when the modulating signal amplitude is zero. For all other values of modulating signal amplitude, *new frequencies are created;* some below f_c, some above f_c. In fact, the amount of frequency change, Δf_c, is *directly proportional to the modulating signal amplitude*. The rate of change is controlled by the modulating signal frequency. Hence, the modulating signal has not been lost—it has merely been "coded" onto the carrier frequency characteristics. The carrier signal peak amplitude is *not changed* by the frequency modulation process—it remains constant at $i_{c(P)}$. Obviously, *the FM process must create many more new frequency components then the* AM *process.*

Mathematically, the frequency modulated signal is given by:

$$i_{c(FM)} = i_{c(P)}[\cos 2\pi f_c t \cos(k_{FM} \sin 2\pi f_m t) \tag{10-17}$$
$$- \sin 2\pi f_c t \sin(k_{FM} \sin 2\pi f_m t)]$$

The factor k_{FM} is the *frequency modulation index,* which is a measure of the relationship between the change in carrier frequency and the modulating signal frequency, and is defined by:

$$k_{FM} = \frac{\Delta f_{c(\text{max})}}{f_m} \tag{10-18}$$

The use of several advanced mathematical concepts results in a new form for Eq. (10–17) that is much easier to interpret:

$$i_{c(FM)} = J_0(k_{FM})\cos 2\pi f_c t \tag{10-17a}$$
$$- J_1(k_{FM})[\cos 2\pi(f_c - f_m)t - \cos 2\pi(f_c + f_m)t]$$
$$+ J_2(k_{FM})[\cos 2\pi(f_c - 2f_m)t + \cos 2\pi(f_c + 2f_m)t]$$
$$- J_3(k_{FM})[\cos 2\pi(f_c - 3f_m)t - \cos 2\pi(f_c + 3f_m)t]$$
$$+ J_4(k_{FM})[\cos 2\pi(f_c - 4f_m)t + \cos 2\pi(f_c + 4f_m)t]$$
$$- \cdots + \cdots -$$
$$+ J_n(k_{FM})[\cos 2\pi(f_c - nf_m)t + \cos 2\pi(f_c + nf_m)t]$$
$$- \cdots + \cdots -$$

where $J_n(k_{FM})$ is a special coefficient (known as the Bessel function) with values as listed in Table 10–1. These coefficients determine the magnitude of each component in the frequency modulated signal. The frequency expressions in Eq. (10–17a) indicate that there are an *infinite number of new signal components created,* starting with the carrier frequency, then occurring in equal-magnitude pairs at every modulating-frequency harmonic above and below the carrier frequency. Fortunately, as can be seen in Table 10–1, the $J_n(k_{FM})$-coefficients decrease very rapidly so that only a finite number of frequency components need be considered in actual practice. (As the modulation index increases, more components remain significant.) Figure 10–18 indicates the effect of various modulation index values on the frequency modulated signal spectrum. [Only the component *magnitudes* are indicated. The phase relationships indicated by the algebraic signs in Eq. (10–17a) and Table 10–1 are not considered.] Unlike the AM signal, the carrier component *is altered* in the FM signal because its magnitude is determined by $J_0(k_{FM})$. In fact, $J_0(k_{FM})$ is zero for certain

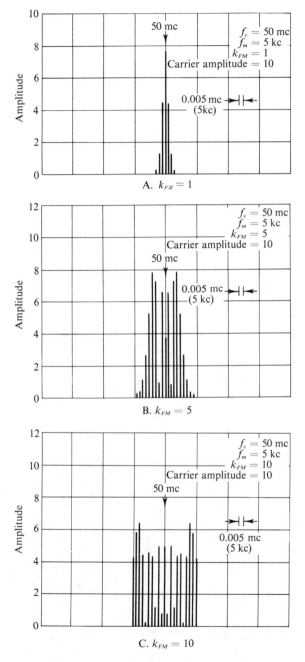

Figure 10-18.   *Effect of Modulating Index on FM Signal Spectrum*

TABLE 10-1

Approximate Bessel-Function Coefficients

k_{FM}	$J_0(k_{FM})$	$J_1(k_{FM})$	$J_2(k_{FM})$	$J_3(k_{FM})$	$J_4(k_{FM})$	$J_5(k_{FM})$	$J_6(k_{FM})$	$J_7(k_{FM})$	$J_8(k_{FM})$	$J_9(k_{FM})$	$J_{10}(k_{FM})$
0	1.00	0.00	0.00	0.00	0.00	0.00	0.00	0.00	0.00	0.00	0.00
1	0.76	0.44	0.15	0.02	0.00	0.00	0.00	0.00	0.00	0.00	0.00
2	0.22	0.58	0.35	0.13	0.03	0.01	0.00	0.00	0.00	0.00	0.00
3	−0.26	0.34	0.49	0.31	0.13	0.04	0.01	0.00	0.00	0.00	0.00
4	−0.40	−0.07	0.36	0.43	0.28	0.13	0.05	0.02	0.00	0.00	0.00
5	−0.18	−0.33	0.05	0.36	0.39	0.26	0.13	0.05	0.02	0.00	0.00
6	0.15	−0.28	−0.24	0.12	0.36	0.36	0.25	0.13	0.06	0.02	0.01
7	0.30	0.00	−0.30	−0.17	0.16	0.35	0.34	0.23	0.13	0.06	0.02
8	0.17	0.24	−0.11	−0.29	−0.10	0.19	0.34	0.32	0.22	0.13	0.06
9	−0.09	0.24	0.14	−0.18	−0.26	−0.06	0.20	0.33	0.31	0.22	0.12
10	−0.25	0.04	0.26	−0.06	−0.22	−0.23	−0.01	0.22	0.32	0.29	0.21

k_{FM}-values (2.405, 5.52, 8.654, 11.79, etc.), so that the carrier component will "dissappear" under these conditions. As with the AM signal, the frequency components above and below the carrier frequency are termed upper- and lower-side frequencies, respectively. Furthermore, the set of upper-side frequencies comprise an upper sideband and the set of lower-side frequencies comprise a lower sideband, also. However, the reader must realize that the two *sidebands* for the FM signal are created by a *single modulating sinewave*—totally unlike the AM signal, which creates only two *side frequencies* for each modulating sinewave. A modulating signal composed of several sinusoidal waves produces two *sets* of side frequencies *for each sinusoidal component* in the frequency modulation process, as shown in Fig. 10–19. A comparison of these spectra with their equivalent AM spectra (Fig. 10–17) will further illustrate the complexity of the FM signal over the AM signal.

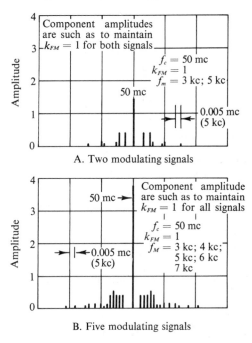

A. Two modulating signals

B. Five modulating signals

Figure 10-19.   *Spread of FM Signal Spectrum with Increasing Number of Modulating Signals*

Example 10-5.   A particular information signal contains sinusoidal components ranging from 20 cycles per second to 20 kilocycles per second. This signal is to be amplitude modulated on a 100-kilocycle per second carrier. The 20-cycle per second modulating signal amplitude is one-tenth the amplitude of the carrier signal and the 20-kilocycle per second modulating signal amplitude is one-half the amplitude of the carrier signal. Draw the composite spectrum for both ends of the modulating band.

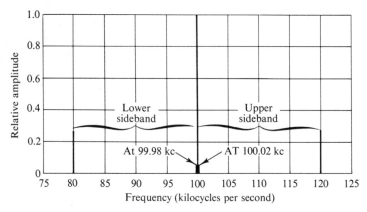

Figure E10-5

Solution. The carrier signal is shown in Fig. E10–5, with a relative amplitude of one. The 20-cycle per second modulating signal produces side frequencies at:

$$f_c + f_m = (100 \times 10^3) + (0.02 \times 10^3) = 100.02 \text{ kc}$$
$$f_c - f_m = (100 \times 10^3) - (0.02 \times 10^3) = 99.98 \text{ kc}$$

Each of these side frequencies has an amplitude of one-half the original modulating signal amplitude, which, when referenced to the carrier amplitude, is:

$$\frac{1}{2} \times \frac{1}{10} = \frac{1}{20}$$

The 20 kilocycle per second modulating signal produces side frequencies at:

$$f_c + f_m = (100 \times 10^3) + (20 \times 10^3) = 120 \text{ kc}$$
$$f_c - f_m = (100 \times 10^3) - (20 \times 10^3) = 80 \text{ kc}$$

Each component has a relative amplitude of:

$$\frac{1}{2} \times \frac{1}{2} = \frac{1}{4}$$

The side frequencies are shown in Fig. E10–5, also. All other modulating components will produce lower- and upper-side frequencies scattered between the two limits shown in the figure.

Amplitude Modulator Circuits

When signals of different frequencies are fed to a linear amplifier, the output consists of a reproduction of the same frequencies unless some of the frequencies lie outside the amplifier bandwidth. Hence, although some frequencies may be lost, *no new frequencies are created* in the linear amplifier. Of course, there is no perfectly linear amplifier. Because of this, new frequencies *are* created, as indicated by the harmonic analysis in Chap. 5. For linear amplification, these harmonics are kept to a minimum. However, the process of amplitude modulation is based on the creation of many new frequency components. For this reason, amplitude modulation circuits are designed to be inherently nonlinear and the AM signal is, in fact, a *controlled nonlinear distortion.*

The volt-ampere characteristic of the junction diode is inherently nonlinear. As described in Chap. 4, this nonlinearity is generally applied in rectifier circuits, taking advantage of the fact that the diode will conduct

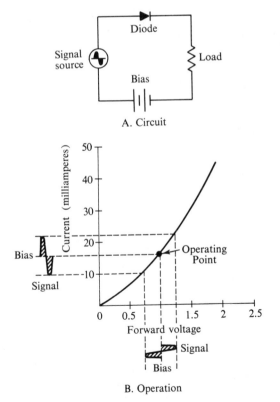

Figure 10-20. *Signal Conduction through Forward Biased Diode*

in only one direction. However, if the diode is forward biased (as in Fig. 10–20, Part A) and a small signal is applied (as in Part B), conduction over the full input cycle is possible. The nonlinear (exponential) shape of the characteristic distorts the signal as shown in Part B and creates a large number of harmonics. A detailed graphical analysis could be performed (as described in Chap. 5) in order to determine the relative values of these distortion components. However, the forward characteristic of the diode is a simple curve and can be described mathematically as a sum of exponential terms:

$$i = Av + Bv^2 + Cv^3 + \cdots + Nv^n \tag{10-19}$$

where i is the current through the diode and v is the voltage across the diode. If a carrier and modulating signal are placed in series with the diode, the first term merely represents the addition of the two signals times a constant, A. Since all terms after the first are raised to an integral power, each of these terms indicates that signal *multiplication* has occurred. The process of multiplication results in amplitude modulation. The second term can be expanded to the exact form indicated by Eq. (10–15a). The higher-order terms in Eq. (10–19) can all be expanded into an even greater number of components. However, these components would be undesirable harmonics (not passed by the amplitude modulator circuitry).

The simple junction diode modulator circuit is shown in Fig. 10–21. The antiresonant circuit is tuned to the carrier frequency, f_c, and has a bandwidth that is designed to pass only the desired AM spectrum. Hence, the lower cutoff frequency must be:

$$f_L = f_c - f_{m(H)} \tag{10-20}$$

where $f_{m(H)}$ is the highest modulating frequency; and the upper cutoff frequency must be:

$$f_H = f_c + f_{m(H)} \tag{10-21}$$

(Antiresonant circuit design is described in Chapter 7.)

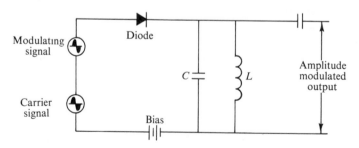

Figure 10-21.   *Diode Amplitude Modulator Circuit*

A primary disadvantage of the diode modulator results from the fact that there is no power gain. In fact, there is always less power out than is put in. Several amplifier stages could be used after the modulator to overcome this. However, modulation and amplification can be made to occur simultaneously within a transistor amplifier, eliminating the need for the additional diode modulator stage. Figure 10–22 illustrates three transistor modulator circuits. Each is distinguished from the other by the branch of the circuit used for coupling the modulating signal into the amplifier. Each achieves modulation by a slightly different phenomenon and each has distinct application criteria. In order to achieve high-efficiency, high-power operation, Class *B* (and, in many instances, Class *C*) operation is used. (This is with respect to the carrier signal. The transistor must conduct during the full modulating cycle in order to avoid distorting this signal.) Class *B* and Class *C* operation are possible with respect to the carrier signal because of the inherent "ringing" nature of the loaded antiresonant circuit. (As described in Chap. 8, although the primary of the antiresonant circuit may be conducting only portions of an input sinewave, the signal induced in the secondary will be sinusoidal because of the energy exchange between the primary inductive and capacitive components.)

Figure 10–23 illustrates the basic principles of collector injection. A separate a-c and d-c load line are shown. As always, the d-c load line establishes the operating point and the a-c load line establishes the limits on the dynamic operation. For this modulator, which is shown in Class *B* operation, the positive halves of the input carrier sinewave must have a peak current equal to the maximum input current that the transistor can handle. This assures that the amplitude of the output current is controlled by the intersection of the a-c load line and the near-vertical portion of the transistor characteristics. In Part A of the figure, no modulating signal is applied. The collector current simply consists of "pulses" clipped off the input carrier signal. In Fig. 10–23, Part B a "positive-going" portion of the modulating signal is shown. This signal, in effect, becomes a part of the supply voltage:

$$v_{oo} = V_{oo} + v_m \tag{10-22}$$

An increase in supply voltage causes the operating point to move to the right, which, in turn, causes the intersection of the a-c load line and the characteristic curves to move upward. This operation causes the output current amplitude to increase. These increases continue until the modulating signal reaches its positive peak. At this point, the operating point begins moving back toward its original position. However, as the modulating signal passes through zero and continues in the negative direction,

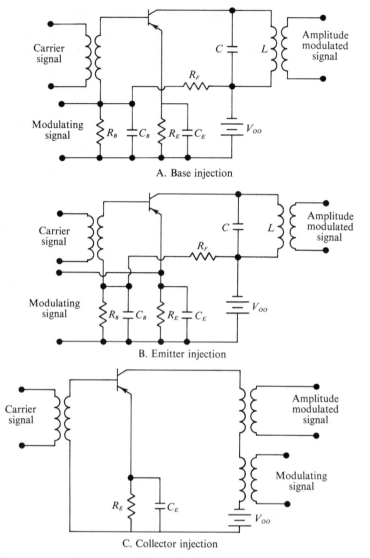

Figure 10-22.   *Three Methods of Achieving Amplitude Modulation within Amplifier Circuits*

the d-c operating point continues moving toward the left. This is shown in Fig. 10–23, Part C. The operating point movement reverses direction again when the modulating signal reaches its maximum negative value. This cyclic movement of the operating point continues in response to the modulating signal throughout its duration. Because of the "ringing" nature of the tuned circuit, the output waveform consists of a complete AM signal variation.

Figure 10–24 illustrates the basic principles of base injection. With no modulating signal, the output current consists of the positive halves of the input carrier signal. The modulating signal adds to the carrier signal:

$$i_B = i_c + i_m \tag{10-23}$$

where the value of i_c (the carrier current, not the collector current) is zero during the negative half of each carrier cycle. This operation causes the peak base and, therefore, the peak output current amplitude to "undulate" at the rate of the modulating signal variation and by an amount proportional to i_m. The complete output waveform is still given by the normal AM signal because of the tank circuit resonance characteristic.

Emitter injection occurs in a manner similar to that described for base injection. In Chap. 5, the current relationships between I_B, I_C, and I_E are described. From this, it can be seen that any variation in one of these current components must produce a similar variation in the other current components. Hence, the emitter injection of the modulating signal current causes an "undulation" similar to that described in the preceding paragraph. The only significant difference is in relative magnitudes.

Base and emitter injection are *low-level*, or low-power, modulator circuits. They are used when the modulating signal values are on the order of microamperes. Collector injection, on the contrary, is a *high-level*, or high-power, modulator circuit. It is used to achieve high-efficiency amplitude modulation. The use of collector injection, then, requires that considerable amplification of the modulating signal be performed *prior to the modulator stage*. This has the additional advantage associated with designing and operating lower-frequency amplifier stages. With base and emitter injection, the majority of the amplification must occur *after the modulator stage*. Any stages following the modulator stage have to work with the AM signal and must, therefore, be high-frequency amplifiers, tuned to the carrier frequency and having a bandwidth as specified by Eqs. (10–20) and (10–21). Such amplifiers are more difficult to design and, because the frequencies are so much higher, have a tendency toward instability.

Amplitude modulation can also be performed directly within the carrier frequency oscillator circuit. Such an arrangement is for very low-level applications. Any subsequent amplification must be performed on the AM signal at higher frequencies with the same tendency toward instability that has been described.

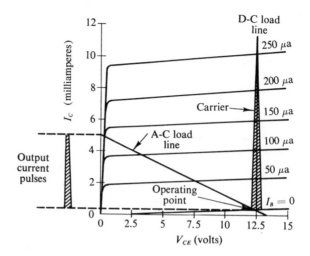

A. No modulating signal

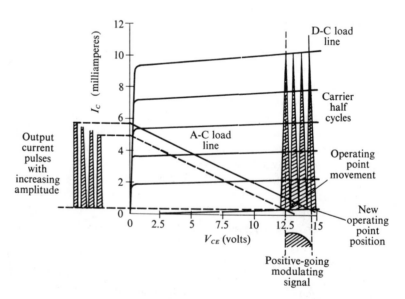

B. Positive-going modulating signal

Figure 10-23.   *Amplitude Modulation with Collector Injection*

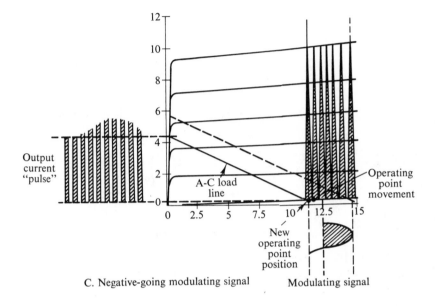

C. Negative-going modulating signal

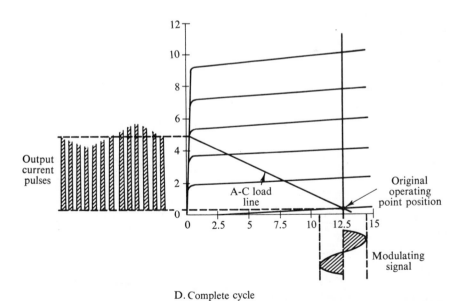

D. Complete cycle

Fig. 10-23.   (*continued*)

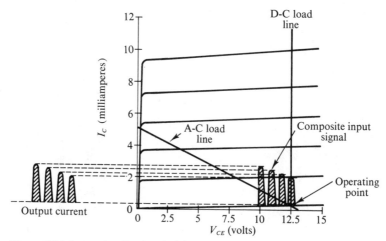

Figure 10-24.   *Amplitude Modulation with Base Injection*

Example 10-6.   Transistor A in Appendix D is to be used in an amplitude modulator with collector injection (Fig. 10–22). A ten-volt supply is used and the modulator is operated Class B with respect to the carrier signal. The modulator is coupled to a device with an equivalent resistance of 100 ohms. Determine the best turns ratio for the transformer.

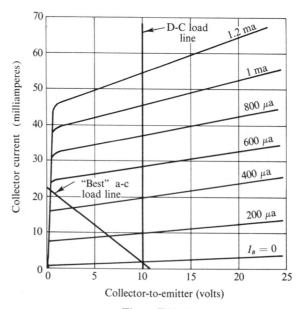

Figure E10-6

Solution. As shown in Fig. 10–23, the best steady-state (no modulating signal) position for the a-c load line is one that intersects the middle of the near-vertical portion of the characteristic curves. This permits maximum excursion of the load line (maximum amplitude variation in the modulating signal) without distorting the AM signal. The appropriate d-c and a-c load lines are presented in Fig. E10–6. The a-c load is:

$$R_{L(a-c)} = \frac{V_{oo}}{I_{int}} = \frac{10}{22 \times 10^{-3}} = 455 \text{ ohms}$$

This requires a turns ratio of:

$$\frac{N_1}{N_2} = \sqrt{\frac{R_{L(a-c)}}{R_D}} = \sqrt{\frac{455}{100}} = 2.14:1$$

Frequency Modulator Circuits

Since frequency modulation requires the creation of many new frequency components, this process must also make use of controlled nonlinear distortion—just as the AM process does. However, the nonlinear distortions that produce FM signals are *frequency sensitive*. The primary frequency-sensitive characteristics of a transistor amplifier include its response (voltage, current, and power gains) and the inherent junction capacitance. The latter "component," associated with both transistor junctions and diode junctions (Chaps. 4 and 5), is commonly used in frequency modulators. This method of achieving FM is termed *reactance modulation*.

Figure 10–25 illustrates a typical reactance modulator, in conjunction with a carrier frequency oscillator. The oscillator is of the Hartley type (see Fig. 10–5) and is designed to produce the desired carrier frequency by the proper selection of inductance and capacitance [Eq. (10–30)]. The transistor and the inductive components must also be selected to satisfy the Barkhausen criterion [Eq. (10–6)]. The output junction capacitance of the reactance modulator (a CE amplifier, fed by the modulating signal) is in parallel with the antiresonant circuit capacitance. Hence, the actual oscillator frequency is given by:

$$f = \frac{1}{2\pi\sqrt{(L_1 + L_2)(C + C_{CE})}} \tag{10-24}$$

Figure 10–26 presents a typical junction capacitance characteristic for a reverse biased junction. With no modulating signal applied, the steady-state capacitance, $C_{CE(0)}$, is "seen" by the antiresonant circuit. For this reason, in order to achieve the desired steady-state carrier frequency, C

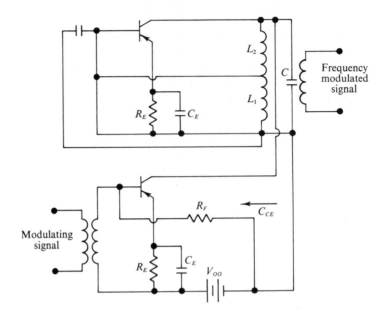

Figure 10-25.   *Reactance Modulator*

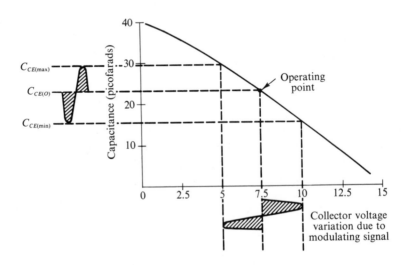

Figure 10-26.   *Sensitivity of Output Junction Capacitance to Modulating Signal*

must be slightly smaller than the value derived directly from Eq. (10–3a). However, such small differences are involved that, in a practical circuit, C is variable. It is adjusted to achieve the proper f_c-value (with no modulating signal present) and is then "locked" in this position. The reactance modulator must operate Class A and, as a rule, the operating point is placed in the center of the linear portion of the junction capacitance characteristic. This assures a uniform frequency variation above and below f_c. It also establishes a maximum value for the peak modulating signal amplitude, as shown in the figure. The variation in C_{CE} is also shown. From Eq. (10–24) it can be seen that increases in C_{CE} above $C_{CE(0)}$ cause a reduction in the oscillator frequency; while decreases in C_{CE} below $C_{CE(0)}$ cause an increase in the oscillator frequency. The maximum frequency change [useful in defining the frequency modulation index in Eq. (10–18)] is given by:

$$\Delta f_{c(\max)} = \frac{1}{2\pi\sqrt{(L_1 + L_2)(C + C_{CE(\min)})}} - f_c \qquad \textbf{(10-25a)}$$

or:

$$\Delta f_{c(\max)} = f_c - \frac{1}{2\pi\sqrt{(L_1 + L_2)(C + C_{CE(\max)})}} \qquad \textbf{(10-25b)}$$

In view of this, it should be apparent that larger-amplitude signals result in a greater frequency excursion, while higher-frequency signals cause a more rapid excursion. Smaller amplitudes and lower frequencies produce the opposite variations in the FM signal.

When the frequency change obtained from C_{CE} is not large enough, the transistor junction capacitance can be supplemented by placing a variable capacitance diode directly across the output terminals of the reactance modulator. These devices are junction diodes (Chap. 4) designed in such a way that the variation in capacitance is extremely sensitive to junction voltage. Equations (10–24) and (10–25) may be used for this arrangement if the C_{CE}-values are replaced by:

$$C' = C_{CE} + C_d \qquad \textbf{(10-26)}$$

where C_d is the diode capacitance. There is a steady-state value, $C_{d(0)}$, and maximum and minimum values, $C_{d(\max)}$ and $C_{d(\min)}$, that must be obtained directly from the diode characteristic.

The transistor in the oscillator circuit also has an output junction capacitance. However, since the oscillator waveform varies at a much higher rate than the modulating signal, the associated frequency components will lie outside the antiresonant circuit bandwidth and need not be considered. This bandwidth must be fixed in accordance with the FM spectrum (Fig. 10–19 and associated text) that is being generated.

The FM signal produced by the circuit in Fig. 10–25 has very little power, as is true of most signals coupled from a high-frequency oscillator. Because of this, several high-frequency amplifier stages must be used in cascade with the frequency modulator. Antiresonant circuits are used almost exclusively at such high frequencies. In order to achieve the necessary bandwidth, stagger tuning (Chap. 7) is frequently used. High-frequency power amplifiers (Chap. 8) may also be used, in stagger-tuned fashion. The resulting frequency modulator is shown in block diagram form in Fig. 10–27.

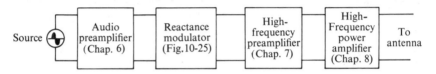

Figure 10-27.   *Block Diagram of Complete Frequency Modulation System*

Example 10-7.   The Hartley oscillator in Example 10–3 is to be used as part of a reactance modulator (Fig. 10–25). The maximum C_{CE}-value is 5 picofarads and the minimum C_{CE}-value is 1 picofarad. The variation is linear over this range. With no modulating signal, the value of C_{CE} is 3 picofarads. Determine the value of C that must be used in the circuit if the carrier frequency is to be 5 megacycles per second. Determine the maximum frequency deviation that can occur.

Solution.   The oscillator frequency is given by:

$$f = \frac{1}{2\pi\sqrt{(L_1 + L_2)(C + C_{CE(0)})}}$$

Rearranging for C:

$$C = \frac{1}{(2\pi)^2(L_1 + L_2)f^2} - C_{CE(0)}$$

$$= \frac{1}{4\pi^2(30.01 \times 10^{-6})(5 \times 10^6)^2} - (3 \times 10^{-12})$$

$$= \frac{1}{2.96 \times 10^{10}} - (3 \times 10^{-12})$$

$$= (33.8 \times 10^{-12}) - (3 \times 10^{-12}) = 30.8 \text{ picofarads}$$

The maximum frequency deviation will be:

$$\Delta f_{c(\text{max})} = \frac{1}{2\pi\sqrt{(L_1 + L_2)(C + C_{CE(\text{min})})}} - f_c$$

$$= \frac{1}{2\pi\sqrt{(30.01 \times 10^{-6})(30.8 + 1)(10^{-12})}} - (5 \times 10^6)$$

$$= \frac{1}{19.4 \times 10^{-8}} - (5 \times 10^6)$$

$$= (5.16 \times 10^6) - (5 \times 10^6) = 160 \text{ kc}$$

Example 10-8.   The maximum C_{CE}-value in Example 10–7 occurs when V_{CE} is 30 volts and the minimum C_{CE}-value occurs when V_{CE} is 10 volts. The stage voltage gain is -50. What is the peak modulating voltage amplitude that can be applied to the stage?

Solution.   Since operation is linear over the range between $C_{CE(\text{max})}$ and $C_{CE(\text{min})}$ (from Example 10–7) the peak-to-peak output voltage ($30 - 10$, or 20 volts) must be undistorted, centered about a value of 20 volts with a peak value of 10 volts. Since:

$$v_{\text{out(peak)}} = A_v v_{\text{in(peak)}}$$

the peak input voltage is limited to:

$$v_{\text{in(peak)}} = \frac{v_{\text{out(peak)}}}{A_v} = \frac{10}{50} = 0.2 \text{ volt}$$

This peak voltage causes the carrier frequency to deviate by the full amount ($\Delta f_{c(\text{max})}$) of 160 kilocycles per second, indicated in Example 10–7.

Example 10-9.   A particular information signal containing sinusoidal components ranging from 2 to 20 kilocycles per second is applied to the reactance tube modulator described in Examples 10–7 and 10–8. The peak carrier signal amplitude is 10 millivolts. Draw the composite spectrum for both ends of the modulating band if the 20-kilocycle per second signal has a peak amplitude of 0.1 volt and the 2-kilocycle per second signal has a peak amplitude of 0.025 volt.

Solution.   From Example 10–8, a peak voltage of 0.2 volt will produce a frequency deviation of 160 kilocycles per second. Hence, the 20-kilocycle per second signal will produce a frequency deviation of 80 kilocycles per second, since its peak amplitude is one-half of 0.2 volt. The 2-kilocycle per second signal will produce a frequency deviation of 20 kilocycles per second, since its peak amplitude is one-eighth of 0.2 volt. The FM spectrum depends on the frequency modulation index, defined by:

$$k_{FM} = \frac{\Delta f_c}{f_m}$$

For the 20-kilocycle per second signal:

$$k_{FM} = \frac{80 \times 10^3}{20 \times 10^3} = 4$$

For the 2-kilocycle per second signal:

$$k_{FM} = \frac{20 \times 10^3}{2 \times 10^3} = 10$$

The following relative amplitude data are obtained from Table 10–1:

Frequency Component	20 kc (0.02 mc)		2 kc (0.002 mc)	
	Frequency (mc)	Relative Amplitude	Frequency (mc)	Relative Amplitude
f_c	5	0.40	5	0.25
$f_c \pm f_m$	4.98;5.02	0.07	4.998;5.002	0.05
$f_c \pm 2f_m$	4.96;5.04	0.36	4.996;5.004	0.26
$f_c \pm 3f_m$	4.94;5.06	0.43	4.994;5.006	0.06
$f_c \pm 4f_m$	4.92;5.08	0.28	4.992;5.008	0.22
$f_c \pm 5f_m$	4.90;5.10	0.13	4.990;5.010	0.23
$f_c \pm 6f_m$	4.88;5.12	0.05	4.988;5.012	0.02
$f_c \pm 7f_m$	4.86;5.14	0.02	4.986;5.014	0.22
$f_c \pm 8f_m$	—	—	4.984;5.016	0.32
$f_c \pm 9f_m$	—	—	4.982;5.018	0.29
$f_c \pm 10f_m$	—	—	4.980;5.020	0.21
$f_c \pm 11f_m$	—	—	4.978;5.022	0.12
$f_c \pm 12f_m$	—	—	4.976;5.024	0.06
$f_c \pm 13f_m$	—	—	4.974;5.026	0.03
$f_c \pm 14f_m$	—	—	4.972;5.028	0.01

The amplitudes of the like-frequency components from both spectra must be combined (Appendix C) by:

$$C_n = \sqrt{A_n^2 + B_n^2}$$

This occurs at 5 mc, 4.98 mc, and 5.02 mc. Since the relative values in the table are referenced to the carrier amplitude, all individual components must be multiplied by 10 millivolts to obtain the actual peak amplitudes. At 5 mc the composite amplitude is:

$$C_n = \sqrt{(4 \times 10^{-3})^2 + (2.5 \times 10^{-3})^2} = \sqrt{22.25 \times 10^{-6}}$$
$$= 4.71 \text{ millivolts}$$

At 4.98 mc and 5.02 mc, the amplitude is:

$$C_n = \sqrt{(0.7 \times 10^{-3})^2 + (2.1 \times 10^{-3})^2} = \sqrt{4.9 \times 10^{-6}}$$
$$= 2.22 \text{ millivolts}$$

The complete FM spectrum for the two modulating components is presented in Fig. E10-9.

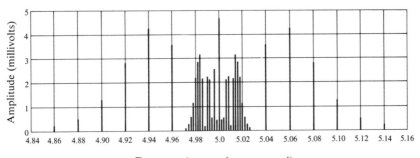

Figure E10-9

10.3 "Mixer" and "Converter" Circuits

As described previously, high (radio) frequencies are used as carrier frequencies in order to facilitate transmission to remote points. The received signals have generally been attenuated severely, so that only fractions of a microvolt are available at the input to the receiving system. Amplification of these signals would require several high-frequency stages. Because of the stability problems associated with high-frequency amplifiers, such arrangements are avoided whenever possible. The technique most often used in receiver systems consists of "stepping down" the frequency, while introducing as little distortion as possible into the AM or FM signals. Hence, the resulting signal is (ideally) an exact reproduction of the original signal amplitude or frequency *variations*, but centered about a frequency that is *much lower* than the carrier frequency.

The creation of sum and difference frequencies, as described for the amplitude modulation process, forms the basic method for achieving new frequencies. The radio-frequency AM (or FM) signal is multiplied with a constant-amplitude, *local oscillator frequency*, producing two new frequencies:

$$f_1 = f_{LO} + f_{RF} \tag{10-27}$$
$$f_2 = f_{LO} - f_{RF} \tag{10-28}$$

where f_{LO} is the local oscillator frequency (higher than the incoming radio frequency). The amplifier circuitry is tuned to reject the sum frequency, f_1—passing only the difference frequency, f_2, or *intermediate frequency*, as it is called. This is illustrated in Fig. 10–28. Standard intermediate fre-

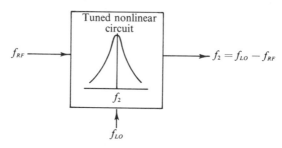

Figure 10-28.   *Creation of the "Intermediate" Frequency*

quencies have been established (455 kilocycles per second for AM receivers and 10.7 megacycles per second for FM receivers) although there are exceptions to these standards. (FM carrier frequencies, and all associated frequencies, are much higher than AM frequencies, in order to accomodate the wider bandwidth requirements associated with FM signals.) For the greatest amount of flexibility, the local oscillator frequency is tuned in unison with the receiver frequency tuning. This permits the generation of a fixed intermediate frequency across the entire receiver band, regardless of the carrier frequency being received. Because of this, all circuitry following the initial receiver stages can be designed around the single, lower intermediate frequency. Since Eqs. (10–27) and (10–28) apply to *all frequency components in the received signal*, a complete spectrum of sum and difference frequencies is produced—distributed about the intermediate carrier frequency.

Two basic methods are available for creating the intermediate frequency. The first method, illustrated in Fig. 10–29, is termed *mixing*, and uses a separate local oscillator stage and "mixing" stage. The second method, illustrated in Fig. 10–30, is termed *frequency conversion*, and accomplishes the functions of local oscillation and mixing in a single stage. In the mixer arrangement, the local oscillator signal may be inserted in the emitter, base, or collector branches (as in the amplitude modulator) of the mixer stage. Generally speaking, emitter or base injection is used, unless a high-power local oscillator signal is available.

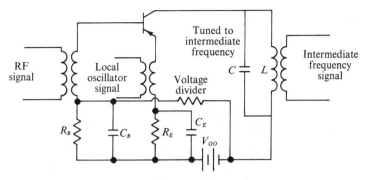

Figure 10-29.   *Mixer Stage (Emitter Injection)*

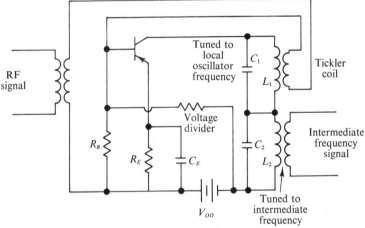

Figure 10-30.   *Converter Stage*

Example 10-10.   The amplitude modulated signal in Example 10–5 is mixed with a local oscillator frequency of 140 kc. Determine and plot the component frequencies in the intermediate frequency spectrum.

Solution.   From Example 10–5, the original frequency components are:

$$f_c = 100 \text{ kc}$$
$$f_c + f_{m(L)} = 100.02 \text{ kc}$$
$$f_c - f_{m(L)} = 99.98 \text{ kc}$$
$$f_c + f_{m(H)} = 120 \text{ kc}$$
$$f_c - f_{m(H)} = 80 \text{ kc}$$

The intermediate frequencies are given by:

$$f = f_{LO} - f_{RF}$$

leading to a spectrum of:

$$f_c = 40 \text{ kc}$$
$$f_c + f_{m(L)} = 39.98 \text{ kc}$$
$$f_c - f_{m(L)} = 40.02 \text{ kc}$$
$$f_c + f_{m(H)} = 20 \text{ kc}$$
$$f_c - f_{m(H)} = 60 \text{ kc}$$

These components are plotted in Fig. E10–10 and can be compared to those in Fig. E10–5.

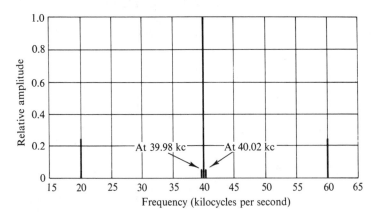

Figure E10-10

10.4 Demodulator Circuits

In order to recover the original modulating signal information (music, speech, etc.), the process of demodulation must be accomplished. Demodulator circuitry consists, essentially, of a half- or full-wave rectifier, in combination with a filtering network that passes only the modulating frequency components (Fig. 10–31). Because of the symmetrical nature of AM and FM signals, a rectified version of the signal contains the same information (modulating signal amplitude and frequency) as the full cyclic variation. This is illustrated in Fig. 10–32.

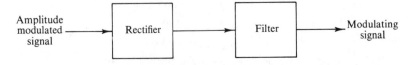

Figure 10-31.   *Amplitude Demodulator Block Diagram*

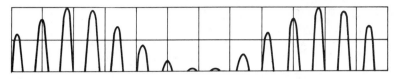

Figure 10-32.   *Rectified* AM *Signal* ($k_{AM} = 1$)

Amplitude Demodulation

Two basic amplitude demodulator circuits are shown in Fig. 10–33. In the RC demodulator (or *detector*), the diode serves as a half-wave rectifier and the RC combination serves as a filter (the shunt-capacitor arrangement described in Fig. 4–46 and the associated text). The design relationships are quite similar to those described in Chap. 4. However,

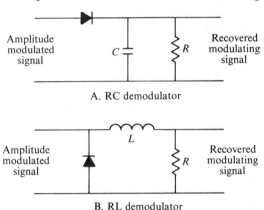

Figure 10-33.   *Amplitude Demodulator Circuits*

the design frequency is f_c (the AM carrier frequency), or the intermediate carrier frequency, as appropriate. With such a design, the capacitor will not discharge appreciably between each of the high-frequency half cycles. However, the output signal variation will track (very closely) the *peaks* of the high-frequency signal, as shown in Fig. 10–34. Since the variation in these peaks represents the original modulating signal, *the desired information is recovered.* The RL demodulator is similar to the inductive rectifier circuit described in Chap. 4. However, for the detector circuit, the diode is placed in shunt with the RL combination. Again, as with the RC detector, with appropriate component values, only the high-frequency peaks will be tracked, resulting in the recovery of the original information.

Transistor stages may also be used as amplitude demodulators. One junction serves as a rectifier (Class *B* operation with respect to the high-frequency signal), with the RC-filter combination built into an appropriate

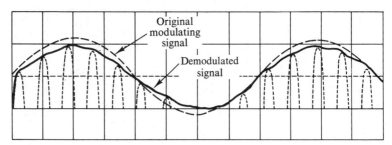

Figure 10-34.   *Recovery of Modulating Signal (Peak-Amplitude "Track-ing")*

branch (emitter, base, or collector) of the circuit. Such an arrangement serves to amplify the recovered signal, also. A typical arrangement is shown in Fig. 10–35. Rectification takes place at the emitter-to-base junction. R and C form the shunt-capacitor filter, permitting only the modulating frequency components to appear across R. Since the variation across R controls the input current to the transistor (as an amplifier), the predominant output signal is an amplified version of the modulating signal components. Some high-frequency component amplification also occurs. However, these components are bypassed around the amplifier load. In essence, the presence of the capacitors in Fig. 10–35 causes the amplifier to have a bandwidth that will pass only the modulating signal frequencies.

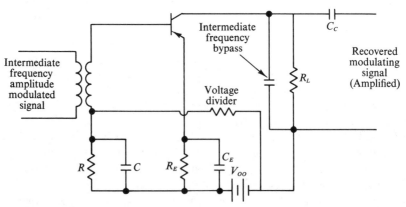

Figure 10-35.   *Transistor Amplitude Demodulator (CE Configuration)*

Frequency Demodulation

A basic, although indirect, method of obtaining frequency demodulation consists of converting the frequency variations into amplitude

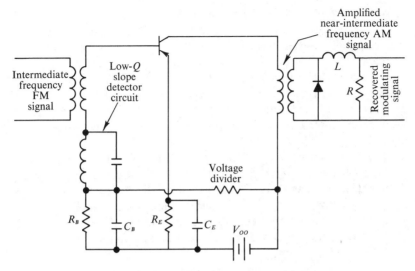

Figure 10-36.   *Slope Detector Frequency Demodulator*

variations (FM signal to an AM signal), rectifying the AM signal, and performing amplitude demodulation as described in the previous section. This technique is termed *slope detection* and is accomplished by a circuit such as the one illustrated in Fig. 10–36. The antiresonant circuit in the input loop is tuned slightly off the intermediate carrier frequency, as shown in Fig. 10–37. This circuit forms a *frequency-sensitive biasing impedance*. When only the intermediate carrier frequency is present, the steady-state bias current flows in the input (and, consequently, in the output) loop. Frequencies below the intermediate carrier frequency tend to reduce the impedance, resulting in more current flow in the amplifier. Frequencies

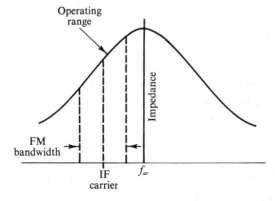

Figure 10-37.   *Tuning and Sensitivity of Slope Detector Circuit*

above the intermediate carrier frequency tend to increase the impedance, resulting in less current flow in the amplifier. Hence, the signal reproduced in the amplifier output has a frequency that is equal to the antiresonant frequency of the tuned circuit in the input loop (slightly different from the intermediate carrier frequency), but has a *peak amplitude variation* that represents the original modulating signal. The modulating signal components are recovered (and the high-frequency components rejected) by the amplitude demodulator, which serves as a part of the input loop to the next stage.

The direct conversion of frequency variations into the original modulating signal can be obtained with the *discriminator* circuit shown in Fig. 10–38. This circuit is a rectifier-filter combination placed in the output loop of the last intermediate frequency amplifier stage. Parallel half-wave rectification is used. The discriminator is *phase sensitive*, with the phase relationship dependent upon the incoming frequency.

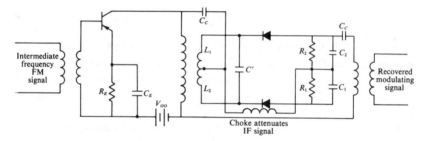

Figure 10-38. *Frequency Discriminator*

The two discriminator loops are *balanced;* that is, the input to the discriminator portion is a center-tapped transformer secondary, R_1 and R_2 are equal, C_1 and C_2 are equal, and the two junction diodes are as nearly matched as is possible. The choke in the circuit acts as an open circuit to the intermediate range of frequencies, developing a *reference voltage* for the two discriminator loads. C' and the individual halves of the secondary winding are *resonant* at the intermediate carrier frequency. In view of this, the discriminator actually consists of two parallel series-resonant branches, tuned to the intermediate carrier frequency—operating as a half-wave rectifier with RC filtering.

The series resonant portion of the circuit controls the phase of the secondary current, making the device sensitive to frequency variations. At resonance, the impedance of the circuit is zero and the current and voltage are in phase. For frequencies below the resonant frequency, the impedance is capacitive and the current leads the voltage by an increasing

angle as frequency decreases. Above the resonant frequency, the impedance is inductive in nature and the current lags the voltage by an increasing angle as frequency decreases. The voltage across the inductive portion
of the circuit must *always lead the circuit current by* 90°.

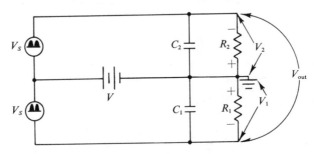

Figure 10-39.   *Electrical Equivalent for Discriminator Loops*

An equivalent circuit for the discriminator is presented in Fig. 10–39.
It must be remembered, however, that the generators labeled V_S are very
unique: they supply a current of variable phase and a voltage which always
leads this current by 90°. From this, it can be seen that V_1 is always determined by the *vector sum* of V and V_S, while V_2 is always determined by the
vector difference of V and V_S, where V is the reference voltage across the
choke. The filter networks smooth the intermediate frequency half-wave
pulses so that V_1 and V_2 become fairly constant d-c values when only a
single-frequency signal is applied. Since V_1 and V_2 are of opposite polarity,
V_{out} will be equal to the difference in their magnitudes. As shown in
Fig. 10–40, Part A at resonance (when the intermediate carrier frequency
is applied), V_{out} is zero. When the signal frequency is below the resonant
frequency, the output voltage is a *positive* d-c *voltage with a magnitude that
is proportional to the frequency deviation below resonance.* This is shown
in Part B of the figure. When the input frequency is above the resonant
frequency, the output voltage is a *negative* d-c *voltage with a magnitude that
is proportional to the frequency deviation above resonance.* This is shown in
Part C.

Although the discriminator operation is simply analyzed in terms of
single-frequency input signals and the associated d-c output voltage (as in
the preceding paragraph), in reality, the FM signal is continuously varying
in frequency. Hence, V_{out} is not a d-c voltage—it is a constantly fluctuating
voltage with amplitude variations following the input frequency variations.
Since the input frequency variations follow the original modulating
signal *amplitude variations,* V_{out} is similar to the original modulating
signal.

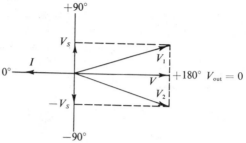

A. Resonance

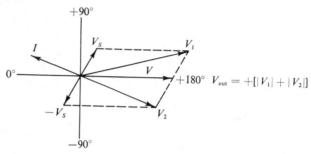

B. Below resonance

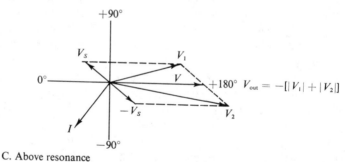

C. Above resonance

Figure 10-40.   *Vector Relationships for Discriminator Circuit*

PROBLEMS

1. Transistor A in Appendix D is used in an oscillator circuit. An operating point is established at V_{CE} equal to 12 volts, I_B equal to 400 microamperes, and I_C equal to 20 milliamperes. The oscillator output is transformer coupled to a device with an equivalent resistance of 1K. If a peak output current of 18 milliamperes is to be obtained from the transistor, what must be the transformer turns ratio?

2. Transistor E in Appendix D is used in an oscillator circuit. A 25-volt supply is used in the output loop. A shunt feedback resistance of 12.5K is used. The d-c resistance is 5 ohms and the oscillator is RC coupled to a device with an equivalent resistance of 2K. Determine the peak output current from the transistor.

3. An amplifier with a power gain of 50 decibels is to be converted into an oscillator. How much positive feedback much be used to exactly satisfy the Barkhausen criterion and obtain sustained oscillations?

4. A Hartley oscillator with a frequency of 5 megacycles per second is desired. The transistor with parameters listed in Table 6–5 is to be used. L_2 is to be 50 microhenries. Determine a suitable value for L_1 and for C.

5. The oscillator described in Problem 4 is to be developed with a Colpitts circuit. L is to be 50 microhenries. Determine a suitable value for C_1 and C_2.

6. A transistor with the h-parameters listed in Table 6–5 is to be used in a Clapp oscillator. The inductance is 100 millihenries. C_1 is to be 50 microfarads. Determine the necessary value for C_2 if sustained oscillations are to be achieved. Determine the range over which C_3 must vary if the oscillator is to be tunable from 5 to 40 megacycles per second.

7. A particular phase-shift oscillator uses a transistor with an h_{fE} of 60. A three-stage ladder is used with R equal to 2K. What is the R_L-value necessary to achieve sustained oscillations? What capacitance must be used in each branch in order to obtain oscillations at 5 kilocycles per second?

8. A particular phase-shift oscillator has an R_L-value of 1800 ohms and an R-value of 800 ohms. What is the minimum value of h_{fE} necessary to obtained sustained oscillations?

9. Determine the upper and lower cutoff frequencies for an amplifier that is to be used in amplifying an AM signal. The carrier frequency is 500 kilocycles per second and is fed by a 5-kilocycle per second sawtooth waveform. Nine of the sawtooth components must be passed by the amplifier to produce the low degree of distortion required for this application.

10. The carrier peak amplitude in Problem 9 is 10 milliamperes and the peak current for the sawtooth is 5 milliamperes. Plot the AM spectrum for the nine sawtooth components.

11. Transistor B in Appendix D is to be used in an amplitude modulator with collector injection. A 6-volt supply is used and the modulator is operated Class B with respect to the carrier signal. A transformer with a 3:1 turns ratio is used. The modulator is to feed a device with

an equivalent resistance of 6 ohms. Determine the maximum peak modulating voltage that can be used.

12. Transistor B in Appendix D is to be used in an amplitude modulator with base injection. A 9-volt supply is used and the modulator is operated Class B with respect to the carrier. The carrier amplitude is 10 microamperes. The transformer coupled circuit has a 2:1 turns ratio and feeds a device with an equivalent resistance of 1K. Determine the peak modulating current that can be applied.

13. A maximum frequency deviation of 200 kilocycles per second is associated with a particular reactance modulator. Determine the frequency modulation index for a 20-kilocycle modulating signal whose amplitude produces one-fourth the maximum frequency deviation. Repeat for a 5-kilocycle per second modulating signal whose frequency deviation is one-tenth the maximum value. Plot the spectrum for each of these signals.

14. The output capacitance of the amplifier stage in a reactance modulator varies linearly over a total range of 10 picofarads when the peak-to-peak collector-to-emitter voltage is 10 volts. The carrier frequency is 20 megacycles per second. The total inductance ($L_1 + L_2$) in the oscillator is 100 microhenries. Determine the frequency modulation index for a 2-kilocycle per second, 5-volt peak collector-to-emitter voltage. Repeat for a 10-kilocycle per second, 2-volt peak collector-to-emitter voltage.

Further Reading

"Basic Theory and Applications of Transistors," TM11–690. Washington, D. C.: U.S. Government Printing Office, 1959.

Martin, T. L., Jr., *Electronic Circuits*. Englewood Cliffs, N.J.: Prentice-Hall, Inc., 1955.

Ryder, John D., *Electronic Fundamentals and Applications*. Englewood Cliffs, N.J.: Prentice-Hall, Inc., 1959.

Schwartz, M., *Information Transmission, Modulation, and Noise*. New York: McGraw-Hill Book Co., Inc., 1959.

Seidman, A. H. and S. L. Marshall, *Semiconductor Fundamentals*. New York: John Wiley and Sons, Inc., 1963.

Surina, T. and C. Herrick, *Semiconductor Electronics*. New York: Holt, Rinehart, and Winston, Inc., 1964.

11

Other
Semiconductor Devices

In the preceding chapters emphasis has been placed on developing and applying the characteristics of the first and most basic of semiconductor devices, the junction diode and the transistor. A considerable amount of material is also presented on the analysis of these devices in basic circuits for amplification, oscillation, modulation, and rectification. A special category of applications, known as *switching circuits*, has not been considered. This subject is treated in many separate texts devoted entirely to these applications. Likewise, there are many semiconductor devices other than the junction diode and transistor that have not been treated. New devices are discovered and applied almost faster than textbooks can be written. However, most of these devices take advantage of the same microscopic phenomena that have been emphasized for semiconductor materials and for P-N junctions. It is hoped that the reader might extend these ideas to new devices as they are encountered.

Initial limitations in the field of semiconductor applications included upper cutoff frequencies and maximum dissipation powers far below those of vacuum tube circuitry. Solutions have been achieved, often by accident;

occasionally by deliberate design. A direct outgrowth of junction diodes is the *tunnel diode*, a device used as an extremely high-frequency amplifier and oscillator, *but not as a rectifier*. Much of the advancement in transistor devices has come about through the development of better fabrication techniques. *Thin-film* deposits of materials, no thicker than several molecules, have lead to the development of miniaturized components far beyond the imagination of the originators of the semiconductor revolution. Such techniques have led to the practical development of *field-effect transistors*, three-junction PNPN devices, and *integrated circuits*. The latter development provides the capability for placing entire amplifier cascades, transmitters, and receivers on a single *chip* of material. Etched into, and deposited upon, this material are transistors, diodes, resistors, capacitors, and inductors—connected into complete electronic networks.

This chapter is devoted to a brief discussion of the operating phenomena, operating characteristics, and predominant applications of the tunnel diode and the field-effect transistor.

11.1 Tunnel Diodes

Conventional junction diode operation is described in Chap. 4. As noted there, the conventional diode serves as a convenient rectifying device (supporting a large forward current and a very small reverse current) and as a voltage reference device (when reverse biased to the Zener voltage value). When the N- and P-type materials in a junction diode are very heavily doped with impurities (concentrations on the order of 10^{-3} to 10^{-2}), a diode with an entirely different volt-ampere characteristic may be obtained if the depletion region is narrow enough. The characteristic displays a *negative resistance region*. That is, over a particular range of voltage and current values, *increases in bias voltage cause decreases in current*. Furthermore, the unilateral chatacteristic of the diode is destroyed; rectification can no longer be achieved. This change in operating characteristic results from an entirely new current mechanism, akin to the diffusion current phenomenon, called the *tunneling effect*.

Tunnel diodes can be used to achieve signal amplification, and can also be operated as an oscillator. The primary disadvantage of the device lies in the fact that voltages are restricted to values less than one volt. Hence, tunnel diodes are restricted to extremely small-signal applications. However, since their cutoff frequencies are extremely high (several hundred megacycles) even with such a disadvantageous signal amplitude range, the devices find considerable application.

The Tunneling Effect

The inherent diffusion current across a conventional P-N junction when it is formed is described by Fig. 4–16 and the associated text. This flow creates a depletion region in the vicinity of the junction (Fig. 4–17 and associated text), resulting in a junction potential (Fig. 4–18 and associated text). This junction potential represents an electrostatic barrier, maintaining a state of equilibrium as long as no external bias voltages are applied. Majority carriers cannot cross the barrier because they do not have enough thermal energy to overcome the potential difference that exists. However, electrons in the N-type material *do* continue to migrate toward the junction. As they attempt to cross the barrier, they lose energy and eventually become absorbed by one of the ions in the depletion region.

This is shown in Fig. 11–1. Each electron absorption releases a photon of electromagnetic energy. These photons are propagated in all directions (randomly) and eventually cause the thermal activation of other electrons (maintaining the proper number of electrons for the equilibrium condition).

The extremely high concentration of impurities in the semiconductor materials used for tunnel diodes assures that enough electrons are present in the N-type material to cause an almost continuous "bombardment" of the depletion region. Hence, a large number of photons are propagated through the material. Furthermore, the structure of the tunnel diode is such that the depletion region is very thin (on the order of 10^{-8} meter); much thinner than that of the conventional diode. Because of this, the photons propagated in the direction of the junction *cross the junction* before they cause the thermal activation of other electrons (Fig. 11–2). In effect, *a new current flow occurs across the junction* even though electrons in the N material do not physically cross into the P material. This indirect current mechanism is known as the *tunnel effect.*

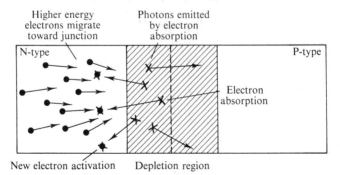

Higher energy electrons migrate toward junction

Photons emitted by electron absorption

N-type

P-type

Electron absorption

New electron activation   Depletion region

Figure 11-1.   *Energy Emission in the* P-N *Junction*

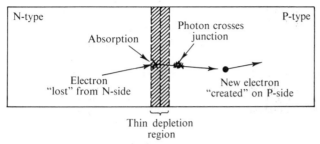

Thin depletion
region

Figure 11-2.   *The Tunnel Effect*

Two conditions have been specified in order to achieve the tunnel effect: an extremely high concentration of electrons, and a very thin depletion region. The first condition is required because of the inefficiency of the process. That is, since the photons created on the N-side of the junction propagate in a random fashion, only a small percentage of the total will travel toward the P material. Hence, there must be a large number of photons if the tunnel current is to reach an appreciable value. The second condition is essential so that the photons will enter the P material before they are absorbed. Any photon absorption (and associated electron activation) on the N-side of the junction is not equivalent to a current flow across the junction. This equivalency is obtained only when the electron activation occurs on the P-side.

A third condition must also be satisfied if the tunnel effect is to occur. This condition is associated with the availability of an empty energy level on the P-side equal, in value, to the newly filled energy level on the N-side.

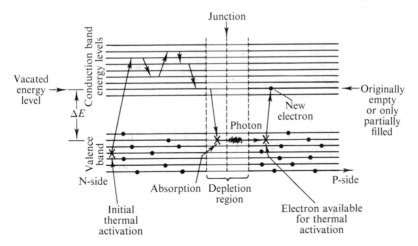

Figure 11-3.   *Tunnel Effect in Terms of Energy Exchanges* (*Example*)

Figure 11-3 illustrates the tunnel effect (from Fig. 11-2) in terms of energy levels. As the electron approaches the depletion region on the N-side, it is changing energy levels in a random fashion. Abruptly, it is absorbed by an atom, losing the energy ΔE. The photon (also with a total energy of ΔE) crosses the junction and, in order to cause the release of a new electron, must raise the electron by exactly the same energy value. This requires that the energy level in the P material directly opposite (of the same energy value as) the vacated energy level in the N material be empty, or only partially filled.

Since the tunneling effect is electromagnetic in nature, rather than the physical movement of particles, the transfer occurs in about 10^{-16} second. This is much faster than the normal diffusion and drift current transfers. Hence, the tunnel diode can handle signal variations on the order of several hundred megacycles per second before its operational effectiveness is reduced by a significant amount.

Energy Band Structure

Carrier energy distributions in N- and P-type semiconductor materials are discussed in Chap. 4. As shown in Fig. 4-8, the donor impurity introduces a band of energies (filled with electrons) just below the normal conduction band, and the acceptor impurity introduces a band of energies (empty) just above the valence band. This occurs with normal amounts of impurity concentrations (10^{-7} to 10^{-6}). With extremely high concentrations (10^{-3} to 10^{-2}), the impurity energy band spreads, occupying a wider range of energy values, so that these bands *overlap into the valence and conduction bands*. This is shown in Fig. 11-4. In the P-type material, the empty impurity band (Part A) becomes a part of the valence band. As shown in Part B of the figure, the filled impurity band in the N-type material spreads until it becomes a part of the conduction band. At absolute zero, the valence electrons in the P material remain in their covalent bonds (occupying the lowest possible energy levels) and the excess electrons in the N material remain attached (only in a very weak manner) to the impurity atoms. Hence, both materials have insulator properties at absolute zero.

As temperature is raised above absolute zero, the thermal activation associated with conventional impurity materials occurs. This raises the excess electrons of the N material into the higher conduction band energy levels at a very low temperature. At higher temperatures, some of the covalent bonds in the valence band are broken (valence electrons are raised to the conduction band, creating holes in the valence band). How-

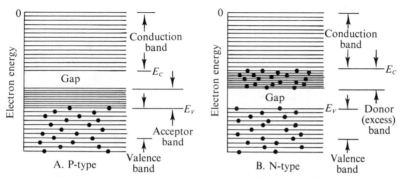

Figure 11-4.   *Energy Bands in Heavily-Doped Materials (Absolute Zero)*

ever, because of the mass action law (Chap. 4), the increased number of majority carriers results in a smaller number of minority carriers than would be present in a conventional material at the same temperature. This is shown in Fig. 11–5, Part A. Part B shows the similar action in the P material, with the creation of a larger number of holes (majority carriers) and a smaller number of electrons (minority carriers). In view of this discussion, the thermal activation in tunnel diode materials is similar to that in conventional materials; only the relative numbers of carriers are different.

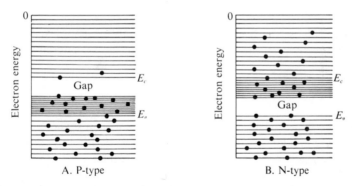

Figure 11-5.   *Energy Bands and Electron-Hole Distributions (Above Absolute Zero)*

Figure 11–6 illustrates the energy-level arrangement in an unbiased tunnel diode. The presence of the junction potential causes an equivalent energy shift $(E_j = V_j Q)$ between the levels on the P- and N-sides of the junction. This energy difference prevents the flow of majority carriers across the junction via the normal current mechanisms. Examination of the figure also indicates that *no tunnel current will flow in the unbiased*

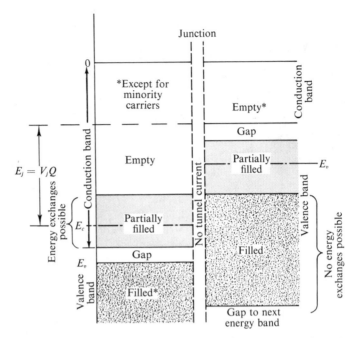

Figure 11-6.   *Energy Band and Carrier Relations in an Unbiased Tunnel Diode*

condition. This is true because there are no empty energy levels in the P material directly opposite filled energy levels in the N material.

Operating Characteristics

With no bias applied, the equilibrium currents across the tunnel diode junction are similar to those shown in Fig. 4–19 for the conventional diode. This leads to a net current of zero across the junction. Figure 11–7 presents the forward voltage-current characteristic of the tunnel diode, as compared to the characteristic for a conventional diode. The unique characteristic of the tunnel diode, which makes its circuit applications entirely different from those of the conventional diode, is the presence of a *negative conductance region* between the *peak* and *valley* points. From Ohm's law, an increase in voltage across a normal conductance must result in a current increase. However, over the region indicated in the figure, an increase in voltage produces a *decrease* in current.

The nature of the tunnel diode characteristic can be explained by referring to Fig. 11–8. In Part A, the application of a small forward bias

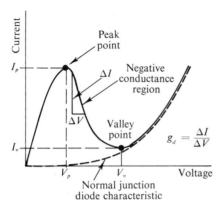

Figure 11-7.   *Tunnel Diode Characteristic*

reduces the relative energy shift between the levels in the N and P materials. This is similar to the reduction in barrier potential indicated in Fig. 4–23. This permits an increase in the diffusion currents across the junction (some of the majority carriers have enough thermal energy to overcome the barrier) as shown in Fig. 4–24. However, the third condition for tunneling is also satisfied. That is, partially filled energy levels in the P material are opposite filled energy levels in the N material. As a result, a small tunnel current will flow. Since the tunnel current carriers are majority carriers, this constitutes *an additional component of forward current*. As forward bias is increased, larger diffusion currents, and a larger tunnel current, will flow. The tunnel current increases because the additional reduction in energy shift across the junction causes more partially filled energy levels in the P material to "line-up" with filled energy levels in the N material (Fig. 11–8, Part B). The maximum tunnel current flows (producing the peak point in Fig. 11–7) when the forward bias condition in Part C is reached. For larger forward bias voltages (such as in Part D), fewer partially filled energy levels in the P material correspond to filled energy levels in the N material and the tunnel current begins decreasing. This marks the beginning of the negative conductance region. The reduction in tunnel current (and, therefore, total forward current) continues until the relative energy levels reach the condition shown in Part E. This constitutes the valley point in the operating characteristic. Increases in bias voltage above this value merely cause increases in the diffusion currents (as in a conventional diode). For this reason, the two diode characteristics become identical when the forward bias is greater than V_v.

For most applications, the tunnel diode is biased in such a way as to achieve an operating point in the middle of the negative conductance

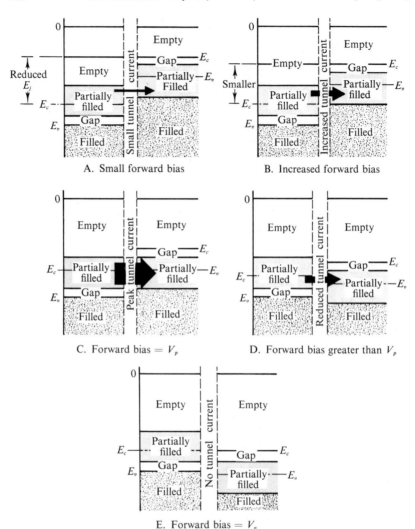

Figure 11-8.   *Phenomena Associated with Tunnel Diode Characteristic*

region. This is shown in Fig. 11–9. The procedure for plotting the d-c load line is identical to the procedure for plotting transistor amplifier load lines (Chap. 5). However, because of the extremely high-frequency operation of the tunnel diode, a different biasing arrangement must be used. This is also shown in Fig. 11–9. The RF choke is placed in series with the supply in order to prevent high-frequency signals from overheating the supply. Hence, the a-c and d-c circuits are isolated from one another. The bias resistor, R_B, is adjustable since placement of the operating point is critical over a very narrow region. The tunable inductance, L, and the adjustable resistor, R, are present in the a-c circuit in order to control the circuit response characteristics (gain and bandwidth).

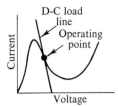

A. Normal operating point

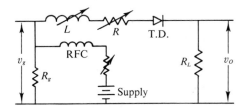

B. Circuit arrangement

Figure 11-9.   *Tunnel Diode Amplifier*

Amplification

The presence of a negative resistance in a normal resistive network tends to nullify a portion of the equivalent series resistance of the circuit. Because of this, for a given input voltage, a circuit containing a negative resistance device will circulate a higher current, drop a higher voltage across the load, and dissipate a higher power in the load than the same circuit without a negative resistance device. In effect, then, the presence of the negative resistance device results in a current, voltage, and power amplification. Consider the circuit in Fig. 11–10, Part A. Defining R_T as the total equivalent a-c series resistance of the circuit, the current in the load is:

$$i_L = \frac{v_g}{R_T} \tag{11-1}$$

and the voltage across the load, $i_L R_L$, is:

$$v_L = \frac{v_g R_L}{R_T} \tag{11-2}$$

The power $i_L^2 R_L$ is:

$$p_L = \frac{v_g^2 R_L}{R_T^2} \tag{11-3}$$

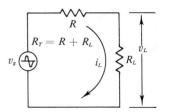

A. Circuit without negative
resistance

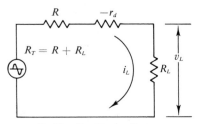

B. Circuit with negative
resistance

Figure 11-10.   *Development of Insertion Gain for Negative Resistance
Device*

Part B of the figure contains a negative resistance device, $-r_d$. The current
in the load is:

$$i_L' = \frac{v_g}{R_T - r_d} \tag{11-4}$$

and the voltage across the load is:

$$v_L' = \frac{v_g R_L}{R_T - r_d} \tag{11-5}$$

The power is:

$$p_L' = \frac{v_g^2 R_L}{(R_T - r_d)^2} \tag{11-6}$$

Hence, it is possible to define *insertion gains* for the negative resistance
device:

$$A_i = \frac{i_L'}{i_L} = \frac{R_T}{R_T - r_d} \tag{11-7}$$

$$A_v = \frac{v_L'}{v_L} = \frac{R_T}{R_T - r_d} \tag{11-8}$$

$$A_p = \frac{p_L'}{p_L} = \frac{R_T^2}{(R_T - r_d)^2} \tag{11-9}$$

Since the denominators in all of these expressions are smaller than the numerators, all of the *insertion gains are greater than one*. These equations cannot be used directly to calculate tunnel diode amplifier gain. However, they are useful in demonstrating the existence of the diode's inherent gain characteristic.

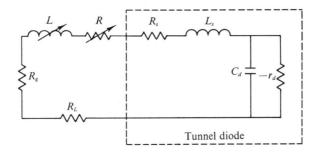

Figure 11-11.   A-C *Equivalent Circuit For Tunnel Diode in Amplifier Arrangement*

Figure 11–11 presents the a-c equivalent circuit for a tunnel diode in an amplifier arrangement (such as the basic amplifier circuit of Fig. 11–9). The series inductance, L_s, and resistance, R_s, are associated with the leads permanently attached to the device. The capacitance, C_d, is associated with the leads and with the tunnel diode junction. The negative resistance, $-r_d$, is obtained when the operating point is as shown in Fig. 11–9. Its value is:

$$r_d = \frac{1}{g_d} \qquad (11\text{-}10)$$

These parameter values are specified by the manufacturer for a particular tunnel diode. Because of the series resonant nature of the tunnel diode, linear Class A amplification is obtained only when:

$$\frac{L_T}{C_d r_d} < R_T < |r_d| \qquad (11\text{-}11)$$

Maintaining this relationship is very critical to good amplifier operation.

The frequency response characteristic of the tunnel-diode amplifier is similar in shape to that of the singly-tuned amplifier circuits discussed in Chap. 7. The center frequency of the response characteristic is given by:

$$f = \frac{1}{2\pi} \sqrt{\frac{|r_d| - R_T}{R_T (C_d r_d)^2}} \qquad (11\text{-}12)$$

As R_T is made smaller, the center frequency increases and the bandwidth of the amplifier is decreased. As R_T is made larger, the center frequency decreases and the bandwidth increases. As is usual in amplifier response characteristics (the law of conservation of energy, again), a change in bandwidth is accompanied by an opposite change in gain. Hence, as R_T is made smaller, the gain increases; as R_T is made larger, the gain decreases. These relationships are illustrated in Fig. 11–12.

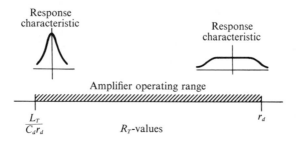

Figure 11-12.   *Manner in Which R_T Controls Amplifier Response*

Example 11-1.   A tunnel diode with the following parameters:

$$L_s = 10 \text{ m}\mu\text{h} \qquad R_s = 3 \text{ ohms}$$
$$C_d = 6 \text{ pf} \qquad r_d = -150 \text{ ohms}$$

is used in an amplifier that is to have its response centered at 100 mc. What value R and L must be used in the circuit, if R_g and R_L are both equal to 40 ohms?

Solution.   Solving Eq. (11–12) for R_T:

$$R_T = \frac{|r_d|}{1 + (2\pi f C_d r_d)^2} = \frac{150}{1 + [2\pi(10^8)(6 \times 10^{-12})(150)]^2}$$
$$= \frac{150}{1.319} = 114 \text{ ohms}$$

Since R_T is the sum of all circuit resistances except the negative resistance of the diode:

$$R = R_T - (R_g + R_s + R_L) = 114 - (40 + 3 + 40) = 31 \text{ ohms}$$

From Eq. (11–11):

$$L_T < R_T C_d r_d = 114(6 \times 10^{-12})(150) = 103 \text{ m}\mu\text{h}$$

and:

$$L < L_T - L_s = (103 - 10)(10^{-9}) = 94 \text{ m}\mu\text{h}$$

Oscillation

When the conditions:

$$R_T \leq \frac{L_T}{C_d r_d} \tag{11-13}$$

or:

$$R_T \geq |r_d| \tag{11-14}$$

are satisfied, the tunnel-diode circuit becomes unstable. The range of values specified by Eq. (11–14) is used for special, *switching*, applications which are beyond the scope of this text. For most values over the range specified by Eq. (11–13), the instability results in nonlinear oscillations. These values are used to achieve amplitude modulation or frequency conversion (see Chap. 10). However, the exact condition:

$$R_T = \frac{L_T}{C_d r_d} \tag{11-15}$$

results in sinusoidal oscillations with a frequency given by:

$$f = \frac{1}{2\pi} \sqrt{\frac{1}{L_T C_d} - \frac{1}{(C_d r_d)^2}} \tag{11-16}$$

The oscillator operation ranges between the peak and valley points on the

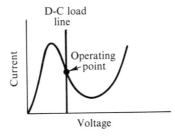

A. Load line

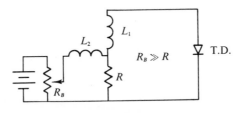

B. Circuit arrangement

Figure 11-13.   *Tunnel-Diode Oscillator*

tunnel-diode characteristic, resulting in an output power of:

$$P_o = \frac{(V_v - V_p)(I_p - I_v)}{8} \tag{11-17}$$

A typical oscillator circuit (with operating point) is shown in Fig. 11–13.

Example 11-2. If the inductance, L, used in the amplifier of Example 11–1 is 90 mμh, what value must R be adjusted to if the circuit is to become a sinusoidal oscillator? What is the frequency of oscillation?

Solution. In order to achieve sinewave oscillation, the total resistance must be:

$$R_T = \frac{L_T}{C_d r_d} = \frac{L_s + L}{C_d r_d} = \frac{10^{-7}}{(6 \times 10^{-12})(150)} = 110 \text{ ohms}$$

leading to a resistance value of:

$$R = R_T - (R_g + R_s + R_L) = 110 - (40 + 3 + 40) = 27 \text{ ohms}$$

The frequency of oscillation will be:

$$f = \frac{1}{2\pi} \sqrt{\frac{1}{L_T C_d} - \frac{1}{(C_d r_d)^2}}$$

$$= \frac{1}{2\pi} \sqrt{\frac{1}{(10^{-7})(6 \times 10^{-12})} - \frac{1}{(6 \times 10^{-12})(150)^2}}$$

$$= \frac{1}{2\pi} \sqrt{(1.67 \times 10^{18}) - (1.25 \times 18^{18})} = 31.5 \text{ mc}$$

11.2   Field-Effect Transistors

A field-effect transistor (FET) uses a high-intensity electric field, directed transversely across a bar of semiconductor material, to control the total conductance of a current loop. This process is called *conductance modulation* since the path conductance varies in a manner proportional to the input signal amplitude. Since the magnitude of an electric field can be changed very rapidly, FET's inherently have a high-frequency response. However, since physical current carriers must still cross this field (as in crossing a semiconductor junction), degradations are introduced at higher frequencies, limiting the operation to values below those associated with the tunnel diode.

One type of FET construction is shown in Fig. 11–14, Part A. Here, a lightly doped semiconductor material is shaped into a rectangular bar (called the *channel*) and two small regions of heavily doped material (of

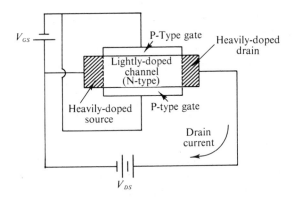

A. Junction type

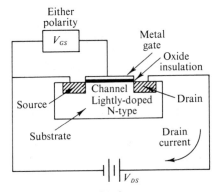

B. Insulated-gate type

Figure 11-14.   *Two Types of* FET *Construction*

opposite type with respect to the channel) are formed on the upper and lower surfaces. These two regions are connected (electrically) and are referred to as *gates*. One end of the bar is known as the *source*; the other, the *drain*. These ends are doped more heavily than the major portion of the bar. The gates are normally reverse biased with respect to the source (as shown by V_{GS} in the figure), and a drain current is established by placing a d-c voltage across the two ends of the channel (V_{DS} in the figure). The second type construction (Part B) has a thin film of metal oxide (usually silicon dioxide) separating the gate and the channel. The gate, in this case, is metal (usually silicon), also deposited in a thin film. This type is termed the metal-oxide-semiconductor (MOS) FET, or the insulated-gate (IG) FET. Since the gate is not in direct electrical contact with the drain-source region, no semiconductor junction is formed and the gate may have a positive or negative potential applied to it. This increases the flexibility of the device (the junction FET *must have* the gate reverse biased with respect to the channel). This changes the cutoff characteristics of the device considerably. The lightly doped *substrate* forms the bulk of the device; the channel region occupies only a portion of the substrate material between the more heavily doped source and drain regions.

Operating Characteristics

When a d-c voltage is placed across the ends of a semiconductor bar, the bar limits the current flow in the circuit because of its basic resistivity. The total resistance of the bar (from Chap. 3) is:

$$R = \rho\left(\frac{L}{A}\right) \qquad \text{(ohms)} \qquad \textbf{(11-18)}$$

where ρ is the material resistivity, L is the length of the bar, and A is the cross-sectional area of the bar. In terms of conductivity:

$$G = \sigma\left(\frac{A}{L}\right) \qquad \text{(mhos)} \qquad \textbf{(11-19)}$$

where σ is the conductivity of the material (see Chap. 3). Hence, any variation in σ, L, or A will provide a variation in G (and, therefore, a variation in circuit current). The basic operation of an FET consists of one (or more) of these parameters varying in accordance with an input signal (a form of "modulation").

The depletion area between the gates and the channel region of a junction FET are shown in Fig. 11–15, Part A with no bias voltage applied to the gates. Since the channel is lightly doped, the depletion region extends farther into the channel material than into the gate material (see Fig. 4–28 and associated text for explanation). When a d-c voltage is applied across the drain and source regions (Fig. 11–15, Part B), the voltage is dropped proportionately along the channel region causing the indicated change in the depletion area. This condition establishes a specific conductance value for the channel, in accordance with Eq. (11–19), and controls the amount of drain current, I_D, that will flow. This establishes point A on the characteristic curve, as shown in Fig. 11–16, Part A. A slight increase in V_{DS} (Fig. 11–15, Part C) causes further widening of the depletion area, especially at the drain end. Notice that the cross-sectional area available for current flow in Part C is less than that of Part B. Hence [from Eq. (11–19)], *the channel conductance is decreased.* This indicates that an increase in V_{DS} will not produce a proportional increase in I_D (doubling the V_{DS}-value in Part A will not double the I_D-value obtained in Part A). This new conductance establishes point B on the characteristic curve in Fig. 11–16,

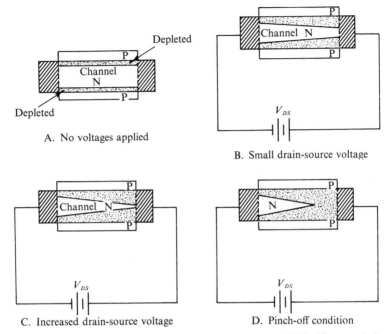

Figure 11-15.   *Phenomena Associated with Junction* FET *Characteristic*

Part A. This phenomenon continues until V_{DS} reaches a value that depletes the entire width of the channel at the drain end (Fig. 11–15, Part D). This V_{DS}-value is known as the *pinch-off voltage*, and is shown as point C in Fig. 11–16, Part A. Throughout the region of operation that has been described, the FET is said to display an *ohmic behavior*. When V_{DS} is increased beyond the pinch-off value, large changes in voltage are required to produce small changes in current. Operation in this region is not well understood, but it is in this region that most FET applications are accomplished.

When a reverse bias, V_{GS}, is applied from gate to source, the depletion area is widened (Fig. 11–17), reducing the area available for channel current flow. This means that the conductance of the channel is less with a gate voltage applied than without, even when no drain-to-source voltage is used. Applying V_{DS} causes the same sequence of events described previously. *However, a given V_{DS}-value will produce a lower I_D-value than that obtained when V_{GS} was zero.* This results in a similar, but lower-valued, characteristic curve for each increase in V_{DS} (Fig. 11–16, Part B). The pinch-off voltage, V_p, is an important FET parameter. For a given device it is a constant. Furthermore, V_{GS} and V_{DS} must always satisfy the condition:

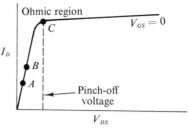

A. Basic characteristic

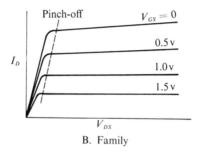

B. Family

Figure 11-16.   *Typical Junction FET Characteristics*

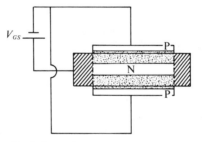

Figure 11-17.   *Depletion Area in Junction FET with Gate-Source Voltage Applied*

$$V_p = |V_{GS}| + V_{DS} \tag{11-20}$$

when pinch-off occurs. Another important FET parameter is the maximum (saturation) drain-to-source current when V_{GS} is zero, denoted by the symbol, I_{DSS}.

The insulated-gate FET also works on a conductance modulation principle. However, the variation in conductance is not achieved by a variation in a semiconductor junction. Rather, the area available for current flow in the channel is achieved through a capacitance effect between

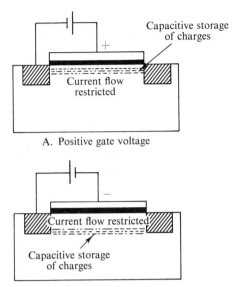

A. Positive gate voltage

B. Negative gate voltage

Figure 11-18.   *Current Control Phenomena in the Insulated-Gate* FET

the metal gate and the semiconductive substrate. As shown in Fig. 11–18, Part A, placing a positive voltage on the gate causes the upper portion of the channel region to become more negative than the lower portion. Hence, it is easier for the channel current to flow through the lower portion. Varying the positive gate voltage varies the area of the current path. Part B of the figure indicates a similar action when a negative gate voltage is applied. However, the current path is restricted to the upper portion of

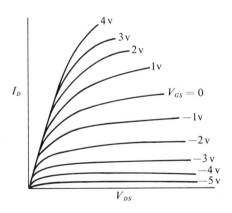

Figure 11-19.   *Family of Characteristics for the Insulated-Gate* FET

the channel in this case. The application of V_{DS} alters the shape of the current path in a manner similar to that in the junction FET. Hence, an effect similar to pinch-off is achieved. Because a gate voltage of either polarity may be used, the characteristic curves for the insulated-gate FET appear as shown in Fig. 11–19.

Amplification

For either type FET, amplification is achieved by biasing the device in the region to the right of pinch-off. The d-c load line is developed in a manner similar to that described for the junction transistor (Chap. 5). Once the operating point is established, the a-c load line may also be constructed in a manner similar to that for the junction transistor. A typical circuit, and the associated load lines, are shown in Fig. 11–20. Gate-to-

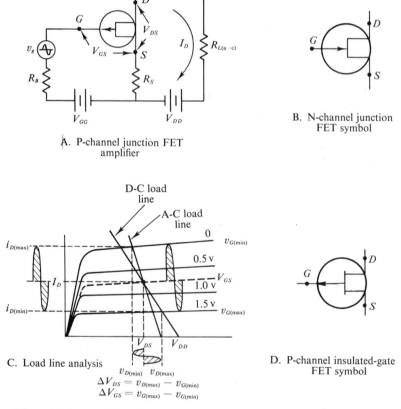

A. P-channel junction FET amplifier

B. N-channel junction FET symbol

C. Load line analysis

$$\Delta V_{DS} = v_{D(max)} - v_{G(min)}$$
$$\Delta V_{GS} = v_{G(max)} - v_{G(min)}$$

D. P-channel insulated-gate FET symbol

Figure 11-20.   FET *Amplifier Circuits and Load Line Analysis*

source bias is established with a biasing resistor, R_B, which serves to drop most of the supply voltage, V_{GG}, prior to the device terminals. The gate-to-source loop represents an extremely high resistance (the FET is similar to the vacuum tube in this respect) so that, for all practical purposes, the input current is negligible. The input signal is applied in the gate-to-source loop; the output signal is extracted in the drain-to-source loop. The voltage gain may be determined graphically (also shown in Fig. 11-20) from the relationship:

$$A_v = \frac{\Delta V_{DS}}{\Delta V_{GS}} \qquad (11\text{-}21)$$

Thermal stabilization for an FET amplifier may be obtained by inserting a resistor in the source branch. This is similar to the use of the emitter resistor in the junction transistor (Chap. 9). Distortion may be analyzed graphically, as in Chap. 5, as can many other operating characteristics.

Example 11-3. The insulated-gate FET with characteristics given in Appendix D is used in an amplifier with a bias V_{GS} of zero volts. A two-volt peak input signal is applied in the gate-to-source loop. What is the voltage gain of the amplifier if the equivalent a-c load resistance is 2.8K and the drain-to-source supply voltage is 20 volts?

Solution. The current intercept for the d-c load line (which must be equal to the a-c load line in this example), is given by:

$$I_{D(\text{int})} = \frac{28}{2.8 \times 10^3} = 10 \text{ ma}$$

The voltage gain is given by:

$$A_v = \frac{\Delta V_{DS}}{\Delta V_{GS}} = \frac{19 - 8}{4} = 2.75$$

PROBLEMS

1. A tunnel diode has the following parameters:

   $$L_s = 8 \text{ m}\mu\text{h} \qquad C_d = 4 \text{ pf}$$
   $$R_s = 2 \text{ ohms} \qquad r_d = -120 \text{ ohms}$$

   The total circuit resistance (including R_s) is 110 ohms. What is the center frequency of the response characteristic?

2. What value L must be used in Problem 1 if the amplifier is to have maximum gain and minimum bandwidth?

3. What type response could be expected from the amplifier in Problem 1 if L is made equal to 40 mμh?

4. What value L must be used with the tunnel diode in Problem 1 if it is to form a sinusoidal oscillator?

5. What is the frequency of oscillation in Problem 4?

6. Calculate the distortion associated with the output waveform in Example 11–3.

Further Reading

Oppenheimer, S. L., *Semiconductor Logic and Switching Circuits.* Columbus, Ohio: Charles E. Merrill Books, Inc., 1966.

Pierce, J. F., *Semiconductor Junction Devices.* Columbus, Ohio: Charles E. Merrill Books, Inc., 1967.

Ristenbatt, M. P. and R. L. Riddle, *Transistor Physics and Circuits.* Englewood Cliffs, N. J.: Prentice-Hall, Inc., 1966.

Seidman, A. H. and S. L. Marshall, *Semiconductor Fundamentals.* New York: John Wiley and Sons, Inc., 1963.

Appendices

APPENDIX A

List of Physical Constants

Quantity	Value	Unit
Electron charge	$-(1.6 \times 10^{-19})$	Coulomb
Electron mass	9.1×10^{-31}	Kilogram
Proton charge	$+(1.6 \times 10^{-19})$	Coulomb
Proton mass	1.67×10^{-27}	Kilogram
Neutron charge	0	——
Neutron mass	1.67×10^{-27}	Kilogram
Permittivity (vacuum)	8.85×10^{-12}	Coulomb/Newton·Meter
Permeability (vacuum)	1.256×10^{-6}	Newton/Ampere
Planck's constant	6.62×10^{-34}	Joule·Second
	4.15×10^{-17}	Electron Volt/Second
Boltzmann's constant	1.38×10^{-23}	Joule/°Kelvin
	8.62×10^{-5}	Electron Volt/°Kelvin
Velocity of light* (vacuum)	3×10^8	Meter/Second

* Also applies to other electromagnetic radiation

577

APPENDIX B

Electromagnetic "Particles"

The classical concept of electromagnetic waves is mathematically described by Maxwell's electromagnetic field equations. However, Maxwell's equations do not fit all the phenomena observed at the microscopic level of atomic and molecular structure. At this level, the charged particles responsible for creating electromagnetic energy (electrons, in general) cannot accelerate in a continuous fashion. Rather, they accelerate abruptly, changing velocity by small, discrete values in order to match the permissable atomic orbits—jumping from one orbit to another. These transitions may decrease the electron velocity (moving to a larger orbit), requiring that energy be absorbed from some external source. They may increase the electron velocity (moving to a smaller orbit), resulting in the emission of energy. (Material structure and the energy transitions are discussed in Chap. 1.)

Since the electron velocity and, therefore, energy, changes occur in discrete steps, the associated electromagnetic energy absorptions and emissions must occur in distinct segments. Such segments of electromagnetic energy are termed *photons*. Each photon has an energy:

$$E_{ph} = \Delta E_T \qquad \text{(B-1)}$$

where ΔE_T is the total change in electron energy. (Positive values of ΔE_T and E_{ph} indicate an increase in energy: *photon absorption*. Negative values indicate a decrease in energy: *photon emission*.) Velocity changes and the associated photon absorption and emission processes are illustrated in Fig. B-1.

Theory, verified by extensive experimentation, indicates that the actual electron velocities in a material are *distributed across a wide range of values* with different numbers of particles having different values of velocity. This movement is the result of thermal energy absorptions and emissions. In graphical form, the distribution looks like Fig. B-2. The quantity v_0 is the most probable, or average, velocity for a given temperature:

$$v_0 = \sqrt{\frac{2kT}{m_e}} \qquad \text{(meters/second)} \qquad \text{(B-2)}$$

where k is Boltzmann's constant (Appendix A), T is the the temperature in degrees Kelvin, and m_e is the electron mass. No single particular particle will always travel at the same velocity. Rather, each particle will change velocity and direction of motion many times per second. However, all the

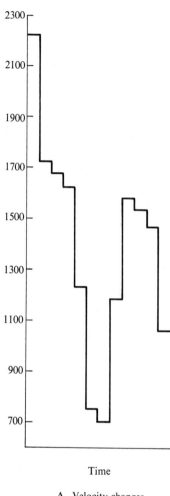

Time

A. Velocity changes

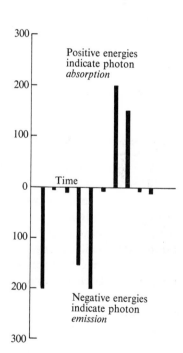

B. Associated photons

Figure B-1. *Typical Particle History Showing Photon Emission and Absorption*

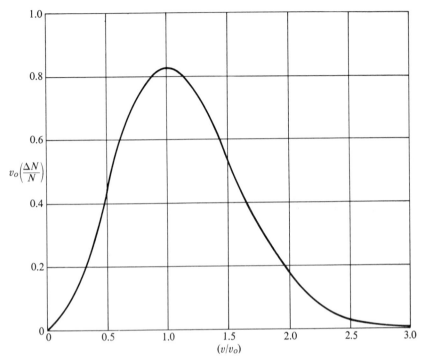

Figure B-2.   *Maxwell-Boltzmann Velocity Distribution*

particles are undergoing such changes so that, when the overall effects are observed, the velocity distribution of Fig. B-2 is maintained.

Every cubic meter of matter contains millions of particles. According to the Maxwell-Boltzmann distribution, hundreds of thousands of these particles will have a specific velocity, v. Hence, these particles must be executing a specific change in velocity, Δv, and an associated change in energy, according to a similar distribution curve. Each particle making the same energy change emits an identical photon. The myriads of *identical photons*, in effect, *add together to make a single frequency electromagnetic wave* of frequency:

$$f = \frac{E_{ph}}{h} \qquad \text{(B-3)}$$

Each photon in this wave contains exactly the same energy. The emission of photons having different energy values results in different electromagnetic field frequencies—one frequency for each different-size photon. The total energy of each wave is determined by the *number of photons* contributing to it. Since the number of particles having specific energy-change values follows a distribution similar to that in Fig. B-2, the number of photons having a particular energy value must follow a similar distribution, as in Fig. B-3, Part A. Since each energy value results in a single-frequency electromagnetic wave, there is an *electromagnetic emission spectrum* (or

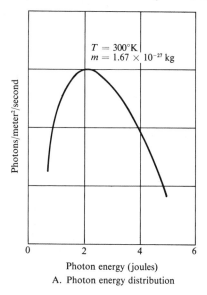

A. Photon energy distribution

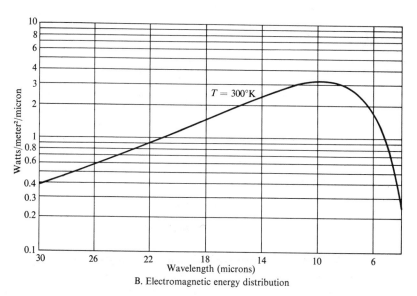

B. Electromagnetic energy distribution

Figure B-3.   *The Natural Emission of Electromagnetic Energy*

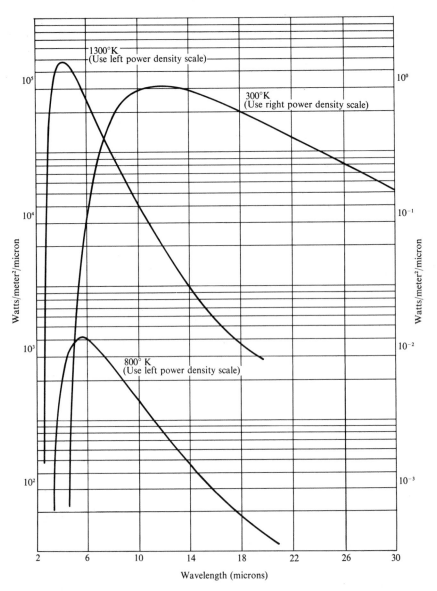

Figure B-4.   *Distributions of Electromagnetic Energy*

frequency distribution) associated with all matter, as shown in Part B of the figure. The shape of this final curve changes as temperature changes since the particle velocity and particle energy distributions are temperature dependent.

Figure B-4 shows the electromagnetic spectrum associated with an object at several different temperatures. The general trend, with increasing temperature, is for the object to emit a more intense radiation at all frequencies, and for the energy to be concentrated at successively higher frequencies. At low temperatures, the energy is concentrated at radio and microwave frequencies. When the temperature is high enough for the spectrum to extend into the infrared region, the intensity and frequency is such that the human skin can feel the *heat radiation*. As the spectrum crosses the visible light region, the object begins to glow. As the temperature increases, the intensity of the glow increases and the color changes from red to white to blue as the energy is concentrated at higher and higher frequencies.

APPENDIX C

Waveform Analysis

Since the amplitude value of an alternating waveform varies from instant to instant, an *effective* value has been defined for application to all waveforms. This value is based on the heating (power) effect of the waveform since this effect is independent of direction (positive and negative values). There is also an *average* value associated with an alternating waveform. This value is equivalent to the reading that would be obtained on a d-c meter with the alternating waveform applied. The techniques to be described apply to all waveforms; sinusoidal and nonsinusoidal.

Although it is common practice to analyze electronic signals and circuits on the basis of pure sinusoids and their effects, it is extremely rare (in actual practice) for a signal to consist of such a simple waveform. Rather, all waveforms that represent speech, music, and other information consist of nonsinusoidal signals. Electronic circuits *can be* analyzed in terms of such signals. However, the analysis may become quite complex and will, almost always, require the application of advanced mathematics. Fortunately, a French mathematician, named *Fourier*, has proven that nonsinusoidal signals can be represented by a simple trigonometric series (sum) of sine and cosine functions. Hence, it is possible to convert a complex signal into its pure sinusoidal components, performing the circuit analysis across the entire band of frequencies that are produced.

C-1. Effective (RMS) Value

An alternating waveform has an effective value of one ampere (or one volt) if it produces heat in a given resistance at the same rate as heat is produced in an equal resistance by one ampere (or one volt) of d-c current (or voltage). The heating value must be computed from the square of the alternating signal waveform. Figure C–1 illustrates the square of a sinewave. All values are positive, since squaring a negative value produces a positive value. There is an axis about which the squared waveform is symmetrical. The value of this axis is the mean (average) value of the squared waveform. The square root of this value is the desired *effective value*. Since the process involves obtaining the square root of a mean value, it is referred to as the *root-mean-square* (rms) *value*.

The following step-by-step procedure may be used for a graphical determination of the rms value of any alternating waveform:

1. Plot a waveform whose amplitude is equal to the square of the original waveform amplitude.

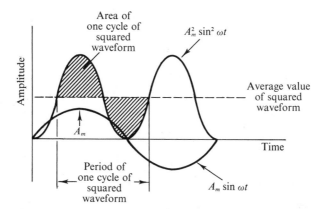

Figure C-1.   *Determining the Effective Value of a Sinewave*

2. Find the mean amplitude-squared value by dividing the area under the plotted waveform (for one cycle) by the duration of the cycle (one period).

3. Determine the square root of the mean amplitude-squared value.

Step 2 is generally the most difficult. This is especially true for complex waveforms. However, the area can be obtained with a planimeter. Figure C–2 shows the determination for a simple pulse waveform, where the values can be calculated directly.

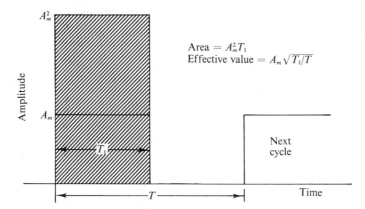

Figure C-2.   *Effective Value of a Pulse Waveform*

C-2. Average Value

The average value of any alternating waveform is the value found by adding the amplitudes at incremental times over the duration of one period, and dividing this summation by the value of the period. The accuracy of this determination will depend on the number of increments that are used. The value can also be determined by finding the value of the area under the plotted waveform for one cycle and dividing by the value of the period. Again, a planimeter may be used for finding the area. Applying this latter rule to the pulse waveform in Fig. C–2, the area for one cycle is $A_m T_1$ and the average value must be $A_m T_1/T$.

The average and rms values for several common waveforms are indicated in Fig. C–3.

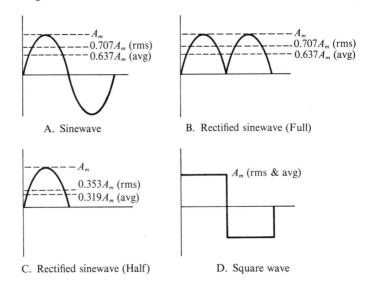

A. Sinewave

A_m
$0.707A_m$ (rms)
$0.637A_m$ (avg)

B. Rectified sinewave (Full)

A_m
$0.707A_m$ (rms)
$0.637A_m$ (avg)

C. Rectified sinewave (Half)

A_m
$0.353A_m$ (rms)
$0.319A_m$ (avg)

D. Square wave

A_m (rms & avg)

Figure C-3. RMS *and Average Values for Several Alternating Wave-forms*

C-3. Fourier (Harmonic) Analysis

Any periodic function of time [denoted by $f(t)$] with a period of T seconds can be represented by the *Fourier series*:

$$f(t) = \frac{A_0}{T} + \frac{2}{T} \sum_{n=1}^{\infty} (A_n \cos 2\pi f_n t + B_n \sin 2\pi f_n t) \qquad \text{(C-1)}$$

where:

$$f_n = \frac{n}{T} \qquad [n = 1, 2, 3, \cdots] \qquad \text{(C-2)}$$

The summation sign, Σ, simply means that all components are to be added. For example, if two components ($n = 1, 2$) are to be considered:

$$f(t) = \frac{A_0}{T} + \frac{2}{T}\left[A_1 \cos 2\pi\left(\frac{t}{T}\right) + A_2 \cos 2\pi\left(\frac{2t}{T}\right)\right.$$

$$\left. + B_1 \sin 2\pi\left(\frac{t}{T}\right) + B_2 \sin 2\pi\left(\frac{2t}{T}\right)\right] \tag{C-3}$$

is the Fourier series expression.

The coefficients A_0, A_n, and B_n *must be determined separately for each different waveform.* This is what makes one Fourier series different from another. The term (A_0/T) is a constant, and, for electrical signals, expresses *the* d-c *component*. The sine and cosine terms have the same frequency value, f_n, which is related to the period of $f(t)$. This fact also makes one Fourier series different from another. In summary, then, the component *frequencies* and *amplitudes* make the Fourier series for one nonsinusoidal signal distinct from that for all other nonsinusoidal signals. Notice, also, that the frequency values (f_n's) are *integral multiples* of each other. For this reason, the Fourier series is also termed the *harmonic series*; that is, each successive component is a harmonic (an integral multiple) of the fundamental component, which is given by f_1, or $1/T$.

The evaluation of the coefficients requires the use of calculus techni-

TABLE C-1

Fourier (Harmonic) Expressions for Typical
Nonsinusoidal Signals

Waveform	Harmonic Expression
Rectified sinewave (Full)	$A = \frac{2}{\pi} + \frac{4}{\pi}\left[\frac{1}{3}\cos 4\pi f - \frac{1}{15}\cos 8\pi f + \cdots + \frac{(-1)^{n+1}}{4n^2 - 1}\cos 4n\pi f\right]$
Rectified sinewave (Half)	$A = \frac{1}{\pi} + \frac{1}{2}\cos 2\pi f + \frac{2}{\pi}\left[\frac{1}{3}\cos 4\pi f + \cdots + \frac{(-1)^{n+1}}{4n^2 - 1}\cos 4n\pi f\right]$
Square wave	$A = \frac{4}{\pi}\left[\sin 2\pi f + \frac{1}{3}\sin 6\pi f + \frac{1}{5}\sin 10\pi f + \cdots\right.$ $\left. + \frac{1}{2n+1}\sin 2(2n\pi + 1)f\right]$
Sawtooth wave	$A = \frac{2}{\pi}\left[\sin 2\pi f - \frac{1}{2}\sin 4\pi f + \frac{1}{3}\sin 6\pi f + \cdots\right.$ $\left. + \frac{(-1)^{n+1}}{n}\sin 2n\pi f\right]$

Note: Expressions assume unit peak amplitude for nonsinusoidal waveforms. To convert to other values, multiply all terms in expression by peak amplitude.

ques. This permits the direct calculation of their values for any $f(t)$. Graphical methods based on a plot of $f(t)$ also exist. However, this approach is very time-consuming and yields only an approximation for the coefficients. Table C–1 presents the Fourier (or harmonic) series for several common nonsinusoidal signals.

Notice that, in the general definition, the summation is indicated from n equal to one to n equal to infinity. This means (at least, in theory) that an infinite number of sine and cosine terms must be added together in order to truly represent the nonsinusoidal signal. Fortunately, in practice, a near perfect approximation can be achieved with a reasonably small number of components (see Fig. C–4).

A convenient method of presenting the Fourier series of a waveform consists of plotting an amplitude-frequency *spectrum* rather than the

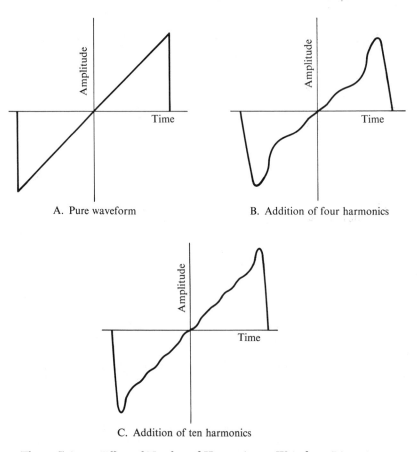

A. Pure waveform   B. Addition of four harmonics

C. Addition of ten harmonics

Figure C-4.   *Effect of Number of Harmonics on Waveform Distortion*

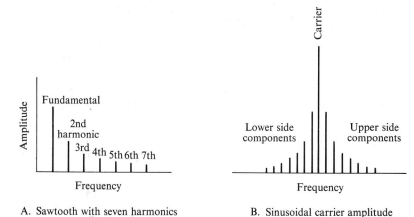

A. Sawtooth with seven harmonics

B. Sinusoidal carrier amplitude modulated by sawtooth

Figure C-5. *Amplitude-Frequency Spectrum* (*Example*)

amplitude-time waveforms that are generally seen (Fig. C–5). Since the frequency of each successive sine and cosine component is the same, it is possible to determine a *composite amplitude* for each:

$$C_n = \sqrt{A_n^2 + B_n^2} \qquad \text{(C-4)}$$

This expression is used to construct the amplitude-frequency spectrum.

Several of the Fourier series in Table C–1 contain only sine or cosine terms—not a mixture of the two as indicated in the defining equations. This is brought about by the *symmetry* of some nonsinusoidal signals. An *even waveform* is symmetrical about the amplitude axis. Thus, the amplitude is the same for specific positive and negative values of t (Fig. C–6).

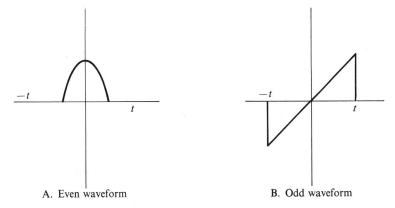

A. Even waveform

B. Odd waveform

Figure C-6. *Waveform Symmetry*

The *odd waveform* has an amplitude that is equal in numerical value, but of opposite algebraic sign for positive and negative values of t: (Although there is no such thing as *negative time*, the concept can be used to show even-odd symmetry. The point where t is equal to zero may be placed anywhere on a waveform—only relative phase relationships will change when this is done.) *Even waveforms contain only cosine terms in the Fourier series. Odd waveforms contain only sine terms in the Fourier series.*

APPENDIX D

Semiconductor Characteristics

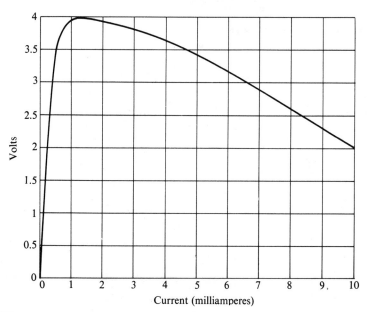

Figure D-1. *Thermistor*

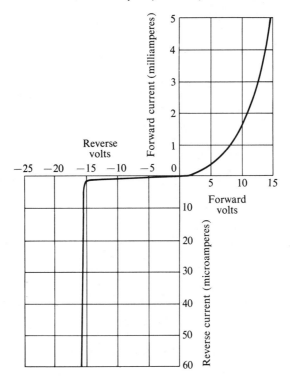

Figure D-2.   *Junction Diode*

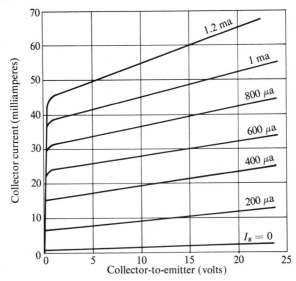

Figure D-3.   *Transistor A—Medium-Signal Amplifiers*

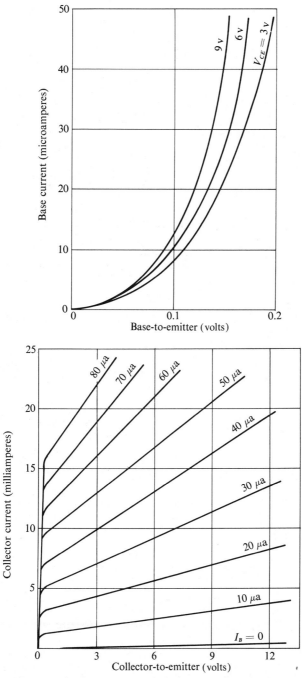

Figure D-4.   *Transistor B—Small-Signal Amplifiers*

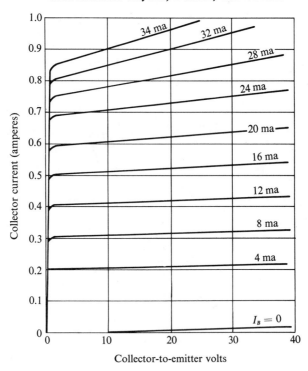

Figure D-5.   *Transistor C—Power Amplifiers*

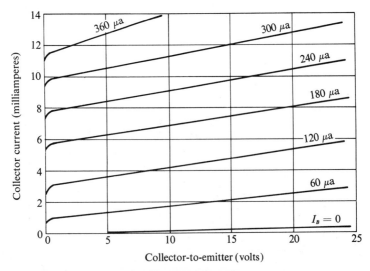

Figure D-6.   *Transistor D—Medium-Signal Amplifiers*

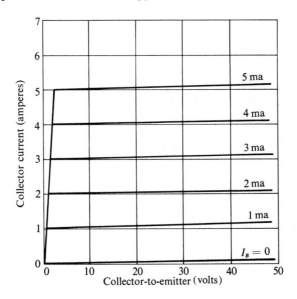

Figure D-7.   *Transistor E—Power Amplifiers*

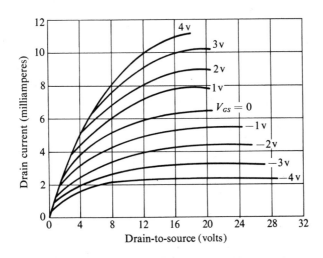

Figure D-8.   *Transistor F—Insulated-Gate* FET

APPENDIX E

Summary of Transistor
Parameters and Conversions

The hybrid parameters defined in Chap. 6 and applied throughout the rest of the text comprise only one method of representing the transistor in an equivalent circuit. Two other sets that are frequently used include the impedance (or resistance) parameters and the admittance parameters. The hybrid parameters are generally specified by the manufacturer because they are easiest to measure. However, for the sake of completeness, and in order that the reader might better compare the techniques of this text to those in other texts, the other two sets will be described. The resistance (r) parameters are defined by:

$$r_{iG} = \frac{\Delta V_{IG}}{\Delta I_I}\bigg|_{I_o} \tag{E-1}$$

$$r_{fG} = \frac{\Delta V_{OG}}{\Delta I_I}\bigg|_{I_o} \tag{E-2}$$

$$r_{rG} = \frac{\Delta V_{IG}}{\Delta I_o}\bigg|_{I_I} \tag{E-3}$$

$$r_{oG} = \frac{\Delta V_{OG}}{\Delta I_o}\bigg|_{I_I} \tag{E-4}$$

and are termed the input impedance, forward transfer impedance, reverse transfer impedance, and the output impedance, respectively. The admittance (y) parameters are defined by:

$$y_{iG} = \frac{\Delta I_I}{\Delta V_{IG}}\bigg|_{V_{OG}} \tag{E-5}$$

$$y_{fG} = \frac{\Delta I_o}{\Delta V_{IG}}\bigg|_{V_{OG}} \tag{E-6}$$

$$y_{rG} = \frac{\Delta I_I}{\Delta V_{OG}}\bigg|_{V_{IG}} \tag{E-7}$$

$$y_{oG} = \frac{\Delta I_o}{\Delta V_{OG}}\bigg|_{V_{IG}} \tag{E-8}$$

TABLE E-1

Conversions between Hybrid, Resistance, Admittance Parameters

To convert from → / to ↓	r		y		h	
r	r_{iG}	r_{rG}	$\dfrac{y_{oG}}{\Delta_y}$	$\dfrac{-y_{iG}}{\Delta_y}$	$\dfrac{\Delta_h}{h_{oG}}$	$\dfrac{h_{rG}}{h_{oG}}$
	r_{fG}	r_{oG}	$\dfrac{-y_{fG}}{\Delta_y}$	$\dfrac{y_{iG}}{\Delta_y}$	$\dfrac{-h_{fG}}{h_{oG}}$	$\dfrac{1}{h_{oG}}$
y	$\dfrac{r_{oG}}{\Delta_r}$	$\dfrac{-r_{rG}}{\Delta_r}$	y_{iG}	y_{rG}	$\dfrac{1}{h_{iG}}$	$\dfrac{-h_{rG}}{h_{iG}}$
	$\dfrac{-r_{fG}}{\Delta_r}$	$\dfrac{r_{iG}}{\Delta_r}$	y_{fG}	y_{oG}	$\dfrac{h_{fG}}{h_{iG}}$	$\dfrac{\Delta_h}{h_{iG}}$
h	$\dfrac{\Delta_r}{r_{oG}}$	$\dfrac{r_{rG}}{r_{oG}}$	$\dfrac{1}{y_{iG}}$	$\dfrac{-y_{rG}}{y_{iG}}$	h_{iG}	h_{rG}
	$\dfrac{-r_{fG}}{r_{oG}}$	$\dfrac{1}{r_{oG}}$	$\dfrac{y_{fG}}{y_{rG}}$	$\dfrac{\Delta_y}{y_{iG}}$	h_{fG}	h_{oG}

$\Delta_r = r_{iG}r_{oG} - r_{fG}r_{rG}$
$\Delta_y = y_{iG}y_{oG} - y_{fG}y_{rG}$
$\Delta_h = h_{iG}h_{oG} - h_{fG}h_{rG}$

TABLE E-2

T-Equivalent Circuit Components Expressed in *r*-Parameters

T-Circuit Component	Common Base	Common Emitter	Common Collector
Current factor	$\dfrac{r_{fB}}{r_{oB}}$	$\dfrac{-r_{fE}}{r_{oE} - r_{fE}}$	$\dfrac{-r_{fC}}{r_{oC} - r_{fC}}$
r_B	r_{rB}	$r_{iE} - r_{rE}$	$r_{iC} - r_{rC}$
r_E	$r_{iB} - r_{rB}$	r_{rE}	$r_{oC} - r_{rC}$
r_C	$r_{oB} - r_{rB}$	$r_{oE} + r_{rE}$	r_{rC}

and are termed the input admittance, forward transfer admittance, reverse transfer admittance, and the output admittance, respectively.

Conversions are possible between all of these parameters, as indicated in Table E–1.

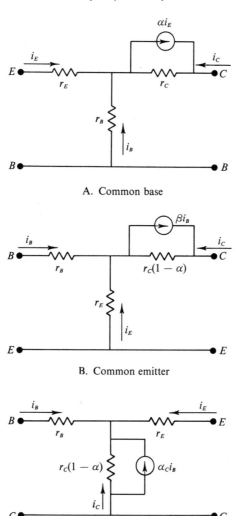

A. Common base

B. Common emitter

C. Common collector

Figure E-1.   T-*Equivalent Circuits*

The resistance parameters are most frequently used in T-*equivalent circuits* as illustrated in Fig. E–1. Table E–2 defines the T-equivalent components in terms of the resistance parameters. These components are converted into the hybrid parameters in Table E–3.

TABLE E-3

T-Equivalent Circuit Components Expressed in h-Parameters

T-*Circuit* *Component*	*Common* *Base*	*Common* *Emitter*	*Common* *Collector*
Current factor	$-h_{fB}$	$\dfrac{h_{fE}}{1 + h_{fE}}$	$\dfrac{1 + h_{fC}}{h_{fC}}$
r_B	$\dfrac{h_{rB}}{h_{oB}}$	$h_{iE} - \dfrac{h_{rE}}{h_{oE}}(1 + h_{fE})$	$h_{iC} + \dfrac{h_{fC}}{h_{oC}}(1 - h_{rC})$
r_E	$h_{iB} - \dfrac{h_{rB}}{h_{oB}}(1 + h_{fB})$	$\dfrac{h_{rE}}{h_{oE}}$	$\dfrac{1 - h_{rC}}{h_{oC}}$
r_C	$\dfrac{1 - h_{rB}}{h_{oB}}$	$\dfrac{1 + h_{fE}}{h_{oE}}$	$\dfrac{-h_{fC}}{h_{oC}}$

Index

Index